CONCORDIA UNIVERSITY

QL45.R33
NATURAL HISTORY LONDON   C001 V

3 4211 000092204

NATURAL HISTORY

Contributors :

INVERTEBRATES (other than Insects) : G. C. Robson, M.A., *Deputy Keeper, Department of Zoology, British Museum (Natural History).*

INSECTS : D. Aubertin, M.Sc., F.L.S., *Assistant Keeper, Department of Entomology, British Museum (Natural History).*

FISHES : Charles Tate Regan, D.Sc., F.R.S., *Director of the British Museum (Natural History).*

REPTILES AND AMPHIBIANS : E. G. Boulenger, *Director of the Zoological Society's Aquarium, London.*

BIRDS : W. B. Alexander, M.A., *Director of Research in Economic Ornithology, University of Oxford.*

MAMMALS : R. I. Pocock, F.R.S., F.L.S., *formerly Assistant Keeper, Department of Zoology, British Museum (Natural History); formerly Superintendent of the Zoological Society's Gardens, London.*

LIONESS (*Felis leo*)

[*By courtesy of*]　　　　　　　　　　　　　　　　　　　　　　[*British Museum (Natural History*)]

LION (*Felis leo*)

NATURAL HISTORY

Edited by

CHARLES TATE REGAN, D.Sc., F.R.S.

DIRECTOR OF THE BRITISH MUSEUM (NATURAL HISTORY)

With Sixteen Colour Plates, and
Over a Thousand Photographs

WARD, LOCK & CO., LIMITED

LONDON AND MELBOURNE

Distributed in U.S.A. by

John de Graff, Inc.

64 West 23rd Street
New York 10, N. Y.

MADE IN ENGLAND

Printed in Great Britain by

L. T. A. ROBINSON LIMITED, THE BOTOLPH PRINTING WORKS
LONDON

48798

PREFACE

THE ever-widening range of knowledge due to discoveries of hitherto unrecorded forms of life, and still more to improved methods of observation under natural conditions, have, to a large extent, rendered obsolete existing compendiums of natural history. Yet there has never been a time when it was of greater importance that such knowledge should be both easily accessible and widely diffused.

In attempting, regardless of expense and trouble, to meet this real and often-expressed demand, the Publishers have been fortunate in securing the services as General Editor of Dr. Charles Tate Regan, M.A., F.R.S., Director of the British Museum (Natural History), and he in his turn has been successful in enlisting the help of probably as distinguished a team of specialists—each an acknowledged authority on the subject of which he writes—as has ever collaborated in a work of the kind.

The result can safely be left to speak for itself. The guiding principle has been to secure by systematic arrangement and modern method of classification a volume easily read, and easily referred to, and at the same time of the strictest accuracy, meeting at once the needs of the general reader and of the student. The language throughout is lucid and straightforward, and where scientific names are used (as they must and in such a work should be) they are accompanied, wherever possible, by the common names.

It is claimed, in short, that this work will be found in actual use both detailed and comprehensive, affording a survey of the Animal Kingdom, from the lowest unicellular organisms to the highest and most complex forms. New light is thrown on such intensely interesting aspects of Natural History as the inter-relationship of the various species and families ; the evolution of types to suit the conditions under which they live, their characteristics, range, distribution, food, habits, and economic value.

In a work of this kind the illustrations are of hardly less importance than the letterpress, those in this volume form a collection that, in the opinion of several authorities well qualified to judge, is unique. Numbering well over a thousand, they have been collected from all parts of the world. Wherever possible, the photographs depict living forms of animals in their natural habitat, stuffed and caged specimens having been carefully avoided except in cases where no alternative is to be had. The sixteen coloured

PREFACE

plates are reproduced in four colours, mostly from originals loaned by kind permission of the Trustees of the British Museum (Natural History).

Here, then, is a volume of high scientific value and at the same time of popular appeal, which it is confidently hoped will find an honoured place in every library and on the shelves of all who are interested in even the most general way in a subject of endless fascination.

WARD, LOCK & CO., LIMITED
6 Chancery Lane
London, W.C.2

CONTENTS

CONTENTS

INSECTS (*continued*)—

VERTEBRATA (Vertebrates)
by Charles Tate Regan, D.Sc., F.R.S.

BATRACHIA (or Amphibia)
by E. G. Boulenger, F.Z.S.

REPTILIA (Reptiles)
by E. G. Boulenger, F.Z.S.

CONTENTS

REPTILIA (*continued*)—

BIRDS (Aves)
by W. B. Alexander, M.A.

CONTENTS

MAMMALIA (Mammals)
by R. I. Pocock, F.R.S., F.L.S.

COLOUR PLATES

INDEX

To facilitate reference, a very full index, including the common names, as well as the scientific names and indicating species illustrated, will be found at the end of the book.

INTRODUCTION

NATURAL HISTORY, strictly interpreted, is the history of the whole world of nature, animal, vegetable, and mineral, and includes not only the earth and its inhabitants as they are now, but as they were in the past also. The history of the earth from the beginning, possibly two thousand million years ago, and of the animals and plants that have lived on it for perhaps half that time, is a vast subject, and it is fortunate that nobody expects to find the whole of it covered by a book entitled " Natural History." Nor, indeed, will most readers expect to find in such a book anything about minerals and rocks, or flowers and ferns, and not much about fossils, but mainly some account of the forms of animal life that now exist.

It has been estimated that some 600,000 kinds, or species, of insects have been described and named, and that the Animal Kingdom of to-day may include about ten times as many species as there are words in this book. This estimate will make it clear that not only most of the species, but whole groups of species, must be omitted altogether, and that if, for example, the salmon and the tiger get a hundred words each, they do so at the expense of some other kinds of animals considered to be of less general interest.

If we attempt to classify animals, we find that they can be grouped into about fourteen main branches, or phyla, in each of which a fundamental structural plan can be recognized, although endless modifications of it occur. These phyla are named and diagnosed in the introduction to the chapter on Invertebrates, and it need only be mentioned here that the phylum Vertebrata, or back-boned animals, is one of the smallest, but that as it includes Man it is naturally the one that interests him most, and therefore occupies the greater part of this book, although it is not placed first. The plan of the book is to begin with the simpler and more primitive forms of animal life, and to trace the steps that lead upwards.

The diversity of living animals is amazing, and can be understood only if certain general principles be accepted. The main difference between animals and plants is that plants obtain from air and from water relatively simple nutritive substances, and are passive, whereas animals need as food either plants, plant products, or other animals, and are typically active, moving about in search of food. There are, certainly, a number of sedentary animals and some, like polyps and sponges, that are fixed, but these are able to produce currents that bring food to their mouths, or are provided with tentacles to reach out and seize prey ; moreover, they have active free-swimming larvae. The activity of animals leads to a greater complexity of organization than is found in plants, and to the development of organs of locomotion, and of organs of touch, smell, sight and hearing.

The purpose of every living individual animal is to maintain itself for a time, to find food, to escape enemies, and to leave descendants to continue the race, objects that may be accomplished in many different ways. Animals may live in the sea, in freshwater, on land, in trees, and in the air ; they appear to have explored every possible habitat, to have left no sort of food and no device for obtaining it untried, and to have perfected all kinds of methods of harming, avoiding or deceiving their enemies.

The relation of differences in structure, form, and colour of animals to differences in habits and conditions of life is one of the problems that the zoologist has to study. But when he has found out where and under what conditions an animal lives, what it is and what it does, there are still many questions to be answered, and these concern the problem of evolution.

About eighty years ago was published the " Origin of Species " in which Darwin showed that the classification of animals into groups within groups, and the facts of their structure, development, geographical distribution and geological succession, were inexplicable unless evolution, or descent with modification, had taken place. Since that time knowledge in all these fields has increased enormously, evidence has accumulated and has been tested, all tending to confirm Darwin's conclusion.

As has been said, animals are classified into groups within groups, species being grouped into genera, genera into families, families into orders, orders into classes, and classes into phyla. In large, or diverse, groups it is often necessary to recognize other categories, some of which, such as sub-class, suborder, etc., have names that quite clearly indicate their rank, whereas others, such as division, tribe, etc., are less definite. In all modern work on classification, evolution is accepted as basic ; it is assumed that the characters common to all the members of a group, by which it is diagnosed, are those of its ancestral form, and that the differences between members of a group, which are used in classifying it, are divergent modifications of the ancestral form. The systematist, who is concerned with classification, must, if he can, frame exact diagnoses, but he is more concerned, in the first place, with considering the evidence as to the meaning of the resemblances and differences between the animals of the group he is studying, to what extent these may be due to the nearness or remoteness of a common ancestor and to what extent to other circumstances. He has to get an idea of the origin and evolution of the group, and to classify it in such a way that his views are made clear.

Classifications may differ for several reasons ; when two or more workers have reached the same conclusion as to relationships, they may not agree as to the best way of expressing this in classification ; more often, perhaps, different workers do not interpret the available evidence in the same way, and so have different views to express. These things may perhaps be made clearer if a definite problem be shortly discussed, particularly if one be taken about which much has been written, but about which opinions still differ, namely "Man's Place in Nature."

Taking the groups named above as common to all systems of classification, everybody is agreed that Man (*Homo sapiens*) belongs to the phylum Vertebrata, class Mammalia, order Primates, family Hominidae, and genus *Homo*. Most authorities would agree also that the family Hominidae belongs to a group Catarrhina, which includes all the apes and monkeys of the Old World, and to a section, the Anthropomorpha, that includes the Gibbons (Hylobatidae) and the Great Apes—Chimpanzee, Gorilla, Orang—(Simiidae). The fact that opinions differ as to whether Man is more nearly related to the Gibbons or to the Great Apes, and as to the precise relationship of these three families to the old-world monkeys (Cercopithecidae) does not affect our classification so far ; but a word or two may be said about these matters. The Catarrhines are easily defined by the number of the teeth, eight on each side, two incisors, a canine, two premolars, and three molars. The Monkeys of Africa and Asia are more primitive than the Gibbons, Great Apes, and Man in several ways ; most of them have tails, the thumb emerges from the middle of the palm, and they are quadrupedal, walking or running with the undersides of the fingers and toes on the ground. However, in the structure of the skull they are so highly specialized that it is clear that if some remote ancestor of Man might have been termed a Catarrhine Monkey, it could not have been placed in the same family as the recent members of this group.

The Anthropomorpha are tailless, and in them the thumb emerges from the base of the palm. The three families of this group differ in their manner of locomotion. Gibbons are bipedal ; they walk, run, and even dance, but are flat-footed and hold out their arms to keep their balance. The Great Apes are habitually quadrupedal, but walk on their knuckles. Man is distinguished by having the big toe in line with the other toes and by the arched instep ; he is better balanced than the Gibbons, but would seem to have perfected their method of locomotion, and, therefore, is more likely to have been evolved from some primitive Gibbon than from a Great Ape. But as the Great Apes more nearly approach Man in size of body, size and convolutions of the brain, etc., there are many who do not accept this conclusion.

The classification of the Primates as a whole is much more difficult than that of the Catarrhines. Some authorities divide the order Primates into three suborders, namely : Lemuroidea, Tarsioidea, and Anthropoidea. The Lemuroidea include the Lemuriformes and Lorisiformes, the Anthropoidea the Platyrrhina and Catarrhina. This classification expresses the view that the Lemurs are the most primitive Primates, that the little Tarsier of Malaysia leads from the Lemurs to the Monkeys, and that the structural resemblances between the Platyrrhines, or South American Monkeys, and the Catarrhines, are sufficient to indicate that

INTRODUCTION

these are descended from a common ancestor that had the essential characteristics of a monkey.

The present writer is, perhaps, more inclined to stress the evidence from present and past distribution, which indicates that the Catarrhines originated in Africa, later spread to Europe and Asia, but have never, except Man, reached America, and that the Platyrrhines originated in South America, later invaded Central America, but have never gone further afield. He is also, perhaps, more inclined to be critical of resemblances as evidence of relationship if there be differences that suggest a different conclusion, and to accept parallel and convergent evolution as more common than it was formerly considered to be.

Applying these ideas to the Primates, he has proposed to classify them into five suborders : Lorisoidea, Tarsioidea, Platyrrhina, Lemuroidea, and Catarrhina, and to express the view that the Tarsioids and Platyrrhines are derived independently from Lorisoids, and Catarrhines from Lemuroids. In this classification the Lorisoidea and Lemuroidea correspond respectively to the Lorisiformes and Lemuriformes of that given on the preceding page.

Enough has been said to show that no finality has been reached in the classification of animals, nor could be unless our knowledge of their evolution were complete.

Species are the units that the systematist recognizes, but they may be divided into subspecies or races. Most species can be assigned to one or the other of two main types, that may be termed geographical and habitudinal. Within a group of related species, the geographical species represent each other in different areas, as a rule living the same sort of life in each, whereas the habitudinal species inhabit the same area, but differ in habits, most frequently in food and in feeding habits. This indicates that the evolution of species may have been either geographical, the differentiation of local forms adapted to local conditions, or habitudinal, in order to take full advantage of the different possibilities of an area.

The writer's views on evolution are that it has always been adaptive, related to habits and conditions of life. Some species are sufficiently well known to enable it to be said where, when, and even why they have evolved ; but the question " how ? " still remains to be answered, and no attempt to answer it need be made here. Whether the theory of Lamarck, generally termed " the inheritance of acquired characters," or the Natural Selection theory of Darwin, offers the most satisfactory explanation, and whether any of the more modern hypotheses come nearer the truth, are controversial matters that need a separate book for their discussion.

SOUTH KENSINGTON   C. TATE REGAN.

DIANA GUENON (*Cercopithecus diana*)

By courtesy of]   [*British Museum (Natural History)*

CHESTNUT-BROWED GUENON (*Cercopithecus neglectus*)

INVERTEBRATES
(Other than Insects)
BY
G. C. ROBSON, M.A., F.Z.S.

INTRODUCTION

The classification of animals into vertebrates and invertebrates is hardly justified, as the invertebrates comprise a number of phyla of diverse organisation, and constitute by far the larger part of the Animal Kingdom, both in number of species and of individuals.

The relationships of these phyla to each other is a difficult question, for each is characterised by a distinct plan of structure. Moreover, their origins are lost in obscurity, for all seem to have existed and evolved on the earth for countless ages. Zoologists agree in placing at the base of the series the Protozoa, or unicellular animals, whose bodies are supposed to be equivalent to the units of structure of the tissues of other animals. The somewhat inappropriate name " cell " is given to these units because, when plants were first investigated microscopically, they were found to have a sort of honeycomb structure consisting of numerous minute chambers with hard walls, each filled with protoplasm, or semi-fluid living matter, containing a more definite and firmer central part, the nucleus. The name " cell," given at first to such hard-walled chambers, and then to their living contents, was afterwards transferred to the similar elements of animal tissues, although, except in skeletal tissues, these may be bounded only by thin membranes, or may even be imperfectly defined. The essential feature of a cell, or of the body of a unicellular animal, is that it consists of protoplasm and a nucleus.

The Protozoa are mostly of minute size and many are invisible to the naked eye. They multiply either by division into two (fission) or more (spore-formation), this division sometimes being preceded by the union of two individuals (conjugation). If we are correct in supposing that this phylum includes the most primitive animals, and that the earliest forms of animal life to appear on the earth were Protozoa, then the phylum has had a longer evolutionary history than any other. Consequently, it is not surprising that living Protozoa exhibit a great diversity of structure and of habits, or that some may be highly organised and may have complicated life-histories. Nevertheless, it is difficult to imagine a simpler form of animal life than Amoeba, named from its continual changes of shape Proteus. This little animal, which creeps about on the mud at the bottom of ponds, consists of a granular plasm containing a nucleus, and with a clear and somewhat firmer outer layer ; finger-like processes, into which the plasm flows, may be protruded from any part of the body and again be drawn in ; in this way the animal moves and captures food, which may be taken in anywhere. Other forms of Protozoa afford interesting parallels to certain multicellular animals in having, for example, a definite mouth, or in secreting a skeleton either as an internal support or a protective shell ; also there are forms that obtain food by the action of cilia, little vibratory " hairs " that produce in the water currents that bring food to the mouth, a method also adopted by several groups of higher animals. One group, the Flagellata, which swim about by the lashing movements of one or two whiplike appendages, includes several forms that contain chlorophyll, the substance that gives plants their green colour. Some or all of these green Flagellates are ranked by botanists as plants, and, indeed, appear to be the group from which the green plants originated. The Flagellates are also of interest from their resemblance to the motile germs of the males of other animals and of the lower plants.

All animals other than Protozoa are termed multicellular, but the vexed question whether one of these animals is equivalent to a single Protozoon or may be regarded as an aggregation of numerous Protozoa, will never be finally answered. Those who favour the first view, point to the unity of the organism, and the co-ordination of its activities ; they regard its development as a process of increase in size, accompanied by a multiplication of nuclei. On the other hand, every individual multicellular animal starts life as a single cell, comparable in structure to a Protozoon ; growth is accomplished by division into two, then into four, etc., a process comparable to the continued fission of a Protozoon, but with the difference that the cells produced do not separate and live apart, but remain connected together to form a single animal, which may thus be considered to be formed of many Protozoa. A further analogy is furnished by the fact that in the Protozoa, fission may be preceded by conjugation, the union of two unicellular individuals, and that a similar process generally precedes the development of a higher animal.

The Porifera or Sponges are assigned to a distinct grade under the name Parazoa, because they appear to be a sideline, without evident relationship to other animals except the Protozoa and possibly the Coelenterates. In their organisation these aquatic animals are quite unlike any others, for instead of a single mouth, they have numerous minute openings over the whole surface of the body ; through these openings food-currents pass into the system of canals and chambers that permeate the body, and eventually emerge through one or more larger exhalent openings. In other stationary animals, food-currents are produced by the action of cilia, minute " hairs " that vibrate in unison, but in sponges they are produced by the movements of larger lashes, flagella, each borne by a single cell. The resemblance of the collar-cells that line the chambers of the sponge to certain Protozoa that have a similar collar and flagellum may be an indication as to the origin of sponges. The development of a supporting skeleton in the network between the canals enables these animals to attain a considerable size and to exhibit a great diversity of form ; but however large they may be, and however complicated the ramifications of the canal system, they are essentially animals of simple structure, in which water and food are brought direct to all parts of the body by the canals. The free-swimming larvae of some sponges are not unlike those of Coelenterates, but their development after they settle down and become fixed is so different that it is difficult to attach much importance to this resemblance.

The multicellular animals other than sponges have a single mouth and are grouped together as Metazoa. The simplest Metazoa are the Coelenterates, radially symmetrical animals with the mouth in the middle of the free end of the body, in the fixed polyps, or of the under surface in the free-swimming jelly-fishes. The mouth leads into the single cavity of the body ; the walls of the body enclosing this cavity are formed of two membranes with a layer of jelly between them. The inner membrane that lines the cavity of the body is digestive, and there are no special organs of circulation, excretion or respiration ; cells of either membrane may be contractile, functioning as muscles, and some of those of the outer membrane may be nerve cells with branching processes ; in the jelly-fishes organs of sight, hearing and smell may be present, placed round the edge of the umbrella-shaped or bell-shaped body.

[*H. Bastin.*

VENUS'S FLOWER BASKET
SPONGE
(*Euplectella aspergillum*).
The siliceous skeleton forms a trumpet
of delicate lattice-work.

A cylindrical or oval, ciliated larva, the *planula*, is known in most groups of Coelenterates, and may represent the ancestral form from which this and the other phyla developed. Probably the peculiarities of Coelenterate structure, such as their radial symmetry and the development round the mouth of tentacles for catching prey, are due to the adoption of the habit of fixation. The fixed polyps are more primitive than the free-swimming Medusae, which, indeed, are produced from them. Fixation seems to have determined the Coelenterate structure, and to have prevented

[W. S. Berridge.
CORAL (*Turbinaria conspicua*).
A reef coral that forms growths of complicated structure.

the further advance which was made by the animals that remained free; these developed under the skin a muscular layer that enabled them to crawl or swim in the sea, and some sort of blood system for the transference of food materials from the digestive cavity to other parts of the body. These animals, collectively termed "triploblastic" from the presence of the muscles and other tissues between the outer and inner membranes of the body, commonly pass through a Coelenterate stage—known as the *gastrula*—in their development, when the body is formed of two layers of cells, and contains a single cavity with one opening. Thus it seems certain that the triploblastic phyla have a Coelenterate ancestry, or rather that they are derived from the same primitive animals as the living Coelenterates. Parasitism may produce degeneration, and most phyla contain animals that exemplify the facts that the adoption of sedentary or fixed habits may lead to a simplification of structure, and may also produce great changes, such as the development of ciliated tentacles round the mouth, and may even lead to a radial organisation, as in the Echinoderms. But normal animals that move about freely are bilaterally symmetrical, with the front end of the body generally differentiated as a head, which contains the brain, in close association with the eyes, feelers and other sense-organs.

Many of the phyla are represented by fossils in Cambrian strata. They have lived on the earth for a time estimated at hundreds of millions of years, and thus it is difficult to say much about their relationships.

Probably the most primitive of the triploblastic animals are the Flat-worms (Platyhelminthes), which resemble the Coelenterates in having a digestive cavity with one opening only, but which differ from them fundamentally in having a muscular layer under the skin, a spongy tissue between this and the digestive cavity, the spaces of which may serve as a blood system, and an excretory system of branching tubules. Many Flatworms are parasitic: the free-living forms are flat and oval, with the mouth at the end of a protrusible proboscis on the underside of the body.

The remaining invertebrate phyla are characterised by a digestive cavity in the form of a tube open at both ends; some of them exhibit little advance in other respects on the Flatworm structure, whereas others are highly-organised animals with digestive glands, special respiratory organs, and a blood system with a heart, arteries and veins.

The principal phyla may be shortly described as follows:

20

Nematoda. Threadworms, very elongated in form, unsegmented ; without proboscis, but sometimes with horny jaws. Mostly parasitic.

Nemertinea. Long, unsegmented worms with very contractile bodies ; at the front end of the body is an evertible proboscis, armed with stings or spines. Mostly marine and carnivorous.

Rotifera. Wheel Animalcules ; minute aquatic animals with a circle of cilia at the edge of a disc at the front end of the body. Mostly fresh water.

Echinoderma. Radially symmetrical animals ; skin with plates or spines ; a water vascular system of a circular and five radial canals, from which protrude the tube-feet. Marine.

Brachiopoda. Fixed animals enclosed in a bivalved shell, with a row of ciliated tentacles below the mouth. Marine.

Polyzoa. Small fixed colonial animals, with a crown of ciliated tentacles round the mouth. Marine and fresh water.

Mollusca. Animals typically protected by a shell, crawling about by means of a muscular foot, and having a tongue armed with horny teeth. Aquatic and terrestrial.

Annelida. Worms with the body divided into a series of segments. Aquatic and terrestrial.

Arthropoda. Segmented animals with a hard outer skeleton, and jointed limbs, one or more pairs of which are used as jaws. Aquatic and terrestrial.

These diagnoses suffice to indicate the distinctness of the phyla. It may be noted that several are entirely aquatic and mainly marine, that only a few are represented in the land fauna, and that the most primitive members of these live in the sea. Apart from the Vertebrates, the Arthropoda may be considered the most successful animals ; insects, spiders, scorpions, lobsters and crabs are some of the characteristic types of this great group.

Strange as it may seem, the Echinoderms appear to be the nearest allies to the Vertebrates, for similarities in the early development of the Star-fishes and their allies and of certain lowly Vertebrates, lead to the conclusion that both phyla may have evolved from the same group.

The Echinoderms are a very ancient group. The structure of the early fossils, and the development of the living forms lead to the conclusion that they originated from bilaterally-symmetrical worm-like animals that became fixed down by the head and acquired a protective covering of bony plates. As is usual in fixed animals, the mouth moved to the free end of the body.

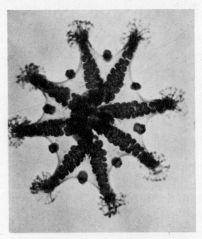

[John J. Ward.
A SCYPHOMEDUSAN JELLY-FISH
(*Lucernaria*) WITH EGGS.

21

Phylum PROTOZOA

The Protozoa—or unicellular animals—are nearly all of minute size, many being invisible without the aid of a microscope. They are generally considered to be simple in structure, each individual corresponding to one of the cells of the tissues of other animals. They have a world-wide distribution, in the sea, in fresh water and on land ; many are parasitic.

Class 1. SARCODINA

This class includes Protozoa that have no definite shape, but move about and capture prey by pushing out processes of the body—or pseudopodia.

Amoeba. If a little water, with mud, from the bottom of a pond, be poured into a shallow and fairly wide vessel, some examples of *Amoeba proteus* may be seen, just visible to the naked eye as minute brown specks moving slowly among the mud at the bottom. Under a microscope they appear as irregular blobs of a semi-fluid, granular, jelly-like substance, with a denser more or less circular body in the middle—the nucleus. No definite and permanent organs other than the nucleus are visible, but by attentive watching it will be found that temporary organs may be formed. Thus it will be seen that the Amoeba moves and also captures food by pushing out finger-like portions of its substance. The animal does not move by levering itself along, as creatures with muscular and bony limbs do, but the movement is a flowing one. Another feature that is revealed by study is the appearance from time to time of circular or oval semi-transparent cavities, in which the food is received and digested.

Amoeba proteus reproduces itself by a process known as fission. First the nucleus divides into two and then the body is similarly divided, so that two daughter cells are produced from the original cell. It will be noted that in this method of reproduction there is no trace of sexual phenomena or fertilisation. However, in other Protozoa, cell-division may be preceded by the union of two individuals which may either be structurally identical, or be of different form and size.

Foraminifera. These have a horny or calcareous shell, that may be many-chambered and coiled, some of them resembling miniature shells of Gastropod or Cephalod Molluscs (snails, ammonites). The shell may be pierced with holes, and through these, and the main opening of the

[H. Bastin.
SHELLS OF FORAMINIFERA.
The minute shells of these animals show great diversity of form.

shell, are protruded the long, thread-like pseudopodia, which often unite to form a network. These animals are marine, and mostly crawl about at the bottom of the sea, but some float near the surface, and these are very abundant. Most of them are minute, comparable in size to the head of a pin, but some have a diameter of an inch or more. Large tracts of the sea-bottom are covered by a thick deposit of the shells of the pelagic *Globigerina* ; the shells of Foraminifera, especially nummu-lites, also play a considerable part in the formation of chalks and limestones.

[*H. Bastin.*
CAPSULES OF RADIOLARIA.
These siliceous capsules are pierced with holes or have a latticed structure.

Radiolaria. These take their name from the manner in which the slender pseudopodia radiate from the body ; they differ from the Foraminifera in having a siliceous skeleton, which is not an external shell, but an internal capsule enclosing the nucleus. These capsules exhibit a diversity of form, being spherical, conical, ring-shaped, etc., and are pierced with holes, or have a latticed structure. These animals abound near the surface of the warmer parts of the oceans, and their skeletons form the principal con-stituent of the Radiolarian Ooze that covers large areas of the ocean floor in the tropics.

Class 2. FLAGELLATA

These Protozoa have a definite shape, the body being enclosed in a membrane ; special organs of locomotion are present and there is generally a mouth. The Flagellata swim by means of the lashing movements of one or two, rarely more, whip-like threads. Some greenish freshwater forms are sometimes regarded as plants. Those Flagellata that have a collar round the base of the single flagellum are of interest from their resem-blance to the collar-cells of sponges. *Noctiluca* is a remarkable form that may occur at the surface of the sea in such numbers as to form bands miles in length, red in the day and phosphorescent at night. The *Trypanosomes* are blood-parasites of vertebrates. Sleeping sickness is caused by *Trypanosoma gambiense*, which is transmitted from man to man by the bites of Tsetse-flies.

Class 3. INFUSORIA (Ciliata)

The name of the class has reference to the fact that they were first dis-covered in a bowl of stagnant water, and that they appear in any infusion of water that contains animal or vegetable matter. In the Infusoria or Ciliata the organs of locomotion are cilia, numerous minute vibratory filaments distributed over the surface of the body. Most Ciliata are free-living, but a few are parasitic. The Slipper Animalcule

[*H. Bastin.*
STENTOR.
In this fixed trumpet-shaped Protozoa the marginal
cilia produce a current that brings food to the mouth.

(*Paramoecium*) has a flat, oval body and swims about freely. Some Ciliata are sedentary, living attached to weeds or sticks in ponds and ditches. The Bell Animalcules (*Vorticella*) are tiny bell-shaped animals on stalks, with a fringe of cilia at the rim of the bell, the movements of which produce a current that brings food particles to the mouth ; the trumpet-shaped *Stentor* feeds in a similar manner.

Some Ciliata are free-swimming and provided with cilia when young, but become attached and lose the cilia when adult. These are vase-shaped and have tentacles that bear suckers, which seize the prey and suck it.

Class 4. SPOROZOA

The Sporozoa are parasitic in other animals ; they absorb fluid and are devoid of organs for the capture of food ; they have no mouth and no special organs of locomotion. They take their name from their method of reproduction, which is by the division of the body into a number of spores ; the spores are generally enclosed in a tough capsule, from which they eventually emerge, sometimes after the capsule has passed out of the host and has been taken into another with food. The class is a large one and includes parasites of nearly all groups of animals ; some do no particular damage, but many cause disease by destroying the tissues. Malaria is due to a parasite that is introduced into the blood of man by the bite of a mosquito (*Anopheles*) ; each minute spindle-shaped parasite enters a red blood corpuscle, grows at its expense, and then divides into a number of spores, which emerge, attack other corpuscles, and divide again : the recurrence of a crisis of the fever every third day is due to the fact that this is the time when a fresh liberation of spores occurs. Eventually no more spores are formed, and the parasites become sausage-shaped, ready for transference to a mosquito if it sucks the blood. In the alimentary canal of the mosquito these organisms undergo a number of changes, and conjugate, producing a worm-like form that burrows through the stomach wall and grows into a sphere ; this divides, eventually producing numerous little spindle-shaped forms, some of which enter the salivary glands and are ready to be introduced into the blood of man.

Phylum PORIFERA (Sponges)

The objects commonly known as sponges are the skeletons of animals from which the flesh has been removed. These animals and their allies form a group known as the Porifera, from the little pores that occur all over the surface of the body.

Sponges are mostly marine, although there is one freshwater family with numerous species; they are abundant in all seas, and at nearly all depths. Generally they are fixed to the bottom, or to rocks or weeds.

The simplest kind of sponge may be compared to a vase, fixed at the base, and with the walls perforated by numerous little holes. Each of the cells lining the inside of the vase is known as a collar-cell; it bears a hair-like process, the flagellum, arising from within a cup or collar; by the lashing movements of these hairs currents are produced, water is drawn in through the pores and brings with it microscopic animals and plants and other food-particles and is expelled through the opening at the end. Most sponges are more complicated in structure, although this simple type occurs at an early stage in development; as a rule tubular outgrowths from the walls of the vase branch and unite to form a system of canals and chambers, often with several exhalant "mouths." Generally the sponge body is supported by a skeletal

[H. Bastin.

GLASS-ROPE SPONGES (*Hyalonema sieboldii*).
The cup-shaped sponge is anchored by a rope of long siliceous spicules twisted together.

25

SPONGE (*Chalina polychotoma*). [W. S. Berridge.
An Australian sponge of branching form; it is a shallow-water species, but of the
same group as the deep-sea *Esperiopsis*.

framework, either of calcite, silica, or the horny substance named spongin. Sponges exhibit great diversity in form and size. They may be spherical, cup-shaped, tubular, fan-shaped, tree-like, etc. ; some are quite small, others may have the bulk of a man.

Most sponges produce buds that may separate off as new individuals. Sexual reproduction results in the formation of small larvae that swim out of the canal-system and in a little while settle down, become fixed and grow into a sponge.

The Porifera are divided into three classes, *Calcarea*, *Hexacti-nellida* and *Demospongiae*.

Class 1. CALCAREA
(Calcareous Sponges)

This class contains the sponges that have a skeleton of calcareous spicules. It includes some sponges of the simple vase-like type we have described. *Sycon coronatum*, a common British species, is more advanced in structure, having the collar-cells in numerous small chambers that open into the central one. It is oval, about an inch high, and white ; the opening at the top has a circle of spicules round it. It is a shallow water form, growing on rocks and seaweeds.

[H. Bastin.
A VASE-SHAPED MONAXON SPONGE.
(*Phakelia ventilabrum*).

SILICEOUS SPONGES (DEMOSPONGIAE)

Class 2. HEXACTINELLIDA (Six-rayed Siliceous Sponges)

In this class the skeleton is composed of six-rayed spicules of silica ; there is, as a rule, a large central chamber, and secondary chambers with collar-cells. Most of these sponges inhabit deep water, and are often not fixed, but merely anchored in the mud by a tuft of spicules. In the Glass-rope Sponges (*Hyalonema*) the cup-shaped body of the sponge is rooted by a rope formed of very long spicules twisted together. Venus's Flower-basket (*Euplectella aspergillum*) from Japan has a trumpet-shaped skeleton of a delicate lattice-work, and is used as an ornament.

Class 3. DEMOSPONGIAE
(Siliceous Sponges)

This group includes the majority of sponges ; it is characterised by having a skeleton of either silica or spongin, or of both, but the siliceous spicules are not six-rayed. In one group the spicules are anchor-shaped, with a long shaft and three prongs at one end. The Monaxon sponges have rod-shaped siliceous spicules, pointed at one or both ends. A British species, the Bread-crumb Sponge (*Halichondria panicea*) has a skeleton of minute needle-shaped spicules scattered through the body, and forming a network at the surface. This sponge appears on rocks and weeds as a greenish or yellow crust, from which project little cones, each with a hole at the top, like the craters of volcanoes. The Boring Sponges (*Cliona*) excavate tunnels in lime-stone rocks, and do considerable damage to breakwaters, etc. They also attack shells, and oyster-shells perforated by their tunnels may often be seen near the sea. The Neptune's Cup (*Poterion patera*) from East Indian seas is one of the largest sponges ; the pin-shaped spicules unite

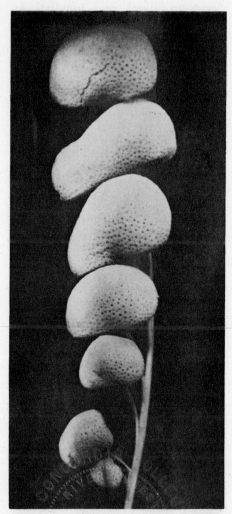

[*W. S. Berridge*
SPONGE (*Esperiopsis challengeri*).
A curious, stalked sponge taken by the "Challenger" at a depth of one thousand fathoms. It belongs to a group with four-rayed spicules of silica.

27

to form a massive skeleton in the form of a cup. The freshwater sponges (*Spongilla*) form green crusts on stems, submerged roots, etc. The sponges with a horny skeleton, generally in the form of a network, are those of commercial value. They are found in all warm seas, in depths down to about one hundred fathoms. They are of various shapes, spheroidal, cake-shaped, conical, or cup-shaped, and belong to a large number of species, of which we may mention the cup-shaped Turkey Sponge (*Spongia officinalis*) and the Bath Sponge (*Hippospongia equina*). When alive they appear as solid, fleshy bodies from grey or yellow to black in colour, attached to the sea-bottom. The Mediterranean fishery is of great antiquity, but that of Florida, Cuba and the Bahamas is now nearly as important. The sponges are obtained in the deeper water by divers, or by means of dredges; in shallower water they are hooked up by means of prongs attached to long poles. They are prepared for the market by allowing the flesh to rot off, and are then beaten or squeezed, cleaned and dried. In recent years has been adopted the method of increasing the supply by cutting live sponges into little pieces, attaching each of them to suitable supports, and allowing them to grow.

[*W. S. Berridge.*

JELLY-FISH (*Chrysaora isosceles*).
A typical Scyphomedusan.

Phylum COELENTERATA
(Jelly-fishes, Sea-anemones and Corals)

This large branch of the Animal Kingdom includes the jelly-fishes, sea-anemones and corals.

They are radially symmetrical animals of simple structure, the mouth opening into the single cavity of the body, which serves both for digestion and circulation. The body-wall is formed of only two layers of cells, with a structureless jelly between them.

Except in the Ctenophores, a very constant feature of the Coelenterata

28

48798

JELLY-FISHES (POLYPS AND MEDUSAE)

is the presence of stings, or thread-cells, which occur in the skin in great numbers, particularly on the tentacles. Each thread-cell consists of a little capsule containing fluid, in which lies a long thread spirally coiled ; the thread can be suddenly uncoiled and ejected, and the barbed end may pierce the skin of enemy or prey, introducing some of the poisonous fluid.

Nearly all the Coelenterata are marine, but some inhabit fresh water ; they are either

[John J. Ward.
SEA-MOSS (*Sertularia*).
Growing on the shell of a Horse-mussel.

solitary, or form colonies by budding ; they are of two main types, named polyps and medusae.

Polyp. The polyp is generally cylindrical, attached at one end, with the mouth, surrounded by one or more circles of tentacles, at the other. These sedentary creatures often feed on small animals that they seize with their tentacles and paralyse with their stings : when they are not feeding, the soft body is contracted, and the tentacles are drawn in.

Medusa. The medusa, or jelly-fish, floats or swims in the sea. It is circular and generally shaped like a bell or an umbrella ; there is a circle of tentacles round the

[W. S. Berridge.
JELLY-FISH (*Aequorea forskalea*) [glass model].
This belongs to the class Hydromedusae.

29

A BRANCHED COLONY OF
POLYPS (*Obelia*).

edge, and from the middle of the under surface a stalk hangs down, at the end of which is the mouth. From the central cavity a number of canals radiate, and join a circular canal near the margin. Swimming is accomplished by the slow contraction of the body.

It is of great interest that in some groups (*Hydromedusae* and *Scyphomedusae*) the polyps form buds that separate off as free-swimming medusae, which give rise by sexual processes to a larva that settles down, becomes fixed, and grows into a polyp. This occurrence of two quite different kinds of individuals in the regular life cycle is termed " alternation of generations."

Four classes of the Coelenterata are generally recognised : *Hydromedusae*, *Scyphomedusae*, *Anthozoa* and *Ctenophora*.

Class 1. HYDROMEDUSAE (Freshwater Hydra and the Portuguese Man-o'-War)

This class includes solitary polyps and colonies of polyps that may or may not give rise to medusae. The polyps are of simple structure, with the mouth opening directly into the undivided body cavity ; the medusae are characterised by the presence of a membrane attached to the edge of the bell, and are generally small.

The common freshwater polyp of Britain (*Hydra viridis*) is an example of a solitary polyp that has no medusoid generation. It is very small, with a body about as thick as a thread, and may be found adhering to weeds.

The polyp colonies often form delicate branching growths of various shapes, frequently like ferns or trees, on which the little polyps, sometimes bright pink in colour, are borne. The stem may be enclosed in a horny sheath, which forms cups for the polyps. The medusae are produced by special individuals without mouth or tentacles, which are nourished through the

Photos]   [*John J. Ward*.
A PORTION OF THE BRANCHES OF
THE SEA-MOSS (*Sertularia*).
Magnified to show the mouthless polyps that
give birth to little jelly-fishes.

[F. Schensky.

SEA-ANEMONE (Cerianthus).
A beautiful species with very slender tentacles.

stem at the expense of the other polyps. Many kinds of these hydroids occur in British seas, growing on the bottom, or attached to shells, seaweeds, etc.

Siphonophora. The Siphonophora are free-swimming colonies of medusae. The best-known example of this group is the Portuguese Man-o'-War (*Physalia*), which is often found floating at the surface in

[*Topical.*
CORAL (*Madrepora*).
The branches are studded with little prongs.

warm seas; it is noted for its beautiful colouring and also for its dangerous powers of stinging. It has a large float, below which are attached the long, trailing sting-ing tentacles, a number of nutri-tive individuals, tube-shaped, with a terminal mouth, and mouthless reproductive individuals. Other Siphonophora may have some of the medusae modified for swim-ming, as contractile bells, without tentacles or internal organs.

Class 2. SCYPHOMEDUSAE
(True Jelly-fishes)

This class includes jelly-fishes that differ from the medusae of the preceding class in their larger size, thicker umbrella, with the edge lobed and without a mem-branous fringe, and in having four large oral tentacles. They produce larvae that become fixed and develop into small polyps, each of which becomes constricted into a number of segments that separate off, swim away, and develop into medusae. A common British jelly-fish is *Aurelia aurita*, which is very abundant in the summer months; it is transparent and may be nearly a foot across. Some jelly-fishes of this group have a diameter of six feet.

Class 3. ANTHOZOA (Sea-anemones and Corals)

This class includes the sea-anemones and corals; the polyps are distinguished from those of the Hydromedusae by having a tube that extends down from the mouth into the body-cavity, which is sub-divided by a number of membranous partitions, extending between the tube and the body wall. These are marine, solitary or colonial animals, without a medusoid generation.

32

[F. Schensky.

DAHLIA SEA-ANEMONES (*Tealia crassicornis*).
In this species the tentacles are rather stout.

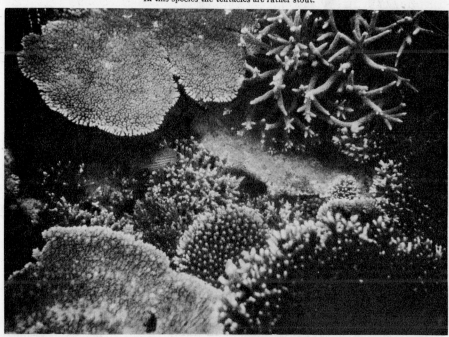

[Otho Webb.

UNDER-WATER PHOTOGRAPH OF CORAL GROWTH, GREAT BARRIER REEF, AUSTRALIA.

Alcyonaria. The Alcyonaria, with eight tentacles, include the " Dead-man's Finger " found on the British coast, between tide-marks, as a soft mass of pink finger-shaped lobes bearing the transparent polyps. In the Sea-fans (*Gorgoniacea*) the colony branches to form a spreading fan-shaped growth, studded with little polyps. The Sea-pens (*Pennatulidae*) live in deep water ; they have a long stalk imbedded in sand or mud, with a plume of branches bearing the polyps.

Zoantharia. In the Zoantharia, the tentacles are generally six, or some multiple of six, in number. This group includes the sea-anemones and corals.

The sea-anemones are solitary polyps with several circles of tentacles, and are found attached to rocks, piers, etc., generally in shallow water. Many of them are brightly coloured, and some, when fully expanded, are very beautiful. A curious association is that between a hermit-crab (*Eupagurus*) and the sea-anemone (*Adamsia*) that grows on the shell it inhabits. The anemone protects the crab by its long stinging tentacles, and shares its food.

CORALS

Coral polyps are similar to sea-anemones, but they form colonies and secrete a hard calcareous skeleton in the form either of a branching structure, or a massive rock, the surface of which is covered with cups containing the polyps.

The reef-building corals occur in tropical seas : by continuous division the polyps increase in number, always keeping at the surface of the large, solid, calcareous masses that they secrete, which are the principal constituents of coral-reefs. The largest coral-reef is the Great Barrier Reef, that extends for over twelve hundred miles off the coast of Queensland.

The polyps of the reef-building corals cannot live at a depth of more than about thirty fathoms, and the occurrence of many ring-shaped coral islands, perched on mountain-tops in the ocean, is puzzling ; the question how so many mountains come near enough to the surface for corals to grow on them is not yet satisfactorily answered.

*Class 4. CTENOPHORA (Comb-bearing Jellies or Sea-gooseberries)

The Ctenophores are transparent creatures of tropical and temperate seas, generally spherical in shape, that swim by means of the rapid movements of eight rows of little plates on the body. They have no stings, but some forms, such as *Pleurobrachia*, have two long tentacles with cells that contain coiled threads ; when released these threads do not pierce the prey, but stick to it. The beautiful phosphorescent Venus's Girdle (*Cestus veneris*) is ribbon-shaped, and may reach a length of over four feet.   * See page 30

Phylum PLATYHELMINTHES
(Flat-worms, Flukes and Tape-worms)

Class 1. TURBELLARIA

The Turbellaria are soft-bodied, unsegmented animals that are flat and generally oval in shape. The mouth is on the under surface of the body, and is at the end of a muscular proboscis that can be withdrawn, or be thrust out for a considerable distance.

These animals live either in the sea, or in freshwater, or in damp places on land. They are mostly carnivorous, and often suck the juices of small worms, insect larvae, etc. In the marine *Acoela* the pharynx opens into the soft spongy tissue of the body, but in other groups a stomach is present, either simple or branched, and there is an elaborate excretory system of branching canals penetrating to all parts of the body.

Planaria and *Dendrocoelum* are common flatworms, found in ponds in Britain.

Class 2. TREMATODA
(Flat-worms and Flukes)

These differ from the Turbellaria especially in being parasitic and in having suckers or hooks for attachment to the host. Many have a complicated life history, in the course of which they pass from one host to another.

[*H. Bastin*

TURBELLARIA (*Eurylepta cornuta*).
A marine flat-worm found on the British coast.

The cause of the disease known in sheep as liver-rot is the liver-fluke (*Distomum hepaticum*). The fluke lives in the liver of sheep, and there becomes sexually mature; the eggs hatch out as little larvae, and if these pass from the sheep into water, or on to grass in water meadows, they find a small water-snail (*Limnaea truncatula*) and bore their way into it, and after a time produce a number of tiny tadpole-like creatures, which swim away, attach themselves to blades of grass, and lose their tails; if the grass is eaten by a sheep, they enter its liver, and so the life cycle is completed.

Class 3. CESTODA (Tape-worms)

The Tape-worms are parasitic, elongate worms, attached by hooks

35

and suckers borne on the swollen anterior end of the body, which consists of a large number of flat segments, each of which appears to represent an individual, and has a complete set of reproductive organs and a branched excretory system, but no mouth or stomach. Tape-worms are parasitic in the alimentary canal of vertebrates: the posterior segments break off and are voided by the host, and produce eggs that are laid on the ground or in water. The eggs are taken in by another animal, the intermediate host, when it eats or drinks, and in it hatch out as larvae, with hooks on their heads that enable them to bore into the tissues of the host, where they grow into vesicles—or bladder-worms—from the walls of which a tape-worm head, with hooks and suckers, develops. If this intermediate host be eaten by an animal of the same kind as the original host, the bladder-worms develop into mature tape-worms in the alimentary canal of the new host.

Taenia solium, which may reach a length of several feet, is a tape-worm found in man; the bladder-worms of this species generally occur in the flesh of pigs. Carnivorous or omnivorous animals are the ones that generally harbour tape-worms in the alimentary canal, but all sorts of animals may serve as intermediate hosts.

PHYLUM NEMATHELMINTHES (Round-worms)

The Thread-worms (*Nematoda*) are an interesting and important group of animals, owing to the fact that many are parasitic in animals and plants, and some are responsible for certain serious diseases in Man.

They are a group of worm-like creatures, with unsegmented bodies clothed in a tough cuticle. They range in size from under a millimetre in length up to about a metre. The mouth is situated at one extremity of the body and the alimentary canal, which is fairly simple, runs straight through the body. There is an anterior nerve collar round the oesophagus; simple sense organs (tactile papillae and eye spots) and an excretory system are present. There are no special circulatory or respiratory organs.

The sexes are usually distinct and the male tends to be smaller than the female. Some kinds are viviparous, others lay eggs enclosed in horny cases. The young Nematode develops into the adult more or less directly and without any clearly marked metamorphosis.

Thread-worms are found in nearly all parts of the world. A large number of them are free-living and are found in the sea, in freshwater and on land. The terrestrial forms live in moss, soil, and decaying organic substances. The parasitic forms have either a simple life-history, passing directly from one host to another of the same species, or else they require an " intermediate host," which may be of an altogether different group. Thus the Guinea Worm (*Filaria bancrofti*) is transmitted from one human sufferer to another by the bite of an insect, which is the intermediate host.

Ascaroidea. The Ascaroidea contain both free-living and parasitic forms, the latter usually with a direct life-history. *Ascaris* is a large genus of well over two-hundred and fifty species, all of which are parasites of vertebrates. *A. lumbricoides* is found in man, pigs and oxen; the method of infection is not certainly known. *A. megalocephala*, found in the horse, ass, ox, etc., sometimes attains a length of seventeen inches. The *Anguillulidae* cause the well-known galls in corn, "ear-cockles."

Strongyloidea. The Strongyloidea include the *Ancylostomidae*, or Hook-worms, of which *Necator* and *Ancylostoma* are the most common. These forms cause ulceration of the intestine in man, and are probably mildly poisonous. "Hook-worm disease," without being very deadly, is most destructive to human health, mental and physical.

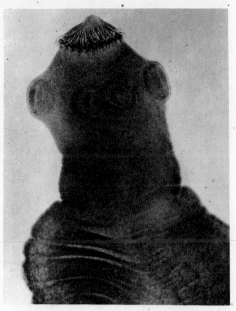

Filarioidea. The Filarioidea have an indirect life-history. The Guinea Worm of West Africa (*Dracunculus medinensis*) is transmitted from one human subject to another by a small crustacean (*Cyclops*) that lives in drinking water. Many forms of *Filaria* are carried by mosquitoes.

Dioctophymoidea. The small order Dioctophymoidea comprises only three genera, one of which is *Dioctophyme*, the largest living Nematode.

[John J. Ward.
HEAD OF TAPE-WORM FROM THE HARE.
Showing hooks and suckers with which it grips and moves about on the intestines of its host.

Trichinelloidea. In the Trichinelloidea is found the single family Trichinellidae, which include various forms found in man and acquired by him through eating "measly" pork, infected by the encysted larvae of the parasite.

Desmoscolecidae and Chaetostomatidae. Two families, Desmoscolecidae and Chaetostomatidae, which are both marine and free-living, are usually ranked as Nematoda, though their correct position is rather uncertain.

Nematomorpha. Sometimes associated with the Nematoda are the Nematomorpha, which are thread-like, unsegmented worms living in the larval stage as parasites in various aquatic and terrestrial invertebrates.

PHYLUM ACANTHOCEPHALA (Thorny-headed Worms)

The Acanthocephala are related to the Nematodes; they are parasitic in the adult stage in aquatic or semi-aquatic vertebrates, and pass their larval stage in certain invertebrates, such as Crustacea.

In the adult, the body is divisible into proboscis, neck and trunk. The proboscis is armed with hooks by which the animal clings to the tissues of its host ; it can be withdrawn into a special sheath. The skin is like that of a Nematode, and below it is a remarkable system of canals and cavities full of a clear fluid. There is no alimentary canal, the animals living by absorbing the fluids of the host's body through their skin. The sexes are separate, rather an unusual phenomenon in parasites. *Echinorhynchus proteus* lives as an adult in freshwater fishes (pike, gudgeon, etc.), and its larvae are found in the Amphipod Crustacean *Gammarus pulex* (Freshwater Shrimp) or in other fishes. Other forms are found in birds, swine, fin-whales and seals.

Phylum NEMERTINEA (Ribbon-worms)

The Nemertines are a group of worm-like animals of doubtful affinities. They are mostly found in the sea, but a few live in fresh water and on land.

A typical Nemertine, such as our common *Lineus marinus*, is an elongate animal with a smooth unsegmented body covered with cilia. The mouth is situated on the ventral surface near the anterior end, at the tip of which is a small pore from which a proboscis can be thrust out. This proboscis, which in one group is armed with spines, is an organ of touch and also of defence. The alimentary canal runs straight through the body. There is a well-developed nervous system, and several eyes are usually found on the head. There is a blood-system, but no heart. In the Nemertines the sexes are distinct, and development is either direct, or a larval stage is found (*Pilidium* larva).

The Nemertines have a nearly world-wide distribution. The group as a whole is carnivorous, and they are described as very voracious. The marine forms live in shallow water and are found under stones or on muddy and sandy bottoms. The larger kinds are solitary, but the smaller live in coiled masses.

Phylum CHAETOGNATHA (Arrow-worms)

The Chaetognatha or " Arrow-worms," of which *Sagitta* is the best-known genus, are a conspicuous feature in the floating life of the sea (plankton). They are, at certain times of the day and in certain latitudes, so plentiful that the surface seems alive with them. In appearance they are transparent, torpedo-shaped creatures, rarely exceeding two inches in length. The head is blunt and somewhat rounded ; it is surrounded by a kind of hood, inside which are some rows of spines. Flat, horizontal projections from the body form a tail-fin, and one or two pairs of lateral fins.

WHEEL ANIMALCULES (ROTIFERA)

There is a straight alimentary canal and a nervous system, but no special respiratory, circulatory or excretory organs. The Chaetognatha are hermaphrodite, and the eggs are shed into the water and develop without a larval stage.

These animals feed on unicellular floating plants and animals, but they will also attack larger creatures, such as Copepods and young fishes. They swim about by movements of the whole body, the fins being used as balancing organs. They are found at depths down to seven hundred to eight hundred fathoms, and seem to perform daily or periodic migrations from the surface to deep water and back again.

[F. Schensky.

RIBBON-WORMS (*Langia*).
The long, flat body, frilled at the edge, is distinctive of this marine Nemertean.

PHYLUM ROTIFERA (Wheel Animalcules)

The Rotifera or " Wheel Animalcules " are aquatic animals of minute size ; their most obvious structural feature is a ciliated disc at the anterior end of the body. Their affinities are very obscure.

A typical Rotifer has a body divisible into two distinct parts, a broad trunk enclosed in a transparent cuticle, and a slender, wrinkled tail. In front the body projects as a disc, the edge of which is fringed with cilia, by means of which the animal may be driven through the water. The mouth, situated at a point on the circumference of the disc, leads into a muscular pharynx armed with hard elements of complex structure that serve as masticatory organs. There is a simple nervous system, but no definite blood-system.

Rotifers are strange little creatures, mostly inhabiting fresh water. Many crawl about, or swim, but anchor themselves when at rest by means of pincers at the end of the tail; others fix themselves by means of a sucker at the end of the tail, and secrete a gelatinous tube. *Pedalion* is remarkable for having arthropod-like limbs, with which it skips about.

[*H. Bastin.*
Wheel Animalcule (*Rotifer vulgaris*).
Enormously magnified.
It is often seen anchored by its pointed tail to a leaf or stem of some water-plant.

Many Rotifera, if the ponds or ditches dry up in the summer, form a gelatinous sheath that protects them from evaporation, and so enables them to live until water returns.

A remarkable thing about Rotifers is the difference between the sexes. The males are much smaller than the females, and hatch from the egg fully developed; they have no gut, and neither feed nor grow, but live for a short time only to breed. During the summer the females produce parthenogenetically thin-shelled eggs of two kinds, the large developing into females and the small into males. Thick-shelled eggs are probably the result of fertilisation; these remain dormant for a considerable time; they resist drought and often rest throughout the winter, hatching out in the spring.

Phylum ECHINODERMATA
(Starfishes, Sea-urchins, Sea-lilies and Sea-cucumbers)

The Starfishes and Sea-urchins are the best-known representatives of this phylum. Although they are highly organised animals, they resemble the Coelenterata in having the main lines of the body and the chief organs arranged radially about a common centre. They are found only in the sea, and, with the exception of a few species that live in estuaries and similar areas, seem quite incapable of living in fresh or brackish water.

The Starfishes (*Asteroids*), Sea-urchins (*Echinoids*), and their relations the Sea-cucumbers (*Holothurians*), Sea-lilies (*Crinoids*) and Brittle-stars (*Ophiuroids*) differ very markedly in their shape, but they agree in the main architecture of the body. The symmetry of the body is five-rayed (or on some system based on a multiple of five), that is to say, the organs are arranged along five lines that radiate from a common centre. The body is generally either spherical or disc-like. In sea-urchins and starfishes the mouth is in the centre of the under surface.

STARFISHES, SEA-URCHINS AND SEA-CUCUMBERS

The Echinoderm body is generally covered with an external skeleton, which may form a compact armour of closely fitting plates, as in the Echinoids, or may be composed of isolated spicules, as in the Sea-cucumbers. The plates are formed from concretions of crystalline carbonate of lime (calcite) and may carry prickles or spines jointed to them. In the Asteroids and Echinoids some of the prickles are modified as pincers of various kinds, used either for cleaning, for defence, to hold prey, or to kill small animals. The spines are primarily defensive, but in the Sea-urchins they assist in locomotion.

The alimentary canal is simple and without any glandular appendages.* There is no heart, no regular circulation, and no definite excretory system. The nervous system is well-developed, but there are no special organs of sense. The sexes are separate; the eggs are discharged into the sea, except in some deep - water

[*Herbert Flower.*

STARFISHES (*Asterias*).
The armed form contrasts with the disc-like *Pentaceros*.

and Polar species, which incubate the young. In the course of development there is usually a free-swimming, bilaterally symmetrical larval stage.

One of the most characteristic features of the group is the water vascular system, a system of tubes which terminate in the tube-feet. A circular canal round the mouth gives off a branch to each ray ; each branch bears a double series of small tubes with sucker-like tips, that can be protruded or retracted. This system is connected with the exterior by a canal leading to an external plate pierced with pores, and the water it contains is passed to the tube-feet, where, under varying degrees of pressure, it provides the suckers with the power by which they drag the body along.

* Glandular "pyloric caeca" are found in the Asteroids.

INVERTEBRATA (PHYLUM ECHINODERMATA)

The Echinoderms nearly all live on the sea bottom, and very few adult floating forms are known. Most of the Crinoids are fixed down by a stalk. Though well-organised and complex, they are extremely sluggish and inert creatures. Their feeding habits vary a good deal.

The phylum has had a long geological history and several groups became extinct before Secondary times. There are five classes of living forms : *Asteroidea* (Starfishes), *Ophiuroidea* (Brittle-stars), *Echinoidea* (Sea-urchins), *Crinoidea* (Sea-lilies), and *Holothuroidea* (Sea-cucumber).

Class 1. ASTEROIDEA (Starfishes)

[H. Bastin.

STARFISH (*Pentaceros reticulatus*).
A large West Indian species. The shilling shows its relative size.

The Starfishes, of which our common *Asterias rubens* is an example, are star-shaped or pentagonal in outline, and have the body flattened. *Asterias* has a simple five-rayed organisation, but the number of rays may be as high as forty-five (*Labidiaster*). *Asterias* also shows the star-shaped form in which the rays are distinct arms, as contrasted with the form in which the body is a five-sided disc.

The skin is well protected either by a regular pavement of plates, or by a loose meshwork of irregularly arranged rods ; the plates are often studded with spines. The water vascular system is well developed, and the tube-feet are numerous, at the sides of a groove that extends down each arm from the mouth. In some Asteroids the young are incubated in the maternal body, and in *Stichaster nutrix* they are said to undergo their early development in outgrowths of the stomach. The development is rarely direct ; there is usually a larva (*Bipinnaria*) in which the body is encircled by two ciliated bands.

Starfishes vary very much in size, and some very large examples are known. *Freyella remex*, which was obtained by the *Challenger* Expedition off New Guinea at the great depth of two-thousand four-hundred fathoms, has

42

an arm radius measuring eighteen inches.

Starfishes live on the sea-bottom, and obtain their food by means of the tube-feet. *Asterias* is known to prey upon oysters and other molluscs, the valves of which are torn asunder, the body of the mollusc being sucked in by the stomach. A curious capacity is the power of casting off the arms "at will" and subsequently

[*Otho Webb.*

SLATE PENCIL SEA-URCHIN (*Heterocentrotus mamillatus*).
A form with remarkable pencil-shaped spines.

regenerating them. Sometimes a single arm can regenerate a whole animal, and a single large arm may be found with four small regenerated ones.

Among interesting genera we may note the beautiful Sun Star (*Heliaster*) of British seas, which is a brilliant orange colour and may have over twenty-five arms, the deep-water *Brisinga*, which has many very long arms, and the *Pentagonasteridae*, in which the interbrachial region is filled out so as to obscure the individual arms.

Class 2. OPHIUROIDEA (Brittle-stars)

The Brittle-stars have long, slender arms without grooves, clearly marked off from the small central region of the body. These animals live on the sea bottom. They move fairly rapidly by bending their arms sideways, and in some large forms by a wave-like vertical movement resembling that of a snake.

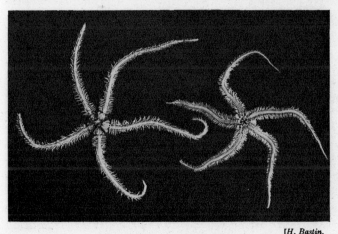

They get the name "Brittle-star" from their habit of breaking off the arms when irritated; they are able, however, to regenerate them.

The Ophiuroids have usually a very

[*H. Bastin.*

BRITTLE-STARS (*Ophiuroidea*).
These take their name from their habit of breaking off their arms when they are disturbed.

43

perfect armour of plates, which forms a series of segments on each arm. The water vascular system resembles that of the Asteroidea, but the tube-feet are modified, and are sensory in function.

The development is usually indirect, and there is a special ciliated larval stage (" *Ophiopluteus* "). In some Ophiuroids the arms are branched, and in species of *Gorgonocephalus* they divide repeatedly, the animal being a remarkable mass of slender, branching arms. *Ophiothrix fragilis* is a common British species.

Class 3. ECHINOIDEA (Sea-urchins)

The Sea-urchins are either spherical, oval, or disc-like, generally enclosed in a shell composed of closely-fitting plates, supplied with movable spines. The tube-feet protrude through rows of pores extending nearly to the dorsal part of the sphere. The sea-urchins live on the bottom, over which they crawl slowly by means of the long tube-feet and spines. Some live on rocky bottoms, but others prefer burrowing in sand. Many are omnivorous. There are five pairs of " gills." In a few forms development takes place inside the mother's body; but it is usually external, and a larval stage, the *Pluteus*, is regularly found.

A very large number of living and fossil Echinoids are known. The Spatangoids (Heart-urchins) are more or less heart-shaped. The Common Heart-urchin (*Echinocardium cordatum*), which burrows in sand, has no teeth and feeds on minute animals. The Clypeastroids, or Cake-urchins, are remarkably flattened forms (*Rotula* and *Mellita*) with resemblance to some kind of biscuit. *Echinus esculentus*, a common British urchin. is

[*H. Bastin.*

COMMON SEA-URCHIN (*Echinus esculentus*).
Shown with and without spines.

globular, and red or purple in colour. *Echinus* has an elaborate system of teeth, known as "Aristotle's Lantern," which consists essentially of five stout teeth surrounding the mouth and projecting somewhat from it, borne on a complex basal mechanism, the whole being shaped not unlike an old-fashioned lantern.

Class 4. CRINOIDEA
(Sea-lilies or Feather-stars)

The Sea-lilies or Feather-stars are fixed to the sea-bottom during the whole or part of their life. They are usually anchored down to the bottom

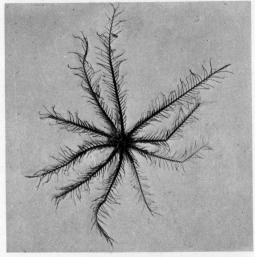

[*H. Bastin.*
SEA-LILY OR "FEATHER-STAR" (*Antedon*).
The feathery arms are used to catch minute organisms.

by a flexible jointed stalk, which is a prolongation from the apical part of the body. The body consists of a disc-like "calyx" from which the long, branching arms project, with the mouth in the centre. The tube-feet are devoid of the mechanism for locomotion, and may be sensory and respiratory.

The number of living Crinoid genera is small, but the group was an exceedingly flourishing one in Primary and Secondary times. A good number of Crinoids are found in deep water. They feed upon minute organisms which are brought to the mouth by currents set up by the cilia on the grooves of the arms.

In the permanently-anchored forms the stalk may be very long; it is formed of a number of separate segments which are jointed together. The British Feather-star (*Antedon rosacea*) is fixed by a stem when young, but later breaks off all but the top segment of the stem and swims away. This segment bears a number of fibrous processes which are used to anchor the animal when it comes to rest. The plume-like arms of this species are used to catch minute organisms.

Class 5. HOLOTHUROIDEA (Sea-cucumbers)

The Sea-cucumbers take their name from their shape, which is quite unlike that of other Echinoderms; indeed, they are more like worms in appearance. The mouth is at one end of the body and is surrounded by a circle of tentacles, which are used either for catching small prey, or to help pass into the mouth the mud from which these animals derive some nutriment. The skin is flexible and somewhat leathery, and contains scattered spicules. The tube-feet, when present, may be arranged

45

more or less definitely in five longitudinal series. *Holothuria nigra* is a British species; it reaches a length of about a foot and crawls about by means of the tube-feet of one side of the body, which is flattened. The *Synaptidae* have a cylindrical, worm-like body, and no tube-feet; these burrow in sand or mud. Some species of the Pacific are valued as food, and are known as *Trepang* or *Bêche-de-mer*. The animals are captured at low tide by spearing or in deeper water by divers. They are usually eviscerated, boiled, dried and smoked. The product is greatly appreciated by the Chinese.

[W. S. Berridge.
SEA-CUCUMBER (*Holothuria*).
Sea-cucumbers are worm-like Echinoderms that crawl about or burrow.

PHYLUM BRACHIOPODA ("Lamp Shells")

The Brachiopoda or "Lamp Shells," like bivalve Mollusca, are encased in a shell composed of two plates.

The Brachiopoda are marine, and mostly live in rather deep water. They are not particularly numerous at the present day, but the group is a very old one, which flourished in Primary times, over two thousand species being known from Silurian rocks.

One valve of the shell is usually larger than the other, and has a prominent beak. The valves are not placed one on each side of the body as in a bivalve Mollusc, but one in front and one behind. They are secreted by a sheath of skin that encloses a cavity, in which lies the main part of the body. The mouth is surrounded by an expansion prolonged as two long arms, often coiled, fringed with tentacles; these are covered with cilia (vibrating hair-like processes), which drive food particles towards the mouth. Posteriorly the body is continued as a stalk (peduncle) which passes between the valves and anchors the animal down. The Brachiopoda live on the sea-bottom, and nearly all are fixed by the stalk. The sexes are separate, and the young pass through a larval stage in development.

Lingulidae. The most interesting forms are the *Lingulidae*, which are found in Lower Cambrian rocks and have persisted down to the present day, without any alteration. The Indo-Pacific *Lingula* has a small shell and a long stalk; it lives in tubes excavated in the sand, and is generally at the mouth of the tube; but if it is disturbed, the stalk contracts and rapidly draws the animal down into the tube.

Phylum POLYZOA

The Polyzoa are small aquatic animals that form colonies, appearing either as fixed, branching growths, or as crusts on stones, shells or weeds. These growths are generally made up of numerous little adjacent chambers, usually horny or calcareous; sometimes the chambers project separately from the stem. Each chamber has an opening through which the animal it contains

[H. Bastin.

POLYZOON.
An encrusted Polyzoon growing on a water-weed.

can protrude the circle of long tentacles that surround its mouth; in some forms this opening can be closed by a hinged lid when the tentacles are withdrawn. The alimentary canal of the Polyzoa is U-shaped; there is a nerve ganglion, but no blood-system, nor special organs of excretion or respiration. There is a free-swimming larva, which comes to rest, fixes itself, and develops into a colony by budding.

[M. H. Crawford.

SEA-MAT (*Flustra foliacea*).
A growth of branching fronds, formed of a double layer of chambers.

Most of the Polyzoa are marine, and some live at considerable depths; there are, however, a good many freshwater species. They feed on minute organisms, which are brought to the mouth by the continuous vibration of the hair-like cilia that cover the tentacles.

Sea-mats. The Sea-mat (*Flustra*) forms a seaweed-like

47

growth of flat, branching fronds, made up of a double layer of chambers set back to back. Fragments of sea-mat may often be found among seaweeds cast up on the shore, and show a fine network pattern on the surface, which a lens reveals to be due to the outlines of the walls of the chambers. This species belongs to a group in which the chambers can be closed by lids; some of these exhibit remarkable modifications, some individuals assuming the form of a bird's head, with the lid of the chamber as a kind of jaw that performs snapping movements; these "bird's heads" may seize and hold small animals. In other individuals the lids may be produced into long lashes; the movements of these lashes may keep the colony clean.

[M. H. Crawford.
COWRIES (Cypraea).
Cowry shells are used as ornaments and in some places, as money.

Of the British marine species that have chambers with lids, we may mention *Lepralia foliacea*, in which thin calcareous plates, formed of two layers of chambers, back to back, unite in places to form a massive growth penetrated by channels. *Alcyonidium gelatinosum*, which is attached to stones or shells as a fleshy growth, often of large size, is a common lidless form.

In one group of Polyzoa the tentacles are borne on the edges of a horseshoe-shaped support. All the members of this group inhabit fresh water; they form peculiar internal buds, which are protected by a capsule, and live through the winter, when the rest of the colony dies, to start growth again in the spring.

PHYLUM MOLLUSCA
(Whelk, Snail, Slug, Oyster, Octopus, etc.)

The Mollusca, on account of their numbers, their remarkable diversity of form, and their success in colonising the sea, fresh water, and the land, may be considered the third most important of the phyla of the Animal Kingdom. They include such animals as the Whelk, the Snail, the Slug, the Oyster, and the Octopus. Though the Snail and the Octopus are at

BAILER OR MELON SHELL (*Melo amphora*).
An underwater photograph showing the siphon that conducts water into the mantle cavity.

first sight very unlike each other, they are placed in the same group because of the similarity of their general organisation.

The Mollusca are mainly elongated animals, the under surface of whose bodies is very muscular and forms a foot. At one end of the body the mouth and chief nerve-ganglia are situated. Usually the mouth is furnished with a rasping tongue (radula) beset with numerous small teeth. The body is sheathed in a thin fold of skin, the mantle, by which a shell is secreted. The shell, which is mainly formed of carbonate of lime, usually covers the animal completely ; but in certain forms it is internal and degenerate or it may be entirely absent. The mantle hangs down around the body like a skirt and encloses a cavity (mantle-cavity) in which the breathing-organs are situated.

The Mollusca are essentially slow-moving animals and rely on the shell for protection. Some molluscs, indeed, have become swimmers, and others are adapted for floating ; but the majority move about by crawling and are " sluggish " creatures. They live in all parts of the world from the tropics to the Polar regions. They are found at very great heights on mountains, and some have been brought up from great depths in the sea. Their inert constitution enables them to live in places that would be fatal to many other animals. They are of considerable economic importance as human food in many parts of the world, and as the source of pearls and mother-of-pearl. They are obnoxious to man only to a very limited extent.

Photos]   *[Otho Webb.*
CHITON (*Acanthozostera gemmata*).
The Chitons bear a series of eight plates ; they can roll up like woodlice.

THE "FIG" SHELL.
(One of the Gastropoda.)

The Mollusc Phylum is divided into five classes : the *Amphineura* ("Coat-of-Mail Shells "), the *Gastropoda* (Whelks, Snails, etc.), the *Scaphopoda* (" Tusk Shells "), the *Lamellibranchia* (Mussels, Oysters, etc.), and the *Cephalopoda* (Octopods, Squids, etc.).

Class I. AMPHINEURA (Chitons or "Coat-of-Mail Shells ")

This class mainly consists of the Chitons or " Coat-of-Mail Shells." These are marine animals recognisable by their flat bodies covered by eight overlapping shell-plates, from which the popular name is derived. As they can roll up into a more or less spherical shape, they are sometimes compared to Woodlice. They are usually small and inconspicuous, though the Giant Chiton of the north-eastern Pacific (*Cryptochiton stelleri*) often attains a length of ten inches.

Outside the shell-plates the skin of the mantle is covered with spicules, which are often so thick and long as to give the animal a shaggy look. The shell-plates themselves are pierced by numerous holes, through which pass the nerves supplying numerous sense-organs called "shell-eyes." The Chitons have a flat foot on the under surface of the body, and between the foot and the edge of the mantle on each side is a row of gills. The head is very slightly differentiated from the rest of the body and bears no special sense-organs.

Photos]   *[H. Bastin.*
LIMPETS (*Patella vulgata.*)
Limpets adhere to rocks and are difficult to dislodge.

50

SNAIL, SLUG, LIMPET, ETC. (GASTROPODA)

"Top Shells" (*Trochidae*).
These are common on the shores of Britain.

The Chitons are found in all seas, and three to four hundred species have been described. The majority live in shallow water, on or under stones. A good many, however, have been obtained from deep water.

Among the more interesting Chitons we may mention the *Acanthochitonidae*, in which the shell valves are deeply sunk in the mantle, and the *Cryptoplacidae*, in which the valves are degenerate. Related to the Chitons are two very interesting forms, *Chaetoderma* and *Neomenia*, which have no shell at all and look very like worms. *Chaetoderma* has at the posterior end of its body a bell-shaped cavity in which the gills are placed. It lives on muddy bottoms at all depths, and feeds on minute organisms such as Protozoa. *Neomenia* is found on corals and hydroids, on which it feeds.

Gastropod Shells.

Class 2. GASTROPODA (Snail, Slug, Limpet, Whelk, etc.)

This is the largest of the classes into which the Mollusca are divided, and includes marine, freshwater and terrestrial forms. The most characteristic feature of these animals is the spirally coiled shell, as seen in the Snail and the Periwinkle. The head region is well-developed, and bears one or two pairs of tentacles ; the internal anatomy is peculiar owing to the atrophy of the gill, kidney and other organs of the original left side of the body.

Photos]   *[John J. Ward.*
Great Triton Shell.
(One of the Gastropoda.)

The Gastropoda are slow-moving creatures, and spend their lives crawling about on the sea-bottom or on rocks, on the bottoms and submerged vegetation of lakes and streams, or on trees, grassy banks and among plant-debris. A few groups live permanently floating in the sea (plankton). They are essentially plant-eaters, but many of them have become carnivorous. A few families are parasitic, and the *Eulimidae* and

51

[*John J. Ward.*
ROCK WHELK (*Murex*).
From this gastropod purple dyes were formerly made.

Entoconchidae are internal parasites of Echinoderms. A vast number of species of Gastropods have been described. The exact number is uncertain, but probably not less than thirty-five thousand.

The Gastropoda are divided into two great sub-classes, the *Streptoneura* and *Euthyneura*.

Sub-Class I.. STREPTONEURA
(Limpets, River-snails, Land-snails, Periwinkles, Cowries, Whelks)

The members of this large sub-class are distinguished by having the visceral loop of the nervous system twisted into a figure-of-eight. The sexes are separate, and after fertilisation the developing animal passes through a larval stage (Trochosphere).

The most primitive members of the group still have distinct traces of a symmetrical organization. The Limpets (*Patellidae*) are probably the most familiar examples of such primitive Streptoneura. The Common Limpet (*Patella vulgata*) is found on most of the rocky coasts of the British Isles, adhering to the rocks by its flat foot. Its powers of adhesion are very considerable, and it has been calculated that it can resist a pull equivalent to fifty-four pounds weight. This power of adhesion is useful in enabling the Limpets to resist both the force of the waves (which might otherwise wash them away to unsuitable habitats), and the efforts of enemies (such as sea-birds) to dislodge them.

Rhipidoglossa. The genus *Pleurotomaria* includes only five living species, in the West Indies, the Moluccas and Japan ; but there are several hundred extinct species.

The " Ear-shells " or Ormers (*Haliotis*) are remarkable on account of the large size of the last chamber (whorl) of the shell, which is widely open and not unlike a human ear.

The " Top-Shells " (*Trochidae*) have a world-wide distribution. They are to be found on our own shores, where the little speckled *Trochus cinerarius* (" Ashy Top ") and the

[*F. Martin Duncan.*
SEA-HARES (*Aplysia punctata*).
These animals emit a purple secretion when irritated.

[W. S. Berridge.
GREAT BLACK SLUG (*Arion ater*).
Slugs may be described as snails without external shells.

delicate pink *Trochus zizyphinus* (" Common Top ") are common objects. The *Helicinidae* have taken to living on land, and their gill is replaced by a lung. *Titiscania*, a Pacific form, is slug-like and devoid of a shell.

The forms described above with several other families form a group named the *Rhipidoglossa*, and may be generally regarded as more primitive than the *Taenioglossa*, which include all forms related to the common Periwinkles. They are mainly marine, but there are some very common fresh water forms. Species of *Paludestrina* may be found swarming in ditches and streams in England, and the River Whelk (*Vivipara*) is a common inhabitant of larger streams and rivers.

[M. H. Crawford.
GARDEN SNAIL AND EGGS (*Helix aspersa*).

Littorinidae. The Periwinkles are a large family of marine Gastropods, with some species that are on the way to becoming terrestrial. Thus our common *Littorina rudis* has been found living over a mile from the sea. In these molluscs the gill is in process of modification, and the mantle-cavity is changing into a lung.

Other interesting groups allied to the Periwinkles are the Apple-snails (*Ampullariidae*), an amphibious family found in tropical swamps and rivers, the Cowries (*Cypraeidae*), the Purple-snails (*Ianthinidae*), which live floating at the surface of the sea and tow their eggs about suspended

[John J. Ward.
THE ROMAN OR EDIBLE SNAIL (*Helix pomatia*).

53

on the underside of a gelatinous raft or float, the parasitic *Eulimidae*, and the " Cup-and-Saucer " and the " Slipper " Limpets (*Calyptraeidae*).

Rhachiglossa. These have the mouth formed into a proboscis, which can be protruded from the head. They are mainly carnivorous, and some of them attain a considerable size. The most familiar family is that of the true Whelks (*Buccinidae*). The *Coralliophilidae* burrow into corals ; their shell is irregular and its spiral is unwound. Some genera of Rock Whelks (*Muricidae*) have the shell covered with long and sharp spines. The Cones (*Conidae*) have very handsome and elaborately patterned shells, and their mouth is furnished with a poison-gland.

[*M. H. Crawford.*
FRESHWATER SNAILS (*Limnaea stagnalis*).
Feeding on water-weed in an aquarium.

Sub-class 2. EUTHY-NEURA (Bubble-shells, Sea-butterflies, Sea-hares, Sea-slugs and Snails)

In nearly all these Gastropods the nervous system is untwisted in the adult. The sexes are united in a single individual (hermaphrodite).

Opisthobranchia. The first order is that of the Opisthobranchia. These are marine forms, which show a very marked tendency for the shell to disappear. Among those which retain the shell are the *Bullomorpha* or " Bubble-shells " (*Actaeon,*

Scaphander, etc.), which have the head provided with a " digging-shield " by which they burrow in sand, and the *Pterota* or " Sea-butterflies." The latter are sometimes united with another group of Opisthobranchia, the shell-less *Gymnosomata*, as a single tribe—the " Pteropoda." These animals are very small and delicate, and form an important part of the minute floating life of the sea.

At certain places on the south and west shores of the British Isles, there is to be found a curious form, the Sea-hare (*Aplysia*), so-called from its resemblance to a crouching hare. These animals have an internal shell ; they emit a purple secretion when irritated.

The Sea-slugs (*Eolidae*) are shell-less molluscs, very often of attractive and fantastic shape and colour. Many species may be found in rock

54

pools on British coasts, and are immediately recognizable by the prominent papillae that stud the back. These papillae contain stinging cells which are derived from the hydroids on which they feed, and can be discharged if the animal is irritated or attacked.

Pulmonata. The last order of Gastropods is the great group of the Pulmonata, which includes nearly all the land snails and some aquatic forms. In the land forms the mantle-cavity is converted into a lung. None of the Pulmonata has a true gill, but in some, which have returned to an aquatic life, a secondary or " false " gill is developed.

The large group of the Pulmonata have a world-wide distribution. The order is divided into two suborders.

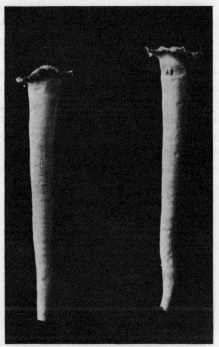

THE WATERING-POT SHELL (*Brechites*). This is a Lamellibranch, see page 57.

Photos]   [*H. Bastin.*
Some of the large land snails lay hard-shelled eggs like those of birds. This species of *Borus* and its egg are from the West Indies and South America.

the *Basommatophora*, which include certain marine and freshwater genera and have on the head a single pair of tentacles, at the base of which the eyes are situated, and the *Stylommatophora*, the large group of terrestrial " snails " which have two pairs of tentacles, with the eyes at the ends of the hinder pair. It is difficult to estimate exactly the number of species in the latter suborder, but there must be well over ten thousand. The most familiar examples are : our Common Snail (*Helix aspersa*), whose freckled and roughly-banded brown and yellow shell may be found in gardens, hedges, etc., and the Wood and Garden Snails (*Cepea nemoralis* and *C. hortensis*).

55

Allied to these genera are the small *Helicellas* of our downlands, and the long, pointed *Cochlicella* of the south and west of England. Other families of land snails contain forms with more brilliant shells, e.g. the *Papuinas* of New Guinea, the Solomon Isles, etc., and the *Helicostylas*. The Giant Snail of South America and the West Indies (*Borus*) is remarkable for its large egg, which is sometimes as large as that of a pigeon. Other interesting families are the *Cylindrellidae*, which have long, turreted shells, the *Clausiliidae*, in which the aperture of the shell is closed by a spoon-shaped plate when the animal retreats inside, and the curious marine *Oncidiidae*, which are slug-like creatures with eyes scattered all over the back. The true slugs (*Limacidae, Arionidae*) have an internal degenerate

[Dr. F. Ward.
LIMA (*Limidae*).
The Limas are like scallops, but have thread-like filaments at the edges of the mantle.

shell, and in some other slug-like forms of tropical countries the shell is absent.

The majority of land Pulmonates are vegetable-eaters, but a few families are carnivorous. Our common British *Testacella* (" Snail-slug ") lives principally on earthworms.

Class 3.
SCAPHOPODA
(Tusk-shells or Tooth-shells)

These molluscs are known as the " Tusk-shells." Though they are ranked as a distinct class on account of their peculiar structure, they contain but two families and a limited number of species. They are an exclusively marine group and have sometimes been taken at very great depths. They live in nearly all seas and are usually found burrowing in the sand.

The shell of the common genus *Dentalium* is elongate, tubular, and open at both ends. One of these openings is larger than the other, and from it the foot of the animal projects. It is easy to understand the structure of these molluscs in relation to that of a Gastropod, if it be realised that the flaps or skirt of the mantle have grown down and joined each other below the body and foot, thus forming a tube, around which the shell is formed. The foot is long and powerful and ends in a prow-like termination (hence the name Scaphopod or " Boat-foot "). The head is very little developed, but projecting from its dorsal side is a bunch of delicate tentacles which are very sensitive, and are used for capturing prey.

The Scaphopods feed on minute animals and plants.

There are two families, *Dentaliidae* and *Siphonopodidae*; in the latter the foot is expanded at the tip into a disc which facilitates progress through the sand, as it seems to act as a kind of lever.

[H. Bastin.
SHELL OF PIDDOCK
(*Pholas*).
Piddocks are marine, and have the power of boring into rocks.

Class 4. LAMELLIBRANCHIA (Bivalves : Oysters, Mussels, Cockles, Clams)

The " Bivalves " (*Lamellibranchia*) are the second largest class of the Mollusca and comprise such forms as the Oysters, Mussels, Cockles and Clams. They are exclusively aquatic and are found both in the sea and in fresh water. In the sea they may be found burrowing in sand or adhering to rocks and submerged objects. In fresh water they inhabit ponds, lakes, rivers and streams.

The Bivalves are at once recognizable by their shell, which is in two parts (valves) placed one on each side of the body, and joined in the middle line by a special apparatus, usually including a hinge and a ligament. The head is rudimentary, and there is no radula. The mantle is well developed, and shows some interesting modifications. Thus it may be joined at one or more points under the body and may be extended backwards to form tubes (siphons). The gills, however, a r e the most important organ in this class. Essentially they are breathing-organs, but they are also important in feeding, as the tiny vibratory hairs (cilia) with which they are covered, drive towards the mouth

[John J. Ward.
THORNY OYSTERS (*Spondylus*).
These shells are heavy and spiny.

57

the minute organisms and broken-down particles of animals and plants on which these molluscs feed.

In some families the gills are modified into pouches (Marsupia), in which the young are incubated.

The foot is usually adapted for burrowing and in many genera it contains a cavity into which a secretion is poured from certain glands; this secretion is extruded as a bunch of tough, horny threads (the byssus) by which the animal attaches itself to solid objects.

The Lamellibranchia are nearly all slow-moving, burrowing creatures. A few move rapidly by hopping movements of the foot (*Tellina*) or by clapping together the valves of the shell, as the Scallops (*Pecten*). A good many are permanently fixed to the bottom (the Oysters, *Spondylus*), and some burrow into wood or rocks [Shipworm (*Teredo*); Piddock (*Pholas*)]. They live almost exclusively on minute floating organisms and organic debris.

The sexes are either separate or are united in a single individual, and the fertilized egg usually passes through a larval stage (*Veliger*) before the adult condition is reached. In several genera the eggs are incubated in the maternal mantle-cavity.

The Lamellibranchia have a considerable economic value as articles of food (Oysters, Cockles, Clams, Scallops, Mussels) and as supplying pearls and mother-of-pearl shell. This class is divided into four main orders, each containing one or more suborders.

Order 1. PROTOBRANCHIA

These are Lamellibranchs with simply-constructed gills, a foot with a flat surface adapted for crawling rather than burrowing, and a very imperfectly-developed byssus.

This is a very small group, though it was larger in earlier geological times. It contains very primitive forms like the *Nuculidae*, *Ledidae* and *Solenomyidae*. These are found in most parts of the world, and some of them have been obtained from great depths in the sea.

Order 2. FILIBRANCHIA (Pearl Oysters, Scallops, Mussels, etc.)

This group contains several well-known genera, such as the Scallops and Mussels. The gills are more complicated than in the Protobranchia, and the byssus is very well developed.

One of the most common British species is the Rainbow Shell (*Anomia*). The iridescent shells of this mollusc are found on many shores and are often collected for the artificial flower industry, as the valves have a resemblance to flower petals. The Anomiidae are fixed down on one side by the byssus, which passes through a deep notch in the right-hand valve. The " Window-pane Oysters " (*Placuna*) belong to this family. They have

58

PEARL OYSTERS, SCALLOPS, MUSSELS (FILIBRANCHIA)

flat, pearly shells, which in the young are so transparent that they are used in certain parts of the East for glazing windows.

Like the Gastropod *Pleurotomaria*, the *Trigonias* may be regarded as "living fossils." At present only six species are known, all of which come from Australasian waters. In Secondary times, however, they were widely distributed, and were represented by a great number of species.

The Mussels (*Mytilidae*) are found in most of the seas of the world. Their byssus is very well-developed, and they may be found

[Otho Webb.

GIANT CLAM (*Tridacna gigas*).
This is the largest living shell-fish, reaching a weight of five hundred pounds.

in thick masses ("mussel scaups") adhering to each other and to pieces of shingle. Some of the genera of mussels that live in warm seas are particularly handsome, the shells being of a rich brown and green colour.

Pectinacea. In the suborder Pectinacea are placed two important groups, the Scallops (*Pectinidae*), and the Pearl Oysters (*Meleagrina*) of the family Aviculidae. The Scallops are important as an article of food, and zoologically they are very interesting on account of the highly-complex eyes with which the fringes of the mantle-lobes are studded.

The Pearl Oysters are found in nearly all warm and tropical seas, though the pearl fisheries are mainly concentrated in India, Japan and Northern Australia. The oysters are fished both for the pearls that are

59

found imbedded in their tissues, and for the shell itself, which has a highly-developed nacreous layer (mother of pearl).

Order 3. EULAMELLIBRANCHIA (True Oyster, Cockle, River and Pond Mussel, etc.)

This is the largest order of Lamellibranchs and contains nine sub-orders. The most familiar examples are the Oyster, the Cockle, and the river and pond Mussels.

Edible Oysters (Ostraeidae) are fixed down to the sea-bottom or to submerged structures by the left valve, which is larger than the right. . They pass through a free larval stage in their development and eventually settle down as " spat," which are young oysters less than one inch in length. In the cultivation of oysters, which is carried out in extensive grounds in shallow water (e.g. at Whitstable in England and Cancale in Brittany), the most important activity is the provision of a suitable bottom on which the spat may settle down. On a very soft bottom they run the risk of finding no solid substance on which to fix themselves, and of being smothered by fine sand and mud. In such places artificial supports such as faggots, tiles, etc., are provided for them.

The *Pinnidae* are amongst the largest shelled Mollusca. *Pinna nobilis*, a Mediterranean species, is over two feet in length. The byssus, which is very fine and silky, is used in some parts for making gloves, bracelets, etc.

Freshwater Oysters and Mussels. The *Unionidae* are the largest family of Lamellibranchia. They include the freshwater Oysters (*Unio*) and freshwater Mussels (*Anodonta*). The former are especially plentiful in the rivers of North America, where they are cultivated for the sake of the shells, which are used for button-making. In this family the young, after being incubated in the gills, are liberated as a special type of larva (*Glochidium*), which becomes attached to the external parts of fishes and passes through a parasitic stage in a cyst in the skin of the fish.

The Ship-worm (*Teredo*) is worm-shaped, and has rows of spines on the valves of the small shell, by means of which it excavates long tunnels in the wood of ships, piers, etc.

The Cockles (*Cardiidae*), Venus-shells, Giant Clams (*Tridacna*), which attain a length of three feet, and Razor-shells (*Solenidae*) are other examples of this large order.

[*John J. Ward.*

SHELLS OF THE PEARLY NAUTILUS
(*Nautilus pompilus*).
Median section and external view. The many-chambered
shell resembles that of the extinct *Ammonite.*

[*Raoul Barba.*

SQUIDS (*Sepia officinalis*).
The sepia of commerce is obtained from the ink produced by these animals.

Order 4. SEPTIBRANCHIA

This is a very small group consisting of three families. They are carnivorous marine forms living at considerable depths and have the gills transformed into a muscular partition which is pierced by holes. Through these holes water is drawn into the inner part of the mantle-cavity for respiration, the muscular partition acting as a kind of suction-pump. *Poromya*, *Cetoconcha* and *Cuspidaria* are examples of this Order.

Class 5. CEPHALOPODA (Squids, Cuttlefish, Octopods and Pearly Nautilus)

This class contains the Squids, Cuttlefish, Octopods and the Pearly Nautilus. The last-named has a coiled external shell, and is superficially not unlike a Gastropod. In the other living members of the class the shell is internal, usually degenerate, or even absent. These Cephalopods with internal shells bear very little external resemblance to the other Mollusca, and the Squids and Cuttlefish look far more like fish. However, their internal structure and general organization are essentially those of a typical mollusc. Their most characteristic feature is that the head, instead of being situated above and in front of the foot (as in a chiton or a limpet), is fused up with it, and the mouth has moved into the middle

61

of the foot. The edges of the foot have become drawn-out as a number of long, sucker-bearing appendages (tentacles and arms), and the body has become high and dome-like. The foot is also modified to form a tube or funnel, out of which the animal can squirt jets of water, by means of which it propels itself through the water.

The Cephalopods are marine animals and are never found in fresh water. They are carnivorous and aggressive in their habits, and the Squids and Cuttlefish are vigorous swimmers, moving by means of the funnel and a pair of fins placed on each side of the body. They feed on crustacea, small fishes and other mollusca. A good many are known to be nocturnal in their habits. The sexes are separate. The male fertilizes the female by means of a specially modified tentacle, which in one group, the Argonautidae, is a highly complex apparatus and can be thrown off by the animal.

All the Cephalopoda lay eggs, which are fixed to the sea-bottom, and the young Squid or Octopus develops directly into the adult without a definite larval stage.

This class of Mollusca is represented at the present time by a relatively small number of living forms. In the remote past it was much larger, and many forms have become extinct. The Ammonites did not survive after the Cretaceous period. The Cephalopoda are divided into two sub-classes, one of which (*Tetrabranchiata*) is constituted by the Nautili (living and fossil) and the Ammonites, the other by the living and extinct Squids, Cuttlefish and Octopods (*Dibranchiata*).

Sub-class 1. TETRABRANCHIATA (Nautilus)

The Nautiloids are represented at the present time by three species of the genus *Nautilus*. These are more primitive than the other members of the class. The shell is completely external and fully formed. The living species of Nautilus are distributed through the seas between the Philippine Islands, New Caledonia and Fiji.

These animals live in relatively shallow water, though they appear to go into deep water to breed. They feed on crabs and prawns, and are often caught by the natives, who use them for food, in a kind of trap like a " crab-pot."

The extinct Ammonites were a very flourishing group in Secondary times, and their coiled shells, which are found very plentifully as fossils in many parts of England, are often elaborately ornamented with knobs and ridges. Some of them are uncoiled, or wound in fantastic shapes.

Sub-class 2. DIBRANCHIATA (Squids, Cuttlefish, Octopods)

In the members of the second sub-class the shell is internal and degenerate in the living forms, except in the single genus *Spirula*, in which it is partly external, and is still calcified and well-formed. In the Squids it is mainly represented by the horny " pen." There is a gland which secretes a dark fluid ; when the animal is attacked, it emits into the water a mass of this fluid, under cover of which it can slip away from its enemy.

The Dibranchiata are divided into two orders, the *Decapoda* (Squids and Cuttlefish) and the *Octopoda* (Octopus and its allies.)

Decapoda (Squids and Cuttlefish). Chief among these animals are the Giant Squids (*Architeuthis*). Some members of this group attain a total length (including the tentacles) of over fifty feet and many stories

[*Dr. F. Ward.*

OCTOPUS.
The suckers on the arms are clearly visible.

(mainly exaggerated) are told of their ferocity and strength. The *Ony-choteuthidae* have the horny rings of some of their suckers converted into formidable hooks. Allied to these forms are some Squids (*Lycoteuthis, Thaumatolampas*), which are deep-sea forms and have light-organs placed in various parts of their bodies, that emit a brilliant light, which is no doubt serviceable in the lightless abyss of the sea.

The *Cranchiidae* include some very strange forms. They are mainly delicate floating animals, and some have gelatinous bodies.

In *Bathothauma* the eyes are on the end of long stalks, and the arms are reduced to a very small size. The Cuttlefish (*Sepiidae*) live in most warm and temperate seas and some of them attain a considerable size. They are distinguished by their long, narrow fins and flat bodies. Both the Cuttlefish and the true Squids (*Loliginidae*) live in shallow coastal waters.

Octopoda. The members of this order have eight arms only, the tentacles found in the Decapoda being absent. The Common Octopus (*Octopus vulgaris*) of European waters and its allies are mainly inhabitants of shallow water, where they hunt for crabs, which they paralyse by ejecting over them the secretion of their poisonous salivary glands. The Giant Octopus of the North Pacific attains a total span of thirty-two feet. The majority of the Octopod genera are deep-water forms and include some very strange and highly modified specimens, the most remarkable of which are the *Cirroteuthidae* and the *Vampyroteuthidae*.

The Paper Nautilus (*Argonauta*) and its allies are remarkable on account of the great difference in size between the males and females, the female being often fifteen times as large as the male. Argonauta has no remnant of the true shell; but from a pair of its arms a new (secondary) shell is secreted, in which the eggs are carried until the embryos hatch out. This secondary shell is extremely delicate and fragile and the name " Paper Nautilus " is given to this animal for this reason.

[*John J. Ward.*
SHELL OF THE PAPER NAUTILUS (*Argonauta argo*).
This delicate shell is secreted by a pair of arms and is used to carry the eggs.

PHYLUM ANNELIDA (Ringed Worms)

The name "worm" is given to a number of soft-bodied animals, more or less elongate in form, which, however, belong to a number of distinct and unrelated phyla. Of these the Annelida, or Ringed Worms, rather closely resemble the Arthropoda in their organization. The body of these animals is made up of a series of segments, appearing externally as rings; internally it is divided by a number of transverse partitions into more or less similar compartments. The gut extends the whole length of the body, there is a head ganglion and a ventral nerve-cord, and a well-developed system of blood-vessels. Very characteristic of the group is the presence on the body of horny bristles.

Class I. POLYCHAETA (Marine Bristle-worms)

The marine Bristle-worms are a large group distinguished from the rest of the Annelida by the prominent lateral feet (parapodia) on which the bristles are borne. The most familiar example is the common Lug- or Sand-worm (*Arenicola*), which is found burrowing in sand between tide-marks.

A typical Polychaet has a long, segmented body, the front end of which is modified as a head, and bears eyes, and tentacles in which are located organs of touch. Each segment behind the head bears a pair of feet, one on each side ; each foot is bilobed, with a bundle of bristles on each lobe. The feet are used for locomotion ; the bristles may be dug into the mud or sand and serve as levers. The feet have also a respiratory function. Many forms have gills, which may be plume-like structures on the head. In many Polychaets the mouth is furnished with a proboscis, which can be thrust out to seize prey, and is furnished with horny jaws.

[Central Press.

FEATHERED SEA-WORMS.
These inhabit tubes that project from the mud ; at the free end are the feathery gills.

Unlike the earthworms, the Polychaeta are normally unisexual. The eggs are liberated in the sea, and development is indirect, there being a characteristic larval form known as the Trochophore, which swims by means of one or more bands of cilia that encircle the body.

In some of the Nereidae mature individuals have the feet of the hinder part of the body modified into flat swimming organs. In the Syllidae similar modifications occur, but the tail of the body breaks off and swims away to breed at the surface of the sea, the head end remaining at the bottom to grow another tail ; in some members of this family one swimming worm after another is produced, breeds and then dies.

The habits and mode of life of the Polychaeta are very varied. The

INVERTEBRATA (PHYLUM ANNELIDA)

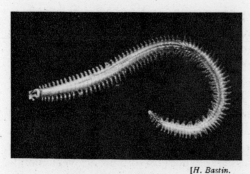

RAG-WORM (*Nereis*). [*H. Bastin.*]

majority live between tide-marks and near the shore, though some have been obtained from deeper water. They either burrow in sand, or live in tubes or holes. A certain number are sedentary and live permanently in calcareous tubes, which are fixed to rocks, the shells of molluscs, the tests of Echinoderms, etc. The food of the Polychaeta is equally varied. Some, such as the Nereidae, are active and carnivorous ; others browse on algae. The sedentary forms feed on minute organisms, which are caught and entangled in their tentacles. Some of the forms that burrow in sand seem to live on the organic matter contained in the sand, which they pass through their alimentary canal ; an example is the Lug-worm (*Arenicola marina*), whose casts are often to be seen on sandy shores. The Rag-worm (*Nereis diversicolor*) is a common British species. The Sea-mouse (*Aphrodite aculeata*) is a curious form ; it is about six inches long, and lives on sandy ground ; the broad back is covered with numerous slender bristles, which are matted together. The Boring-worm (*Polydora ciliata*) inhabits U-shaped tunnels that it excavates in rocks. *Spirorbis* makes the little coiled snail-like shells that are often found attached to rocks or seaweeds. *Sabella* makes long tubes by cementing sand-grains together ; the tubes project from the mud, and at the free end appear the long, feathery gills. The " Palolo " worm of the Pacific is famous ; it lives among the corals, but the hind ends break off and swim to the surface to breed ; they appear each November in enormous swarms, making the water soupy. The natives of Samoa and other islands scoop them up in buckets and hold an annual feast.

[*John J. Ward.*]
BRISTLE-WORM (*Gattiola spectabilis*), WITH EGGS.

Class 2. OLIGOCHAETA (Earthworms)

By far the greater part of this class is constituted by the Earthworms. There are a small number which live in fresh water, and a few marine forms.

The Oligochaeta differ from the Polychaeta in having no feet, and in being hermaphroditic.

The body of the Common Earthworm

66

EARTHWORMS (OLIGOCHAETA)

(*Lumbricus terrestris*) is divided into a number of segments, which are manifest by the characteristic external ringing. In the adult worm a certain number of segments towards the front end of the body form a glandular swelling (the clitellum), which secretes a cocoon for the eggs. As in most Earthworms, each segment has eight bristles, two pairs on each side, one pair being placed low down, the other nearer the back.

The alimentary canal is characterized by a strong muscular gizzard, in which the earth, which the animal swallows in bulk, is ground down and prepared for digestion ; respiration is carried on by means of the skin, which is well supplied with blood-vessels. The sense-organs are very simple.

Each individual is hermaphroditic. The fertilized eggs of Earthworms are covered over, as they are extruded, by a hard-shelled cocoon ; the growing young are nourished while they are in the cocoon by an albuminous fluid produced from the clitellum at the time the cocoon is formed. The young worms hatch out some weeks after the eggs are extruded. In the *Aeolosomatidae* and *Naididae* the normal sexual reproduc-

[*John J. Ward.*]

SEA-MOUSE (*Aphrodite aculeata*).
A curious worm, with numerous bristles matted together on the back (underside).

tion is generally not found, new individuals being formed by the division of one worm into two.

Earthworms are nocturnal and spend the daytime in their burrows. They feed mainly on the organic debris contained in the soil, which they obtain by passing a great quantity of earth through their alimentary tract. They burrow mainly near the surface, but in very hot or cold weather they are known to retreat to a depth of six feet or more. They have a very important part in the economy of Nature, as was pointed out by Charles Darwin in his interesting study of the group. By grinding up the soil below ground, and casting it out on the surface, they prepare the soil for plants ; their burrows promote the aeration of the soil, and the downward passage of roots.

It is customary to divide the class into two orders, the *Megadrili* (Earthworms) and *Microdrili* (the smaller forms which live in water or mud). The most important families of the Megadrili are the *Megascolecidae*

67

of Southern Asia, Australasia and parts of Africa and South America, and the *Lumbricidae*, in which most of the earthworms of Europe, Northern Asia, and North America are placed. The aquatic forms, most of which are distinguished by having very long and hair-like setae, include the *Tubificidae*, which have red blood that shows through the thin skin ; our common *Tubifex rivulorum* may often be seen in scarlet masses at the bottom of ponds and tanks. The Indian genus *Branchiodrilus* has structures projecting from the body which may be regarded as gills. Gills are also found in a single representative of the Megadrili, the " Nile Worm " (*Alma nilotica*). The *Branchiobdellodrilidae* are external parasites of Crayfish.

Class 3. HIRUDINEA (Leeches)

The Leeches are distinguished by the presence of a sucker at each end of the body, by the fact that the segments of the body are obscured by numerous subsidiary rings, and by the absence of bristles. In a typical form there may be over a hundred rings, though there are but twenty-seven segments.

The Leeches are carnivorous and parasitic. They attach themselves by their suckers to a great variety of other animals, and suck their blood by means of the specially modified mouth, which contains teeth capable of piercing the skin.

Leeches vary in size from a few millimetres up to eighteen inches. Their shape is very varied ; they may be sub-cylindrical, ovate, or leaf-like. Many species are brilliantly coloured and exhibit very elaborate patterns.

These animals reproduce themselves in very much the same way as do the Oligochaeta. The eggs are laid in cocoons formed from glands in the clitellum. After leaving the cocoon, the young, in many species, attach themselves to the under surface of the parent's body.

The medicinal Leech (*Hirudo medicinalis*) was very extensively used for blood-letting in order to

By courtesy of]   *[Carl Hagenbeck's Tierpark, Stellingen.*
EARTHWORMS (*Lumbricus terrestris*).
The Earthworms differ from the Polychaeta in having no feet, and but few bristles.

reduce local inflammation ; but the practice has been almost entirely abandoned in modern medicine.

Leeches are divided into two main groups, the marine and certain freshwater leeches (*Rhynchobdellida*), which are devoid of jaws and have colourless blood, and the rest of the freshwater and the terrestrial leeches

[*W. J. Clarke.*

SKATE LEECH (*Pontobdella muricata*).
Leeches have a sucker at each end of the body.

(*Gnathobdellida*), which have jaws and red blood.

Class 4. MYZOSTOMARIA

The Myzostomaria are small Annelids that live as parasites on Echinoderms. The body is usually oval or disc-shaped, and its edge is furnished with about ten pairs of slender appendages (cirri). On the under surface are five pairs of parapodia provided with bristles and hooks, and four pairs of suckers.

The majority of the Myzostomaria live on Crinoids, but a few are found on Brittle-stars and Starfishes. They climb about the disc and arms of the host, or form a kind of gall on them ; some live in its alimentary canal or reproductive organs. They are hermaphroditic and pass through a trochophore larval stage in their development.

Four families of Myzostomaria are distinguished, and some hundred and ten species are known.

Phylum GEPHYREA

This is a small group of marine worm-like or saccular creatures of which the *Echiuroidea* may be related to the Annelida. *Bonellia*, which occurs in the North Sea, is remarkable for having minute males, numbers of which may be associated with one female, and appear to be parasitic on her. The *Sipunculoidea* may be related to the Echiuroidea : they are unsegmented marine worms with the mouth surrounded by tentacles. These animals live in crevices of rocks, or make tunnels in the sand. Another group, of very uncertain relationship, includes the single genus *Phoronis*, marine worms that live in tubes, projecting a crown of tentacles which are covered with cilia that produce food-currents.

PHYLUM ARTHROPODA
(Lobsters, Crabs, Spiders, Scorpions, Centipedes, Millipedes and Insects)

The Arthropoda, like the Annelida, are highly-organized animals in which the body is formed of a series of segments. They are distinguished by having a hard, chitinous outer covering, and by the possession of jointed limbs, one or more pairs of which are modified for use as jaws. To this group belong Lobsters and Crabs, Spiders and Scorpions, Centipedes, Millipedes, and Insects. It is by far the largest phylum of the Animal Kingdom, containing perhaps one million living species. The Arthropoda were probably marine in origin, and many are aquatic; others have become terrestrial, and of these the Insects may be considered particularly successful.

[*James's Press.*

BRAZILIAN PERIPATUS (*Peripatus braziliensis*).
These terrestrial caterpillar-like animals live in damp places.

Class 1. ONYCHO-PHORA

Peripatus and its allies are small terrestrial caterpillar-like animals, found in many tropical and some temperate countries. *Peripatus* has a segmented body, a pair of antennae on the head, and a number of pairs of legs. It was at first mistaken for a slug, and then classified as a worm, but it is now accepted as an Arthropod, the presence of a pair of jaw-appendages, and air-tubes similar to the tracheae of insects, being decisive.

These animals shelter under stones, on the bark of trees, or in crannies; they are nocturnal, and appear to be carnivorous; they walk like caterpillars. Some fifty to sixty species are known.

Class 2. ARACHNIDA (Spiders, Scorpions, Mites and " Harvesters ")

The Arachnida are typically represented by such animals as the Spiders, Scorpions, Mites and "Harvesters." With the exception of the small group of *Xiphosura* (King Crabs), the extinct *Eurypterids*, and a few other forms, they are terrestrial air-breathing animals, distinguished from insects by having four pairs of legs instead of three.

The body of a typical Arachnid is composed of a series of distinct segments, in which three separate regions are to be recognized. The anterior segments may be covered by a carapace; they bear the two

70

pairs of jaw-appendages, the second of which are large " pincer-claws," and the four pairs of walking legs ; six segments in the middle of the body bear the gills (when present), and six posterior segments are without appendages.

The primitive Arachnids seem to have lived in the sea, and the King Crabs represent this evolutionary stage. These ancestral forms breathe by means of external gills (" gill-books "), each consisting of a number of thin plates like the leaves of a book. In the terrestrial forms the gill-books have become internal (" lung-books "), though they still retain a connection with the exterior by a number of slits. In some Arachnids the lung-books are replaced by tufts of small tubes (tracheae), which resemble those of insects.

The sexes in this group are nearly always separate, and the fertilized eggs develop into the adult usually without metamorphosis.

The Arachnids are mainly predacious animals, some of them being nocturnal. There are a certain number of parasitic forms, some of which are degenerate and highly modified. A number are provided with " silk glands " and make webs.

[*W. S. Berridge.*

KING CRAB (*Xiphosura* (or *Limulus*) *polyphemus*).
A marine Arachnid with helmet-like carapace and a long movable spine.

The Arachnida are a more diversified class than the Insects, and exhibit as much structural divergence among themselves as do the Crustacea.

Order 1. XIPHOSURA (King Crabs)

The King Crab, *Xiphosura* (or *Limulus*) *polyphemus*, ranges on the eastern American coast from Maine to Yucatan. Four species inhabiting Eastern seas, from Japan to India, belong to two other genera.

In the King Crab, the body is divided into two parts which are jointed together, and are covered by a broad, vaulted carapace, on the front segment of which are situated two median and two lateral eyes. A long movable spine projects from the hinder end. On the under surface are to be seen the characteristic appendages, with five pairs of " gill-books " behind the legs.

These creatures live in shallow water, and spend most of their time burrowing in sand and mud in search of food, which consists mainly of worms. They are also known to eat bivalve mollusca. They deposit their eggs in the sand between tide-marks. According to some observers a kind of nest is formed. The young escape from the egg as larvae.

INVERTEBRATA (PHYLUM ARTHROPODA)

The *Eurypterids*, found as fossils in palaeozoic strata, are allied to the King Crabs, but they had a relatively small carapace, and the last legs were paddle-like. They seem to have been free-swimming, predacious marine animals.

The remaining Arachnids are, with a few exceptions, terrestrial creatures with internal breathing organs.

Order 2. SCORPIONIDEA (Scorpions)

[E. A. Robins.
THE WHIP SCORPION
(*Thelyphonius caudatus*).
The whip is at the end of the tail. The first pair of legs are used as feelers.

The Scorpions have a body divisible into a cephalothorax, covered by a carapace, and an abdomen, of which the posterior segments are narrowed to form a tail.

The first pair of jaws is strong and nipper-like, the second is typically long, and ends in powerful nippers, the biting edges of which are toothed. The last segment of the body is globular, and is furnished with a curved point, the poisonous sting.

The Scorpions are terrestrial animals, and breathe by means of lung-books, placed in cavities that open to the exterior by four pairs of slits. They are the largest air-breathing Arachnids.

This group is found in the Northern Hemisphere in all regions between the Equator and 40° N. In the Southern Hemisphere they occur over all the habitable land, except New Zealand and South Patagonia. They are nocturnal in their habits, and pass the daytime beneath logs of wood, stones, etc., or in burrows which they dig with their claws. Some of them live in forests and others in deserts, and they are well adapted for arid conditions, as they can dispense with water for long periods. They feed upon insects and other small animals, which they seize and tear to pieces. If the prey is large, they kill it with the poison secreted by the " poison-gland," which is injected into the victim by the " sting." Scorpions are viviparous, and after they are born, the young are carried on the mother's back till they can fend for themselves.

Six families of Scorpions are usually recognized. The *Buthidae* include the European *Buthus occitanus*, the habits of which have been vividly described by the celebrated French naturalist, J. H. Fabre.

Order 3. PEDIPALPI (Whip Scorpions)

In this group are placed the Whip Scorpions. They have powerful and formidable pincer-claws, and the first pair of legs are long and slender, and are used as organs of touch and not for walking. They seem to feed principally on insects, and are of retiring habits. The Whip Scorpions have a long, lash-like appendage at the end of the abdomen. In the genus *Tarantula* (not to be confused with the true Tarantula "*Lycosa tarentula*," which is a spider), the female carries her eggs in a sac beneath the abdomen. Whip Scorpions are widely distributed in the Old and New Worlds, and are known to have existed as early as the Carboniferous period.

[F. W. Bond.
INDIAN SCORPION (*Palomnaeus*).
Scorpions seize and tear their prey with their claws, and if it is large inject poison with the "sting" at the end of the tail.

Order 4. ARANEAE (True Spiders)

The true Spiders resemble the Pedipalpi in having the cephalothorax separated from the abdomen by a "waist." They differ from them in that the abdomen is generally unsegmented, and the appendages of the third and fourth abdominal segments are retained as "spinnerets," by which the "silk," a secretion of certain abdominal glands, is handled in web-making and other operations.

The Spiders are a large group and are very widely distributed. Though they are terrestrial air-breathing animals, there are many amphibious species, and the Water Spider (*Argyroneta aquatica*) passes nearly the whole of its life under water, breathing air provided by a bubble attached to the long hairs of its abdomen. All spiders have poison-glands, which open on the first pair of jaws. The effect of the venom has been much debated. It seems to be undoubted that in some forms (e.g. the Tarantula) it has an instantaneous fatal effect on insects and other small animals.

The food of spiders consists mainly of insects, but certain forms prey on other animals such as lizards and mice, and the tropical *Aviculariidae* are said to capture and eat small birds.

[Chace (Dorien, Leigh Ltd.).
WOOD SPIDER WITH COCOON OF EGGS.

73

INVERTEBRATA (PHYLUM ARTHROPODA)

Spiders exhibit a great diversity of habits. Some go in active pursuit of their prey; the Jumping Spider (*Epiblemum scenicum*) of Britain is an example. Others lie in wait for their prey, concealed by their resemblance to their surroundings, like a British species (*Misumena vatia*), which inhabits flowers. Others conceal themselves under stones, or in the mouths of burrows that they excavate; and of the burrowing type, the Trap-door Spiders close the mouth of the tunnel with a trap-door. A burrowing spider (*Atypus affinis*), found in southern England, lines its tunnel with silk, and produces this beyond the opening as a long tube, which serves as a trap for flies.

Many spiders construct webs in which the prey is snared; these are of various designs. The circular form (orb- or wheel-web) is characteristic of the Epeiridae. This design may be modified by additional parts, e.g. the dome-web made by the American *Hentzia basilica*. The Theridiidae or Line-weavers make a web of fine irregular strands running in all directions. The sheet-webs of the Agelenidae and Dictynidae are closely woven. The common house-spider of this country (*Tegenaria civilis*) forms a web of this kind familiar to all as the "cobweb."

[*Chace (Dorien, Leigh Ltd.*).
GOLDEN SPIDER WITH COCOON OF EGGS.

The courtship habits of spiders are very remarkable. Display and courtship antics similar to those seen in birds are found in the Attidae (Leaping Spiders). The most remarkable phenomenon in the group, however, is the behaviour of the female towards the male in certain groups. In the Epeiridae the female, which is much larger than the male, will

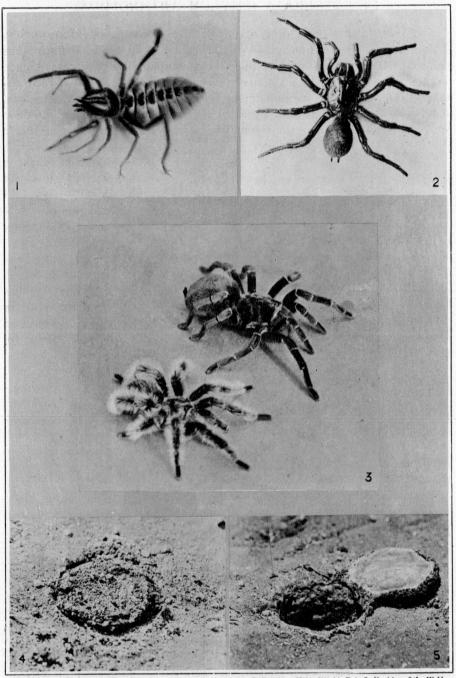

Photos]   [W. S. Berridge, Wide World, Eric J. Hosking, Otho Webb.

1. FALSE SPIDER (*Paragaleodes barbarus*). The False Spiders of warm countries are terrestrial and predacious. 2. AUSTRALIAN TRAP-DOOR SPIDER (*Atrax robustus*). 3. BIRD-EATING SPIDERS. These large tropical spiders are protected by a hairy covering. 4. TRAP-DOOR SPIDER'S NEST, door closed. 5. TRAP-DOOR SPIDER'S NEST, door open.

INVERTEBRATA (PHYLUM ARTHROPODA)

[*James's Press.*
A LYCOSID OR WOLF SPIDER CARRYING YOUNG.
The Lycosids are hunting spiders.

often kill and devour him, if she is not ready to accept his advances.

The eggs of spiders are enclosed in cocoons of silk, or in silk nests, or silk-lined burrows, which are often guarded by the mother. The young spiders spin one or two long threads, which support them in the air; they allow themselves to be carried by the wind, and so are dispersed.

Order 5. PALPIGRADI

This very small order consists of a single genus (*Koenenia*), of which several species have been described from Europe, Asia, Africa and America. They are minute animals living in damp places under stones. They resemble the Spiders and Whip Scorpions in having a " waist," but differ from them in having the second pair of jaw-appendages adapted for locomotion, and not for the holding and mastication of food.

Order 6. SOLIFUGAE (False Spiders)

The Solifugae, or False Spiders, are a very distinct group of Arachnids, somewhat spider-like, but with cephalothorax and abdomen segmented, and no waist. They are exclusively terrestrial animals, and breathe by air-tubes.

The Solifugae inhabit warm and tropical countries, many species being found in Africa. They are predacious, and feed on insects, lizards and mice. Some of them (e.g. *Galeodes*) are large and formidable looking creatures, and some of them are venomous.

Order 7. CHERNETIDEA
(False Scorpions)

The False Scorpions resemble the Scorpions in having large pincer-claws, but are not closely

[*M. H. Crawford.*
WHEEL WEB OF THE GARDEN SPIDER.

76

related to them, and have no " tail."
They are small animals of retiring
habits, usually to be found in damp
places in moss, or beneath stones. They
feed very largely on mites, and some of
them may be found clinging to beetles and
blue-bottles, which they visit in order
to catch parasitic mites. The order has a
world-wide distribution. Several species
of *Chelifer* and *Chernes* are found in
England.

Order 8. PODOGONA

This order contains but two genera,
Cryptostemma and *Cryptocellus*, which
are found in the tropical forests of
West Africa and Brazil. They are
characterized by having a movable
plate, jointed to the carapace, and hanging over the mouth and jaws like a
hood. They are small, sluggish animals. The hood-like plate may prevent
the mouth-parts from being clogged
by soil, in which the animals may
burrow.

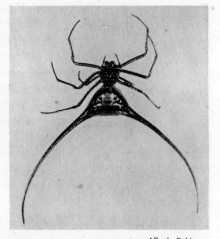

[*E. A. Robins.*
A BRAZILIAN SPIDER (*Gastrocantha
arcuatum*).
These spiders have the abdomen armed with spines

Order 9. OPILIONES (Harvesters
or Harvest Spiders)

The Harvesters or Harvest Spiders
are superficially like Spiders, but
have no " waist " and no spinning
organs. The group is a large one,
and its members are found in all
parts of the world. They eat insects, worms, etc., but seem to be
more omnivorous than other Arachnids, as they will eat carrion, and
have been seen feeding on plants.
The eggs are laid in cracks and
holes, and no special provision is
made for them or the young.

The family Phalangidae is well
represented in England, the species of *Phalangium* (" Long-legged
Spiders ") and *Oligolophus* being our
common " Harvesters."

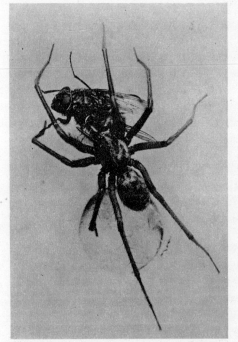

[*H. Bastin.*
HOUSE SPIDER AND PREY (*Tegenaria atrica*).
This spider spins the familiar cobweb.

Order 10. ACARI (Mites and Ticks)

This order contains the Mites and Ticks, a large group of Arachnids distinguished by many peculiarities of habit and structure. They are very small, some of them being less than a hundredth part of an inch in length, and few exceed half an inch. They are roughly divisible into two main groups as far as their habits are concerned, some being free-living and predacious, whereas others are parasitic on plants and other animals.

The cephalothorax and abdomen are fused into a compact mass and there is no " waist." The individual segments of the abdomen are seldom visible. The predacious Acarines have the mouth-parts adapted for mastication, but in the parasitic forms they are modified for sucking. Parasitic Acarines are of considerable economic importance. They are the cause of certain skin-diseases, and many of the galls on various useful trees and plants are due to Mites. The " Red Spider " (*Tetranychus telarius*) causes extensive damage to fruit-trees and flowers, and the North American Tick (*Boophilus annulatus*) has been shown to be the carrier of the disastrous Texas fever of cattle. *Eriophyes tiliae* causes " nail-galls " in lime leaves and *E. ribis* is the Gall-mite of the Black Currant. The species of *Demodex* are entirely parasitic, and have very much reduced appendages; they cause mange in mammals. The Cheese-mites (*Tyroglyphinae*) and Itch-mites (*Sarcoptinae*) are more or less globular in shape. The Ticks (*Ixodoidea*) are parasitic on reptiles, birds and mammals. Finally we may mention the Marine Mites (*Halacaridae*), Freshwater Mites (*Hydrachnidae*) and the Spinning or Harvest Mites (*Trombiinae*) or "Harvest Bugs," which attack man and cause a painful and irritating rash.

The following two groups are usually placed near the Arachnids :

[*H. Bastin.*

TICKS DISTENDED WITH BLOOD.
(*Dorsal.*)   (*Ventral.*)

PENTASTOMIDA

These are worm-like parasitic animals which live as adults in the respiratory cavities of certain Carnivora (Wolves, Foxes, etc.), Reptiles and Birds.

The body of an adult Pentastomid (e.g. *Porocephalus*) is worm-like, and marked off by a number of prominent rings. The anterior end bears a mouth, and a number of hooks by which the animal attaches itself to the interior of the nasal cavity. There are no respiratory or circulatory organs. *Linguatula* is the best-known genus.

TARDIGRADA

The Tardigrada are minute animals which live in moss, heather, etc., and are to be found only by careful and close searching. They have a roughly ovoid body covered by a transparent chitinous skin, and move by means of four pairs of short, clumsy legs. They have an alimentary canal, excretory organs and nervous system, but no respiratory or circulatory organs. They feed upon the sap of mosses, which they suck by means of a specially-adapted pharynx. The Tardigrada have a remarkable capacity for resisting drought, and it is said that they can continue in a desiccated stage for years. They are found in all parts of the world and are the most widely distributed of all segmented animals. The genus *Echiniscus* is of world-wide occurrence, and is found in both the Arctic and Antarctic regions.

[*James's Press.*
SCARLET-MITE
(*Trombidium hirsutissimum*).

Class 3. DIPLOPODA (Millipedes)

The Millipedes are given the name Diplopoda ("double-footed") because most of the segments of the body carry two pairs of appendages. The segments of the body are generally numerous; the head is equipped with a pair of short antennae, and two pairs of jaws. Millipedes are terrestrial, and breathe by means of tracheae, or air-tubes.

Millipedes are rather sluggish animals, avoiding the light and living under stones, etc. They tend to frequent damp places. They feed mainly upon vegetable matter, and have a useful rôle in that they destroy decomposing organic substances. They range in size from one-twelfth of an inch (*Polyxenus*) to nearly eight inches in length (tropical species of *Iulidae*). When crawling, the body is kept fully extended; the movement of the legs is not simultaneous, but a hinder leg precedes the one in front, and there seems to be a series of waves passing up the legs from behind forwards. Millipedes are quite harmless creatures; many of them, however, are equipped with "stink glands," which give off an unpleasant odour, and are supposed to protect them from birds and other enemies. All the known Millipedes lay eggs, which they deposit in masses in damp earth, sometimes a sort of nest is made for them.

[*John J. Ward.*
RED SPIDER (*Tetranychus telarius*).
A spinning mite that does much damage to fruit trees and flowers (×100).

79

Iulidae. This is one of the largest families, and is represented by the large *Iulus sabulosus* and other species in the British Isles. They are elongated, worm-like forms, and have as many as one hundred and forty pairs of legs. The *Oniscomorpha*, which can roll themselves up like Woodlice, are represented in England by the common Pill Millipede (*Glomeris marginata*).

Class 4. CHILOPODA (Centipedes)

In the Centipedes each segment of the body bears one pair of legs. The head bears a pair of long, many-jointed antennae, and four pairs of appendages behind the mouth are modified as jaws. The posterior jaws are killing-organs, and are provided with a strong piercing stylet, at the tip of which is the orifice of a poison gland. The number of pairs of legs varies from fifteen to over a hundred.

Centipedes are active, mainly carnivorous, animals which prey on worms, insects, slugs, and even lizards and mice. They bite their prey with the ferocious mandibles, and kill it by injecting poison into the wound. Certain tropical species are large enough to inflict dangerous bites on man. The majority of Centipedes lay eggs and some (e.g. the European species of *Scolopendra*) seem to incubate them by rolling themselves round them. Our common English Centipede is *Lithobius forficatus*. The species of *Scutigera* are remarkable for the length of their legs, which are thrown off if the animal is seized by them.

[*Otho Webb.*
CENTIPEDE (*Scolopendra morsitans*).
Centipedes bite their prey and inject poison into the wound.

Class 5. SYMPHYLA

This group contains two genera, *Scolopendrella* and *Scutigerella*, which resemble the Centipedes in appearance and behaviour. They have, however, only twelve pairs of walking legs. They are almost universal in their distribution, and are active, predacious creatures, living principally on insects. They are believed to combine the characters of Centipedes and Insects.

Class 6. PAUROPODA

These are minute Arthropoda that resemble the Millipedes in certain respects, but differ in having branched antennae, only ten pairs of limbs, and no tracheae. They are thought to be a primitive group, with rather close affinity to the Millipedes. They are found in Europe, Asia and

America, and live in damp habitats beneath decaying leaves. Some are carnivorous, and the others live on decomposing animals and vegetable remains. There are two species in Great Britain (*Pauropus huxleyi* and *Stylopauropa pedunculatus*).

Class 7. PYCNOGONIDA (Sea Spiders)

The Sea Spiders, or *Pycnogonida*, are marine Arthropods of curious and often fantastic appearance. They are a small group; as only a few species are found in shallow water, they are very little known to the ordinary observer. They have four or five pairs of very long, spidery legs, and a small body, with only three or four segments behind the head. At the front end of the head is a tubular proboscis, with the mouth at the end. The head bears a pair of appendages ending in pincerlike claws, a pair of jointed feelers, and behind these a pair of appendages to which the name "ovigers" is given, as in some forms the males are found with eggs impaled on the spines by which they are beset; it

[*W. S. Berridge.*
COMMON MILLIPEDE (*Julus terrestris*).
Millipedes are vegetarians and less active than the carnivorous centipedes.

seems, however, that they may have other functions. The internal anatomy is curiously arranged, as part of the gut and the bulk of the reproductive organs are stowed away in the legs. There are two pairs of simple eyes, and no special respiratory organs.

The Pycnogonida seem mainly to move about by crawling, and their movements are slow and deliberate. A few of them are known to swim, but it has been said that they do so "in a laborious and aimless way."

They feed on sedentary Invertebrates like Hydroids and Anemones, and the proboscis is used for sucking the soft tissues of these animals. The eggs are usually small, and there is a larval stage in the development.

The classification of the Pycnogonida is a matter of no little difficulty, and zoologists are as yet in the dark as to their origin and evolution. Dr. W. T. Calman, in a recent summary of the question, believes that they may have been descended from Arachnids.

Some ten families of Pycnogonids may be recognized, and the group has a world-wide distribution. The *Pycnogonidae*, which are short-legged forms, include the common British form *Pycnogonum littorale* ; it may be found under stones near low water, or clinging to Anemones. The *Colossendeidae* are mainly found in Arctic and Antarctic seas, and live at great depths. *Colossendeis gigas*, which has been obtained from very deep water in the Southern Ocean, is about two feet across. Another interesting member of this family is *Pipetta weberi*, taken in the Banda Sea ; it has a remarkably long and slender proboscis.

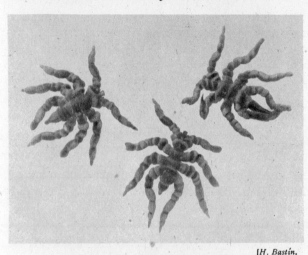

[H. Bastin.
SEA SPIDERS (*Pycnogonum littorale*).
A common British species to be found under stones when the tide is out.

Class 8. CRUSTACEA (Crabs, Lobsters, Shrimps, Woodlice, Sand-hoppers and Barnacles)

The Crustacea form the second largest class of the Arthropoda. They include the Crabs, Lobsters, Shrimps, Woodlice, Sand-hoppers and Barnacles, as well as a large number of less well-known forms. They are mainly aquatic animals, breathing by means of gills, or by the general surface of the body.

Like other Arthropods, the Crustacea have jointed limbs, and an external skeleton formed of a horny substance (chitin), which may be hardened by lime-salts. The body is composed of a number of distinct segments, and may be divided into three main regions, head, thorax, and abdomen. The limbs include two pairs of antennae, which are many jointed and may be double, three pairs of " jaws " (mandibles and first and second maxillae), and a number of thoracic and abdominal appendages, variously modified for swimming, walking, breathing, feeding, and the incubation of the young.

There are two kinds of eyes, median and compound. The median or nauplius eye is found in the larvae, and is the only eye present in the

Eucopepoda. The paired compound eyes are more or less like those of Insects, and in many Crustacea are set on movable stalks.

The sexes are usually separate and in the normal course of development there is a larval stage. Most of the members of the class undergo a series of moults as the result of growth; the animal splits its shell, and withdraws through the opening; it then increases in size before the new shell hardens.

[*John J. Ward.*

WATER-FLEA (*Daphnia*) WITH EGGS.
The branched antennae are used for swimming (× 25)

The Crustacea are mainly free-living, although several are parasitic. Vegetable feeders and carnivores are found amongst them, but a great number feed on carrion and act as scavengers. The majority are of small size, and many species occur in countless numbers in the sea.

The class may be divided into five sub-classes, which, together include twenty-five orders.

Sub-class 1. BRANCHIOPODA (Fairy Shrimps, Brine Shrimps, Clam Shrimps and Water-fleas)

These Crustacea are mainly inhabitants of fresh water. They are of small size, and are distinguished by having flattened and leaf-like limbs. The majority swim with the back downwards, in lakes, ponds and various kinds of streams. Some live in estuaries, and in salt lakes and pools. Their food consists mainly of diatoms and other minute plants, microscopic animals, and plant and animal debris that floats in the water, or settles as mud on the bottom. It is collected in a groove on the under side of the body, and is driven to the mouth by the movement of the limbs.

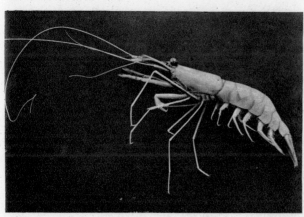

SHRIMP (*Nika edulis*)

[*H. Bastin.*

A very distinctive feature in the group is the occurrence of thick-shelled " resting eggs," which can resist drought, and of parthenogenesis (reproduction from unfertilized eggs).

The Branchiopoda are usually divided into four orders.

Anostraca (Fairy Shrimps and Brine Shrimps). These have

83

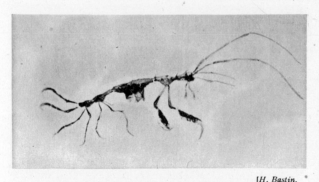

[H. Bastin.

SKELETON SHRIMP (*Caprella*).
These little shrimps climb about among seaweeds and zoophytes.

no carapace; they include shrimp-like forms such as *Artemia, Chirocephalus* and *Branchipus*. The males are remarkable on account of the size and shape of their three-branched antennae, which are used for clasping the female during courtship.

Notostraca (Tadpole Shrimps). These have a broad shield (carapace) over the back. *Apus cancriformis*, which occurs in pools in Great Britain, Europe and Northern Africa, is the most familiar example of this group.

Conchostraca (Clam Shrimps). In this order the carapace is represented by a bivalved shell, like that of a Lamellibranch mollusc, and the body is flattened from side to side.

Nearly all the members of the three preceding orders are found in stagnant ponds, which tend to dry up in the summer. The mud of such pools is often found to contain large quantities of their eggs, and owing to their power of lying dormant in dry mud, the eggs may be transported for long distances, for example, on the muddy feet of wading birds.

Cladocera (Common Water-fleas [Daphnia]). These have a two-valved carapace, and their large, two-branched antennae are used for swimming. A few species are marine, but the greater part live in fresh water, where at certain times of the year they swarm in enormous numbers.

Sub-class 2.
OSTRACODA

These are small marine and freshwater Crustacea which bear a superficial resemblance

[*Sport & General.*

MOLE CRAB (*Hippidae*).
These belong to the Hermit Crab group and burrow in the sand on tropical shores.

84

to the minute Pea Clams (*Pisidium*) among the Mollusca, as their body and appendages can be entirely confined within the bivalved carapace. The eggs are usually carried within the valves of the shell, and when the young are hatched, the bivalve shell is already developed.

The Ostracods are frequently found in

[W. S. Berridge.

TADPOLE SHRIMP (*Lepidurus*).
The broad carapace and whip-like appendages at the end of the tail are distinctive.

great numbers in fresh water and in the sea. They burrow in mud or crawl about over plants. One marine family (*Halocypridae*) is a member of the floating fauna (plankton). They are nearly all minute and many of them are under one-fiftieth of an inch in length. Many species of *Cypris* and its allies appear to be parthogenetic.

Sub-class 3. COPEPODA (Cyclops, etc.)

This is a large and interesting group of marine and freshwater Crustacea, the most familiar example of which is the small flea-like *Cyclops*, found in ponds, etc., in England. It is a widely-distributed group, and occurs in the sea in all latitudes. Such forms as *Calanus* and *Euchaeta* form an important part of the minute floating life of the sea.

[W J. Clarke.

SCALY SQUAT LOBSTER (*Galathea squamifera*).
A relative of the Hermit Crabs, found under stones below tide-marks.

The Copepods have typically a body with about sixteen segments, and no carapace. Their legs are modified for swimming. The group contains a large number of parasitic and semi-parasitic forms. The free-living forms are fairly uniform in their structure, and are distinguished by the fact that the body is divided into two distinct regions, of which that in front may be flattened.

85

Calanidae. These are a very large family of marine forms. They occur in all parts of the world and are one of the most characteristic animals of the sea. They are an important factor in the economy of marine life, as they form one of the main items in the food of fishes. Some species of *Calanus* are very rich in individuals. The shoals which they form are so dense that the sea is said to become discoloured by them. Some Calanidae have a remarkable pair of plumed appendages at the posterior end of the body, in which the plumed hairs (setae) attain an exaggerated size and fantastic arrangement. In northern waters one of the principal causes of phosphorescence in the sea is a Calanid named *Metridia*; the *Centropagidae* also include a number of phosphorescent species. The *Peltiidae* include certain species which can roll themselves into a ball like Woodlice. The parasitic forms can be described only briefly. Some are external parasites and are little modified; others burrow deeply into the skin of the host, and the segmentation of the body may be obscured, and the appendages may be highly modified; some are very degenerate, saccular, and without limbs. They are mainly parasitic on fishes, but a certain number have been recorded from Molluscs, Echinoderms, Tunicates, etc. *Argulus foliaceus* is found in fresh water in Europe, living in the branchial chamber or on the skin of various fishes.

[*H. Bastin.*

GOOSE-BARNACLES (*Lepas anatifera*).
These barnacles are found attached to floating timber.

Sub-class 4. CIRRIPEDIA (Barnacles)

Barnacles at first sight do not look like Crustacea. Indeed, the early naturalists classified them with the Mollusca until it was discovered that they pass through true crustacean larval stages.

BARNACLES (CIRRIPEDIA)

Barnacles are marine animals, fixed by the head, and having the body and limbs enclosed in a carapace strengthened by shell-like plates. The posterior part of the body is little developed. Generally there are six pairs of trunk-limbs, each with two long, feather-like branches. Most Cirripedia are hermaphroditic; the larva swims in the sea, and after several months reaches a stage with a two-valved shell, the *Cypris* larva.

[*H. Bastin.*
ACORN-BARNACLES (*Balanus balanoides*).
These barnacles live attached to rocks or stones between tide-marks.

This attaches itself by its antennae, throws off the shell-valves, and grows into an adult barnacle.

Cirripedes feed "by sweeping the water for floating particles of nutriment, with a net formed by the tendril-like branches of the thoracic limbs" (Calman). Some of them attain quite a considerable size, specimens of *Balanus psittacus* being nine inches in length. The majority live attached to rocks, stones, seaweed, etc., on the bottom. The Goose-barnacle (*Lepas anatifera*) and certain other forms live on floating timber and ships. *Lepas fascicularis* forms colonies round any floating object, such as empty shells of the Cephalopod *Spirula*, and by a secretion from certain glands it makes a mucous float not unlike that made by the Mollusc *Ianthina*. A good many Cirripedes adhere to, or become imbedded in Corals, and sundry forms are attached to the skin of marine animals, such as whales, turtles, etc.

The order *Thoracica* includes barnacles with well-developed limbs. The Acorn-barnacle (*Balanus balanoides*) is a common British species, covering the rocks between tide-marks. The feathery limbs protrude through a hole at the top of the conical shell, but when the tide is out, they are drawn in, and the opening is closed by a lid. The stalked barnacles are

[*Paul Unger.*
SPIDER CRAB (*Maia*).
The Spider Crabs have long legs and a beak-like anterior projection.

attached by a stalk, which may reach a great length; this group includes the Goose-barnacles (*Lepas*) and some forms that live at the bottom in very deep water, which are of great interest, as each large hermaphrodite or female individual has a number of minute males attached to her.

The *Acrothoracica*, *Ascothoracica*, and *Apoda* are three Orders which exhibit a progressive reduction of the appendages, culminating in the Apoda, in which there are no trunk-appendages at all. These forms live on, or in, the shells of molluscs, the branches of Black Corals (*Gorgonians*), etc.

[*Sport & General.*

CRAWFISH OR SPINY LOBSTER (*Palinurus vulgaris*).
This is the Langouste of the French, who value it as food.

The *Rhizocephala* are a very interesting group of truly parasitic barnacles. They have no appendages and no alimentary canal, the place of the latter being taken by an absorptive root-system developed from the peduncle. They are found exclusively on Crustacea. The majority infest Decapods (crabs, shrimps, hermit crabs, etc.). *Sacculina neglecta*, which lives on the spider crab in the Mediterranean, is reduced to a tumour-like or gall-like swelling on the crab's abdomen, and the internal organs are represented only by a generative system and a single nerve-ganglion.

Sub-class 5. MALACOSTRACA (Crabs, Lobsters, Crayfishes, Prawns, Shrimps and Woodlice)

The Malacostraca are a very large group in which the most familiar forms of Crustacea are placed, namely, the Crabs, Lobsters, Prawns, Shrimps and Woodlice. Some of them attain a considerable size. The sub-class is characterized by the fact that the segments of the body and the corresponding limbs are arranged in two distinct divisions, the thorax having eight, and the abdomen usually six segments.

[Otho Webb.

PENAEID PRAWN.
Most of the larger prawns belong to the group Penaeida.

Division 1. Leptostraca

The order *Nebaliacea* differs from all other Malacostraca in having an abdomen of seven segments, and thoracic limbs that are flat and leaf-like, like those of the Branchiopods. The carapace is bivalved. The young do not pass through a larval stage, but are carried between the thoracic feet of the female, and are liberated at a late stage in their development.

These little animals are marine, and most of them occur in shallow water, where they burrow in sand. Some of them have a very wide distribution. *Nebalia bipes* ranges from the British Isles and Greenland to Chili and Japan. These animals feed on minute particles and organisms which are brought to the mouth by the current produced by the movements of the thoracic limbs.

Division 2. Syncarida

In this division there is no carapace, and the segments of the body are distinct. The single family, the Anaspididae, is represented by two genera, one (*Anaspides*) living in tarns and river pools in the mountains of Tasmania, and the other (*Koonunga*) in pools near Melbourne. The

[H. Bastin.

WOODLOUSE (*Porcellio scaber*).
A mother surrounded by her young. This is a common species in gardens.

89

group seems to have been larger at the end of Primary times, and its last survivors may be termed " living fossils."

Anaspides attains a length of nearly two inches. It usually walks about on stones and submerged plants, and takes to swimming only when disturbed. According to the late Mr. G. W. Smith, it browses on the algal slime that covers the rocks of the high mountain tarns and pools. It also seems to take animal food and may even eat carrion.

[*W. S. Berridge.*

HERMIT CRAB (*Eupagurus bernhardus*).
This crab inhabits a whelk shell to which a sea-anemone is attached, and perhaps benefits the crab by its power of stinging.

Division 3. Peracarida (Woodlice, Sandhoppers and Freshwater Shrimps)

The carapace, when present, leaves at least four of the thoracic segments distinct. There is a brood-pouch, formed in the female from expansions of the thoracic limbs. Development is direct (without a larval stage). This group contains the Woodlice, Sandhoppers, a number of freshwater Shrimps of various kinds, and some interesting parasitic forms. It is divided into five orders.

(1) **Mysidacea.** These are mainly marine, though a few occur either as recent invaders or stranded (" relict ") in lakes in the Northern Hemisphere. *Mysis relicta* occurs in lakes in Europe. The Mysidae seem to be a deep-water group, and are rarely found in the surface plankton.

(2) **Cumacea.** The members of this order are also entirely marine, including a peculiar group of species which lives in the Caspian Sea. They are very plentiful in Arctic Seas, where *Diastylis goodsiri*, the largest known form, attains a length of thirty-five millimetres.

(3) **Tanaidacea.** This order includes small marine forms, living at most depths. They burrow in mud and sand, and some may be found in rock-crevices and among algae.

(4) **Isopoda.** This fourth order is a very large one, and its members live in the sea, in fresh water, and on land. They have no carapace and the thoracic limbs are unbranched. Some of them, e.g. the Common Woodlice (*Oniscidae*), are broad and flat, others are more shrimplike. A feature of this class is the large number of parasitic forms.

[*Paul Unger.*

EDIBLE CRAB (*Cancer pagurus*)
A common species among rocks in shallow water.

Among the more interesting kinds are *Asellus aquaticus*, a freshwater form which looks like a Woodlouse, the giant *Bathynomus giganteus*, of the Gulf of Mexico and Indian Ocean, which reaches a foot in length, *Platyarthrus hoffmannseggii*, which lives as a scavenger in ants' nests, and the parasitic *Epicaridae*, which live on and in other crustacea.

(5) **Amphipoda.** In this order the body is flattened laterally, and the gills are attached to the thoracic limbs. They are mainly marine, but some members of the Gammaridea live in fresh water and on land. *Gammarus locusta* is our Common Freshwater-shrimp, and the *Talitridae*, or Sandhoppers, include forms which may be found both on the shore and inland.

Division 4. Eucarida (Prawns, Shrimps, Lobsters, Crayfishes, Crabs, etc.)

Here the carapace is fused in the back region with all the thoracic segments. The eyes are stalked, and there is a complicated larval metamorphosis. The division comprises the

[*H. Bastin.*

SPIDER CRAB.
A small British species.

91

[F. W. Bond.
ROBBER OR COCONUT CRAB (*Birgus latro*).
A crab of the Hermit Crab group; it climbs palms to get coconuts.

Euphausiacea, and the *Decapoda*.

Euphausiacea. These have single series of gills, and all the thoracic limbs are used for swimming. They are marine. *Euphausia superba* has been found to be an important item in the diet of whales in Antarctic Seas, where it occurs in great swarms.

Decapoda. The Decapoda differ from the Euphausiacea in having the first three pairs of thoracic limbs modified, and turned towards the mouth for use as jaws. The gills are in several series, and are enclosed in a special chamber on each side of the thorax.

The Decapoda are a large and world-wide class. Though the majority of them live in the sea, some have established themselves in fresh water and on land. A noteworthy feature is the frequency of parasitism, and that form of association with other animals which is known as commensalism. The Decapoda range in size from the Giant Crab of Japan (*Macrocheira kaempferi*), which may have legs five feet long, to minute forms only one-third of an inch or less in length. The metamorphic stages of the young of Decapoda are numerous and very striking. The series of changes is most complete in the Prawns (*Penaeidea*).

The Decapoda are divided into three suborders, *Macrura* (Lobsters, Crayfishes, Prawns, Shrimps, etc.), *Anomura* (Hermit Crabs, etc.), and *Brachyura* (Crabs).

Macrura (Lobsters, Crayfishes, Prawns, Shrimps, etc.). Here the abdomen is well developed, and ends in a " tail-fan." The various

[Neville Kingston.
LAND CRAB (*Gecarcinidae*).
The land crabs of tropical countries are terrestrial and air breathing.

kinds of Shrimps and Prawns swim in the sea, often in large shoals ; they have the body compressed and the legs slender. The true Lobsters and Crayfishes are distinguished by their large claws. The Common Lobster (*Homarus gammarus*) of Europe crawls about on the bottom or among the rocks, and eats fishes, alive or dead, and any other kind of animal food ; when alive it is blue in colour. The Norway Lobster (*Nephrops norvegicus*) inhabits deeper water. The Crayfishes live in fresh water ; some dwelling in caves in North America are blind. The Spiny Lobster or Langouste, sometimes known as the Sea Crawfish or Rock Lobster (*Palinurus vulgaris*), of the Mediterranean reaches south-west England ; it is a large species, orange in colour, and without pincer-claws ; it is valued as food.

[*H. Bastin.*

ANGULAR CRAB (*Gonophox thomboides*).
Found on the south coast of England. The long eye-stalks are notable.

Anomura (Hermit Crabs, etc.). In this suborder the abdomen is coiled and asymmetrical, or is bent under the body. The best-known examples of this group are the Hermit Crabs (*Paguridae*), which live in the shells of Gastropod molluscs and have the abdomen soft and spirally-coiled to fit the shell. Frequently sea-anemones grown on the shell help to protect the crab, and may share its food. Other organisms, such as sponges, may encrust the shell. The Robber Crab (*Birgus latro*), sometimes known as the Coconut Crab, is a tropical land-crab which does not carry a shell ; it climbs trees to feed on coconuts.

Brachyura (True Crabs). Here the abdomen is short, bent forward under the body, and without a " tail-fan." The carapace is broad and flat. The first pair of legs are large claws. Crabs are found in all seas, and in tropical countries there are many freshwater species, and also terres- trial ones, in which the gill-chambers serve as lungs. British marine species include the Edible Crab (*Cancer pagurus*), the Shore Crab (*Car- cinus maenas*), one of a group in which the last pair of legs is paddle-shaped and used for swimming, the Spiny Spider Crab (*Maia squinado*), which has very long legs, and has the habit of disguising itself by attaching sea- weeds to the spines on its carapace, the Sponge Crab (*Dromia vulgaris*), which uses the last two pairs of legs to hold a piece of sponge, under which it is concealed, and the tiny Pea Crab (*Pinnotheres*), which shelters inside the shells of living bivalve molluscs.

Division 5. Hoplocarida (Mantis Prawns)

This division includes a single Order, the Stomatopoda, and a single Family, the Squillidae. They are large marine Crustacea of somewhat grotesque appearance, resembling the remarkable insects known as " Praying Mantids " (p. 107). The second thoracic limbs are very large, and serve for prehension ; the end segment, which has a series of spines along one edge, can be folded back against the next segment.

The *Stomatopoda* are active predatory animals, but they have retiring habits and seem to lurk in and about burrows in sand or mud. They live chiefly in tropical waters, but range north to England and south to New Zealand.

Some five or six genera are placed in the family *Squillidae*. *Squilla mantis* and *S. desmaresti* are sometimes found on the south coast of England.

[*W. J. Clarke.*

PEA CRAB (*Pinnotheres*).
The crab is inside the shell of a living mussel.

INSECTS

INSECTA

D. AUBERTIN M.Sc., F.L.S.

Definition of Class Insecta

Insects are Arthropods in which the body is clearly divided into head, thorax, and abdomen. The head carries a single pair of antennae, and the thorax one or two pairs of wings and three pairs of legs ; the abdomen in the adult state has no paired appendages. Breathing is effected by a system of air-tubes, termed tracheae, which penetrate into all the recesses of the body. The young seldom resemble the adults in every feature, and very radical changes in appearance may take place before the adult state is attained.

Relationship to Other Classes

The relationship of insects to other groups of Arthropods is not at all clear if only the higher groups such as the bees, flies and butterflies are taken into consideration, but some of the primitive wingless insects show definite resemblances to the less specialized Crustacea and millipedes, and it is probable that all three classes have evolved from an extinct and even simpler group.

The Insecta form the largest group within the Arthropoda ; approximately 500,000 species are known, and it is incontestable that a vast number remain to be discovered. The largest insects are to be found among the beetles and moths. The Elephant-beetle may reach a length of six inches and is bulky in proportion ; certain moths may be fourteen inches from wing-tip to wing-tip, and one of the Stick Insects (*Orthoptera*), although not great in girth, attains a length of thirteen inches. Some of the smallest insects in existence occur among the beetles, many of them measuring less than 1/80th of an inch in length.

Structure

The body of an insect is generally covered with a hard skin formed of a substance named chitin, but soft joints

[*Carl Hagenbeck's Tierpark, Stellingen.*
THE ELEPHANT BEETLE (*Megasoma*).
One of the bulkiest insects known ; it may attain a length of six inches.

95

are left between each segment of the body, or at least of the abdomen, and at the leg-joints, to allow of easy movement. The skin, or cuticle, often bears strong movable hairs, fine immovable hairs, spurs on the legs, and dilatations on various parts of the body ; in addition, it may be pitted or striated ; these manifestations are generally constant for any given species or group of species, and are, therefore, of great value in classification.

[*Laverock*.
Young form of a species of Aphide.
(*Very highly magnified.*)

Insects are predominantly characterized by the brilliant colouring which they frequently exhibit. The colours may be due either to the presence of colouring matter under the cuticle, or to the diffraction and interference experienced by the rays of light on striking a finely-ridged surface, or to a combination of both these factors. Browns, blacks and yellows are generally due to pigment, metallic and iridescent colours to surface structure, and green and magenta to both ; further, the colour of an insect may be affected by the colouring matter in its food.

The head, bearing the eyes, mouth parts and antennae, is formed of six segments fused into a compact mass. Simple eyes, termed ocelli, are often present, but the majority of insects have highly-developed, facetted, compound eyes as well ; these are sometimes so large as to occupy the greater part of the surface of the head. The antennæ are tactile organs, and may have pits connected with the sense of smell ; in primitive forms they are generally lash-like, but in more highly-organized insects they are often compact, and are very various in shape. The mouth-parts consist of a number of separate pieces, which together form an organ suitable for chewing, biting, sucking, or piercing. Sometimes in suctorial insects, such as certain flies, moths, and bees, the proboscis may be considerably longer than the whole of the rest of the body.

[*M. H. Crawford*.
Sculptured eggs of the Yellow Under-wing Moth (*Triphaena pronuba*) on Broom. (*Greatly enlarged.*)

The head is joined to the thorax by a thin, flexible neck, but this is often so short as to be invisible without close inspection. The thorax carries the organs of locomotion, wings and legs ; its three segments are fused into a solid mass.

The wings are primarily membraneous outgrowths of the body wall, supported by longitudinal veins, each of which surrounds an air tube ; these veins are connected together

transversely by thickenings of the wing membrane, so that a network is formed. The most primitive insects are wingless, and many of the most specialized forms have lost their wings, although their nearest relatives have them well developed. There is a tendency towards a reduction in the number of veins in the wings of the higher forms. The true flies have lost the hind wings entirely. The wings vary greatly in shape and texture

and one or both pairs may be concerned with flight. The flight-muscles are attached inside the thorax, and act either directly, as elevator or depressor muscles connected with the inner ends of the wings, or indirectly, inserted on the inside of the plates of the thorax near the wings, and by their expansion and contraction altering the

shape of the thorax, and so moving the wings. It has been estimated that a house-fly makes at least three hundred and thirty wing strokes a second, a bee one hundred and ninety, a moth seventy-two, a dragon-fly twenty-eight, and a butterfly nine.

Insects have three pairs of legs, which are suitable for running and walking, but which are often modified for digging, grasping, carrying pollen, or producing sound. Each leg is composed of three main joints, the femur nearest the body, the tibia, and the

Photos]   *[M. H. Crawford.*
The Male Vapourer Moth (*Orgyia antiqua*) has fully-developed wings, while the female (top picture [natural size]) is wingless; after fertilization, she lays her eggs on or near the cocoon from which she has emerged. The third picture shows the eggs. (× 8.)

[John J. Ward.
Floating egg-cocoon of the Great Silver Water Beetle; two larvae can be seen, one on the leaf to the right and the other emerging from the cocoon. (*Highly magnified.*)

tarsus or foot. The last is composed of from one to five small joints.

The abdomen is primarily composed of eleven segments, but the number tends to decrease in the higher forms, and often only three or four can be seen. The female frequently has a long ovipositor, which may or may not be retractile, projecting from the tip of the abdomen, and in the male the clasping organs sometimes give the tip a knobbed appearance.

Senses

The most highly-developed sense in insects is usually that of sight; certain forms such as grass-hoppers, which emit sounds, are also capable of hearing them; small unchitinized areas are susceptible to touch and smell, and probably function also as organs of taste.

Breathing

As already noted, breathing takes place by means of air-tubes or tracheae, and air-sacs, which permeate the body. The tubes are stiffened by a spiral thickening of chitin in the walls, and open to the exterior by paired openings termed spiracles, generally eleven in number, of which two pairs open on the thorax and the remainder on the sides of the abdominal segments. Air is pumped in and out of the tubes by muscular movements of the body, oxygen and carbon-dioxide being taken up by, and excreted from, the blood wherever it is in contact with the tubes. Terrestrial larvae breathe in the

[M. H. Crawford.
Peacock Butterfly (*Nymphalis io*) resting on puparia. (*Nat. size.*)

same way, but in aquatic forms larval gills are often present.

Waste products, other than insoluble food debris, are stored in various parts of the body, often in the form of pigments.

Insects possess many kinds of secretory glands of which the most remarkable are the salivary glands, modified to form silk-glands in silk-worms, the "stink-glands" of many bugs, the wax-glands of bees and lac insects, and the scent-glands of butterflies and moths.

[John J. Ward.

Larvae (maggots) and puparia of Blow-flies ; the maggots feed on carrion and reach their full size in four or five days. (× 7/4.)

Reproduction

In the majority of insects the young are hatched from fertilized eggs, but in some the eggs are few in number and hatch before leaving the body of the female, this form of reproduction being termed "viviparous" as opposed to the "oviparous" method.

In certain groups such as the ants, colonial bees and wasps, and aphides, unfertilized eggs may hatch and give rise to perfectly formed adults. This is known as Parthenogenesis. Parthenogenetic generations often alternate with a sexual generation in the life cycle of a species. Further modifications of normal methods of reproduction are Paedogenesis—the larva producing more larvae—and Polyembryony—the development of two or more larvae from a single egg.

Eggs are laid singly, or in masses, in water, in the earth, or in cracks in plants, and are sometimes provided with a protective covering ; any period from a day to six months may elapse before they hatch.

[John J. Ward.
The larva of the Garden Chafer (order *Coleoptera*) lives just below the surface of the ground, feeding on the roots of plants. (*Nat. size.*)

Development

The larvae vary greatly in shape in the different orders. In the more primitive forms they are active, and resemble the full-grown insect in general plan. As they grow, they shed their skins, and with each moult

99

[H. Fischer.

The Comma Butterfly (*Polygonia c-album*) derives protection from the irregular outline of its wings and the broken colouring of their lower sides. (*Nat. size.*)

become more like the adults; when full-grown they cease to moult, and become sexually mature. During this development there is no resting stage. In the higher forms the larvae are frequently legless and are totally unlike the adults; when they have attained their full size, they secrete a tough covering and pass through a resting stage during which the larval tissues are broken down, and are reformed into the likeness of the adult. Insects in which this type of development occurs are said to undergo metamorphosis. The resting stage is termed the pupa. The development is in some cases further complicated by the occurrence of two or three changes of shape before the larva is full grown. When the transformation into the adult insect, or imago, is complete, the pupal skin splits, the insect crawls out, stretches and dries it wings and, after a shorter or longer period, begins to reproduce.

In certain butterflies and flies no food is taken in the adult state, and consequently they die immediately after pairing and laying eggs. The greatest age, fourteen or fifteen years, is probably attained by the queens in groups which have developed a colonial mode of life.

Protective Resemblance

It is generally acknowledged that the insects form one of the

[H. Bastin.

Tropical Leaf-insects from Ceylon. (× 9/10.)

most successful groups in the animal kingdom ; this is attributable to their small size, rapid and prolific methods of reproduction, and general adaptability. This last characteristic is demonstrated when the shape and colour of insects are studied in relation to their surroundings. A large number will be found to resemble closely the leaves, twigs or bark on which they are habitually found ; this type of coloration is termed Protective Resemblance and is most remarkable among the butterflies, moths, stick-insects, and leaf-insects ; it undoubtedly serves as a protection against discovery by birds, toads, and other enemies. A contrast to this type of protection is afforded by the brilliant coloration of many butter-

[H. Bastin.
A Japanese moth which closely resembles the surface on which it is resting ; when at rest, the brightly-coloured hind wings are hidden by the fore wings. (× 4/5.)

flies, beetles, and Hymenoptera. Investigation has shown that many insects of this type are extremely unpalatable, and it is thought that enemies associate the brilliant colours with an unpleasant taste, and consequently leave the possessors of " warning coloration " alone. It has also beeen shown that many species, not apparently unpleasant to the taste, closely resemble the nauseous forms which occupy the same region, although the relatives of the former group in other parts of the world may be quite differently coloured ; these insects are said to " mimic " the unpalatable f o r m s, termed " models," and derive protection

[H. Bastin.
These beetles occur in Madagascar. They are almost invisible when resting on a lichen-covered branch. (× 5/6.)

from the fact that their enemies are incapable of distinguishing between pleasant and distasteful insects, when similarly coloured.

Polymorphism

A striking characteristic of insects is their capacity for producing individuals in the same species which are so dissimilar that one would hardly suspect them of close relationship. This phenomenon is termed Polymorphism, and is present in varying degrees in all groups. It is incipient in the differences between the sexes and reaches its maximum development in the seasonal races of butterflies, and in those insects which have adopted a colonial mode of life.

The colonial habit represents the culmination of insect evolution, and involves division of labour, care of the young, and potential immortality of the community, though not of the individual.

Economic Importance

Of all animals, insects most closely affect the welfare of man. A few are beneficial, but an overwhelming majority are harmful. Of the former type silk-worms and lac insects give rise to products of commercial value, and many flies and Hymenoptera are of value in that they parasitize destructive insects, or feed on rampant weeds, thus keeping them in check. Such insects have been artificially introduced into countries suffering, for instance, from the depredations of scale insects, or from the rapid growth of blackberry bushes, and their influence has been of immediate value. Great care, however, must be exercised in employing the method of Biological Control, as it is possible that the introduced insect may itself, in fresh surroundings, become a serious pest.

Innumerable insects, in some stage of their life history, are destructive to crops, cultivated fruit, stored products or manufactured goods. A smaller group affect man himself either by breeding in wounds and ulcers, or by transmitting such virulent diseases as yellow fever, bubonic plague, sleeping sickness and malaria.

Photos]   *[H. Bastin.*
Species A & B ($\times$ 1/3) are closely related and distasteful to birds; species C ($\times$ 5/12) is unrelated and is edible; it derives protection from its enemies by its similarity to species A & B.

CLASSIFICATION OF CLASS INSECTA

Sub-class 1. APTERYGOTA
Primitive insects without wings. There is no metamorphosis, or but a very slight one.

Order 1. *Thysanura* (Bristle-tails).
    2. *Collembola* (Spring-tails).
    3. *Protura*.

Sub-class 2. PTERYGOTA
Insects with wings, unless these have been lost.

[*H. Bastin.*
BIRD-WINGED PARADISE BUTTERFLY (*Ornithoptera paradisea*), NEW GUINEA. The male (above) and female of this species are very different in size and appearance. (× 1/4.)

Division 1. EXOPTERYGOTA
Pterygota in which the wings develop outside the body. Metamorphosis is slight, without a pupal stage.

Order 1. *Orthoptera* (Cockroaches, Sooth-sayers, Stick and Leaf Insects, Locusts, Grasshoppers and Crickets).

Order 2. *Dermaptera* (Earwigs).
    3. *Plecoptera* (Stone-flies).
    4. *Isoptera* (Termites).
    5. *Embioptera*.
    6. *Psocoptera* (Book-lice).

Order 7. *Anoplura* (Lice).
    8. *Ephemeroptera* (May-flies).
    9. *Odonata* (Dragon-flies).
    10. *Thysanoptera* (Thrips).
    11. *Hemiptera* (Bugs).

Division 2. ENDOPTERYGOTA
Pterygota in which the wings develop inside the body. Metamorphosis complex, with a pupal stage.

Order 1. *Neuroptera* (Lace-wing Flies).
    2. *Mecoptera* (Scorpion-flies).
    3. *Trichoptera* (Caddis-flies)
    4. *Lepidoptera* (Butterflies and Moths).
    5. *Coleoptera* (Beetles).
    6. *Strepsiptera* (Stylops).
    7. *Aphaniptera* (Fleas).
    8. *Diptera* (True Flies).
    9. *Hymenoptera* (Ants, Bees, and Wasps).

[*H. Bastin.*
Sexual dimorphism in a species of weevil (*Brenthus*); the male is much larger than the female and has an immense rostrum. (× 1⅔).

Sub-class APTERYGOTA

Order THYSANURA (Bristle-tails)

This order may be considered to be the most primitive in the class Insecta. Bristle-tails are small insects, rarely more than a quarter of an inch in length. They live in the soil, in rotting wood, in leaf deposits, or under stones; some are found in ants' and termites' nests.

Members of this order have biting mouth-parts, a tracheal system, lateral, paired appendages at the base of the abdomen, and either two or three long bristles at its tip. Metamorphosis is very slight, or absent.

The commonest bristle-tail is the "Silver-fish" or "Slicker." It occurs in England, and is frequently seen running about the floor or on furniture. It feeds on paper, book-bindings, and similar substances, but rarely does any appreciable damage in temperate climates.

[H. Bastin.
One of the Bristle-tails (*Campodea staphylinus*); a blind, wingless insect found in damp places in north-temperate regions. (*Photograph from a wax model,* × 3.)

Order COLLEMBOLA (Spring-tails)

Collembola are minute insects, about a quarter of an inch or less in length, living in the soil, on plants, or under bark, and sometimes in ants' or termites' nests. The mouth-parts are of the biting type, the eyes are simple, and the six-segmented abdomen generally has a forked springing organ at the tip and an adhesive organ at the base. The tracheal system is absent, and breathing is effected through the soft skin. There is no metamorphosis.

Order PROTURA

The insects of this order are even smaller than the Spring-tails. They live in much the same type of habitat, but have piercing and sucking mouth-parts. The abdomen has twelve segments in the adult, but in the nymphal stage there are fewer. The group is divided into two families characterized by the presence or absence of the tracheal system.

Sub-class PTERYGOTA

Division EXOPTERYGOTA

Order ORTHOPTERA (Cockroaches, Sooth-sayers, Stick and Leaf Insects, Grasshoppers and Crickets)

Cockroaches, sooth-sayers, stick and leaf insects, grasshoppers and crickets belong to this order; they are comparatively large insects, some

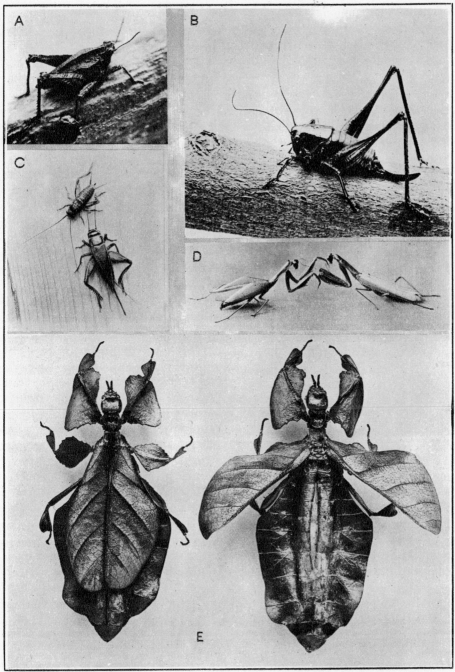

Photos]   [*H. Bastin and M. H. Crawford.*

A. The Grouse-locust, a short-horned Grasshopper (*Tetrix sp.*) (× 2); B. Long-horned Grasshopper (*Pholidoptera griseoaptera*) (× 5/4); C. House Cricket (*Gryllus domesticus*) (*Nat. size*); D. Praying Mantis (*Mantis religiosa*) (× 1/2); E. Leaf Insects (*Phyllium sp.*) (*Nat. size*).

of them being among the largest known; about twelve thousand species have so far been discovered; of these five hundred are found in Europe, and about forty in Great Britain.

Orthoptera have biting mouth-parts, and the order as a whole may be said to be omnivorous. They are predominantly terrestrial and, although typical forms have wings, prolonged flights occur in only a few families. Certain forms are devoid of wings, but this is a secondary condition, since it occurs sporadically in all the families. When wings are present, the front pair is narrow, straight and hard, and closes over the extensive hind wings, which are membraneous and are covered with a network of veins.

The members of this group have great powers of running and jumping, and the order is divided roughly into two sub-orders based on these modes of progression; in the runners (*Cursoria*), the three pairs of legs are all

[*M. H. Crawford.*
A Cockroach (*Blatta sp.*) just after moulting. The insect is white at first, but soon darkens; it eats the cast-off skin. (× 5/4.)

alike; in the jumpers (*Saltatoria*), the hind legs are very long, and have swollen femora. Certain species in the families *Blattidae*, *Acrididae* and *Gryllidae* have become aquatic, but they do not show any marked modification in relation to this mode of life.

The eggs are generally long and oval, and are dropped on the ground, or buried in " egg-pods." These egg-cases are formed by a secretion produced by the female, which hardens in the air, forming a tough protective coat. When the young hatch, they burst the case and struggle out with worm-like movements, moult immediately, and then begin to crawl. Several moults occur as they grow, but there is no abrupt metamorphosis.

Sub-Order Cursoria (Cockroaches, Praying Insects, Stick and Leaf Insects)

The cockroaches (*Blattidae*) are flat, broad insects, nocturnal in habit, and found all over the world. They are most frequently seen in tropical countries, although some forms occur naturally in colder regions; *Blatta orientalis*, the cockroach or " black beetle " of our kitchens, has been introduced from ships trading with the East, and may now be termed " domesticated." About one thousand two hundred species are known, two of which are indigenous in England, and live in the undergrowth of woods and on the seashore.

Cockroaches are generally brownish, and have large eyes and long antennae; they run very quickly; also they possess glands which produce an unpleasant smell. Those living in houses will eat anything, including

[*H. Bastin.*
A Mole-cricket (*Gryllotalpa vulgaris*) as it appears in flight.
(*Nat. size.*)

clothing, books, or dead insects. The female lays about forty eggs into an egg-pod which projects from her body as it gradually becomes filled ; when ready, it is dropped into a convenient crack. The young may become full-grown within a year, but in some species two or more years may pass before the adult state is reached.

The Praying Insects (*Mantidae*) occur only in the warmer regions, none being known further north than central France. They are exclusively carnivorous, and their popular name is connected with the attitude in which they sit while waiting to seize their food. The anterior part of the thorax is very much lengthened, and is raised at an angle to the rest of the body ; the front pair of legs is attached to this region ; they are elongated and the tibia folds back on the femur like the blade of a clasp knife ; this pair of legs is held in the air ready to grasp any prey within range ; some of the larger Mantids are known to attack small birds, lizards or frogs.

These insects vary enormously in shape, some being very attenuated and others having outgrowths of chitin causing them to resemble leaves and flowers ; they always blend perfectly with their surroundings, an assistance when catching unwary insects and a protection from their own enemies.

The females are not very active and are rarely seen flying. They attach their egg-purses to twigs, walls, the bark of trees or other objects.

The Stick and Leaf Insects (*Phasmidae*) are remarkable for the peculiar faithfulness with which they mimic the twigs and leaves among which they live; the resemblance is increased by their habit of feigning death when disturbed, and they are often incredibly difficult to detect, although some species may reach a length of thirteen inches.

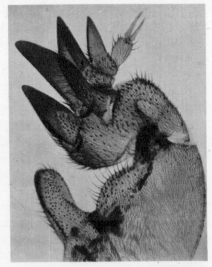

[*John J. Ward.*
Front leg of a Mole-cricket showing the broad blades used in digging. (*Highly magnified.*)

Like the Mantids, these insects also inhabit warmer regions, but they feed entirely on plants. Occasionally they are introduced into England with imported plants, and may become very destructive if they establish themselves in hot-houses.

Males are rare, and reproduction can be carried on parthenogenetically for many generations ; each egg is enclosed in a capsule which is dropped on the ground ; one or two years may pass before hatching takes place, and a further considerable period elapses before the adult state is reached.

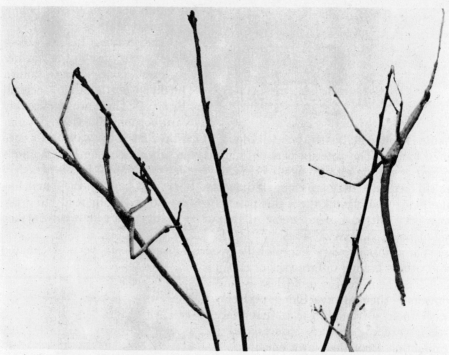

[Carl Hagenbeck's Tierpark, Stellingen.
Stick Insects, which closely resemble the twigs among which they sit. (Nat. size.)

Sub-order Saltatoria (Crickets, Grasshoppers, Katydids and Locusts)

This sub-order comprises the crickets, long-horned grasshoppers, short-horned grasshoppers, and locusts. The males of all these groups are capable of producing a considerable volume of sound, and all have organs of hearing.

The Crickets (*Gryllidae*) have long antennae, and strongly-developed legs ; they are sometimes winged and sometimes wingless, and are renowned for their great sound-producing powers. The commonest English forms are the field-cricket, the house-cricket and the ground-cricket. The mole-cricket, an occasional visitor, is peculiar in that it lives underground ; in connection with this habit, the front legs are modified to form short,

Locusts destroying foliage ($\times$ 1/7.)

[Topical Press.

[Wide World Photos.

A swarm of locusts invading a valley in Palestine.

broad, powerful digging instruments, and the compound eyes are much reduced. Certain small wingless crickets live in association with ants in Europe, Asia and America.

The eggs in this family are usually laid freely in the earth, instead of in egg-purses. The adults are omnivorous.

The members of the family *Tettigoniidae* are commonly known as Katydids from their song, which sounds very much like " Katy did, she did." There are nine species in England, characterized by the long antennae which may exceed the length of the body, and the prominent ovipositor in the females. The winged forms are generally green, and live among grass and bushes ; the wingless forms are brown, and live in hollow trees, or beneath stones, or in caves. The eggs in this family are laid separately in the earth, or in the stems of plants.

[*Wide World Photos.*
A female Locust laying eggs ; the abdomen is much extended and is buried in the ground. The egg-purse may be found as deep as eight inches below the surface. (× 2/3.)

The short-horned grass-hoppers (*Acridiidae*) are represented in England by nine species, and are common in our fields and hedges. The antennae are always much shorter than the body, and the ovipositor in the females is inconspicuous. The majority are green in colour, but the small grouse-locusts are brown. The eggs, in this group, are laid in the ground, and an egg-pod is secreted round them.

Although grasshoppers may be present in great numbers on a small area, they may be regarded as solitary insects, that is to say, they do not show any gregarious impulses, each individual pursuing its activities irrespective of the behaviour of its neighbours. This characteristic separates the short-horned grasshoppers from the true swarming locusts. Locusts, in immense cloud-like swarms, appear at irregular intervals in Southern and Central Europe, Siberia, Africa, Madagascar, India, Australia, and North and South America. When the swarms settle, they do incalculable damage to crops and foliage by eating shoots and leaves.

There are several species of locust, but the best-known is probably *Locusta migratoria*, which invades Southern Europe and Western Asia. It breeds in the reed beds of the Danube and other rivers round the Black and

Caspian Seas, the eggs being buried in the soft earth in egg-pods. The young hatch out in the spring and are known as " hoppers." They are white when they first emerge from the egg, but moult at once and rapidly acquire a striking black, yellow, and red coloration. Their activities are very much influenced by the physical conditions of their surroundings ; they do not move about until the air has reached a certain temperature in the morning, and cease moving at night when the temperature has dropped below this point again. Soon after hatching, the hoppers show marked gregarious instincts, collecting together in bands. When a band is formed, the hoppers lose their individuality, and tend to copy the movements of their nearest neighbours. As a result, if the band starts moving, the movement goes on indefinitely until stopped by some external stimulus,

such as the evening fall in temperature. Small bands, when on the move, meet other bands and join them ; ultimately enormous bands of wandering hoppers may be formed. The wandering is entirely aimless, and maintains the direction in which it starts ; no obstacle stops the band, and they are capable of swimming rivers if they cross their path. The hoppers crawl up plants in the evening, if any are available, pass the night on them, feed on them in the morning, and then descend to resume their wanderings. After four or five moults,

[*John J. Ward.*
An Earwig (*Forficula auricularia*) with her brood ; it is just hatching out. The young are pale on emerging from the eggs, but soon darken. (× 4.)

the wings are fully developed, and the hoppers have become locusts, which begin to take short flights that culminate in a migratory flight lasting from one to three days, comparable to the nuptial flight of certain ants. At the end of the flight, the reproductive organs are ripe, pairing takes place, and eggs are laid. The adults are pink when the wings are first fully developed, and gradually become yellow as their reproductive organs mature.

It is well known that several years may elapse between one locust outbreak and another in the same region. Recently it has been discovered that between the outbreaks the migratory locust may be represented by a solitary grasshopper, quite different from it in appearance and in habits. The grasshopper has been described as a distinct species, *Locusta danica*, distinguished from *L. migratoria* by its greenish colour, shorter wings, longer hind legs, etc., and by the uniform green, grey or brown colour of the hoppers. By experimental breeding and rearing, it has been found that eggs of either supposed species are capable of developing into the other ; no matter which is the parent, if the hoppers are crowded together they develop the characters of the hoppers, and ultimately of the adult, of the migratory locust ; but if they are kept apart, they develop into solitary grasshoppers. Moreover, after development has proceeded in one direction, its course may be altered by a change of conditions. From these experiments, it appears that locust outbreaks occur only when conditions are particularly favourable to the hatching out of hoppers in large numbers ;

[H. Fischer.
A STONE-FLY (*Perla abdominalis*)
These insects have fierce aquatic larva. (× 5/4.)

when this occurs, the hoppers form wandering bands, which ultimately develop into locust swarms.

Many methods have been employed to control locust invasions ; possibly the most successful is to spread a poisoned bait before the bands of hoppers. The bait is generally composed of a mixture of bran and sawdust to which a solution containing white arsenic has been added. Efficient control entails a constant watch being kept on the movements of the locusts, and it is thought that, if favourable breeding grounds such as the reed beds of big rivers could be rendered unsuitable, the appearance of the swarming phase might be obviated altogether.

Order DERMAPTERA (Earwigs)

The Order is exemplified by the Common Earwig (*Forficula auricularia*). These insects are dark brown or black and have biting mouth-parts, and long antennae. The hind wings are membraneous and semi-circular in shape, with radiating veins ; they fold up neatly under the much shorter leathery front wings when the insect is not flying ; in some species wings are absent. The abdomen ends in a pair of strong forceps, probably a weapon of defence.

About five hundred species are known ; they are nocturnal in habit, hiding under stones, or among flowers, in the daytime. The most interesting feature in the habits of these insects is the parental care which the female exercises ; the eggs are laid in a group in the earth, the mother watches over them until they are hatched, and the young remain close to her for a considerable period of their development.

Order PLECOPTERA (Stone-flies)

The Stone-flies are rather large insects with long antennae, poorly developed, but functional mouth-parts, two pairs of wings with reticulate veining, the hind pair being the longer, and an elongate abdomen terminated by two hair-like filaments. These insects are found near streams, but do not frequent stagnant ponds. Of the two hundred known species, about thirty, belonging to three different families, are found in Britain.

As many as two thousand eggs may be laid by a single female, and are sometimes carried about on her back before being deposited in the water. The nymphs are aquatic, and breathe either through thin parts of the integument, or by means of tracheal gills. There is a slight metamorphosis, and relics of the larval gills may sometimes be seen on the thorax of the adult, although this has functional tracheae and breathes air.

One of the "soldiers" of a grass-cutting species of Termite. Note the powerful jaws. (*Highly magnified.*)

Order ISOPTERA (Termites or White Ants)

All the species of this order are social and polymorphic, resembling the ants to some extent in their organization and in many of their habits. However, they are not at all closely related to ants, but are very similar in general structure to the Orthoptera. The mouth-parts are adapted for biting and chewing. The two pairs of wings, when present, are similar, long, narrow and membraneous, and are folded flat over the back when the insect is at rest. Metamorphosis is slight, or entirely absent, but at each moult the insects go through a resting stage lasting two or three days, comparable to the pupal stage of more highly-developed groups.

Termites are found only in warm countries. About one thousand species are known at present, and of these, two occur in southern Europe, and a few more in the warmer parts of the United States ; they live either underground, or in trees, or in mounds that they build. The underground nests consist of long tunnels, which may pass up into the trees. The capacity for eating through any amount of wood makes the termites a serious nuisance to man in the tropics, as buildings and

Photos]   [*H. Bastin.*
An arboreal nest of a species of Termité which is found in Brazil.

furniture are apt to collapse as a result of their undetected ravages. The Termitaria are solid structures built of particles of earth cemented together with saliva and excreta. Inside are galleries made of woody material. These mounds may reach a height of twenty feet, and are so strongly built that they are difficult to destroy. An Australian species builds wedge-shaped termitaria, with the side walls invariably facing east and west. Mites, certain beetles, flies, and other insects are found living among the Termites, and occasionally two different species of Termite are found inhabiting the same mound.

The colonies vary in size from species to species; in the primitive forms the number of individuals is small and the social organization is not very complex, but in the more highly-developed species each colony may be made up of over a million individuals representing ten or more castes. Five main castes are recognizable, further differentiation being based on these types. Of these castes three are sexual and two sterile; the former may be long-winged, short-winged or wingless, and the latter, always wingless, are either workers or soldiers; each caste is composed of males and females and all play their appointed part in the economy of the colony.

The long-winged sexual forms may be regarded as typical adults. When fully developed, they emerge from the termitarium in a swarm, and make a flight for the purpose of founding new colonies. At the end of the flight, the wings are snapped off at the base and those which escape from birds and other enemies, pair, and form the nucleus of the new colony; they are termed the Royal Pair. The female has the capacity, unknown in other groups of insects, of growing after the final moult. The growth is confined to the abdomen, which stretches enormously with the development of the reproductive organs, so that the insect may attain a length of five inches; in this state they are considered to be a great delicacy by the natives of Africa and Australia. The Royal Pair inhabit a single cell in the termitarium, the female laying an egg every two or three seconds for the nine or ten years of her life. She is fertilized at intervals by the male. This caste is the only one which comes out into the

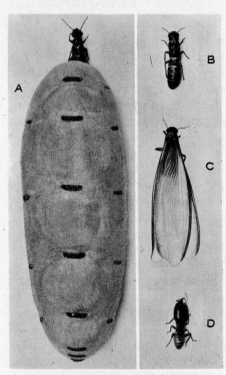

[*Brit. Mus., Nat. Hist.*
Termites have various "castes" in each species. Above are shown a queen (A), a female worker (B), a male (C), and a "soldier" (D), of the White Ant (*Termes bellicosus*). (*Slightly reduced.*)

[Sport & General.
Termite nests built by an Australian species. They are composed of earth cemented with saliva and reach a comparatively immense size. The wedge-shaped nests are always orientated so that the broad sides face east and west.

open air, and so is well chitinized and pigmented, and has functional compound eyes.

The female first lays a number of eggs which develop into workers, who begin the building of the nest. With a few exceptions these workers live underground, or inside termitaria, and are blind, soft and colourless.

The soldiers are concerned with the defence of the colony and fall into two groups. Some have the head and jaws heavily chitinized, and enormously enlarged, sometimes attaining a greater length than the rest of the body; these attack intruders with their jaws, and strike terrifying attitudes. Other soldiers have the head small and pointed and bearing the opening of a gland the secretion from which appears to be deadly and forms an effective defence against ants, the Termite's worst enemies.

The function of the short-winged and wingless sexual forms is not completely understood, but it is thought that they are kept in reserve in case anything should happen to the Royal Pair. Anatomically they are less well developed than the long-winged sexual forms; they are blind, soft and colourless, and may be regarded as nymphs with fully-developed reproductive organs, although even in this connection they are not as efficient as the long-winged forms.

The Royal Pair, the subsidiary sexual forms, and the eggs and young of all the castes are attended to by the workers, who keep the nest clean and prepare the food. The feeding habits of Termites are very curious. Food may consist either of wood or other vegetable matter, dead bodies and cast skins of members of the community, of partially-digested food mixed with saliva and regurgitated through the mouth, or of waste material passed out through the anus (proctodaeal food). In some species fungus gardens are kept and the fungus hyphae are added to the diet. Raw food in the form of wood or other vegetable matter is eaten by the workers, who are able to digest it only with the help of protozoan parasites living in the alimentary canal. The workers then feed the rest of the community, the queen and young nymphs receiving regurgitated food and fungus threads ; the older nymphs receive proctodaeal food, and are finally able to eat wood for themselves.

It is not known whether the development of the various castes is produced by differential feeding as in the bees, or whether it is inherent in the constitution.

CRAB-LOUSE (*Pediculus pubis*).
(*Very highly magnified.*)

Order EMBIOPTERA

This small order contains about sixty species, and is probably more nearly allied to the Orthoptera than to any other group. The insects occur in warm climates, and have not been found further north than the shores of the Mediterranean. They are long and slim, with long antennae, and biting mouth-parts. The front and hind legs are large, with rather swollen joints, but the middle pair is quite small. The males may be winged or wingless, but when winged their powers of flight are very poor ; the females are always wingless. Some of these insects are solitary and others are gregarious, but all live in silken tunnels. The silk is derived from glands which open on the swollen front feet ; males, females and nymphs all have the weaving habit. They live under stones or bark, generally avoiding the daylight. The nymphs resemble the adults, but a slight metamorphosis takes place in the males when the wings appear.

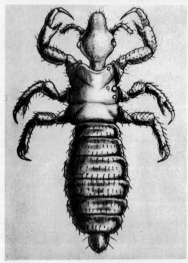

Photos]   *[James's Press.*
BODY-LOUSE (*Pediculus vestimenti*).
(*Very highly magnified.*)

Order PSOCOPTERA (Book-lice)

The insects in this order are very small and have not been widely studied. They have long slender antennae, and biting mouth-parts. They may be winged or wingless, the winged forms having well-developed eyes, and the wingless being blind. When wings are present, they are transparent, the front pair is larger than the back pair, and the transverse veins are much reduced.

Book-lice are wingless forms which are often found among old books and papers in disused rooms. They feed on papers, the paste of bookbindings, and scraps of vegetable and animal matter.

One species shares with a beetle of the genus *Anobium* the title of " Death-watch." The ticking sound is produced by the head being beaten on the ground between the front legs ; if the insect is sitting on a loose piece of paper, this acts as a sounding box, and the noise becomes audible at a distance of several yards.

Many members of this group live under bark, or on leaves, or among lichens. The eggs are frequently attached to leaves, and may be covered by a mass of silken threads. The nymphs are not unlike the adults, and develop without definite metamorphosis or pupal stage.

Order ANOPLURA (Lice)

The members of this order are all ectoparasites of birds and mammals, and are much modified structurally in connection with this mode of life. Lice are small, flattened, wingless, and more or less blind ; the mouthparts are adapted for piercing and sucking, or for biting, and the feet for clinging to the hair or feathers of the host. The eggs are cemented to the body of the host, there is no metamorphosis, and the whole life-cycle is passed through in one place. Two suborders, *Mallophaga* and *Siphunculata*, are recognized.

[*John J. Ward.*
A May-fly (*Ephemera*) after emerging from its nymphal skin. (*Nat. size.*)

Suborder **Mallophaga.** The insects in this group are known as biting lice, and live principally on birds, although one or two are parasitic on mammals. They do not suck blood, but feed on broken bits of skin and feather, and merely irritate their host by crawling about ; birds frequently try to free themselves from their parasites by having dust baths.

It is an interesting fact that the species of lice on closely-related birds are usually more like one another than those on more distantly-related birds. It is possible that the lice may have evolved in conjunction with their hosts, and the comparison of lice from two different birds might be of assistance in determining the inter-relations of the hosts.

Suborder **Siphunculata.** These are sucking lice, and are parasitic on mammals. One hundred and twenty species are known, two occurring on man, six on domestic animals, and others on such improbable hosts as seals and elephants. They have piercing mouth-parts and suck blood.

The human *Head-louse* is about one-sixth of an inch long and lives among the hair of the head. The eggs are cemented to the hairs in lumps, forming " nits " which are very difficult to remove. The lice hatch in six or seven days, and the nymphs undergo three moults, the whole life cycle occupying about seven weeks. A slightly larger variety of this species is known as the *Body-louse*, and is found among the body hairs and in the seams of the clothing. The insect is an agent in spreading typhus, trench fever and relapsing fever, and it has been proved that the virus can be transmitted from one generation of lice to the next.

The other species parasitic on man is the *Crab-louse*. It is broader and shorter than the head-louse, and usually lives in the pubic region. As yet, it has not been connected with the spread of any disease.

Order EPHEMEROPTERA (May-flies)

May-flies are soft-bodied insects, occurring in numbers around streams and ponds. As indicated by the name of the order, the adults have a very brief life, rarely lasting for more than a day. The order contains a single family (*Ephemeridae*), of which perhaps five hundred species are known; about forty of these occur in Great Britain.

The adults have short antennae, large compound eyes, and very degenerate mouth-parts. No food is taken during the short period of adult life, and the alimentary canal is modified to form an air reservoir, which makes the insect very buoyant. The front wings are triangular in shape, with a close net-work of veins, and are very much larger than the hind wings; the legs are small and are useless for walking, and the abdomen is long and narrow, terminating in two or three long, hair-like processes. In addition the male has a clasping organ. Pairing takes place on the wing.

The eggs are laid in water and show considerable variation in shape, some of them having fila-

[*John J. Ward.*
A Dragon-fly after leaving its nymphal skin (*Aeshna sp.*). ($\times$ 5/6.)

ments to anchor them to submerged water plants. They are produced in great numbers, sometimes as many as four thousand being laid by a single female. The nymphs have a comparatively long larval life, sometimes extending over two or three years, and may go through as many as twenty moults. They are vegetable feeders and either lead an active swimming life, or burrow in the mud, or attach themselves to stones in swiftly-running streams. They have compound eyes, well-developed biting mouth-parts, and breathe by means of external tracheal gills.

When the adult state is reached, the nymph floats to the surface, the skin splits down the back, and the

[*John J. Ward.*
Adult Dragon-fly (*Libellula depressa*) emerging from its nymphal skin. (× 7/8.)

winged insect emerges. This group is peculiar in that a moult takes place after the imago has emerged, and it is only after this moult that the insect becomes sexually mature. The first aerial form is called a sub-imago, and is generally duller and more colourless than the perfect insect.

These insects form a staple food of freshwater fish, both in the nymphal and adult stages.

Order ODONATA (Dragon-flies)

This order is small and clearly defined ; about two thousand five hundred species are known at present and of these forty-two occur in England.

Dragon-flies are sun-loving insects, and have tremendous powers of flight ; they are found all over the world, but occur in greatest profusion in South America and Japan. Many species are beautifully coloured, and in some the females are dimorphic, one type resembling the male in coloration, and the other having a striking orange pattern absent from the male. Dragon-flies are often considered dangerous by country people, and have been termed *Horse-stingers* and *Devil's Darning-needles*, but they are perfectly harmless. The nymphs live in fresh water, and are very unlike the adults ; a metamorphosis takes place, but there is no resting stage in the life history.

The head is attached to the body by a very thin neck, and is extremely mobile ; the compound eyes are often enormous. The thorax has a peculiar appearance when seen from the side, as the legs are crowded towards the front and the anterior pair of wings is placed behind the level of insertion of the back pair of legs. The legs are useless for crawling, but are used for climbing up plant stems; they lie close behind the mouth and are covered with slender bristles; as the dragon-fly hunts on the wing, it is possible that the legs form a trap to enmesh the prey, which is then transferred to the mouth. The two pairs of wings resemble one another; they are long, narrow, membraneous, covered with a close network of veins, and with conspicuous stigmata at the tips. The abdomen is a good deal longer than the thorax, and may sometimes be so long and slender that it resembles a bristle. The genital opening is at the tip of the abdomen, but in the male the intromittent organ is situated near the base, so that the

[John J. Ward.
DRAGON-FLY (*Libellula depressa*). (× 5/6.)

spermatophores have to be transferred externally to this organ before pairing can take place. The male also has clasping organs at the tip of the abdomen with which he grasps the female round the neck when mating.

The eggs are laid in fresh water, the female sometimes going below the surface when laying them; occasionally, they are inserted into the stems of water-plants, but they may also be laid freely on the bottom.

The nymphs move about actively, and are predacious; certain of the mouth-parts are modified to form a curious "mask," which can be thrown forward suddenly to grasp an insect and draw it back into the mouth. They feed on all sorts of aquatic insects and very young fish, and may even eat each other if food becomes scarce.

The larvae have a peculiar method of breathing, analogous to the respiration of vertebrates. The terminal part of the alimentary canal or rectum is enlarged to form a fair-sized chamber, the inside walls being covered with small projections; each of these consists of a very thin membrane covering a small tracheole; water is pumped in and out of the rectum and the tracheoles extract oxygen from it and convey it to the main tracheae of the body. In some species the nymphs have simple external gills at the tip of the abdomen, which act in the same way.

When the nymph is full grown, it ceases to feed, crawls up the stem of a water-plant into the air and waits until the cuticle splits ; the adult dragon-fly then crawls out. It dries, the wings harden, and the colour pattern gradually appears.

The Odonata are divided into two suborders, *Anisoptera* and *Zygoptera*.

Suborder **Anisoptera**. In this suborder the wings remain open when the insect is resting, the eyes are close together and the nymphs have rectal gills. There are two families in this suborder, the insects belonging to them being strong flyers. The common European species of *Libellula* is known to collect in swarms which make a definite migratory flight.

Suborder **Zygoptera**. The three families composing the Zygoptera are composed of more delicately-built insects, sometimes called *Demoiselles*. The eyes are widely separated, the wings are folded over the back when the insect is at rest, and the nymphs have external caudal gills.

Order THYSANOPTERA (Thrips)

Thrips are minute insects, yellow, brown or black in colour, which may be found crawling about on flowers, foliage or fungi.

Only about three hundred species are known, and of these one hundred have been found in England. The mouth-parts are adapted for piercing and sucking, and are curious in that they are asymmetrical. The insects feed on plant juices, and injure crops in much the same way as do the Plant-bugs. The wings, when present, are long and narrow, with very few veins, and with stiff fringes all round the edges ; the front wings are linked by hooks to the hind wings when the insect is in flight. Wingless forms crawl or jump, and all species have peculiar pads on the feet, which enable them to walk on any surface. The abdomen has ten segments, and in some forms the females have an ovipositor projecting beyond the tip.

[*John J. Ward.*
CORN THRIPS (*Thrips cerealium*).
(× 26.)

The eggs are laid in the tissues of the host plant, or in crevices under the bark. The nymphs generally moult four times, and, although there is no abrupt metamorphosis, they pass through a resting stage, very similar to the pupal stage of higher groups, before the final moult. Males are very rare in some species, and parthenogenesis is of common occurrence.

Order HEMIPTERA (Plant-bugs, Bed-bugs, Pond-skaters, Water-boatmen, and Aphides)

The order Hemiptera includes, among other insects, the Plant-bugs, Bed-bugs, Water-boatmen, and Aphides. There are many thousand different kinds, mostly small, and exhibiting great diversity in shape. The majority are sun-loving insects, often brightly patterned ; most species are plant-feeders, sucking the sap from leaves and young shoots but some suck blood.

The mouth is placed at the end of a proboscis which has a very characteristic and uniform structure throughout the group, and is used for piercing and sucking. Two pairs of piercing stylets are enclosed in a tubular sheath : each member of the inner pair has two longitudinal grooves on its inner surface so that when the two stylets are apposed a double tube is formed. A digestive juice from the salivary glands is forced down one tube into the wound, where it serves to increase the flow of plant or animal juices, which are sucked up the other tube. There are generally two pairs of wings, but they may be absent, or only partly developed in some aquatic forms, or in certain parasites of plants or animals. The hind legs are often well-developed for jumping.

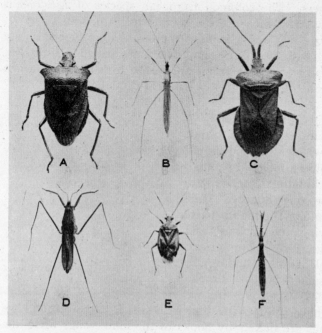

[H. Bastin.
A. Shield-bug (*Pentatoma rufipes*) (*Nat. size*) ; B. *Neides tipularius* (*Nat. size*); C. *Syromastes marginatus* (× 7/4) ; D. *Gerris costae* (*Nat. size*) ; E. *Capsus ruber* (*Nat. size*) ; F. *Hydrometra stagnorum* (*Nat. size*).

The eggs are of various shapes, and are generally deposited in crevices of the host - plant. The larvae go through a number of moults, generally six, after the third of which the wing rudiments appear. There is no definite pupal stage ; the nymph becomes more and more like its parent at each moult, and with the final one, assumes the adult form.

The habits of these insects place them among the worst enemies to the welfare of man, since almost all cultivated plants are attacked and injury proceeds not only from removal of sap, but also from the penetration into the wounds of harmful bacteria and fungi, and the transmission of fungus diseases from plant to plant by the mouth-parts of the insect. Wheat, maize, coffee, cocoa, fruit and cotton are among the crops which suffer most.

Fortunately, the plant-bugs are to some extent held in check by birds, ladybirds, Hymenoptera, Diptera with parasitic larvae, and the free-living carnivorous larvae of certain other Diptera.

[M. H. Crawford.
POND SKATER (Gerris gibbifera). (× 2.)

The Hemiptera are divided into two suborders, *Heteroptera* and *Homoptera*.

Suborder Heteroptera (Shield-bugs, Bed-bugs, Cotton-stainers, Pond-skaters, Water-bugs and Water-boat-men). In this group the front wings are thicker and harder than the back wings, and, when the insect is at rest, they form a kind of roof over the abdomen. Most of the bugs of this group are notorious for their smell, which originates from a pair of "stink glands" opening near the base of the hind pair of legs. They frequently produce sounds, usually by rubbing a leg against the body.

The suborder includes twenty-four families, but only a few of these can be mentioned. The largest family is that of the Shield-bugs (*Pentatomidae*), of which at least four thousand species are known. Bed-bugs (*Cimicidae*) suck the blood of man, but do not live permanently on their host. On the other hand, the Bat-bugs (*Polyctenidae*) live in the fur of the bats on which they are parasitic. The *Coreidae* are vegetable feeders ; many of them have striking expansions of chitin on their hind femora.

[H. Bastin.
THE BED-BUG (*Cimex lectularius*). (× 7.)

The " Cotton-stainers " or " Red-bugs " (*Pyrrhocoridae*) are small, black and red insects which creep into the cotton bolls to suck the juices of the seeds, making wounds which exude an oily secretion that stains

[H. Bastin.
THE FLAG-LEGGED BUG (*Anisoscelis affinis*).
(× 5/3.)

123

[James's Press.
The Giant Water-bug (*Lethocerus*) lives in ponds in warm countries and lies in wait amongst water-plants for its prey, which consists of tadpoles, small fish and insects. (*Photographed as in flight.*) (×1/2).

the cotton; the cotton is also stained by the adult bugs hiding in the bolls and being crushed in the gins.

The Pond-skaters (*Gerridae*) glide about on the surface of the water and are somewhat modified on account of their aquatic mode of life. They have a coat of thick, close hairs, on the under side of the abdomen, which prevents them from getting wet, and there are no scent glands. These insects are carnivorous. Both winged and wingless forms occur. *Halobates*, the only genus of oceanic insects, belongs to this group.

The Giant Water-bugs (*Belostomatidae*) are among the largest insects in the order, some of them attaining a length of four inches; they are very voracious and feed on small fish, tadpoles, young frogs and other insects. They are generally submerged, and air is conveyed to the posterior pair of spiracles from the surface by a retractile tube at the tip of the abdomen, the remaining spiracles being closed. The back of the abdomen is slightly grooved, leaving a hollow space below the wings which is used for the storage of air. In some species the eggs are cemented on to the front wings of the male, where they remain until they hatch.

The Water - boatmen (*Corixidae*) are common in English ponds; the body and legs are flattened and in addition the legs have a row of stiff hairs continuing the plane of the leg, to increase the swimming powers of the insects. Some of the species in this group have stridulating organs. These insects are probably vegetable feeders; in some parts of the world both the adults and the eggs are used as food.

[John J. Ward.
Highly-magnified middle and hind legs of *Corixa sp.* Note the flattened hind leg fringed with long hairs, which act as the blade of an oar.

[John J. Ward
Cuckoo-spit, the frothy excretion of the Frog-hopper nymph
(× 2.)

Suborder **Homoptera** (Cicadas, Frog-hoppers or Cuckoo-spit Insects, Tree-hoppers or Devil Hoppers, Leaf-suckers, Leaf-hoppers, Green-flies or Plant-lice, Candle-and Lantern-flies, White-flies and Scale Insects). In the Homoptera the front and hind wings are alike in texture and are laid flat over the back when not in use; glands which secrete a kind of wax are very highly developed. The best-known members of this group are the Cicadas, Cuckoo-spit Insects, Tree-hoppers, Aphides and Scale Bugs, of which Lac insects are an example.

The Cicadas (*Cicadidae*) are well known on account of the musical propensities of the males, the sound being produced by an elaborate apparatus whereby a membrane is made to vibrate on a soundbox. They are represented by only one species in England. The North American " Periodical Cicada " is interesting since the adults appear in enormous numbers at intervals of seventeen years, the intermediate period being spent underground in the nymphal condition. The adults do great damage to young trees by making such extensive incisions in the soft shoots for the deposition of their eggs that the top of the tree withers away.

The Candle- and Lantern-flies (*Fulgoridae*) are among the most brightly-coloured members of the order ; many of them have extensions

[M. H. Crawford
Nymph of Frog-hopper or Cuckoo-spit without its frothy covering. (× 4.)

of chitin on the head and thorax which gives them a monstrous appearance. Another section of the family contains species which resemble butterflies in shape and colour, and are capable of excreting immense amounts of wax.

The Frog-hoppers or Cuckoo-spit bugs (*Cercopidae*) are very common in England; the nymphs sit on the stems of grasses and flowers in the spring, sucking the plant juices with such vigour that liquid excretion leaves the animal almost continuously, becomes mixed with air and envelopes the nymph in the familiar blob of white foam, keeping it moist and comfortable.

[*H. Bastin.*
THE DEVIL-HOPPER (*Heteronotus vulneratus*). (× 4.)

Among the Tree-hoppers or Devil-hoppers (*Membracidae*) many curious cases of mimicry occur. A South American bug of this family mimics a Leaf-cutter Ant, and resembles not only the ant, but the ant carrying a piece of leaf to its nest. This is only one of the many examples of mimicry in the Hemiptera, which are very striking on account of the curious shapes assumed by these insects.

Members of the families of Leaf-hoppers (*Jassidae*) and Leaf-suckers (*Psyllidae*) are serious pests of fruit trees and other cultivated crops; they are minute insects and often secrete wax or honeydew. The Apple- and Pear-suckers and the Beet Leaf-sucker are among the most notorious species in the group.

Green-flies or Plant-lice (*Aphididae*) are small, soft, sticky green or brown insects, colonial in habit on roses, vines, poplar trees, larches and other plants. The front and hind wings, when present, are of the same membraneous consistency, and winged and wingless forms of the same species may be found on the same plant. Some of the species have a characteristic pair of horns towards the tip of the abdomen, which secrete a sticky substance.

The life-history of the aphis is very complicated, and exhibits the phenomena of viviparity, parthe-

[*H. Bastin.*
MALE (*left*) AND FEMALE CICADA (tropical). (× 8/9.)

nogenesis, polymorphism, and the production of individuals which are sexually perfect, but imperfect in other respects, such as the structure of the mouth-parts, so that they are engaged solely in reproduction. The actual details of the life-history differ from species to species, so that a generalized account will be given here.

The winter is passed in the egg, which is usually laid in some crack or corner of the host plant. In spring the nymph emerges and grows into a structurally imperfect, viviparous, parthenogenetic female who produces a brood of young females rather more perfect in structure than their mother. Reproduction may continue in this way for two or three generations, causing an enormous increase in the number of individuals on the host plant.

THE BROWN CURRANT SCALE (*Lecanium ribes*). (*Nat. size.*)

Photos]   [H. Bastin.
THE COTTONY CUSHION SCALE (*Pulvinaria vitis*). (*Nat. size.*)

In migratory species with two different host plants, over-crowding and consequent diminution of food supply, due to the weakened condition of the host plant, appear to initiate the production among the brood of winged females, who migrate in crowds to the secondary host plant and there produce further broods of wingless, parthenogenetic viviparous young.

Towards the end of the summer, when food on the secondary host begins to decrease in quantity or quality and to become unsuitable for the aphide population, winged females again appear and fly back to the primary host, and broods of sexually-perfect individuals, who may be winged or wingless, appear. Pairing takes place and the females lay one or more eggs on the primary host plant; these remain dormant during the

[H. Bastin.

Colony of aphides on a palm leaf, showing several stages of growth. Note the cast skins. (× 7/2.)

winter and hatch in the spring, thus completing the life-cycle. The details of the life-cycle show an infinite variety, and a much greater degree of complexity is reached in forms where the life-cycle extends over more than one year.

The American Vine Aphis, *Phylloxera vastatrix*, is more or less harmless in America, but has, on introduction into Europe, become a serious pest ; the adults form galls on the leaves, and the winter is passed in the nymphal stage on the roots.

The species of White-fly (*Aleyrodidae*) look like small waxy flies ; the best known is the Tomato Whitefly, which injures the plant by withdrawing sap, and sheds honeydew on the leaves ; the sticky patches form an ideal matrix for the growth of a black fungus which seriously interferes with the life processes of the tomato plant.

The " Scale Insects " (*Coccidae*) are a very serious pest of fruit trees. In the males the front wings are well developed, but the hind wings are vestigial ; the females are wingless and the body becomes very degenerate and incapable of movement. The secretion of wax is highly developed in this family. The wax unites with the cast skins of the nymph and the excreta, and forms a scale, attached at the edges to the host plant, and under this the female lives and rears her young.

The Cochineal Insect (*Dactylopius coccus*) lives on cacti in Mexico, and the dye is obtained from the bodies of the dried females. Lac dye is obtained in the same way, the Lac Insect being cultivated intensively in India.

[Photopress.

White-fly (*Aleyrodes sp.*) on the underside of a leaf. This insect is a serious pest in glass-houses, often doing much damage to tomatoes. (× 3/2.)

THE SMALL TORTOISESHELL (*Aglais urticæ*) AND THE LARGE TORTOISE-
SHELL (*Nymphalis polychloros*). LIFE HISTORY

1. Egg (Magd.) ; 2. Larva ; 3. Seventh Segment of Larva (Magd.) ; 4. Pupa ;
5–6. Female ; 7. Egg (Magd.) ; 8. Larva ; 9. Seventh Segment of Larva. (Magd.) ;
10. Pupa ; 11–12. Female.

Division ENDOPTERYGOTA

Order NEUROPTERA (Alder-flies, Snake-flies, Lacewing-flies, Ant-lions, etc.)

The Order Neuroptera, as currently conceived, is comparatively small, containing Alder-flies, Lacewings, Ant-lions, etc. At one time it was made to include Dragon-flies, Termites, Biting-lice, and several other groups now recognized as separate orders. The insects are large and soft-bodied, with long antennae and biting mouth-parts. The two pairs of wings are similar, membraneous, and covered with a network of veins; when the insect is at rest, they are folded back over the body. The larvae may live on land or in the water; all are carnivorous, and pass through a more or less well-defined pupal stage before the last moult.

The structure of the mouth-parts of the larvae affords a character for dividing the group into two suborders, *Megaloptera*, in which the mouth-parts of the larva are adapted for biting; and *Planipennia*, in which they form a piercing and sucking organ.

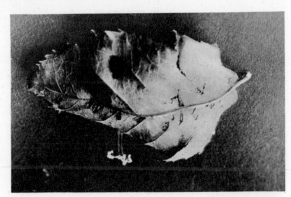

[*M. H. Crawford.*
Eggs of a Lacewing-fly (*Chrysopa*), each one on a slender stalk secreted by the female. ($\times$ 3/2.)

Megaloptera. This suborder contains the Alder-flies and Snake-flies. Only one species of Alder-fly, *Sialis lutaria*, is found in England. It deposits two hundred to five hundred eggs in a mass on plants or stones, near ponds or very slowly-flowing streams; the larvae, on hatching, make their way to the water and crawl about the muddy bottom, feeding on insect larvae and small worms. They have seven pairs of tracheal gills, five-jointed appendages fringed with long hairs, arranged down the sides of the abdomen, and a single terminal gill at the tip. The pupal period is passed in the mud, but the pupa retains sufficient power of motion to work its way to the surface of the water before hatching.

The Snake-flies (*Raphidiidae*) are characterized by the great elongation of the front of the thorax and back of the head, so that they appear to have a very long neck. About eighty species are known, four of which occur in Britain. The eggs are laid in slits in the bark of trees, and the larvae live under loose bark, feeding on any soft-bodied insects they can find. The pupa is quiescent for a time, then crawls about for a short while, but remains quiet again before the final moult.

Planipennia. This suborder forms a very much larger section of the order than the *Megaloptera*, and, of the thirteen families which compose it, five are represented in Great Britain. Two of these consist of the Brown and Green Lacewing-flies ; twenty species of the former and twelve of the latter have been recorded as British and the members of both families are of some importance on account of the numbers of aphides and other noxious plant bugs which their larvae devour.

Three species of the family *Sisyridae* occur in England. The adults lay their eggs near water, covering them with a silken web ; when the larvae hatch, they find their way to the water and live in association with a freshwater sponge, returning to dry land to pupate.

The members of the family *Nemopteridae* are characterized by the enormous elongation and narrowing of the hind wings.

The Ant-lions (*Myrmeleonidae*) are, perhaps, the most striking family in the order. The adults are nocturnal ; they resemble narrow-bodied

dragon-flies. The larvae, which may be half an inch in length, make pits in dry sand and bury themselves at the bottom, with only the jaws protruding. Insects which slip into the pit are unable to climb up the steep wall of shifting sand, and fall into the jaws of the waiting larva, who sucks them dry and throws the skin out of the pit. These insects are not found in England, but occur in warm, dry regions of Europe, and other parts of the world.

[*M. H. Crawford.*
Larva of an Alder-fly, seeking its prey at the bottom of a stream. (×2.)

Order MECOPTERA (Scorpion-flies)

The insects in this order are medium-sized, slender, and predacious. The head is produced into a rostrum with biting mouth-parts at the tip, and has long antennae, the front and hind pairs of wings are similar, elongate, and with a network of veins, and the abdomen is long and has prominent clasping organs in the male.

The eggs are laid in the soil, and the larvae feed on any small insects which they may find.

Males of the family *Panorpidae* carry the abdomen curved over the back ; hence the term " Scorpion-fly." Members of this family are further characterized by their spotted wings, which are folded flat when the insect is at rest. The *Panorpidae* are very common in northern temperate regions.

Photos]   [*Brit. Mus., Nat. Hist.; H. Bastin ; John J. Ward and M. H. Crawford.*

A. Ant-lion and larva (*Palpares libelluloides*) (× 4/5) ; B. Snake-fly (*Raphidia sp.*) (× 2) ; C. *Nemoptera sp.* (4/5) ; D. Lacewing-fly (*Chrysopa carnea*) (× 3/2) ; E. Alder-fly (*Sialis lutaria*) (× 2).

The family *Bittacidae* is almost world-wide in distribution, but is not found in the extreme north; these insects are very slender, with long, thin legs, and closely resemble a Daddy-long-legs in general appearance. The front tarsi are folded back on the tibiae to

SCORPION FLY (*Panorpa sp.*). (× 3.)   [*H. Bastin.*]

form a grasping organ, as in the Mantids.   The *Boreidae* are wingless; they occur in Europe and North America.

Order Trichoptera (Caddis-flies)

This order contains small moth-like insects with hairy membraneous wings, and rather poorly-developed mouth-parts.   The group is probably nearly allied to the least specialized members of the Lepidoptera.   The adults are inconspicuous, dull in colouring, and often nocturnal in habit.   They are poor flyers, and are generally found near water.   The hind wings are broader than the front wings, and both pairs are held vertically when the insect is at rest; the females are often wingless.   The antennae are long and hairy, and the legs are slender.

CADDIS-FLY.   (× 2.)   [*H. Bastin.*]

In some genera the males have elaborate scent glands. If food is taken at all in the adult condition, it is probably liquid and is licked up from flowers and broken plant stems.

The larvae are known as caddis-worms, and are familiar objects in slowly-flowing streams. In the majority of species each larva builds a tubular case, open at both ends, and held in place by a pair of hooks at the tip of the abdomen. The insect crawls about clumsily, with the head and front legs protruding from the case. Water is circulated through the case by the body movements, and breathing is effected by means of tracheal gills. The cases themselves are made from an infinite variety of materials

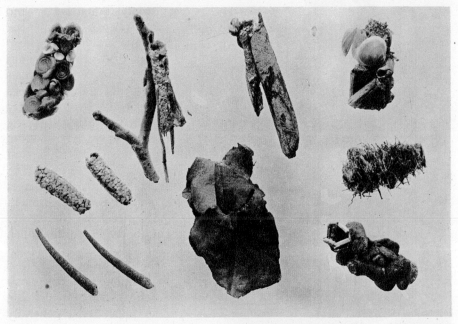

[H. Bastin.

Cases of Caddis-fly larvae made of various materials. (× 5/4.)

cemented together by a secretion of silk : fine gravel, grasses, water-weeds, hollow stems and twigs are most usually made use of, each species having a characteristic case.

When the larva is ready to pupate, it fixes its case to a stone or other stationary object and pupates inside it. Later, the pupa gnaws its way out, crawls up the stem of a water-plant to the surface, and the adult emerges immediately.

About seven hundred species are known, and are grouped in twelve families. One hundred and seventy species have been recorded from the British Isles.

Order LEPIDOPTERA (Butterflies and Moths)

The Lepidoptera are not only one of the most highly-developed, but also one of the most studied groups of insects, and consequently more is known about them than about any other order. At least eighty thousand species have been described and of these two thousand are found in the British Isles. The adults are very constant in shape throughout the group and have similar habits, feeding exclusively, when the mouth-parts a r e n o t atrophied, on flower and fruit juices.

The adults have two pairs of membraneous wings with very few cross-veins and the wings, legs and body are generally covered with broad scales, which vary in colour to form the most striking and intricate patterns. The head bears a large pair of compound eyes and a sucking proboscis, sometimes of abnormal length, which is coiled up under the head when not in use. There is a complete metamorphosis with a resting pupal stage, the pupa being generally enclosed in some kind of cocoon.

The eggs may be laid in thousands and are either dropped at random, or deposited in batches on the food plant, where they hatch from two to thirty days after deposition.

[M. H. Crawford.

AN ADULT TIGER MOTH (*Arctia caia*).
The cocoon from which the perfect insect has emerged is shown in the lower part of the photograph. (*Nat. size.*)

The larva is commonly called a caterpillar; it is wormlike, with a well-developed head with strong biting jaws, three thoracic and ten abdominal segments. It moves by means of three pairs of jointed thoracic legs, and a varying number of pairs of unjointed legs placed on the anterior and posterior abdominal segments. The caterpillar may be either bare or covered with thick tufts of hair, among which there are sometimes poison hairs capable of producing a skin rash if the creature is handled. In addition, glands emitting an unpleasant smell may also be present. The larvae are colourless, protectively coloured, or possessed of a bold and brilliant pattern ; sometimes they conceal themselves in silken cases. They eat voraciously and undergo from four to six moults before pupating. The salivary glands are modified for the production of silk, which is ejected in fluid form through an opening on the front of the head termed the spinneret ; the fluid silk hardens rapidly in the air in the form of fine threads. The pupa, generally enclosed in a silken or earthen cocoon, retains a certain amount of mobility, and emerges from the cocoon before the adult hatches out.

[M. H. Crawford.
Eggs of the Tiger Moth (*Arctia caia*) on a piece of bark. (× 7.)

Lepidoptera are commonly divided into two groups, Butterflies and Moths, the former having the antennae knobbed, and the latter having them fringed, the one flying by day and the other by night. However, these distinctions are not always valid, and are not at all acceptable in a scientific classification. The order can most satisfactorily be divided into two suborders based on the wing venation. In the *Homoneura* t h e venation of the fore and hind wings is almost identical, whereas in the *Heteroneura* there are obvious differences.

Homoneura. This suborder is small, containing only two families,

[John J. Ward.
CATERPILLARS OF THE TIGER MOTH.
This type of caterpillar is commonly called a "woolly bear." (× 4/5.)

135

LOBSTER MOTH (*Stauropus fagi*). *[John J. Ward.* (*Nat. size.*)

and is further characterized by the absence of a coiled proboscis ; it may be regarded as containing the more primitive forms among the Lepidoptera.

The family *Micropterygidae* is composed of small, metallic day-flying moths, some of the genera being common in Britain. The mouth-parts are unspecialized, with functional jaws which are used in gathering pollen, the food of the imago. The family *Hepialidae* contains the Ghost-moths and Swift-moths ; they are widely distributed, and differ greatly in size, some of the Australian forms having a wing-spread of six or seven inches, accompanied by brilliant coloration. The five British Swift-moths are small and dull-coloured, and fly at dusk. The mouth-parts are degenerate, so that the life of the individual must be short. In the common Ghost-moth the upper surface of the wings of the male is dazzling white, so that the insect is conspicuous even on the darkest night : the female is brown, and is probably attracted to the male by sight. The larvae live underground, feeding on roots, or they are sometimes internal wood-borers ; some species remain in the larval stage for two or three years.

Heteroneura. This suborder forms a large group, which can be divided on characters afforded by the veining of the wings. As already noted, the front and hind wings are diversely veined, and in addition, a coiled proboscis is present, unless it has become degenerate.

The Clear-wing moths (*Aegeriidae*) are characterized by the absence of scales on parts of the wing, leaving

[H. Bastin.
THE PURPLE EMPEROR BUTTERFLY (*Apatura iris*).
The method of closing the wings, when at rest, may (except in a few instances) be used to distinguish between butterflies and moths. (*Nat. size.*)

Photos]   [*John J. Ward ; Hugh Main ; H. Bastin.*
A. Five-spot Burnet and cocoons (*Zygaena loniceræ*) (× 5/6) ; B. Clear-wing, Lunar Hornet Moth (*Trochilium crabroni-formis*) (× 2/3) ; C. Plume Moth (*Orneodes hexadactyla*) (× 3) ; D. Clothes Moth (*Tinea pellionella*) (× 3) ; E. Male Goat-moth (*Cossus cossus*) (× 5/6) ; F. Female Oak Eggar (*Lasiocampa quercus*) (× 2/3).

[*H. Bastin.*
Case constructed by the caterpillar of one of the
African Bag-worm Moths. (× 2.)

patches of transparent membrane. They are active day-flyers, and very often bear a very striking resemblance to wasps, bees, and ichneumons. The larvae are wood-borers, and pupate in the larval burrow ; this habit of tunnelling in wood makes them injurious to cultivated fruit trees. Fourteen species are known in the British Isles, but they are not very common.

The family *Tineidae* forms a large group, of which seven hundred British species are known. A common example of this family is the Clothes-moth, a small golden insect, with narrow wings which have long fringes, developed particularly on the back of the hind wings. The eggs are laid among wool, hair, clothing, carpets and skins which afford food for the larvae, who increase the damage produced while feeding, by spinning themselves silken webs and galleries.

The Goat-moths and Carpenter-moths (*Cossidae*) are night-flyers. The larvae are wood-borers, and frequently do considerable damage to fruit trees. The members of the family *Tortricidae* are closely related to the Cossids. About three hundred species occur in Britain. The larvae roll themselves up in the leaves on which they feed and many even form galls. The larvae of the

[*H. Bastin.*
Male (above) and female Ghost-moths (*Hepialus humuli*). These moths fly at dusk ; the male is far more conspicuous than the female. (*Nat. size.*)

Photos]   *John J. Ward ; Hugh Main ; James's Press ; H. Bastin.*

A. Peacock (*Nymphalis io*) (× 2/3); B. European White Admiral and chrysalis skin (*Limenitis camilla*) (× 1/2); C. Painted Lady (*Vanessa cardui*) (× 1/2); D. *Morpho anaxibia* (S. America) (× 2/5); E. Purple Emperor (*Apatura iris*) (× 2/3); F. Grayling (*Satyrus semele*) (× 4/5).

139

Wet season form of a Tropical Butterfly (*Precis octavia*). (*Nat. size.*) Deep orange ground, spotted and edged black.

Codling-moth burrow in apples and pears, often causing serious damage.

The commonest British members of the family *Pyralidae* are the Grass-moths of the genus *Crambus*. They rest during the day-time, with their narrow wings folded back parallel to the grass stems on which they are sitting, and begin to fly in thousands at dusk. The larvae build themselves silken tunnels, and feed on grass-shoots. Certain species in this family have aquatic larvae; they begin life as leaf-miners in submerged water plants, and afterwards spin themselves into a cocoon under water. The adult females are dimorphic, those with long wings living aerially, and those with reduced wings living entirely in water.

The families *Pterophoridae* and *Orneodidae* comprise the Plume-moths in which one or both pairs of wings are divided into three or four lobes or plumes, each division having a long fringe on either side. The larvae frequently burrow in shoots and flower stems, and may produce galls.

The Bag-worm moths (*Psychidae*) have wingless females who spend their life inside the larval cocoon which, in the genus *Apterona*, is made of

Photos] [*Brit. Mus., Nat. Hist.*
Dry season form of *Precis octavia* (*Nat. size.*). Purple-blue ground, black lines and orange spots. Note the complete change of colour and increased size in the dry season.

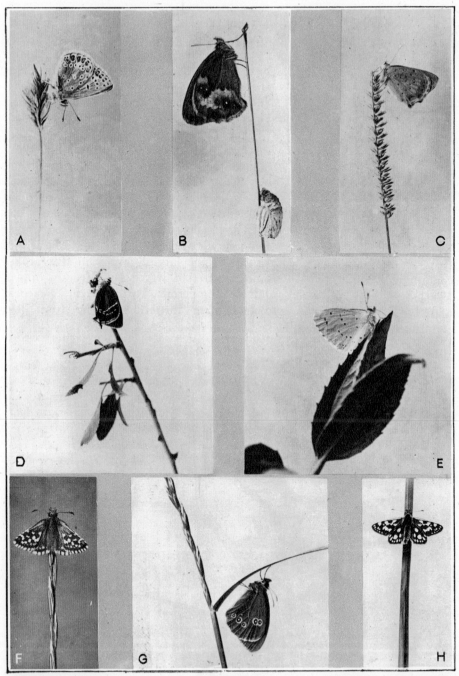

Photos]   [*Hugh Main and John J. Ward.*

A. Common Blue (*Polyommatus icarus*) (*Nat. size*) ; B. Hedge Brown (*Maniola tithonus*) (*Nat. size*) ; C. Small Copper (*Lycaena phlaeas*) (*Nat. size*) ; D. Black Hairstreak (*Strymon pruni*) (× 2/3) ; E. Holly Blue (*Lycaenopsis argiolus*) (×9/10) ; F. Grizzled Skipper (*Pyrgus malvae*) (*Nat. size*) ; G. Ringlet (*Aphantopus hyperanthus*) (× 2/3) ; H. Chequered Skipper (*Carterocephalus palaemon*) (× 2/3).

[M. H. Crawford.
Clay Triple Lines (*Ephyra linearia*), a British
Geometrid Moth, whose caterpillar feeds on
Beech. (*Nat. size.*)

silk and is coiled like a snail-shell. The best-known British representatives of the family *Zygaenidae* are the Burnet-moths and Foresters. The former are common in fields and sand-dunes, where the tough parchment-like cases enclosing the pupae are familiar objects on the grass stems.

The Eggars and Lappet moths (*Lasio-campidae*) are mostly nocturnal, but those belonging to the genus *Lasiocampa* are strong day-fliers. The larvae of the Lackey-moth live gregariously in silken webs, and are frequently very destructive to foliage.

The insects generally known as butterflies form a very much more uniform group than the moths. The *Nymphalidae* is the largest family in this group, containing at least five thousand species, of which the Meadow-brown, Heath, Grayling, Ringlet, Purple Emperor, Tortoiseshell, Peacock, and Painted Lady are familiar British butterflies. The front legs

[*John J. Ward.*
" Stick Caterpillars " of the Swallow-tail Moth (*Ourapteryx sambucaria*) ; they resemble twigs when at rest and are difficult
to detect. (*Slightly reduced.*)

Photos]   *[Hugh Main and John J. Ward.*
A. Clouded Yellow (*Colias croceus*) (*Nat. size*); B. Green-veined White (*Pieris napi*) (× 2/3); C. Black-veined White and puparia (*Aporia crataegi*) (*Nat. size*); D. Orange Tip (*Euchloë cardamines*) (× 2/3); E. Large White, male and female, (*Pieris brassicae*) (× 1/2).

143

[Hugh Main.
The Larch Pug (*Eupithecia lariciata*) on pine.
(*Nat. size.*)

are functionless and are reduced in size in both sexes, and are often covered with long, soft hairs, whence the name "brush-footed" butterflies. The adults of the sub-family *Danaidae* are probably protected from their enemies by possessing an unpleasant taste, and are the "models" for many mimicry associations in the tropics. The wings of the brilliant metallic-blue butterflies of the genus *Morpho* are used in the manufacture of jewellery. Many species form well-marked local races and the females are frequently seasonally dimorphic, exhibiting "dry-weather" and "wet-weather" forms.

The Blues, Coppers, and Hair-streaks belong to the family *Lycaenidae*; they are predominantly South American, but eighteen of the eleven hundred known species occur in Britain. The caterpillars of some species are carnivorous, feeding on Aphides, Coccids and Ant larvae.

The Whites, Brimstones, Orange-tips, and Clouded Yellows belong to the family *Pieridae*. The larvae sometimes cause great damage to green vegetables, and the adults of certain species are remarkable for their migratory flights.

The Swallow-tails (*Papilionidae*) are predominantly tropical butterflies, characterized by the tail-like extensions of the hind wings; one species still occurs locally in Britain. In some species the females differ greatly from the male and may be polymorphic; many forms mimic danaine butterflies.

The family *Hesperiidae* contains the Skippers, of which there are eight British species. The adults have a characteristic rapid, darting flight; the larvae may be wood-borers, or may conceal themselves by drawing leaves together in a silken web.

The *Sphingidae* (Hawk-moths) number about five hundred species, of which seventeen are found in the British Isles. The adults are thick-bodied, and have long narrow front wings with oblique outer margins. A few species

[H. Bastin.
The Tissue-moth (*fam. Geometridae*) resting on bark in a characteristic position; the colour of the wings blends well with that of the background. (*Nat. size.*)

AGRIAS AMYDON, SUB-SPECIES *zenodorus* (Ecuador)

By courtesy of]   [*British Museum (Natural History)*

AGRIAS CLAUDIA, SUB-SPECIES *sardanapalus* (Upper Amazons)

Photos]   [*H. Bastin and M. H. Crawford.*
A. Ghost Butterfly (*Ideopsis perakana*) (× 2/3);   B. Apollo Butterfly (*Parnassius apollo*) (*Nat. size*);   C. Swallow-tail
Butterfly (*Papilio machaon*) (*Nat. size*);   D. Caterpillar of Swallow-tail Butterfly (× 5/6).

The domesticated Silk-worm Moth (*Bombyx mori*) with eggs. (*Nat. size.*)

are diurnal, but the majority are night fliers. The Death's-head moth, with the " skull and cross-bones " on the back of the thorax, has a curious habit of entering beehives to obtain honey. It is also one of the few members of this order capable of making a sound both in the larval and adult stage. The larva, when disturbed, makes a crackling sound with its jaws, but the method by which the shrill chirp of the adult is evoked is still uncertain.

The family *Geometridae* contains the moths commonly known as Carpets, Waves, and Pugs ; it consists of many thousand species, of which about two hundred and seventy are British. The caterpillars are peculiar in having a smaller number of legs than those of other groups, which causes the characteristic looping movement, the tip of the abdomen being drawn up to the base with each " step." Most of these caterpillars closely resemble twigs, and are difficult to detect when at rest. Certain larvae known as

Photos] Silk-worms feeding. (*Nat. size.*) [*M. H. Crawford.*

Photos]   [*John J. Ward* ; *M. H. Crawford* ; *Sport & General.*
A. Elephant Hawk-moth (*Chaerocampa elpenor*) (× 3/4) ;   B. Broad-bordered Bee-Hawk-moth (*Haemorrhagia fuciformis*) (× 7/8) ; C. Male and female Eyed Hawk-moths (*Smerinthus ocellatus*) (× 3/4) ; D. Death's-head Hawk-moth (*Acherontia atropos*) (× 6/5).

[H. Bastin.
The Emperor Moth (*Saturnia pavonia*) (female) and cocoon. (×2/3.)

Canker-worms are a serious pest of fruit trees in North America.

The *Bombycidae* comprise the Silk-worm moths. The best commercial silk is obtained from the domesticated species *Bombyx mori*, which is no longer known in the wild state. The larvae are fed on mulberry leaves, and to obtain good silk, great care must be taken in selection of food, and regulation of temperature and moisture, in the sheds where they are housed. After the silken cocoon has been spun, the pupae are killed by dropping them in boiling water, and the continuous thread of silk is then reeled off. The adults selected for breeding purposes mate very shortly after emerging from the cocoon, and die after laying their eggs, without feeding.

The Emperor-moth is the only British species of the family *Saturniidae*,

[John J. Ward.
Caterpillars of the Emperor Moth. (× 2/3.)

Photos]   [*M. H. Crawford ; H. Bastin ; and Hugh Main.*

A. Gold-tail Moth (*Euproctis chrysorrhaea*) (× 3/4) ; B. Male (above) and female Gipsy Moth (*Lymantria dispar*) (× 5/6) ;
C. Heart & Dart Moth (*Agrotis exclamationis*) (× 3/2) ; D. Female Drinker Moth (*Cosmotriche potatoria*) (× 2/3).

[*Hugh Main.*
CATERPILLAR OF THE SMALL
ELEPHANT HAWK-MOTH. (*Nat.
size.*)

which contains some of the largest moths in the world. The silken cocoons of the larvae of the moths of this family are also used to produce commercial silk, but the quality is inferior to that obtained from the Bombycidae.

The European Processionary Moth belongs to the family *Eupterotidae*. The popular name is derived from the gregarious habit of the caterpillars, who march in long processions, keeping their ranks together by means of a head and tail contact. The Pine Processionary Moth is very destructive to pine trees around the Mediterranean.

The Tiger, Ermine and Footmen moths are representatives of the family *Arctiidae*.

The Owlet moths (*Noctuidae*) are a very large and homogeneous family. They fly by night and spend the day resting on tree-trunks, where they are protected by the sombre and cryptic coloration of the front wings. Certain larvae are the destructive cut-worms of North America, others are Boll-worms attacking cotton, and the larva of yet another species is the gregarious Army worm.

The Gold - tail Moth is a common European member of the family *Lymantriidae*. Another species, the Gipsy Moth, has, on introduction to North America, become a serious pest of foliage trees.

[*John J. Ward.*
CATERPILLAR OF THE DEATH'S-HEAD HAWK-MOTH (*Acherontia
atropos.*) (*Nat. size.*)

Order COLEOPTERA (Beetles)

This is probably the largest order, not only among insects, but in the whole animal kingdom, approximately one hundred and eighty thousand species being at present known ; of these some 3,600 have been recorded from the British Isles. The name Coleoptera (horn-winged) is derived from the fact that the front wings form hard cases, termed elytra, which take little or no part in flight, but give protection to the hind wings when the insect is at rest. In flightless forms the elytra are often fused together in the middle line and are consequently immovable. Beetles vary enormously in size and are very adaptable, being found in almost every conceivable locality ; they are very common in dung, carrion, rotting wood, and fungi, and they act as excellent scavengers. Members of five families live in fresh water, and certain species are daily submerged by the tides.

Other forms occur in woollen goods, furs, furniture, foodstuffs, etc., where they often cause great damage.

The various parts of the body are heavily chitinized. The head is often produced forwards into a rostrum which bears the mouth-parts at the tip ; the eyes vary in size and are sometimes absent in cave-dwelling forms, and the shape of the antennae is useful for purposes of classification. Great

[Ray Palmer.

The Tiger Beetle (*Cicindela hybrida*) is brightly coloured, and may frequently be seen flying in the sun, along dusty paths. (× 5/3.)

variety is seen in the structure of the jaws, which are adapted for biting ; in the males of certain forms they may be longer than the whole of the rest of the body ; they may differ very considerably in size and shape in the males and females of the same species. The legs are generally suitable for running and walking, and may be modified for digging or swimming. The more primitive forms have five-jointed tarsi, but the number is often reduced in more specialized forms ; this character is used, along with others, for dividing the group into super-families and families.

The venation of the hind wings falls into three main groups, a character used in determining the major divisions of the order. The adults in a large number of families possess stridulating organs.

The eggs are generally oval and the number laid varies inversely with their size. They may be deposited in the earth, on leaves, in carrion, or in the stems of plants. The larva has well-developed biting mouth-parts, which do not differ essentially from those of the adult. Legs are generally present in the larvae, which may be either extremely active and carni-

151

INSECTA (ORDER COLEOPTERA)

A Water-beetle (*Dytiscus sp.*) as in flight. [*H. Bastin* (× 4/3.)

vorous, or almost immobile, feeding on vegetable substances or decaying matter. Many forms pupate in earthen cells below the surface of the ground; others may remain within the food plant. A cocoon is sometimes formed, or the pupa may be protected by the remains of the last larval skin. Metamorphosis is complete.

The order is divided into two suborders, *Adephaga* and *Polyphaga*.

Adephaga (Predaceous Beetles). The members of this suborder are characterized by having the first three ventral segments of the abdomen more or less fused, and by having five-jointed tarsi; these are the least-specialized beetles. The larvae are active and predaceous; they have well-developed legs, each usually bearing two claws.

The Tiger-beetles (*Cicindelidae*) are large and brightly coloured, and are very voracious in larval and adult life. About eighteen hundred species are known, but the family is not largely represented in Britain. The larvae live in burrows in the ground, and lie with the head and shoulders flush with the surface, waiting to snap up any unwary insects that may come within their reach.

A certain number of families of Adephaga are more or less aquatic, the best-known being the *Dytiscidae* (True Water-beetles) and the *Gyrinidae* (Whirligig Beetles).

Out of two thousand known species of Water-beetles, about one hundred occur in the British Isles. They are active swimmers under water, and are also good fliers; the larvae are aquatic, but the pupal stage is usually passed in moist earth. The hind legs are much flattened and are fringed with stiff hairs, and are used as oars. In the males of certain forms the front tarsi are modified into sucker-like pads to hold the females while pairing. Both adults and larvae come to the surface of the water periodically

[*Ray Palmer.*
Great Water-beetle (*Hydrophilus piceus*) as in flight. (× 2/3.)

152

for air, which they take in through spiracles at the tip of the abdomen ; the adults are capable of keeping a supply of air beneath the elytra ; this is renewed from time to time. The eggs are laid in the stems of water plants. The larvae are very voracious, feeding on worms, insects, tadpoles, and even small fish. Their prey is seized by the mandibles, which are hollow, each perforated by a canal leading into the gut ; a digestive juice is ejected through these canals into the captured insect, where it breaks down the tissues, which are absorbed by the larvae in liquid form ; in the adults, however, digestion is internal.

The Whirligig Beetles are sur-

[W. S. Pitt.
WATER-BEETLES (*Dytiscus sp.*). (× 3/8.)

face swimmers ; they are generally a compact oval in shape, and are metallic in colour ; they are gregarious, swimming rapidly around one another in a bewildering maze. The larvae feed in much the same way as those of the true Water-beetles, but, unlike them, they breathe by means of tracheal gills attached to the abdomen.

The family *Paussidae* contains about three hundred known species, all of which live in association with ants or termites, and are curiously modified in relation to this mode of life. The antennae and various parts of the body are swollen, and secrete an aromatic substance much appreciated by the ants, who welcome the beetles as guests. The secretory patches are marked by tufts of yellow hairs.

[John J. Ward.
Larva of the Great Water-beetle (*Hydrophilus piceus*) sucking the juices of a worm. (× 4/7.)

153

Polyphaga (**Burying Beetles, etc.**). Members of this suborder are characterized by having all the abdominal segments free ventrally. The habits of the larvae are very various, but the legs are less well developed than in the Adephaga, and bear single, instead of paired, claws.

The *Staphylinoidea* include mainly very small forms, of which the Burying and Carrion Beetles (*Silphidae*) are perhaps the best known. The adults live on carrion, fungi and decaying vegetable matter ; some are found in ants' nests, and certain blind forms inhabit caves. The black and orange Burying Beetles excavate the ground underneath small dead animals, ultimately burying them ; eggs are laid in these corpses and the

Burying Beetles around the body of a dead Greenfinch. (× 5/6.)

[*H. Bastin.*

developing larvae feed on the decaying flesh. About one hundred out of nine hundred known species may be found in Great Britain.

Members of the family *Pselaphidae* live as inquilines in ants' nests, and are modified in much the same way as the Paussid beetles.

In the *Diversicornia* the wing venation is generally of the type shown in *Hydrophilus piceus*, but may be greatly reduced. The larvae usually have legs, but a number are legless.

One of the most easily recognized families (*Coccinellidae*) contains the Lady-birds. They are generally small, rounded and convex, and have characteristically-spotted elytra. About two thousand species are known, and the majority are carnivorous in both the larval and adult stage, preying on Aphides, Coccids and other soft-bodied insects. They are therefore of considerable use to man and certain forms have proved themselves to be successful agents in controlling the scale insects infesting orange and lemon trees, when imported into the countries where these fruits are cultivated.

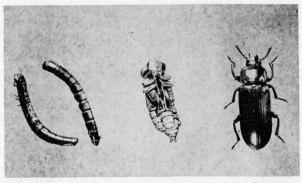

[H. Bastin.
The common Meal-worm (*Tenebrio molitor*) as larva, pupa and perfect insect. A pest of stored grain. (× 8/5.)

The larvae are compact, oblong, soft-bodied creatures, often with a number of feathery processes projecting from the body. The pupae generally suspend themselves head downwards from bushes or palings, and are frequently brightly coloured.

The *Dermestidae* contain relatively small beetles which in the adult stage are often covered with fine hairs or scales; they may be found among furs, hides, wool, bacon, cheese and other substances, and are extremely voracious and destructive in the larval stage.

[John J. Ward.
Lady-bird Beetle (*Coccinellidae*) beside pupa case. The insect is cream-coloured when it emerges; the black spots appear in about four hours. (× 10/3.)

Two families are partially aquatic, although the adults in the *Dryopidae* are incapable of swimming. They live in, or near, water, clinging to submerged plants by their claws. The larva lives in torrents and waterfalls, the whole body being modified to form a kind of sucker, whereby it adheres to the rocks and stones. In the family *Hydrophilidae* a certain number of species are truly aquatic, but the remainder live on land. This family contains the largest British beetle, *Hydrophilus piceus*; it has a very intricate mechanism for storing air not only under its elytra, but on the under surface of the body.

The beetles comprising the family *Cantharidae* are generally long, slender and soft-bodied. About two thousand four hundred

155

[*H. Bastin.*
Larvae of the Colorado Beetle (*Leptinotarsa decemlineata*)
on potato leaves. (× 5/2.)

species are known, the most remarkable being the Glow-worms and Fire-flies. These are nocturnal insects and many of them are capable of emitting a greenish light. In the common glow-worm the female is wingless, and the male is attracted to her by the bright light which she emits. The adults feed very little, but the larvae prey on snails and slugs; digestion is largely external, much as in Dytiscus (page 153).

The family *Anobiidae* contains beetles which are very injurious to timber, books, foodstuffs, and furniture. The Death-watch Beetle is probably the best-known species; its larvae form burrows in wood, from which the adults emerge, leaving the familiar small round holes behind them. The tapping noise, from which this beetle gets its name, is a sexual call, the lower part of the head being beaten on the wood on which the insect is standing.

The family *Buprestidae* contains over five thousand species; they are frequently large, active fliers, and are brilliantly metallic, consequently, they are often used in embroidery and jewellery. They are mainly tropical, but ten species occur in Britain. The larvae generally live in burrows beneath the bark of trees.

The *Heteromera* are characterized by having the front and middle pair of tarsi five-jointed, and the hind pair four-jointed. About twenty thousand species are known, and are grouped into fifteen families, of which the largest is the *Tenebrionidae*. The adults of this family are diverse in size and shape, but the larvae are very uniform. Certain larvae live in flour and stored products, and are known as " meal - worms "; others live in dead animals, in fungi, or under bark.

The *Rhipiphoridae* are parasites in wasps' nests, the larva being first an internal and then an external parasite of the wasp grub, which it completely destroys.

[*H. Bastin.*
TWO KINDS OF OIL BEETLES (*Melöe spp.*)   (× 2.)

The family *Meloidae* contains one thousand five hundred species, the larvae of which are parasitic on Orthoptera and Aculeate Hymenoptera. The larvae are remarkable in that, in the earliest stage, they move about actively in search of a host, and in the later stages, in the brood cell of the host, are non-motile and quite different in shape, feeding, after having destroyed the grubs of the host, upon the food laid up by the latter for its own progeny. A pharmaceutical product, cantharidin, is obtained from the dried bodies of certain species, one of which, known as the "Spanish Fly," inhabits Southern Europe.

[*H. Bastin.*
Death-watch Beetle (*Xestobium rufovillosum*) (× 3), and wood damaged by the beetle. (*Nat. size : Beetle enlarged.*)

The *Phytophaga* are, as the name implies, all plant feeders. They are recognizable by the structure of the tarsus, which appears to be four-jointed, the third join being flattened and lobed, and the fourth minute and inserted in the centre of the third. There are three families, of which the most important is the *Chrysomelidae*, the component species numbering about twenty thousand. The eggs are often laid in

[*John J. Ward.*
Furniture Beetle (*Anobium punctatum*) (× 9), and wood damaged by the beetle (× 2).

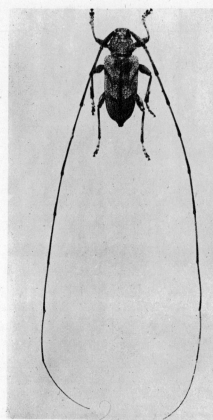

A LONG-HORNED BEETLE. (× 3/2.)

cases, and the larvae and pupae are sometimes similarly protected. Certain of these, e.g. the Colorado Potato-beetle, and the Turnip-flea, are very injurious to crops.

The Longicorn beetles (*Cerambycidae*) are not common in Britain, the family being essentially tropical. Some of the species are among the largest living insects, measuring four or five inches from the head to the tip of the abdomen. The larvae are generally wood-borers and have much reduced legs, but move about in their tunnels by means of dorsal and ventral swellings on the abdominal segments.

The Cerambycidae are remarkable for the degree in which they exhibit the phenomenon of mimicry. This subject has been studied by Gahan, who remarks first of all that mimicry occurs only in day-flying beetles, those that fly by night resembling the ground, plant, or other object on which they rest during the day (cryptic or protective coloration). The Cerambycidae, harmless and palatable, exhibit an extraordinary diversity of form, owing to their

Photos]   [H. Bastin.
HARLEQUIN BEETLE (*Acrocinus longimanus*).
(× 2/3.)

158

imitation either of stinging insects, such as wasps, or noxious ones, such as unpalatable beetles of other families. In the wasp mimics the elytra are generally reduced, exposing the wings; their resemblance to the models in size, form, colour and mode of progression is remarkable. Gahan contrasts with the diversity of the Cerambycidae the uniformity of the *Lycidae*, a family of beetles protected by a distasteful secretion; these have a characteristic shape, with the elytra rounded and expanded posteriorly; in South America all are black and yellow, in Asia, red.

[*H. Bastin*
Weevil, with cocoons, among fig-wort seed-pods. (× 4/3.)

A giant Longicorn Beetle which lives in Saõ Thomé. (× 3/5.)
[*Dr. F. Barns.*

Thus they are readily recognized and avoided, and they serve as models for moths, flies, and other beetles, including members of several different groups of the Cerambycidae.

The *Rhynchophora* are characterized by the head being produced to form a beak or rostrum. There are four families, of which that containing the weevils (*Curculionidae*) is the largest and most important. Some thirty thousand species are already known, but it is thought that at least two hundred thousand may exist. The rostrum is used by the female for boring holes in which to lay her eggs; its use in the male is unknown,

159

but it is sometimes considerably smaller in this sex than in the female. The larvae are usually borers or miners in plants, and a number of them develop in grains of maize, wheat, barley or rice ; others are found in dried peas and beans, flour and meal. A notorious species is known as the Cotton-boll weevil ; it attacks the flower-buds of the cotton crop in America, and it is estimated that an equivalent of four hundred thousand bales is destroyed by this insect every year. One of the most destructive species in this country is the Apple-Blossom weevil ; the eggs are laid in the flower-buds, which are destroyed by the larvae before they are ready to open.

[Brit. Mus., Nat. Hist.
GRUB OF STAG-
BEETLE. *(Nat. size.)*

The Bark beetles (*Scolytidae*) burrow in the bark, and between the bark and the wood of trees, leaving characteristic sinuous marks on the wood. The burrows may penetrate deep into the living wood, causing serious damage to the trees. Some of these beetles live together in a primitive kind of social community in which all phases of mating habits from mono-gamy to complete promiscuity may be observed. The Ambrosia beetles prepare fungus beds in their burrows, each species being associated, apparently, with a special fungus.

The *Lamellicornia* are among the most easily recognized of beetles, on account of the antennae ter-minating in a curious lamellate club ; the legs are often modi-fied for digging. These are, for the most part, active fliers, the wingless condition being rare. One of the most remarkable features of the group is the occurrence of extreme sexual dimorphism, the males and females being sometimes so dis-similar that they have inadver-tently been placed in separate genera. Both adults and larvae commonly possess stridulating organs, and are capable of pro-ducing a high-pitched squeak. The larvae are thick, fleshy grubs with very small powers of locomotion ; they feed on dead vegetable and animal matter and are generally sur-rounded with sufficient food

[*H. Bastin.*
Elm Bark Beetle (*Scolytus destructor*) (× 4), and inner surface of a piece of elm bark showing burrows made by this beetle and its off-spring. (× 3/5).

Photos]   *[H. Bastin.*

A. Male Stag-beetle (*Lucanus cervus*) (× 5/6); B. A Lamellicorn Beetle found in Central America (× 7/5); C. A Tropical Weevil (× 5/4); D. Female Stag-beetle (× 5/6); E. A Weevil which is found in Sikkim (× 3/5).

to last them for the whole of their development.

Of the three families into which the group is divided the Lucanidae and Scarabaeidae contain some of the best-known beetles. The Stag beetles (*Lucanidae*) are characterized by the enormous development of the jaws in the male. The larvae live in rotting wood, and may take from four to six years to complete their development. Of the six hundred known species, three occur in England, each belonging to a different genus.

[H. Bastin.
COTTON-BOLL WEEVIL
(*Anthonomus grandis*). (× 3.)

The family *Scarabaeidae* contains the Cockchafers and the Dor-beetles. About fourteen thousand species are known, ninety occurring in the British Isles. The Cockchafers are large brown beetles common among lime trees in summer. The larvae feed on decaying vegetable matter and the roots of plants, often causing serious injury. At the end of three years they pupate; the adult stage is attained in October, but the beetles do not leave the ground until the following spring.

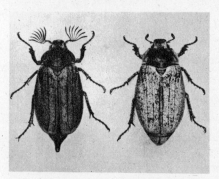

[Brit. Mus., Nat. Hist.
MALE AND FEMALE COCKCHAFER (*Melolontha vulgaris*). (*Nat. size.*)

The Dor-beetles fly at dusk, and are familiar objects in Britain, where the heavy droning noise accompanying their flight is unmistakable. The adults burrow in the earth below patches of dung, portions of which are stored at the blind ends of branches of the burrow. A single egg is deposited in each mass of food.

The Scarab beetle of Egypt and its close relatives have the habit of collecting balls of dung which they roll to a suitable retreat and feed on continuously for a considerable time. The genus *Copris* constructs similar balls in an underground chamber for the reception of the eggs. The chamber is the joint work of the male and female beetle and is guarded, after oviposition, by the female, who in some species attends her offspring until they reach maturity, and then produces a second brood.

[M. H. Crawford.
DOR-BEETLE OR "DUMBLE-DOR" (*Geotrupes stercorarius*). (× 5/7.)

Order STREPSIPTERA (Stylops)

This order comprises a small group of curious, minute insects commonly termed "Stylops." The larvae are endoparasites of various bugs, wasps and bees, and the female continues to live in this way after the adult state has been reached ; consequently, she remains wormlike in shape, and is wingless. The male, on the other hand, becomes free-living, and has well-developed hind wings, although only vestiges of the front pair can be seen. Insects harbouring these parasites are said to be "stylopized."

The eggs, often numbering many thousand, hatch inside the body of the female ; the larvae are active and crawl out onto the body of the host, where they wait until they can seize on another insect. When this is achieved they are carried back to the nest of the new host, immediately seek out the developing larvae, and bore their way through the cuticle, becoming endoparasitic. The host-larvae are able to develop to the adult state, but the presence of the parasite affects their fertility, and lessens the colour differences between the sexes.

The order is divided into four families containing one hundred and seventy species, sixteen of which are known from Great Britain.

Order APHANIPTERA (Fleas)

This is a small order of very specialized insects, and its relationships to other orders is by no means clear. Fleas are small jumping insects, bristly, wingless, and flattened from side to side. The mouth-parts are adapted for piercing and

[John J. Ward.
The Flea (*Pulex irritans*) is ecto-parasitic on warm-blooded animals. (× 24.)

sucking, eyes may be present or absent, the bases of the legs are enormously enlarged and elongated, and the segments of the thorax are freely movable instead of being fused together as in most other insects. Fleas are responsive to warmth, leaving their host as soon as it dies. The relationship between fleas and their host is not very close, the same species of flea often occurring on different mammals or birds.

The eggs are oval, and are generally white in colour ; they are laid freely in the fur or feathers of the host, and drop to the ground. The larvae are small worm-like creatures resembling, in some respects, the earlier stages of the more primitive flies. They feed on particles of organic matter found in the lair of the host, and when full-grown pupate in a cocoon. The adult, on emerging, can live for some time without food, but seizes the first opportunity to join its host.

About five hundred species are known, and of these forty-six have been found in the British Isles. They are pests not only on account of the irritation of their bites, but because of their agency in transmitting disease. It has been proved that tropical Rat-fleas become infected with the bacilli of bubonic plague from rats, and infect man with them. The "Jigger" flea of tropical regions is peculiar in that the female remains firmly attached to the skin of the host and may burrow underneath, causing great pain, as her abdomen often swells to the size of a pea. Many animals are attacked, and in man the toes are more affected than any other part.

Order DIPTERA (Flies)

Members of this order are characterized by having only a single pair of fully-developed wings, the hind pair being reduced to two small outgrowths termed "halteres." The mouth-parts are suctorial, but may also be adapted for piercing. The larvae are legless; they undergo a complete metamorphosis.

The Diptera form a very large order comprising about fifty thousand species, of which three thousand have been recorded from the British Isles. Structurally, they are highly specialized, and the majority are good flyers. The adults feed mainly on flower-juices, but some prey on other insects, and some suck the blood of man and other mammals. The blood-sucking habit renders those species which practise it dangerous agents in the transmission of malaria, sleeping-sickness, and other diseases.

The head is large, generally bearing compound eyes and three ocelli; the eyes are frequently close together in the male, and wide apart in the female. The antennae vary greatly in shape, and are of much value in classifying the families; in the less specialized forms they are generally thread-like, and may be composed of a large number of joints; in the more specialized forms they take the shape of a compact three-jointed organ with a long bristle either at the tip or at the base. The middle part of the thorax is greatly developed and, along with the head and abdomen, often bears strong, serially-arranged bristles. The abdomen may be composed of from four to eight or nine visible segments. The clasping-organs of the male are frequently prominent, and the female may have a well-developed ovipositor. The wings are transparent, although they may sometimes exhibit a brown pattern, and have a greater number of veins in the more primitive than in the more specialized forms. The legs are strongly developed in carnivorous species, which use them for grasping the prey, and the feet of the Common House-fly and its allies have suctorial pads which enable them to walk vertically or upside down on any surface.

The majority of flies lay eggs, but viviparity frequently occurs in blood-sucking forms. Parthenogenesis is rare, but not unknown.

The larvae are wormlike, with chitinous jaws. As already noted, they are legless, but move about actively by means of protuberances on the skin, which are often beset with small hooks. Their habits are very diverse. Many are plant feeders, some are scavengers, and some are parasitic on the larvae of other insects, and are consequently of immense importance in the control of the insects they select as hosts. Open sores are often attacked by larvae, which eat the injured tissue, inflicting great pain ; when this occurs in man, it is termed myiasis. The Screw-worm fly of South America is particularly notorious in this respect ; its larvae attack the membranes at the back of the nose, frequently eat away the roof of the mouth, and may eventually reach the brain. Among the less specialized species the larvae

A Mosquito (*Culex pipiens*) which has just emerged from its larval skin. Larvae are to be seen at the surface of the water on the left. (× 2.)

are frequently aquatic, obtaining air either from the surface, or from the water by means of blood-gills or tracheal gills. The skin is generally cast three times during growth, the last larval skin hardening to form a rigid pupa-case.

The group is divided into two suborders, based on the method by which the adult emerges from the pupa-case. In the *Orthorrhapha* the case splits straight down the back. In the *Cyclorrhapha* the circular tip of the case is pushed off by a special expansible sac on the front of the head of the emerging insect ; after the adult is free of the pupa case, the sac is gradually re-absorbed into the head until its presence is marked only by a suture round the face and over the antennae.

Orthorrhapha. This suborder contains two series of families, *Nematocera* and *Brachycera*. The thirteen families comprising the Nematocera may be regarded as containing the more primitive flies.

The Daddy-long-legs or Crane Flies (*Tipulidae*) are characterized by their long, fragile legs ; they are very common in grassy places. The larvae of the majority live underground, feeding on the roots of grass and other plants ; they are termed "leather-jackets" and may be destructive to lawns, but unless present in overwhelming numbers they are effectively kept in check by starlings and other

Photos]　　　　　　[*John J. Ward.*
The Drone-fly (*Eristalis tenax*) is one of the Hover-flies; the rat-tailed maggots of this species are found in stagnant water. (*Nat. size.*)

birds. In certain forms the larvae are aquatic, and others live in decaying vegetation.

The family *Culicidae* contains some of the worst enemies of mankind, on account of the part they play in transmitting disease. Mosquitoes are slender flies, with long legs and with scales on their wings. The mouth-parts of the female are generally piercing, but the male is incapable of biting. More than one thousand five hundred species are known, and of these, twenty-five are recorded from Britain. The eggs are laid in or near fresh water, and the larvae and pupae are always aquatic, occurring in ponds, slowly-running streams, or small accumulations of rain water. The larvae are very active, feeding on microscopic food particles suspended in the water; they obtain air from the surface through the spiracles at the tip of the abdomen. The pupae are also active, but breathe through a pair of spiracles on the top of the head. The chief diseases transmitted by mosquitoes are malaria, yellow-fever and filariasis. Malaria is caused by a protozoon parasite which passes part of its life-history in the blood of man. When a female mosquito of a certain species bites a person in-fected with malaria, some of the parasites are taken up in the blood which the mosquito imbibes; they immediately go through a further part of their life-cycle in the body of the mosquito, finally reaching the salivary glands. From this position they are injected into the wound the next time the mosquito bites, and the victim is thus infected with the disease.

Filariasis is caused by the presence of nematode worms in the lymph vessels; the most usual manifestation of this disease is the condition of elephantiasis. The larvae of this worm live in the blood stream, and are transmitted from man to man by the mosquito in much the same way as the malaria parasite.

Various methods of mosquito control have been introduced and have been so successful in the Panama zone that yellow fever is now almost unknown there. The aim of most control campaigns is to destroy the breeding places by drainage; further, the larvae may be suffocated by pouring a film of oil on the surface of the water so that their spiracles cannot come into contact with the air; also they may be eaten by certain fish.

The midges (*Chironomidae*) are delicate flies, similar in shape to the mosquitoes; few of them bite. They have a characteristic habit of dancing in the air in swarms, generally as a preliminary to pairing. The larvae are aquatic, certain of them being red on account of the composition of their blood; these are known as blood-worms and are common in England. Other forms are green. Over one thousand species are known, and of these at least two hundred occur in Britain.

Members of the family *Cecidomyiidae* are generally minute insects; their larvae form galls in the roots, fruits, leaves and stems of willows, grasses and other plants.

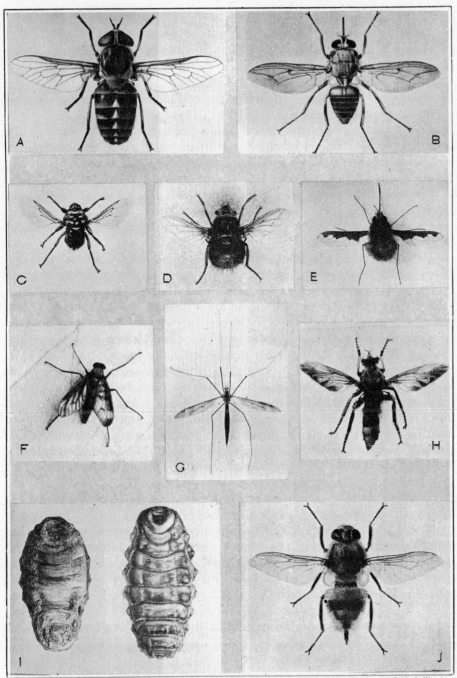

Photos] [*Brit. Mus., Nat. Hist.; H. Bastin; James's Press; M. H. Crawford; and John J. Ward.*

A. Horse-fly (*Tabanus bovinus*) (× 5/4); B. Tsetse-fly (*Glossina brevipalpis*) (× 2); C. Forest-fly (*Hippobosca equina*) (× 5/4); D. Bristle-fly (*Tachina grossa*) (*Nat. size*); E. Bee-fly (*Bombylius major*) (× 3/2); F. Oak-fly (*Rhagio scolopacea*) (*Nat. size*); G. Daddy-long-legs (*Tipula fulvipennis*) (× 1/2); H. Robber-fly (*Asilus crabroniformis*) (*Nat. size*); I. Ox-warble-fly, larva and pupa, (× 11/6); J. Ox-warble-fly (*Hypoderma bovis*) (× 11/6).

167

Closely allied to them are the fungus gnats (*Mycetophilidae*), the larvae of which live in fungi, decaying fruits, and rotting wood. The maggots frequently found in mushrooms may generally be assigned to species of this family.

The Buffalo gnats (*Simuliidae*) are small, stocky flies, generally referred to as midges ; they are most persistent biters, particularly towards evening in the damp places where they breed.

The *Blepharoceridae* are a small family occurring in many parts of the world, but with a discontinuous distribution. The larvae live in mountain torrents, clinging to the rocks and stones by means of a series of suckers on the under side of the body.

Fourteen families are included in the series *Brachycera*, the individual species exhibiting great diversity of structure and of habits. The larvae generally have a retractile head, the pupa is not invested in the last larval skin, and a cocoon is very rarely formed.

The *Stratiomyiidae* contain over one thousand species, of which about fifty may be found in Britain. Many are quite small ; others may reach a length of three-quarters of an inch. Some are black with conspicuous yellow or green markings, and others are a brilliant metallic green. They frequent flowers, and are not very strong flyers. The larvae have a thick skin, and are peculiar in this group in that the head is non-retractile ; they live in water, decaying vegetable matter, or damp earth.

The family *Tabanidae* includes the Horse-flies and Clegs ; they are medium-sized to large flies, and have been extensively studied, over two thousand species being known ; of these twenty-one have been recorded from the British Isles. They are stoutly-built, bristleless flies. The females have mouth-parts adapted for piercing ; they are very persistent biters, and are notorious worriers of horses and cattle. The brown species with more or less clear or boldly-patterned wings are known as Horse-flies, and those with delicately-spotted wings are termed Clegs. The larvae are carnivorous, feeding on earthworms and insect larvae ; they develop in damp soil, mud and rotting logs.

Members of the family *Asilidae* are known as Robber-flies. They are strongly-built, rather elongate, bristly insects, with mouth-parts adapted for piercing. They are exclusively carnivorous, catching their prey, which consists of smaller insects, while on the wing ; the prey is firmly held in the legs, and is sucked after being pierced by the proboscis. The larvae live in soil, sand, wood or leaf-mould. Over three thousand species are known, twenty-three being found in Britain ; of these the most generally noticed is a handsome black and orange species (*Asilus crabroniformis*), which may reach a length of nearly two inches.

The *Empididae* are also predacious flies, but are less hairy and, in general, rather smaller than the Asilidae. Several species exhibit very curious court-ship habits. They fly in swarms, executing "dances" in the air ; the male captures an insect, and, on finding a female, presents it to her while pairing takes place. In some forms the prey is wrapped up in a silken web before being presented, and this practice has reached its highest development in forms where the male omits to capture any prey, but presents the female with an empty silken web.

Members of the family *Bombyliidae* are known as Bee-flies. They are rather large flies, and in many genera are clothed with long, soft hair, which gives them a bee - like appearance. The adults are plant-feeders, and the larvae are parasitic on bees, wasps, locusts and even on other flies.

Cyclorrhapha. This suborder contains two series, *Athericera* and *Pupipara*.

Athericera. The series c o n t a i n s thirty-four families which exhibit great diversity in structure and habits, but all possess a sac in front of the head, by means of which they force their way out of the pupa - case. None of the adults is parasitic.

[*John J. Ward.*

Tachinid flies in the larval stage are parasitic on other insects. The fly puparia are on the left among the caterpillars and cocoons of the Magpie Moth. (*Nat. size.*)

The Hover-flies (*Syrphidae*) are a well-marked family. They frequent flowers, and may often be seen on sunny days hovering motionless in the air. Many have conspicuous black and orange bodies. The larvae have varied habits. Certain species attack Narcissus bulbs and are a serious pest to gardeners. Others are beneficial to man in that they destroy large numbers of aphides. Others, again, live in organic decaying matter or dirty water; they swim with a twisting, rolling movement and have a long, retractile breathing tube at the tip of the abdomen, which is pushed at intervals above the surface of the water. In some species the larvae live in the nests of bees and wasps, feeding on diseased grubs and organic débris.

The *Oestridae* are a small family comprising the Warble or Bot-flies, which, in their larval stages, are much dreaded by cattle and horse-breeders. The adults are large furry flies, with vestigial mouth-parts ; the larvae are endo-parasites of vertebrates. The Warble-fly lays its eggs on the hair of cattle ; the minute larvae bore their way through the skin and migrate through the body of the host ; when nearly full-grown, they return to the surface layers and lie under the skin, piercing it to allow the posterior spiracles to come into contact with the air. At this stage they may be seen and felt under the hide as oval lumps nearly an inch long. When ready to pupate, the larvae burst through the skin, and drop to the ground, becoming enveloped in a hard pupal covering. After a heavy infection, the hide of the host is quite useless for commercial purposes, as it is riddled with holes where the parasites have emerged. The quality of the meat, and the quantity of milk produced, is also impaired.

In the Horse Bot-fly the eggs are also laid on the hairs of the host ; the newly-hatched larvae are swallowed when the horse licks itself ; they attach themselves to the wall of the gut, and develop in this position. When mature, they are voided through the intestine and pupate in the ground. Horses carrying a heavy infection often die.

The *Tachinidae* are medium-sized flies, characterized by a great development of bristles. The larvae are all parasitic, caterpillars being the favourite hosts, but the larvae of many other insects are also victimized. On account of this habit the members of the family are of great importance in controlling insect pests. One species, on introduction to Fiji, completely exterminated the Coconut moth which was endangering the cultivation of coconut palms, by parasitizing its larva ; another species is an active agent in controlling the Corn-borer beetle.

The most familiar members of the *Calliphoridae* are the Blue-bottle and Green-bottle flies, often termed Blow-flies. Blue-bottles have the unpleasant habit of depositing their eggs on meat, which, if left undisturbed, becomes riddled with maggots in a very short time. The Green-bottle flies have similar unpleasant habits and certain species are notorious enemies of the sheep-farmer. The eggs are laid in dirty wool, and the larvae feed on the wool and may even work their way into the flesh of the sheep ; the sheep frequently die, and much of the wool is rendered unfit for use. The large grey Flesh-flies are larviparous ; some of them are parasitic in the larval stage on locusts and snails, and others cause myiasis in man.

The commonest and most widely-spread member of the family *Muscidae* is the Common House-fly. The insect breeds in decaying matter of all kinds and is instrumental in carrying germs of typhoid and other diseases, on account of its habit of coming straight from the dung-heap to the house, and crawling over food and other objects used by man. A fly of another genus, but very similar in appearance to the house-fly, has the proboscis modified for piercing, and is a persistent biter and blood-sucker. The African Tsetse-flies also suck blood, and are notorious as the carriers of the protozoan which causes sleeping-sickness in man, and nagana in cattle. In the Tsetse-flies the larva does not leave the body of the parent until it is almost ready to pupate.

The *Anthomyiidae* are a large family, members of which bear a superficial resemblance to the house-fly. The habits of the larvae are diverse, some living as parasites under the skin of young birds, others mining in leaves, and others, again, attacking the roots of plants of the cabbage family.

In a long series of families related to the Anthomyiidae, the larvae are entirely plant feeders, and are frequently found in ripe or rotting fruits. The Mediterranean Fruit-fly does great damage to oranges and grape-fruit ; other members of this family (*Trypetidae*) form galls in the flower-heads of Compositae, and the larvae of the Celery-fly mine in the leaves of celery and parsnips.

The Frit-fly (*Oscinidae*) is a pest of cereals, the larvae of the first generation destroying the young leaves, those of the second attacking the ripening fruit.

[*John J. Ward.*
Male House-fly (*Musca domestica*) and eggs deposited by the female. This fly breeds in manure heaps. (× 7/2.)

Species of the family *Sciomyzidae* frequent the seashore, and are often immersed in salt water for short periods.

Pupipara. Members of this series are all curiously modified in connection with their habits of living as ectoparasites on mammals and birds. They have a flattened leathery appearance and, with the exception of one group, are blood-suckers. Only some species have wings, and in these the powers of flight are limited. The legs are always long and strong and have well-developed claws, so that these insects are peculiarly well adapted for clinging to their host and crawling about among the fur or feathers.

The females are larviparous, the larvae being retained in the body of the mother until they are ready to pupate ; pupation occurs either in the ground, or in the lair of their host.

The family *Hippoboscidae* contains the Forest-fly, which is found clinging to horses and cattle, the sheep " tick " or " ked," which lives deep in the wool of sheep, and another species which is parasitic on deer. Wings are present in the newly-emerged adults of the Forest-flies, but are broken off when attachment to the host has been effected.

Members of the families *Nycteribiidae* and *Streblidae* are parasites of bats ; in the former family wings are absent, and in the latter the condition varies from species to species. In one Australian form the female sheds not only the wings but the legs as well, and burrows in right under the skin of the host.

The *Braulidae* are minute, blind, wingless insects, found clinging to the queens and drones in beehives. The females are oviparous, and the larvae feed on the honey provided for the developing bees.

Order HYMENOPTERA (Ants, Bees and Wasps)

The Hymenoptera form one of the largest orders among insects. At least sixty thousand species are known, and it is probable that many more remain to be discovered. The order contains not only the ants, bees and wasps which, indeed, form a comparatively small group, but also saw-flies, wood-wasps, ichneumon-flies, and a host of small forms which are parasitic or gall-forming at some stage in their life-history.

The insects in this order vary from two or three inches in length to a size only just visible to the naked eye. They have two pairs of membraneous wings, those on the same side being linked together, hooks on the anterior margin of the hind wing fitting into a fold on the posterior side of the front wing ; the name of the order is derived from this character. The mouth-parts are adapted for biting in the majority of species, but in the more specialized forms a sucking proboscis may be developed ; jaws, how-ever, are always present. The first segment of the abdomen is fused with the thorax, and the second segment may be broad, or narrowed to form a very fine and sometimes elongate " waist " or petiole. In the female the ovipositor is always developed, and may be modified for sawing, boring or stinging.

The eggs are generally oval, those of parasitic species usually having a long stalk which enables the larva to breathe inside the body of the host. The larva has a well-developed head and, in the lower forms, closely resembles a caterpillar, but generally has a larger number of abdominal legs. The boring forms are not very mobile, and the larvae of the ants, bees and wasps are quite helpless.

One of the most interesting features in this group is the development of the social community and consequent differentiation of the individuals

into "castes," each with
its allotted rôle in the
economy of the colony.
This differentiation will
be described in more de-
tail when dealing with
the families concerned.
An analogous form of
social life has been
brought to a high degree
of perfection among the
Termites or White Ants,
but there are certain
fundamental differences
between the two types
and it must be borne

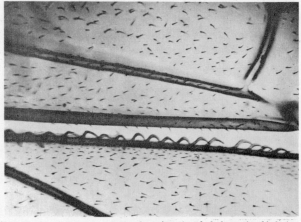

Wing hooks of a wasp, with the fore-wing detached from the hind-wing.
(Highly magnified.)

in mind that the groups in question are only most distantly related.

Parasitism in the larval stage is common in this order. Parthenogenesis
and the alternation of generations (page 99) are also common phenomena.

The order is divided into two suborders *Symphyta* and *Apocrita*.

Symphyta. This suborder contains the more primitive forms in which the
abdomen is not constricted basally; the most important members of this
group are the saw-flies and the wood-wasps. Only one genus is parasitic in
the larval stage, and none shows social behaviour. The larva is very similar
in shape to a lepidopterous caterpillar, but generally has a larger number
of abdominal legs.

The Wood-wasps or Horn-tails (*Siricidae*) are large brilliantly-coloured
insects, black, yellow and metallic blue predominating. In the male there
is a short triangular
spine at the tip of
the abdomen; in
the female an ex-
tremely long ovipo-
sitor extends back-
wards; this has the
appearance of a
peculiarly efficient
sting, but the insect
is quite harmless.
By means of the
ovipositor, holes are
drilled in living
wood, and a single
egg is deposited

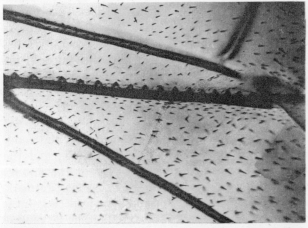

Photos]   *[John J. Ward.*
Wing hooks of a wasp, with the wings locked together. *(Highly magnified.)*

173

in each hole. The larvae are wood-borers, and pupate in their burrows; the adults eat their way out. *Sirex gigas*, the common English Wood-wasp, may reach a length of two inches; the larvae live in conifers, and take two years to complete their life-history.

The Saw-flies (*Tenthredinidae*) derive their common name from the toothed structure of the ovipositor, which is used for sawing. The adults feed either on flower juices or on small beetles and flies. The males are generally fewer in number than the females, and in some species have never yet been found. Parthenogenesis is therefore common in the family, males, females, or mixed broods being derived from unfertilized eggs. The eggs are deposited in slits or pockets, made by the sawing action of the ovipositor, in living wood or in soft plant tissues. The larvae vary considerably in habit, some living in stems or galls, other being leaf-miners, and others, again, living externally on the host-plant. One very destructive form is known as the Pear-slug; in its young stages it is covered with a dark gelatinous secretion, and crawls about the surface of pear-tree leaves, eating the superficial tissues: shortly before pupating it emerges from the secretion with a clear, dry, yellow skin. Other species attack the foliage of currant bushes, turnips and conifers, and some larvae form galls in willow leaves. Pupation generally takes place in the ground, the pupa being enclosed in a silken cocoon with which particles of earth many be mixed; occasionally, the cocoon may be attached to the food plant.

[*H. Bastin.*
Diagrammatic representation of the stinging apparatus of a wasp. The poison gland is at the top, and the alkaline glands with which the poison mixes, are on either side. The sting and paired sensory organs may project from the tip of the abdomen of the female wasp. (*Highly magnified.*)

Apocrita. In this suborder the abdomen is always separated from the thorax by a narrow petiole, and the larvae are legless. In the series *Parasitica* the majority of the species have predacious endo- or ectoparasitic larvae, but some are gall formers.

The *Ichneumonoidea* contain about sixteen thousand known species, but it is probable that a great number remain to be discovered. The larvae are all parasitic on other insects, and are therefore of considerable benefit to

ICHNEUMON FLIES (ICHNEUMONIDAE)

man. In the adults the antennae are long and straight, and the ovipositor leaves the abdomen some distance before the tip.

The Ichneumon flies are mainly parasites of Lepidoptera, but various groups of Hymenoptera, and insects of other orders are also attacked. The adults show remarkably highly-developed instincts in finding hosts for their offspring, some species being known to drill through six

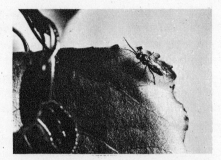

PALISADE SAW-FLY (*Lygaeonematus compressicornis*). (× 2.)

inches of wood to reach the burrow of the host larva. One form is a parasite of an aquatic trichopterous larva, and the adult hymenopteron, when about to lay her eggs, dives and swims through the water seeking the host.

The members of the family *Braconidae* are sometimes known as Supplementary Ichneumon Flies. They are closely allied to the true Ichneumons, and their habits are very similar. Lepidoptera are, again, most frequently chosen as hosts, and as many as one hundred specimens of a Braconid may issue from a single caterpillar. Pupation occurs either within the host or outside it, the pupa being enclosed in a cocoon ; individuals issuing from the same caterpillar often make their cocoons in a close mass and enclose them in a common silken web. One group of Braconids are parasitic on aphides and pupate below the dead body of the host.

The *Chalcidoidea* probably contain the largest number of species of any group in the order, and many of these represent the most minute forms met with among the Insecta. The majority of species are parasites of other insects and are more important even than the Ichneumonidae in keeping economically harmful insects under control, although they themselves attack certain beneficial insects such as the lac-producing Hemiptera, and may be parasites of insects which are already parasites of harmful forms. Butterflies, bugs and flies are the insects most frequently attacked, the parasite being most destructive in the egg and larval stage, although certain species deposit their eggs just before the host pupates.

Photos]   [John J. Ward.
GIANT WOOD-WASP (*Sirex gigas*).
(*Nat. size.*)

INSECTA (ORDER HYMENOPTERA)

In temperate countries the Chalcids appear to pass through two or three generations in the year, but a complete life-cycle may be passed through in as short a time as seven days. In many species the primary larvae are active, and of diverse forms, whereas the secondary larvae are all more or less maggot-like. Pupation occurs in the ground, or in the remains of the host, but no cocoons are formed. There are thirteen families of Chalcids, and so far, one thousand four hundred species have been recorded as British.

The Fig-insects (*Agaonidae*) probably form one of the most interesting families in this group. They are parasites of the wild male fig, known as the caprifig, the females making galls in the male flowers which line the fleshy receptacle. The males are wingless and totally unlike the females; they crawl round inside the fig until they find a gall, gnaw a hole in it, and fertilize the enclosed female. The female comes out through the hole, emerges from the fig and flies off to find another fig in a suitable state of development to receive her eggs. The cultivated or Smyrna fig contains only female flowers and there has long been a tradition among cultivators that the figs do not mature properly unless caprifigs are hung among

[*H. Bastin.*
PINE SAW-FLY, ADULT, LARVA AND COCOONS.
(× 2¾.)

their branches. The underlying explanation of this idea is probably to be found in the fact that the female fig insect unwittingly effects the fertilization of the flowers of the Smyrna fig; after crawling out of the caprifig, covered with pollen, she may enter a Smyrna fig by mistake, wander round inside trying to oviposit, but on finding the flowers unsuitable in shape she emerges again, having incidentally fertilized the flowers, and makes a further attempt to find a caprifig.

The Chalcids of the family *Encyrtidae* are parasites of the eggs, larvae and pupae of a wide range of insects. In certain species where the egg is parasitized, the host larva develops normally with the parasitic larvae in its body cavity; the parasitic larvae then undergo the curious

By courtesy of]

WASPS: (*Triscolia flavifrons*) (*a*) Female; (*d*) Male. (*Dielis collaris*) (*b*) Male; (*c*) Female. Natural Size.

[*British Museum (Natural History)*]

S. AMERICAN BEES: (*Exacrete frontalis*) (*a*) Female; (*b*) *Euglossa piliventris*. Female; (*c*) Female (*Euglossa dimechata var. niveo-fasciata*). Natural size.

phenomenon of polyembryony (p. 99).

The families *Trichogrammidae* and *Myrmaridae* contain very minute insects, all parasites of the eggs of other insects. Certain species parasitize water-bugs, and the adult female may even swim below the surface of the water by means of her wings while seeking the eggs of the host.

The *Cynipoidea* include the *Cynipidae*; these are Gall-wasps, and number about one thousand one hundred known species. They are very minute insects and are usually darkly coloured.

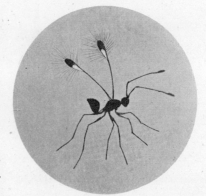

[*H. Bastin.*
A Fairy-fly (*Mymaridae*). These tiny flies are all parasitic, in the larval stage, on the eggs of other insects. (× 9.)

The majority of species form galls on oak trees, a certain number prefer rose bushes, and a few very primitive forms frequent various plants, living in the stems without even forming a gall. In the primitive forms the sexes are approximately equal in number, and parthenogenesis does not occur. In the more highly-specialized forms a sexual and an asexual generation occur in the life-cycle, and in certain species males are unknown and reproduction is consequently entirely parthenogenetic.

A common British species, *Neuroterus lenticularis*, forms lenticular galls on the lower surface of oak leaves in October; the larvae pass the Winter in these galls and emerge in the Spring, the brood consisting entirely of parthenogenetic females who deposit their eggs among the young leaves. The larvae from these eggs give rise to sappy galls, and hatch out to form a sexual generation, which in turn makes lenticular galls on the underside of the leaves. The sexual generation of another species emerges from the common " oak-apple " galls ; the males are winged and the females wingless ; after pairing, eggs are laid and galls are formed at the root of the oak tree. In the Spring wingless parthenogenetic females hatch out, crawl up the tree and lay eggs which give rise to further oak-apples. Yet another species produces the curious " pin-cushion "

[*John J. Ward.*
Long-tailed Ichneumon (*Rhyssa persuasoria*) which, by means of its long ovipositor, lays its eggs deep in the wood close to alien boring larvae of Sirex, which are attacked by the emerging Ichneumon grubs. (*Nat. size.*)

[M. H. Crawford.
Gall-wasp (*Cynips kollari*) emerging from a marble gall. (×3/2.)

galls found on rose bushes.

The process of gall-formation is not thoroughly understood, but irritation of some kind causes the plant to form the gall around the larva. The galls appear rather to be characteristic of the species which causes them, than of the plant on which they are formed.

The *Proctotrypoidea* are small, slender insects, parasitic on a number of different orders, but the majority favour aphides and dipterous gall midges. A number of species are wingless, and in forms where wings are present, the venation is often greatly reduced.

The *Formicoidea* (family Formicidae) includes the ants ; the number of species at present known is about three thousand five hundred. All ants have social habits, though some species are more advanced in this respect than others. They are predominantly a tropical group, but are represented to some extent all over the world. Neighbouring colonies of ants are generally hostile to one another, friends and foes being recognized apparently by means of organs of smell situated in the antennae.

The various parts of the body are well demarcated in the adults, the abdomen in particular being joined to the thorax by a very narrow stalk formed of the first two visible segments, and the remaining segments forming an ovoid swelling known as the gaster. The head bears well-developed compound eyes in the males, but in the

[John J. Ward.
Robin's Pin-Cushion Gall, produced by the Rose-gall Wasp.

Photos]   *[John J. Ward and H. Bastin.*

A. Winged Queen Ants emerging from their puparia ($\times$ 7/8); B. Five Ants moving a " log " ($\times$ 3/2); C. Ants shepherding aphides ; D. Nest of Red Wood Ants (*Formica rufa*).

females they are much reduced; the jaws are prominent and are very diverse in structure and in function. Wings may be present or absent, according to the species or caste, and are used only once during the life-cycle, for the nuptial flight. The females have well-developed stings.

Polymorphism attains its highest expression in this group. The main types to be found in any colony are males, females, and workers, but these castes are capable of sub-division and as many as twenty-nine distinct types of individuals have been recognized.

As in the bees, the development of the egg into a male or female appears to be dependent on the presence or absence of the fertilizing spermatozoon. The workers are under-developed females, and are probably prevented from becoming queens by differential feeding.

[H. Bastin.
HUNTRESS WASP (*Ammophila sabbulosa*). The prey is paralyzed by stinging and is stored, in a helpless state, as food for the young wasps. (× 7/3.)

The feeding habits of ants, as well as their method of life, have become communal, and an ant colony may be said to have but a single stomach. Any worker when taking in food, stores a large part of it in a " crop " from which it can be regurgitated; she is then at the service of any hungry worker who solicits her for food, and this worker will in turn, when satisfied, supply others with food in the same way. The Queen and larvae are also fed by this method in the higher groups.

The eggs and larvae are entirely in the care of the workers, who clean them and carry them about so that they may profit by the most suitable conditions of temperature and moisture. The majority of larvae are fed on food regurgitated by the workers, but some are carnivorous and are supplied with portions of insects, and the fungus-growers feed their larvae on fungus hyphae. The pupae, commonly known as " ants' eggs," are enclosed in cocoons only in the more primitive forms.

In species where both sexes are winged, pairing takes place during the nuptial flight. This phenomenon appears to be controlled by meteorological conditions, since the flights from different colonies of any one species occur simultaneously, thus affording an opportunity for inter-breeding. The fertilized female descends to the ground, breaks off her wings, and excavates a small chamber in which she remains for several months while her eggs ripen. During this period she does not feed, but obtains nourishment from the breaking down of her now useless wing-muscles. The first few eggs develop into workers, who immediately take upon themselves the

Photos]   [*Ray Palmer and John J. Ward.*

A. Queens of six British species of social wasps (× 6/5); B. Wasps (*Vespa vulgaris*) emerging from their cells in the comb (× 3/4); C. Male (top), queen and worker Hornet, (*Vespa crabro*) (*slightly reduced*).

care of the queen and her eggs, and begin to enlarge the nest. The function of the queen is now purely that of an egg-layer, and in this capacity she may live for as long as fifteen years.

The nests are very various in size and structure, each species having its own plan of construction. Some of the more primitive ants do not construct a permanent nest, but live under stones or logs; sometimes subterranean galleries are made to house the larvae, food-stores, or fungus gardens. A characteristic nest met with in parts of England takes the form of a mound, sometimes two or three feet in height, made of soil, twigs, leaves and pine needles. In the tropics nests composed of earth or silk are suspended from trees, or are formed of leaves fastened together by a silken web; the silk is provided by the larvae, which are moved from edge to edge of the leaf by the workers, the thread of silk left behind binding the edges together.

In the more primitive ants, the three castes differ very little in size, and are carnivorous. The Driver-ants of the tropics move about in masses, having no permanent nest, attacking insects, and even larger animals, with great ferocity.

The more highly-evolved groups have adopted a vegetarian diet which includes the seeds of plants, fungi, nectar from flowers, and the honeydew secreted by aphides and other insects. In the Harvesting-ants, seeds are carefully collected and stored, the workers biting off the young roots to prevent germination. Certain South African forms are essentially fungus-growers. The fungi are grown in underground chambers on a specially prepared soil; instead of normal aerial fruits they produce small swellings which are eaten by the ants. The nature of these fungi is not clearly understood, but it is evident that their growth is in some way influenced by the culture-methods of the ants. Before the nuptial flight, each potential queen provides herself with threads of the fungus for the purpose of starting fungus gardens in the new nest.

In the Honey-eating ants curious individuals known as " repletes " have arisen. They are fed by the workers and are capable of being gorged to such an extent that the abdomen is swollen to many times its normal size. These individuals remain permanently in the nest, acting as living food-reservoirs for the remainder of the colony, the food being regurgitated as required.

Ants live in close relationship with a number of other Arthropods, as many as one thousand two hundred and forty-five associations having been recorded. Some species are disliked as intruders, seeking food, others are tolerated, and species producing honey-dew are encouraged and looked after with every possible attention.

In some cases, different species of ants live amicably together in the same nest. This habit has given rise in certain cases to parasitism, the queen of one species entering the nest of a closely-allied species and laying her eggs there. These eggs are tended and reared by the workers belonging

Photos]   [*John J. Ward; H. Bastin; M. H. Crawford and Heinrich Fischer.*
A. Male (left), queen and worker of Honey-bee (*Apis mellifica*) (× 3/2); B. Leaf-cutter-bee (*Megachile sp.*) (× 3/4);
C. Cells made by Leaf-cutter-bee; D. Carpenter-bee (*Xylocopa violacea*) (× 3/2); E. Male and female Solitary-bee
(*Eucera longicornis*) (× 3/2).

to the nest. If the queen of the host-species is killed, the nest ultimately becomes completely occupied by the invaders. From this state of affairs it is but a step to the slave-making habits of certain northern ants, who rob other species of their pupae, rear them, and leave them to attend to the whole business of the colony. Ants with these habits are degenerate in structure, the males being wingless and the females partially blind.

Fossorial Wasps. The fossorial wasps (*Sphecoidea*) do not live in social communities ; in some species a number may live close together, but each pair has its own nest. All the members of the group prey on other insects, and may consequently be regarded as beneficial to man. The *Sphecidae* are slender insects with black-and-yellow or red markings. The petiole is very thin, and often longer than the rest of the abdomen. Nests are made in tunnels in the earth, and are stored with caterpillars or other larvae for the use of the young. The prey, so stored, is stung in a peculiar way, and is subjected to a certain amount of crushing with the jaws ; this treatment has the effect of paralysing the insect without killing it, so that it remains in good condition for the larvae over a considerable number of days. The adults feed mainly on spiders. Members of the family *Bembecidae* deposit their larvae in unsealed cells and feed them from day to day ; this activity takes up a considerable amount of the parents' time, and the broods produced are consequently much smaller than in those forms in which parental care in not manifested.

[H. Bastin.
BEMBECID WASP (*Bembex rostrata*).
(× 7/4.)

Further families of fossorial wasps are peculiar in that the males and females are often extremely dissimilar. Their habits vary, some being endoparasitic, some ectoparasitic and some living as inquilines (i.e., guests of other insects) in the larval stage.

Solitary Wasps. The true solitary wasps (*Eumenidae*) are predaceous. They make their nests in tunnels in the ground, or in hollow stems, or may construct them of mud. The majority prey on caterpillars, treating them in much the same way as do the fossorial wasps.

Vespoid Wasps. The *Vespidae* are colonial. The common British forms are known as Paper-making wasps. The community consists of a queen, males, and workers ; the males and workers die at the end of each summer, but the queen hibernates. In the Spring she emerges and looks for a suitable site for a nest, generally selecting a hole in a bank. The cells of the nest are composed of a papery substance made of chewed wood and saliva ; at first only a few cells are constructed ; eggs are laid, and the larvae are fed daily by the queen. They develop into workers, and immediately begin to enlarge the nest, and to care for the queen. The larvae are fed on a carnivorous diet, and in return secrete saliva which is much appreciated by the workers. The largest British species of this group is the Hornet, which nests mainly in hollow trees. The females in all species have very efficient stings.

Bees (Apoidea). Bees are more or less hairy, have a long sucking proboscis, and feed on the nectar and pollen of flowers, often effecting cross-pollination while crawling in and out of the flower-heads. The larvae are never fed on animal food, but are supplied with pollen and honey, or with regurgitated nectar. The adult females have stiff bristles on the hind legs, which act as pollen baskets.

[John J. Ward.

NEST OF GROUND WASP (*Vespa germanica*).

Solitary bees generally excavate tunnels for their nests, or make mud cells in chinks and holes. One of the best-known species is the Leaf-cutter bee (*Megachilidae*); in this form the cells are thimble-shaped, the walls and lid being made of pieces of rose leaves neatly cut out by the jaws of the adult; they are half-filled with pollen and honey, and an egg is deposited in each; the cells form a string, and are placed in some convenient hole. The Mason-bees (*Osmia*) construct very solid nests, coated on the outside with a mixture of earth and saliva, and divided inside into eight or nine cells.

The Carpenter-bees (*Xylocopidae*) are among the largest bees known. They are mainly tropical, and none occurs in England. They make their nests in tunnels excavated by their strong jaws in seasoned wood; these tunnels may attain a length of a foot or more. Some Carpenter-bees are nocturnal in habit.

INSECTA (ORDER HYMENOPTERA)

Members of the family *Nomadidae* live as guests in the nests of other bees. They are less hairy than most species, do no work for their living, and in connection with this habit, have no pollen baskets on their hind-legs.

The family *Bombidae* includes the Humble- or Bumble-bees. They are very common in temperate regions, and exhibit a form of social life more nearly allied to that of the wasps than to that of the hive-bee. The castes are not very markedly different from one another, and only certain females survive the winter. In some forms the nest is made at the end of a burrow ; in others it may be placed among moss or ivy. The queen, after building her nest, collects a mass of pollen which she forms into a paste, constructs a cell on the top of the mass, and deposits a batch of eggs in it. She also places honey in a wax receptacle for her own consumption. The larvae are fed on regurgitated honey as well as pollen-paste, and eventually develop into workers, later broods giving rise to males and potential queens.

The best-known species of the family Apidae is the Honey-bee, *Apis mellifica* ; it occurs in all countries, but is never found wild in Britain. The three castes are more clearly differentiated than in the Humble-bees, and the colony is potentially everlasting, as only the males are ejected at the end of the Summer, the queen and workers passing the Winter in the hive, feeding on stored food.

A prosperous hive may contain from fifty thousand to eighty thousand workers, as well as a certain number of males, or drones, and the queen. When the hive becomes too crowded, the queen and a certain number of workers emerge in a swarm, and form a new colony elsewhere. A young queen is, in this event, ready to dominate the old hive ; she takes her marriage-flight pursued by the drones, one of whom succeeds in pairing with her, but dies immediately afterwards. The queen returns to the hive, and takes up the duty of egg-laying. The spermatozoa are stored in a close-necked receptacle inside the body of the queen, and she can lay fertilized or unfertilized eggs at will. The former develop into females, and the latter into males. Of the females, those destined to become queens are fed on a richer pabulum than those which are to develop into workers.

The cells which form the honey-comb are hexagonal in shape and are arranged back to back in horizontal rows. They are made of wax, which is secreted from glands in the abdomen of the younger workers. Certain larger cells are set apart for the developing queens, some are used for storing pollen and honey, and the remainder enclose the drone and worker larvae. The cells are open until the larvae are full grown, but are sealed up by the workers while the transformation into the adult insect takes place.

Three wild species of *Apis* occur in India and two other genera of honey-bees occur, mainly in South America, although certain species are found in the Old World. Some of these forms are very minute, and their sting is so degenerate as to be functionless.

186

Phylum VERTEBRATA (Vertebrates)
BY
Charles Tate Regan, D.Sc., F.R.S.
Director of the British Museum (Natural History).

Vertebrates may be defined as animals with an axial skeletal rod, or notochord, formed of elastic tissue, a tubular nerve-cord above it, and a pharynx perforated by gill-slits. Like other groups, the phylum includes certain animals that do not conform to the definition, but the notochord is present in nearly all vertebrates at some period of their life, although in those with a bony skeleton it is an embryonic structure that becomes replaced during development by the backbone. The gill-slits, through which water taken in through the mouth for respiration passes to the exterior, are well developed in fishes; in the terrestrial air-breathing forms they are absent in the adults, but occur constantly as transitory embryonic structures. The tubular nerve-cord, typically expanded in front to form a brain, is very distinctive; both in its structure and in its position along the back it differs notably from the paired ventral cords found in most invertebrates.

The following classification of the Vertebrates is here adopted:

Class 1. Hemichordata
,,   2. Tunicata (Sea-squirts)
,,   3. Cephalochordata (Lancelets)
,,   4. Marsipobranchii (Lampreys and Hag-fishes)
,,   5. Selachii (Sharks and Rays)
,,   6. Pisces (Fishes)
,,   7. Amphibia (Frogs, Newts, etc.)
,,   8. Reptilia (Reptiles)
,,   9. Aves (Birds)
,, 10. Mammalia (Mammals).

Evolution of the Vertebrates

The first three classes include animals that have no brain, or at most a small and simple one, and no skeleton except the notochord. Of these the Lancelet most nearly approaches the higher vertebrates, being fish-shaped, and in relation to active swimming having the lateral muscles divided into a series of segments.

Both Tunicates and Lancelets breathe and feed in the same way, producing by ciliary action a current of water that passes in at the mouth and out through the gill-slits, and brings in food-particles that become entangled in mucus secreted by the pharynx. If this is not the original vertebrate method of breathing and feeding, it is at least an ancient and primitive one.

The remaining vertebrates have a well-developed brain, protected by a cartilaginous or bony skull, and connected with the organs of smell, sight, and hearing.

The *Marsipobranchii* are so named because their gills are contained in a series of muscular pouches, by the expansion and contraction of which water is taken in and expelled. This is an ancient group, as many forms found fossil in Silurian and Devonian rocks belong to it. These differed from the modern Lampreys and Hag-fishes, which are naked, in having the skin covered either with little teeth, or with bony plates and scales. How they fed is not certain, but they do not seem to have possessed the rasping tongue of the living forms.

This class is sometimes termed Agnatha (without jaws) in opposition to the remaining vertebrates, which possess jaws; of these the Selachians (Sharks, etc.) are the most primitive class. Sharks are, in the wide sense of the term, "fishes," that is aquatic, gill-breathing vertebrates with fins; but they differ from the true fishes in having a cartilaginous internal skeleton, no bones, and the skin covered by little denticles, structurally similar to teeth, that occur also inside the mouth.

Sharks breathe and feed in quite a different way from Lampreys, as water is taken in at the mouth and expelled through the gill-openings by the expansion and contraction of the pharynx, movements aided by skeletal elements known as gill-arches. This method of breathing is associated with the capture of prey by opening and closing the mouth, and has led to the use of an anterior pair of gill-arches as jaws, and to the enlargement of the denticles covering them, to serve as teeth.

Fishes differ from Sharks in having a bony skeleton, scales, and an air-bladder or lung. This class has evolved into a great variety of forms, but only the *Crossopterygian* fishes of Devonian times need be considered here, as they were almost certainly the ancestors of the terrestrial Vertebrates. They were slow-swimming freshwater fishes, that may occasionally have come to the surface to breathe air, and may perhaps have journeyed overland when the ponds dried up, as many air-breathing fishes do at the present day.

The paired fins, originally developed as keel-like outgrowths of the body for use in balancing, had become in these fishes paddle-like, with projecting muscular lobes fringed with rays. The skeleton of these lobes is not unlike that of the limbs of the four-footed Vertebrates, and the use of such fins to support the body on land may have led to the formation of the two characteristic joints of the limbs of the terrestrial forms, at wrist and elbow, or ankle and knee, dividing the limb into a part that emerged from the body, a middle erect part, and a distal part that lay flat on the land and had five spreading digits.

The earliest terrestrial Vertebrates were the *Stegocephalia* of Devonian and Carboniferous times, and were in many respects similar to the fishes that gave rise to them, but air-breathing and four-footed. There is good evidence that they resorted to the water to breed, and that the young were aquatic and gill-breathing. For this reason they are placed in the

Amphibia, the group that contains the Frogs, Salamanders, etc. Some were small and newt-like, others large and crocodile-like, but the group soon gave way to the *Reptilia*, who had the advantage that they need not go to water to breed, as their young hatched from shelled eggs and were from the first able to run about on land.

Instead of swallowing air, like Amphibians, most Reptiles expand the chest by movements of the ribs and so inflate the lungs. This superior method of breathing they have handed on to the Birds and Mammals.

In Permian times, and in the succeeding Secondary Period (Triassic to Cretaceous), sometimes termed the " Age of Reptiles," these animals flourished, and developed into land animals, both carnivorous and her-bivorous, some of enormous size, into the marine fish-eating Plesiosaurs and Ichthyosaurs, with paddle-like limbs, and into the flying Pterodactyls, with large membranous wings. Only a few of these ancient groups survive to-day, represented by the Crocodiles, the Tortoises, and the Tuatera of New Zealand ; the Lizards and Snakes are relatively modern.

Birds are distinguished from Reptiles by their warm blood, their covering of feathers, and by their wings, the fore-limbs being modified to support the large feathers used in flight. Other Vertebrates can fly, for example the Bats, but in these a broad membrane connects the fore and hind limbs ; they are clumsy animals on the ground, and have to climb before they can take wing. Birds have the legs unconnected with the wings ; they can hop, walk or run on the ground, and take off from it for flight. These advantages explain the dominance of Birds among flying animals. Some authorities believe that Birds originated from hopping reptiles that extended their jumps into flights ; others think that they evolved from reptiles that launched themselves from a height and planed, aided by a membrane that connected the fore limbs with the body, which degenerated as the flight-feathers developed. The structure of the ancient and primitive lizard-tailed bird (*Archaeopteryx*) of Jurassic times strongly supports the second of these theories. Instead of the short tail with radiating feathers that characterizes modern birds, it had a very long tail with a series of feathers on each side ; with such a tail this bird probably could not take flight from the ground, and that it climbed in order to fly is almost certain, as it was provided with hooked claws on the front edges of the wings, in the same position as the claws used by bats for climbing.

Mammals may be defined as warm-blooded animals that suckle their young. They have evolved from rather primitive Reptiles and are an ancient group, but during the period of Reptilian dominance were un-important. It is noteworthy that the egg-laying mammals, a group with many Reptilian characters, survive in Australia only, and that the Marsupials, in which the young are born early and relatively undeveloped, although formerly a widespread group, are now almost confined to the Australian region.

Elsewhere it is the placental mammals that have replaced the Reptiles as the dominant group on land. The maintenance of their blood at a constant high temperature, allowing them to live in all climates, and the advanced development of their young at birth, appear to be factors in their success. During the Tertiary Period they have evolved into various terrestrial groups, carnivorous, herbivorous, etc. Some, such as bats, have become flying animals, whereas others, such as whales, have become completely adapted to life in the water. The Primates, the order to which Man belongs, mostly live in trees.

Class 1. HEMICHORDATA

This class takes its name from the fact that the notochord, when present, is short and confined to the front part of the body. It includes a number of marine animals that are worm-like in appearance and in habits. These have no brain, or but a small and simple one.

Balanoglossus and its allies have long muscular bodies, with a row of pores along each side that are the openings of the gill-sacs. At the front end of the body is a hollow conical proboscis that can be swollen out by the intake of water, and is used in burrowing. These creatures live in the mud, and pass it through them. They have a free-swimming larva, which is very similar to that of the Starfishes.

Rhabdopleura and *Cephalodiscus* are small sedentary or fixed animals that live in tubes, from the ends of which feathery arms protrude. Some are solitary, others form colonies. They have a single pair of gill-openings, or none. In their manner of life they resemble many tube-inhabiting marine worms.

Class 2. TUNICATA (Sea-squirts)

The Tunicates, like the members of the preceding class, do not appear at first sight to be akin to the back-boned animals, and until their development had been studied their relationship to them was not recognised. This large class of marine animals includes three Orders: Ascidians, Salps, and Appendicularians.

Ascidians or Sea-squirts. In an adult Ascidian, or Sea-squirt, the only trace of vertebrate structure is that the pharynx is perforated by numerous gill-slits. There is, however, a free-swimming tadpole-like larval stage in the life-history, when the animal has a muscular tail with a notochord, and a tubular nerve-cord that expands in front to form a distinct brain, with an eye. These larvae swim in the sea for a time, but then settle at the bottom and become fixed; the tail then disappears, the brain degenerates, and other changes that end in the production of a Sea-squirt occur.

The Ascidians, or Sea-squirts, mostly live attached to rocks, weeds, or other objects. A large British species is the Tube Sea-squirt (*Ciona intestinalis*), which reaches a length of a foot. It is a soft, greenish, translucent animal, cylindrical in form, attached at one end ; at the free end is the tubular mouth, and a little behind it a second similar opening ; the outer skin is tough, forming the " tunic " from which the group takes its name. When touched, the animal contracts, and squirts out water through both its openings.

Other Sea-squirts may form colonies by budding ; a common example on the British coasts is *Botryllusviolaceus* ; this appears as a purplish fleshy mass that spreads over stones and is covered with golden stars ; each star is a cluster of individuals, with their mouths at the end of the rays, and a large exhalent opening common to all in the middle.

In the Sea-squirts the mouth leads into a large pharynx, which is perforated by several rows of slits, that open into a chamber with a single external aperture. The pharynx is lined with cilia, little hair-like processes ; by their lashing movements water is brought in through the mouth and with

[M. H. Crawford.

GOLDEN STAR SEA-SQUIRT (*Botryllus violaceus*).
A colonial form, with the individuals arranged in star-like clusters.

it minute organisms that become entangled in mucus, and serve as food.

A very curious Ascidian is known as *Pyrosoma*. The animals are arranged in a single layer to form a barrel-shaped colony, that swims near the surface in warm seas, and is brilliantly phosphorescent.

Salps. These are free-swimming Tunicates, either solitary or colonial, that have an alternation of generations, the sexually-mature forms being produced by budding from individuals that are unlike them in structure. *Salpa* itself, sometimes found in British waters, is a translucent cylindrical animal with circular bands of muscles round the body, by contracting which it propels itself through the water. By budding it produces numerous individuals that swim about attached to each other in chains, and eventually become mature and produce embryos that develop into the solitary form.

Appendicularians. These resemble in their structure the larvae of the Ascidians. They retain the tail and notochord throughout life, and have a single pair of gill-slits that open directly to the exterior. They are little, transparent animals that swim actively in the sea by means of their tails.

Class 3. CEPHALOCHORDATA (Lancelets)

The Lancelet (*Amphioxus*) ranges from the Mediterranean to Britain. It is a slender animal, pointed at both ends, and transparent ; it reaches a length of about two and a half inches. Along each side of the body the muscles are divided into segments, as in fishes ; there is a continuous low median fin along the back and round the end of the tail, and a fin-like ridge along each side of the abdomen. The mouth is at the front end of the body, and is surrounded by a fringe of tentacles ; it leads into a very large pharynx, which is perforated by numerous long gill-slits ; these lead into a chamber that has a single opening to the exterior. The notochord extends the whole length of the body.

The Lancelet swims about by undulating movements, and often burrows in the sand, with only the head protruding. By the continuous lashing movements of the cilia on the tentacles round the mouth and on the inner surface of the pharynx, water is brought in through the mouth and is expelled through the gill-slits. Minute organisms that enter are entangled in mucus secreted by a groove in the floor of the pharynx ; the mucus, with the food particles, is passed on to the gullet, also by ciliary action. This method of feeding is of great interest, as it is similar to that of the Tunicates and of the larval Lampreys.

The eggs of the Lancelet are very small. The gill-slits of the larvae increase in number from before backwards ; at first they open directly to the exterior, but later become covered by folds that grow out and meet below to form the gill-chamber. About twenty species of Lancelets are known, mostly from warm seas.

Class 4. MARSIPOBRANCHII (Lampreys and Hag-fishes)

The vertebrates so far described are primitive, or in some cases perhaps degenerate animals. The rest may be collectively termed Craniates, as they have a well-developed brain, protected by a skull, and connected with the organs of smell, sight, and hearing. The name " Fish " is generally applied to those craniates that live in water, breathe by gills, and propel and balance themselves with the aid of fins. These are sometimes placed in a single class, but we recognize three classes of fishes : (1) Lampreys and Hag-fishes ; (2) Sharks and Rays ; and (3) Bony Fishes.

The Lampreys and Hag-fishes are naked, eel-shaped vertebrates, with a single median nostril, without paired fins, and without jaws. They have a muscular tongue that bears horny teeth ; this can be protruded, and works like a piston, rasping off the flesh of the fishes on which these animals prey. The gills are vascular ridges on the inner walls of a series of nearly spherical sacs, which are in communication with the pharynx and with the exterior ; the sacs are enclosed in muscular pouches, and water is taken in and expelled by their expansion and contraction. Thus in their methods of feeding and breathing the Lampreys and Hag-fishes are quite peculiar. They show many primitive features in their structure ; the skull is cartilaginous and is open above ; the backbone is represented by a notochord, which in the Lampreys bears a series of cartilages along each side of the nerve-cord.

[H. Bastin.
SEA-SQUIRT (*Ascidia scabra*).
The name " squirt " refers to the fact that when it is touched, the animal contracts and squirts out water.

The group contains about fifty living species, which belong to two families, *Petromyzonidae* and *Myxinidae*.

Petromyzonidae (*Lampreys*)

This family has the mouth surrounded by an expanded suctorial disc, which bears horny teeth ; between the eyes, on top of the head, a pineal eye can be seen under the skin, and in front of it the nostril ; behind each eye is a series of seven small gill-openings, through which water for respiration is both taken in and ejected ; there are two dorsal fins, and a caudal. Lampreys inhabit the seas of the North and South Temperate Zones ; they enter fresh water to breed, and some species live their whole life in fresh water. The southern genera are quite distinct from the northern ones.

Sea-lamprey (*Petromyzon marinus*). This has the sucker covered with conical teeth arranged in curved radiating series. It is greyish or yellowish in colour, and is marbled or spotted with brown and black. The Sea-lamprey reaches a length of three feet and a weight of 5 lbs. ; it is found on both sides of the North Atlantic, and ranges from Iceland to the Mediterranean ; it feeds on cod, mackerel and other fishes, attaching itself to them by means of its sucker. In the spring or early summer, the Sea-lampreys enter rivers to breed, sometimes stealing a ride from salmon, and often resting on their journeys by holding on to stones or other objects ; the males go first and choose sandy places ; here each male clears an oval space by removing stones from it with his sucker, and when he is joined by a female she helps to prepare the nest ; when the eggs are shed both stir up the sand, which adheres to the eggs, so that they sink to the bottom ; the Lampreys now remove stones from above the nest, loosening the sand, which is carried down by the stream and covers the eggs. When these operations are finished, the Lampreys are weak and emaciated, and all die.

Larval Lampreys, or Prides. These live in tubes in the sand or mud ; they are quite different in structure from the adult, having no sucker and no teeth, and rudimentary eyes hidden under the skin. They feed on minute organisms, which are brought into the mouth by currents that are produced, at least in part, by cilia ; the food becomes entangled in slime that emanates from a groove in the floor of the pharynx, and is carried to the gullet by the action of cilia ; this method of feeding is like that of the Lancelet. The Prides live in their burrows for three or four years, and grow to a length of four to six inches before they change into Lampreys, which swim away to the sea, and live there for two or three years, or more, before returning. In former days, the Sea-lamprey was esteemed as food, and an important fishery existed in the Severn.

Other genera with the sucker completely covered with teeth are found in the Caspian Sea, in Transylvania, and in North America.

Lampetra. In this genus the disc bears three large bi- or tri-cuspid teeth on each side of the mouth, and some smaller scattered teeth. The Lampern, *Lampetra fluviatilis*, is white, with greenish back ; it reaches a length of sixteen inches. In its habits it resembles the Sea-lamprey, except that many never go to the sea, but prey on freshwater fishes in lakes and rivers. When breeding, several couples make and share a nest.

Brook-lamprey (*Lampetra planeri*). This is the third British species ; it inhabits brooks and ditches, and in the adult form does not grow, but lives only a few months, dying after spawning. Genera allied to *Lampetra* occur in Japan and North America.

Myxinidae (*Hag-fishes, Borers, or Slime-eels*)

These have no sucker ; the nostril is terminal, above the mouth, and there are four pairs of tentacles near these openings. The eyes are vestigial ; the tongue is very large, and in consequence the gill-pouches are at some distance behind the head. There is a row of glands along each side of the body ; these are able to produce enormous quantities of slime, no doubt for protection. These animals are marine ; they live at the bottom, generally in deep water, and are found mainly in temperate seas. They produce large, heavily-yolked eggs, which are enclosed in horny, oval or sausage-shaped cases ; filaments at the ends of the eggs become entwined and join the eggs to form a cluster, which lies on the bottom of the sea ; when hatched, the young are similar to the adults.

The Hags burrow right into fishes, devouring them until nothing is left but the skin and bones ; they will eat other prey, and can be caught with a bait ; as they are blind, they must find their food by smell. Some-times they lie partly hidden in the mud, with the head protruding, and then breathe through the nostril, which leads into the throat. When

[James's Press.

LAMPERN (*Lampetra fluviatilis*).
The toothed sucker round the mouth is well shown.

they are burrowing inside other fishes, they probably breathe through an opening on the left side, behind the gills.

Heptatretus (*Bdellostoma*) has six to fourteen gill openings on each side ; its species inhabit the North Pacific, and the seas of Chile, New Zealand and South Africa.

Myxine, with five to seven gill-pouches, but only one gill-opening, is a widely distributed genus. *Myxine glutinosa* of the North Atlantic reaches a length of two feet ; its preference for attacking fishes caught on lines, or in nets, makes it a great nuisance to fishermen.

Class 5. SELACHII (Sharks, Dog-fishes, Rays, and Chimaeroids)

The Selachians, or Sharks, Dog-fishes, Rays, and Chimaeroids, have much in common with the Pisces, or Bony Fishes, of which a general description is given later, but differ from them especially as follows: there are no external bones or scales, the skin is generally covered with denticles that have the structure of teeth, the fins are thick and opaque, strengthened with horny fin-rays, the internal skeleton is cartilaginous, the gills are ridges on the walls of the gill-clefts, only at their outer ends becoming detached as filaments, and there is no air-bladder. In the living Selachians the males have paired intromittent organs, which are appendages of the pelvic fins.

The Dog-fishes (*Scyliorhinidae*) lay eggs which are enclosed in large oblong horny cases, with tendrils at the corner that attach them to weeds or stones. The true Rays (*Raiidae*) have rather similar egg-cases. The egg-cases of the Port Jackson Shark (*Heterodontus*) are conical, with a spiral ridge. The remaining sharks and rays are viviparous.

The Selachians date back to Devonian times, but the sharks of those days were very different from the modern ones; these, however, have a considerable antiquity, for many living genera are known from Cretaceous rocks, and some from Jurassic strata. It is surprising that such a specialized genus as that of the Angel-fishes or Monk-fishes (*Squatina*) may have existed for perhaps a hundred million years; beautifully preserved specimens, in the lithographic stone of Bavaria, show that Angel-fishes very like those now living were contemporaries of the *Archaeopteryx*.

Sharks' fins are used by the Chinese in cooking. Shagreen, used for polishing, is the skin of species with little, close-set denticles. Large fisheries for sharks are now established in the tropics; the skin makes leather of high quality, and an excellent oil is extracted from the liver.

Recent Selachians belong to two sub-classes, *Euselachii* and *Holocephali*.

Sub-class Euselachii (Sharks and Rays)

In the Sharks and Rays the gill-clefts open separately to the exterior, and the upper jaw is free from the skull. The teeth are implanted in the membrane that covers the jaws, which is continually moving outwards; behind the teeth in use are others ready to take their place, and there is a constant succession, the used and worn teeth falling off, and being replaced by new ones. The order *Pleurotremi*, with gill-openings lateral and pectoral fins free from the head, includes the Sharks and Dog-fishes. The Rays are placed in a separate order, *Hypotremi*.

Order PLEUROTREMI (Sharks, Dog-fishes, and Angel-fishes)

Hexanchoid Sharks. These have a single dorsal fin above the anal, and six or seven gill-openings on each side. This division includes the Hexanchidae of tropical seas, which have broad compressed teeth, with oblique edges bearing several cusps. *Hexanchus cinereus* occasionally visits British waters ; it is a large piscivorous shark, growing to over twenty-five feet in length.

[*Voyage of H.M.S. " Challenger " ; Permission, Controller, H.M. Stationery Office.*
FRILLED SHARK (*Chlamydoselachus anguinea*).
A curious deep-water shark, eel-shaped and with a terminal mouth.

Chlamydoselachus, found in deep water off Japan and in the Atlantic, is eel-shaped, and has a large terminal mouth with tricuspid teeth in the jaws.

Galeoids. The Galeoids have two dorsal fins, without spines, an anal fin, and five gill-openings on each side. This division includes many typical sharks, large and active, swimming near the surface in warm seas, and feeding on fishes and other prey. They are generally blueish in colour, and in shape may resemble swift oceanic fishes, such as Bonitos or Tunny ; the snout is sharp, the crescentic mouth is on the underside of the head, the teeth are triangular and sharp-edged, and the fins are pointed. Other Galeoids, smaller in size, and with rounded fins, are generally named Dog-fishes ; these live at the bottom. This group includes five families.

The Lamnidae are large oceanic sharks, in which the last gill-opening is in front of the pectoral fin. The Great White Shark (*Carcharodon*) attains a length of forty feet ; it has triangular teeth with serrated edges ; similar teeth, some found as fossils, others from the bottom of the Pacific Ocean, are so large as to suggest that monsters nearly a hundred feet long were formerly in existence. The Porbeagle (*Lamna*) and the Thresher (*Alopias*) may occur round Britain. The Basking Shark (*Cetorhinus*) is a very large shark that takes its name from its habit of basking at the surface ; it differs from other Lamnidae in having minute teeth, and

[*James's Press.*
TIGER SHARK (*Galeocerdo*).
These large sharks are celebrated for their voracity.

197

[Neville Kingston.

EGG CAPSULES OF DOG-FISH.

These fishes produce large eggs enclosed in oblong horny capsules with tendril-like processes at the corners for attachment to weeds or stones.

in feeding on plankton.

The Odontaspidae differ from the Lamnidae in having rounded fins; this family includes the curious *Scapanorhynchus*, which has the snout produced into a broad, flat blade, or shovel; it lives on the bottom in deep water off Japan.

In the remaining Galeoids the last gill-opening is above the pectoral fin. Some Orectolobidae live near the shores of tropical seas; they have blunt heads and rounded fins, and are spotted or barred; in *Orectolobus* the broad, flat head is margined with skinny flaps, much as in the Angler. This family also includes a shark of quite another type, the Whale Shark (*Rhinodon*) a large oceanic shark that is said to reach a length of seventy feet; it has very small teeth, and feeds on plankton; it shows certain resemblances to the Basking Shark, due to similar habits.

The Carchariidae are a large family of sharks, mostly tropical. The Blue Shark (*Carcharias glaucus*) appears off Devon and Cornwall in the summer. The Tiger Sharks (*Galeocerdo*) are spotted sharks that reach a length of thirty feet; they are celebrated for their voracity. The Hammer-heads (*Sphyrna*) are remarkable in having the eyes at the sides of lateral extensions of the front of the head, which is hammer-shaped. The Topes (*Galeus*) and Hounds (*Mustelus*) are relatively small bottom-living Carchariids; each genus has a British species. *Mustelus* feeds on shell-fish, and its teeth are blunt, forming a pavement.

The Scyliorhinidae (Dog-fishes) are found all over the world, some living near the coast, others at considerable depths. There are two British species, both spotted, with rounded fins, and with small, pointed teeth; they feed on all kinds of animals. The species of *Cephalosyllium* inflate themselves like the globe-fishes.

Squaloids. These have two dorsal fins, each of which is preceded by a strong spine, which is not a fin-ray, but an enlarged denticle: in some genera, however, the spines have disappeared. With few exceptions, these are bottom-living forms. The Heterodontidae of the tropical Pacific

198

include the Port Jackson Shark ; they have large crushing teeth at the sides of the jaws. The Squalidae, without an anal fin, are a large and varied family. The Spur-dog (*Squalus acanthias*) is very abundant round Britain ; it swims in large shoals and is very destructive to herrings, pilchards, mackerel, and haddocks ; it is hated by fishermen, as it will destroy nets as well as fish. Some deep-water sharks (*Centrophorus*, etc.) are fished for with long lines off Portugal, down to depths of five hundred fathoms. The Greenland Shark (*Somniosus*) is a large northern shark ; it has cutting teeth, and is said to attack whales.

The Angel-fishes or Monk-fishes (*Squatina*) are flat, with a transverse terminal mouth, sharp, conical teeth, and large, wing-shaped pectoral fins ; they lie in wait for fishes, and occur mainly in temperate seas. Another family related to the Squalidae is that of the Saw-sharks (*Pristiophorus*) of Japan, Australia and South Africa ; the snout forms a long, flat blade, with teeth along each edge.

Order HYPOTREMI (Rays)

In the Rays the pectoral fins are large and are attached to the head, sometimes meeting at the end of the snout ; the transverse mouth and the gill-openings are on the flat lower surface ; on top of the head, immediately behind the eyes, is a pair of large holes, the spiracles, through which water

[*F. Schensky, Helgoland.*

SMALLER SPOTTED DOG-FISH (*Scyliorhinus canicula*).
A common British species.

Reproduced by permission from] [Day's British Fishes.
ANGEL-FISH (*Squatina*).
These flattened sharks take their name from the wing-like form of the pectoral fins.

is taken in for respiration. The dorsal fins are without spines, and there is no anal fin.

Rays form a large group; they are found in all seas, nearly always living at the bottom. The most primitive are the tropical *Rhinobatidae*, less broad and less flat than typical rays, and with smaller pectoral fins; allied to them are the *Pristidae*, or Saw-fishes, which have the snout produced into a long and narrow blade, with a series of strong teeth on each side. Saw-fishes occur on sandy shores in the tropics, and sometimes enter rivers; they have small, blunt teeth and probably use the saw to disturb the small animals on which they feed, by raking the weeds or stirring the sand.

The Raiidae have very large pectoral fins, which form the greater part of a rounded or four-sided disc, which is well marked off from the tail. They are cosmopolitan, and many live in deep water. There are several British species, including the Thornback (*Raia clavata*) with rhombic disc, mottled above and white below, bearing strong thorn-like spines, and the large Skate (*R. batis*), with pointed snout and blue-grey belly.

The Torpedinidae, or Electric Rays, form a very distinct group. They have large electric organs on each side of the head, capable of giving powerful shocks. The skin is smooth and naked, these rays having no need of the spines and tubercles that are commonly present in others, and serve for defence.

The Whip-tailed Rays, found in all warm seas, have a broad disc and a slender tail that carries one or more long, serrated spines, with a poison-gland at the base. By lashing the tail the spines are made to inflict wounds, which are exceedingly painful and difficult to heal in human victims.

The typical Whip-tailed Rays, or *Trygonidae*, are small or of moderate size, and have small, blunt teeth, but the Eagle-rays (*Myliobatidae*) are very large, and have either a pavement of large, flat, hexagonal teeth, or a single series of broad, flat teeth that are joined together; these rays feed on clams and oysters, crushing their shells.

The Sea-devils (*Mobula*) are the largest of all rays, reaching a width of twenty feet; the mouth is wide, terminal, with quite small teeth; on each side of it the front ends of the pectoral fins project forward, and can be rolled up to look like a pair of horns, or be unrolled and meet below the mouth to form a sort of scoop, which is used when these rays are catching little fishes. Sea-devils sometimes swim at the surface, and may make prodigious leaps; they have been described as hovering for a second or two before falling back into the water.

Sub-class Holocephali (Chimaeras)

This sub-class includes the single family *Chimaeridae*, with about thirty species, nearly all of which live at the bottom of the sea in deep water, and feed on small fish. They differ from sharks in having the upper jaw fused with the skull, and in having only one gill-opening on each side. They have a long, tapering tail, and large paired fins; the first dorsal fin, placed just behind the head, has a spine, which is not an enlarged denticle as it is in the Squaloids, but is formed by concrescence of horny fin rays. The eyes are large; the teeth are coalesced to form large plates, with sharp edges, and sometimes with grinding areas. The eggs are enclosed in horny cases.

In *Chimaera* the snout is blunt; in *Harriotta* it is produced and pointed, somewhat like the beak of a bird; in the Antarctic *Callorhynchus* it bears a tactile flap. None of the species grows to more than about four feet long.

Class 6. PISCES (Fishes)

The class Pisces includes the great majority of living fishes, with well over twenty thousand recent species. In having jaws, and gills supported by gill-arches, the Pisces resemble the Selachians, from which they are distinguished by possessing a bony skeleton; in this respect, and in having an air-bladder or lung, they approach the four-footed vertebrates.

External Skeleton. The head is generally covered by bones, and the body by scales. The bones of the head include parietals, frontals, etc., that roof the skull, and on each side bones round the eye. The membrane that covers the gill-chamber is supported by a series of movable rays, the two uppermost of which

[*Douglas P. Wilson.*]

THORNBACK RAY (*Raia clavata*).
Common British Ray.

201

are enlarged to form the bony plates known as the gill-covers; in front of the gill-covers is a fixed praeoperculum. The mouth is bordered above by toothed bones, praemaxillaries in front and maxillaries behind; primitively these are fixed, but in many fishes they are movable, the praemaxillaries often being protractile, and the maxillaries attached at their front ends only. The lower jaw is encased in bones, including a toothed dentary.

Scales. The scales of fishes are primitively rhombic bony plates set edge to edge in parallel oblique and longitudinal series; these plates are covered with a glassy layer of " ganoine " and are termed " ganoid " scales. Among living fishes only the Bichirs (*Polypterus*) and Gar-pikes (*Lepidosteus*) have scales of this kind. In other fishes the scales are generally thin, rounded, and overlapping, and either have the edges entire (" cycloid " scales) or pectinate (" ctenoid " scales); ctenoid scales are generally rough, bearing series of little prickles. In some fishes the scales may be lost, or they may be variously modified, forming, for example, a bony box, or a covering of spines.

Fins. The fins, as in the Selachians, include the median fins, dorsal on the back, anal under the tail, and caudal at the end of the tail, and the paired fins, pectorals and pelvics, corresponding to the fore and hind limbs of terrestrial vertebrates. Each fin consists of a membrane supported by a double series of bony rays, that may unite in pairs to form a single series; typically, the rays are jointed and flexible. The caudal fin may originally have been diphycercal, that is equally developed above and below the end of the tail; in most primitive fishes, however, the end of the tail is turned up, and the lower part of the fin is better developed than the upper; this is termed a " heterocercal " caudal fin.

The terminal and apparently symmetrical " homocercal " caudal fin of most living fishes has been derived from the heterocercal type, but corresponds only to the anterior part of the lower lobe of such a fin, beyond which the end of the tail has disappeared.

In the Sturgeons the paired fins, especially the pelvics, are very like the median fins in structure. In the Lung-fishes the muscular lobes of the paired fins project from the body, and are fringed with rays, forming paddle-like fins. In most modern fishes the pectoral fins have short muscular lobes, and the pelvics none: in some the pelvic fins have moved forward to below the pectorals (thoracic position) or on to the throat (jugular) or even to the chin (mental).

Sense Organs. Fishes have paired eyes, ears, and organs of smell. The ear, which is concerned with equilibrium and hearing, is internal; it generally contains solid calcareous concretions—the otoliths. The organs of smell, placed on the snout, do not communicate with the palate; they are pits, lined with a sensory membrane that generally forms radiating folds; the skin above each pit is pierced by two nostrils, an anterior inhalent and a posterior exhalent. The lateral line is a system of canals on the head and body, containing sense-organs, and opening by pores, or by tubes that perforate the scales; generally, a series of lateral line scales can be seen along each side of the body. This is a very important organ for the perception of vibrations of less frequency than those perceived by the ear, thus enabling the fish to detect movements in the water.

Gills and Gill-arches. The gill-clefts lead from the pharynx into the gill-chamber, which has a single external opening. The gills, supported by the skeletal arches between the clefts, appear as double series of red filaments projecting into the gill-chambers. The gill-arches, which are typically four in number, also bear stiff processes known as gill-rakers, either few and short, or numerous and long, according to the nature of the food; these project into the pharynx and prevent food from passing over the gills. The upper pharyngeals, or upper segments of the gill-arches, generally bear teeth that bite against the lower pharyngeals, a pair of toothed bones in the floor of the throat just behind the gills, remnants of a fifth gill-arch. In many fishes the teeth in the throat are of great importance.

The Air-bladder or Lung. This may originally have been developed as an air-breathing organ, and has this function in some primitive fishes. Generally, its function is to secrete or absorb gas to counteract changes of pressure. In some fishes it becomes connected with the internal ear, and transmits vibrations to it, increasing the sense of hearing: in others it may be a sound-producing organ.

Locomotion. The muscles of fishes are divided into a series of segments. By contractions of these from head to tail, first on one side and then on the other, alternate strokes to right and left are produced. Swift-swimming fishes are typically spindle-shaped, with conical head and tapering tail; they have a strong caudal fin with pointed lobes, and often triangular dorsal and anal fins, that serve as keels; the paired fins also are broad-based and pointed, and are not used in forward swimming, but in turning or slowing movements. Slower fishes may be less graceful in form, and may have rounded fins; in some of these, movements of the dorsal and anal fins may assist the strokes of the tail; in others the pectorals may be used to scull the fish along. Elongate fishes, such as eels, swim by snake-like movements of the body, and by undulations of the long dorsal and anal fins.

Coloration. In most fishes the colour grades from dark above to white below, counteracting the effect of light from above. Many fishes that swim near the surface are silvery, with blue backs; if, like the Mackerel, they have darker spots or bars, these produce a blending effect at a short distance, and help to obscure the outline. Fishes that live on the bottom near the coasts are often barred, spotted, or mottled, harmonizing in colour and pattern with the ground or with the weeds. In the tropics, and particularly among fishes that frequent coral reefs, there occur brilliant colours, and fantastic patterns; the bars, stripes, or blotches of contrasting colours break up the body, obscure the outline, and probably help towards concealment when the fishes are at rest, or are swimming slowly. Many fishes have the power of instantaneously changing colour and pattern, in order to resemble their surroundings; examples of this will be mentioned among the Pipe-fishes, Sea-perches, and Flat-fishes. Fishes that live in the darkness of the ocean depths, or in underground waters, are generally uniformly coloured, black, purplish, or sometimes white.

Breeding and Development. Most fishes assemble in large shoals at the breeding season, and many of them produce enormous numbers of minute eggs that float in the sea. This is true of all the important British food-fishes except the Herring, which produces eggs that lie on the bottom, and the Salmon, which buries its eggs in the gravel of rivers.

When there is courtship and pairing the males are often brightly coloured, and have large and ornamental fins. Fishes of this type as a rule have a relatively small number of eggs, and one or both parents, generally the father, may guard the eggs and young (cf. Cyprinodonts, Pipe-fishes, Cichlids, Gobies, etc.). Some fishes are viviparous (cf. Cyprinodonts). When hatched, the larval fish is transparent, and has a continuous median fin, without rays. The skull is cartilaginous, and the backbone is represented by the notochord. The changes that lead to the formation of rayed fins and to the ossification of the skeleton include one feature of great interest, the development of the caudal fin. At first the end of the tail is straight; at some distance from its end a plate of cartilage, which later gives rise to the bony support of the caudal fin, is formed below the notochord, and in the membrane below it appear the caudal fin-rays; the end of the tail now turns up, so that the caudal fin becomes terminal; afterwards the projecting end of the tail becomes shortened, and eventually disappears. Thus in its larval history a fish like the Herring passes through stages showing the transition from a diphycercal to a heterocercal, and from a heterocercal to a homocercal fin.

Fisheries. The most important food-fishes belong to the families of the Herring (*Clupeidae*), Salmon (*Salmonidae*), Cod (*Gadidae*), and Mackerel (*Scombridae*) and to the Flat-fishes (*Heterosomata*). Although fisheries exist in all parts of the world, those of the North Atlantic and the North Pacific are far more valuable than any others, Britain, Japan, and the United States being the leading fishing nations. In the northern seas there are large banks, at depths down to two hundred fathoms or more, which are inhabited by the cod, halibut, and other bottom-living fishes that are caught by trawl or line. Here also herring abound, and to the south of them pilchards and mackerel, fishes that swim near the surface, and are caught by gill-nets, seines, etc. On the Pacific coast of North America several kinds of salmon are taken in enormous numbers as they run into the rivers to breed ; these are the basis of the canning industry.

Classification. The class " Pisces " is divided into three sub-classes, the two first of which, *Palaeopterygii* and *Crossopterygii*, date back to Devonian times and are represented in the living fauna only by remnants. The third sub-class, the *Neopterygii*, which dates back to the Permian, contains the great majority of recent fishes, which are arranged in thirty-one orders (page 208).

Sub-class Palaeopterygii (Sturgeons and Bichirs)

The living Palaeopterygii belong to two very distinct orders, both of which, however, retain certain characters of the palaeozoic Palaeoniscidae, which were predacious fishes with blunt snout, large mouth, sharp teeth, ganoid scales, heterocercal tail, and fins with series of numerous close-set rays.

Order 1. CHONDROSTEI (Sturgeons and Paddle-fishes)

The Sturgeons and their allies are the only living bony fishes with a heterocercal tail, and with many-rayed fins of Palaeoniscid structure. They are distinguished by a projecting snout, a toothless mouth, and a scaleless body, naked or with some bony plates.

The Polyodontidae include the Paddle-fish or Spoon-bill (*Polyodon spatula*) of the Mississippi, a curious naked fish, with small eyes, and with a very long, flat blade, broad and rounded at the end, projecting in front of the mouth. The Spoon-bill stirs up the mud with its paddle-like snout, and feeds on little crustaceans and other minute animals ; it grows to six feet long. A related fish (*Psephurus gladius*) from China has the snout narrower and pointed in front ; it is said to grow to twenty feet long in the Yang-tse-Kiang.

The Acipenseridae, or Sturgeons, are distinguished by a shorter snout, with a transverse series of four long barbels on the flat lower surface, in front of the mouth, which is protractile downwards ; along the body are five series of bony plates, each generally bearing a spine. There are some thirty species of this family ; some are marine, but enter rivers to spawn, in Europe, northern Asia, and North America ; others are restricted to fresh water.

The Sturgeon (*Acipenser sturio*), found on both sides of the North Atlantic, ranges in the east from Norway to the Black Sea. It is a large fish, growing to eighteen feet in length ; it is not a regular visitor to British rivers, preferring larger streams for breeding. It feeds at the bottom, feeling for small prey with its barbels, and sucking food into the mouth ; the name " Sturgeon " refers to its habit of stirring up the mud.

Round the Black and Caspian Seas there are important fisheries for

205

[*W. S. Berridge.*

SENEGAL BICHIR (*Polypterus senegalus*).
The Bichirs are freshwater fishes of tropical Africa.

several kinds of Sturgeons ; the flesh is esteemed as food ; caviare is prepared from the roe, and isinglass from the air-bladder.

The shovel-nose Sturgeons of North America and Central Asia belong to a separate genus (*Scaphirhynchus*) with the snout flat and the tail completely enclosed in bony scutes.

Order 2. CLADISTIA (Bichirs and Reed-fish)

The Polypteridae of tropical Africa are more primitive than the Sturgeons in having a terminal mouth, sharp teeth in the jaws, and the body covered with ganoid scales. They are, however, more specialized in the structure of the fins, especially the dorsal and caudal. The dorsal forms a series of strong well-separated spines along the back ; behind these is a part formed of jointed rays connected by membrane, and this is united with the caudal ; the two together, dorsal above and caudal below, form a rounded fin at the hind end of the body. The Bichir of the Nile (*Polypterus bichir*) is a carnivorous fish, eating other fishes, frogs, crustaceans, etc. ; it grows to about four feet long. There are about ten other species of *Polypterus*, and the family also includes the eel-like *Calamichthys*, or Reed-fish, of West Africa.

In these fishes the air-bladder is very lung-like, and is used for breathing air. The young are peculiar, being provided with a pair of long, feather-like external gills, inserted above the pectoral fins.

Sub-class 2. Crossopterygii
Order DIPNEUSTI (Lung-fishes)

The fringe-finned fishes are a very ancient group ; they are characterized by paired fins with rays fringing a long muscular lobe, which contains an elongate bony axis divided into segments. Only one order survives, that of the Dipneusti, or Lung-fishes, so named from the lung-like structure of the air-bladder, and from their air-breathing habits. In the Lung-fishes praemaxillaries and maxillaries are absent, and a pair of tooth-plates on the inside of the lower jaw bites against a pair on the roof of the mouth. The living genera have continuous median fins, and cycloid scales ; they belong to two families.

The family Ceratodontidae dates back to the Triassic, but includes

206

only one living species, the Barramunda (*Neoceratodus forsteri*) of Queensland, which is moderately elongate in form, has large scales, and paddle-shaped paired fins ; the flat surface of the tooth-plates is transversed by several low radiating ridges. The Barramunda is a large fish, reaching six feet in length ; it lives in stagnant pools, and often comes to the surface to breathe air ; it swims about quietly, cropping the weeds and eating the small crustaceans and other animals that frequent them. The eggs are laid among the weeds or on the mud, and the larvae lack the peculiarities of those of the next family.

The Lepidosirenidae include *Protopterus* of tropical Africa, and *Lepidosiren* of South America ; they are more elongate in form than the Barramunda, have small scales, and rayless paired fins that appear as tapering filaments ; the tooth-plates have three strong, sharp-edged ridges. These fishes live in swamps and marshes, eat fishes and other animal prey, and often come to the surface to breathe air. In the dry season they sleep in burrows in the mud, living on their own fat, and breathing air through one or more small openings that they leave when closing the mouth of the burrow ; when the rainy season arrives, they leave the burrows and resume an active life. They make nests, either a hole at the edge of a swamp (*Protopterus*), or a burrow at the bottom of the water (*Lepidosiren*) ; in these holes or burrows the eggs are laid, and are guarded by the male fish. The larvae adhere to the mud by means of a sucker behind the mouth, and they have four pairs of feathery external gills, that are necessary to enable them to breathe during this stationary period of their existence, when they cannot rise to the surface. After a time, the sucker disappears and the young fish become free, lose their external gills, and swim out of the nest.

[*James's Press.*

AFRICAN LUNG-FISH (*Protopterus*).
These fishes inhabit swamps ; during the dry season they live in burrows in the mud and breathe air.

Sub-class 3. Neopterygii

This sub-class includes the great majority of living fishes, which are distinguished by the structure of the fins. Each ray of the dorsal and anal fins has its own pair of muscles and is articulated to its own skeletal support ; the caudal fin is abbreviate heterocercal or homocercal. The pelvic fins have no muscular lobe, and that of the pectorals is short.

The sub-class originated at the end of the Palaeozoic era, its first members being slow-swimming, bottom-feeding fishes ; the shortening of the upturned end of the tail, and the reduction in number and spacing out of the rays of the dorsal and anal fins, were related to the habits of these fishes, the fins being less fitted to cleave the water, but more capable of delicate movements, than those of their swift, predacious ancestors. Although their descendants have become adapted to many ways of living, some being swift fishes with close-set dorsal and anal rays, some eel-shaped, with many-rayed fins, the essential feature, that each ray has its own support, has been retained in all. A list of the orders of the *Neopterygii* follows :—

1. Protospondyli (Bow-fin)
2. Ginglymodi (Gar-pikes)
3. Isospondyli (Herring, Salmon, etc.)
4. Haplomi (Pikes, Mud-minnows)
5. Iniomi (Lantern-fishes)
6. Lyomeri (Gulpers)
7. Ostariophysi (Carps, Cat-fishes)
8. Apodes (Eels)
9. Heteromi
10. Synentognathi (Gar-fishes, Flying Fishes)
11. Microcyprini (Cyprinodonts)
12. Salmopercae (Trout-perches)
13. Anacanthini (Cods, etc.)
14. Allotriognathi (Opah, Ribbon-fishes)
15. Solenichthyes (Snipe-fishes, Pipe-fishes)
16. Berycomorphi (Berycoids)
17. Zeomorphi (Dories)
18. Percomorphi (Perches, Blennies, etc.)
19. Gobiomorphi (Gobies)
20. Scleroparei (Mail-cheeked Fishes)
21. Thoracostei (Sticklebacks)
22. Hypostomides (Dragon-fishes)
23. Heterosomata (Flat-fishes)
24. Discocephali (Sucker-fishes)
25. Plectognathi (Trigger-fish, Globe-fish)
26. Malacichthyes (Rag-fishes)
27. Xenopterygii (Cling-fishes)
28. Haplodoci (Toad-fishes)
29. Pediculati (Anglers)
30. Opisthomi (Spiny Eels)
31. Symbranchii (Symbranchoid Eels).

Order 1. PROTOSPONDYLI (Bow-fin)

The only living member of this order is the Bow-fin (*Amia calva*), of the fresh waters of North America, from the Great Lakes southwards. The Bow-fin is rather elongate in form, with a long dorsal fin and the other fins rounded ; the caudal fin has a somewhat oblique base. The mouth is moderately large, with strong jaws, and some rather large conical teeth ;

208

[W. S. Berridge.

BOW-FIN (*Amia calva*).
The only living member of its order, which is, however, an ancient one; it inhabits the fresh waters of North America.

there is a large, bony gular plate between the branches of the lower jaw, and the scales are thin and rounded.

The Bow-fin is a greenish fish, mottled with darker colour; the female grows to about thirty inches long; the male, who is smaller, is distinguished by an ocellus, black edged with yellow, at the base of the caudal fin. This is an active and voracious fish, which can live a long time out of water, breathing air with its lung-like air-bladder. In the spring the Bow-fins pair, and clear a nest among the weeds in a shallow place; the male guards the nest, and may swim with his brood for a time.

Order 2. GINGLYMODI (Gar-pikes)

The Lepidosteidae, or Gar-pikes, of North and Central America, are more primitive than the Bow-fin in having the body covered with ganoid scales, rhombic bony plates with shiny surface, but are more specialized in having the jaws produced, and in lacking a gular plate; the dorsal fin is short, above the anal. There are half-a-dozen species of these sluggish and voracious fishes, the largest of which is the Alligator Gar (*Lepidosteus tristoechus*) of the southern States and Mexico, which has a broad snout, and very strong conical teeth; it takes its name from its crocodile-like head, and is said to reach a length of twenty feet. Of the other species, the com-

[F. W. Bond.

GAR-PIKE (*Lepidosteus*).
The Gar-pikes inhabit the fresh waters of North America; except the Bichirs of Africa they are the only living fishes with ganoid scales.

[*Voyage of H.M.S. "Challenger"; Permission, Controller, H.M. Stationery Office.*
Bathytroctes rostratus.
An example of the Alepocephalidae, dark-coloured fishes that inhabit the depths of the ocean.

monest is the long-nosed Gar (*L. osseus*), which has very long and slender jaws and is abundant in the Great Lakes, and southwards.

Order 3. ISOSPONDYLI (Herring, Salmon, etc.)

This order includes the most primitive fishes with a homocercal caudal fin ; they are soft-rayed, with abdominal pelvic fins, with an open duct to the air-bladder, and generally with the mouth bordered above by the praemaxillaries in front and the maxillaries at the sides.

Elopidae. These have a large terminal mouth, with bands of small conical teeth in the jaws, and a bony plate under the lower jaw. The. Tarpon (*Megalops atlanticus*), found on both sides of the tropical Atlantic, has very large scales ; it is a celebrated sporting fish, that reaches a weight of over one hundred pounds ; it feeds on small fishes, and will pursue the shoals into rivers. The ten-pounders (*Elops*) are slender, silvery fishes, active and piscivorous ; they are found in tropical seas, but one African species is confined to fresh water.

Albulidae. These include *Albula vulpes*, a silvery fish with prominent snout, small subterminal mouth, and a large patch of blunt teeth on the tongue, opposed to others on the palate, used for crushing the shells of molluscs ; it reaches a length of three feet, and is common on sandy shores in tropical seas.

Chanidae (*Chanos*). This family comprises a single species, the Milk-fish, a large, silvery fish with a small, toothless mouth ; it feeds on algae, and is found throughout the Indo-Pacific, sometimes entering rivers ; it is valued as food, and can be kept and fattened in freshwater ponds.

Alepocephalidae. These are deep-blue, purple, or black fishes, with the dorsal fin above the anal ; about fifty kinds are known, all living in the ocean depths.

Clupeidae. This, the Herring family, comprises some three hundred species, most of which swim in shoals. The majority have minute teeth, and feed on plankton, the most notable exception being the Dorab (*Chirocentrus*), of the Indian Ocean, a long and lean predacious fish, with strong, sharp teeth.

The Herring (*Clupea harengus*), of the North Atlantic, ranges from Iceland and Northern Europe south to the Bay of Biscay and Cape Hatteras ; another species occurs in the North Pacific. The Herring is a silvery, blue-backed fish, with a median row of strong scales with back-wardly-directed points along the abdomen ; it seldom exceeds a foot in length, and swims in enormous shoals, feeding on little Crustacea and other minute animals that abound near the surface of the sea. There appear to be a number of races that spawn at different times ; the eggs, which are about the size of small shot, are deposited on the sea-bottom. In economic importance the Herring exceeds any other European fish.

The Sprat, a smaller fish, with more strongly-serrated abdomen, ranges from Norway to the Mediterranean ; unlike the Herring, it produces small floating eggs. In Norway large quantities of sprats are tinned in oil.

The Pilchard (*Sardina pilchardus*) is a plumper fish than the Herring, with the abdomen only weakly serrated ; in summer some may enter the North Sea, but the species is common only from the Mediterranean to Cornwall. It is a plankton feeder ; it breeds well out at sea and produces very small floating eggs. The French name of this fish is Sardine, and under this name are sold the young fish, tinned in oil, that are caught off France and Portugal. Another species of Pilchard (*S. sagax*) inhabits the seas of South Africa, Japan, California and Chile, and a third is found off Australia and New Zealand. All the Pilchards have about fifty-four scales in a longitudinal series, but in the European species the scales of every alternate row are enlarged and cover the row behind, so that only half that number can be counted ; occasionally specimens have been taken with the scales of one side of equal size, and apparently more numerous, as in *S. sagax*. The Indian Oil Sardine belongs to an allied tropical genus, *Sardinella*.

The Shads (*Alosa*) have a notch in the middle of the upper jaw ; they are found on both sides of the North Atlantic, and enter rivers to spawn in fresh water. The American Shad (*A. sapidissima*) is a valued food fish. The British species are the Allis Shad (*A. alosa*) and the Twaite Shad (*A. finta*) ; the former is distinguished by very long, slender, and numerous g i l l - rakers, in relation to a diet of plankton ; it is the l a r g e r species, reaching a weight of eight pounds. Both enter rivers from April to June; the eggs lie on the

[*W. J. Clarke.*

TWAITE SHAD (*Alosa finta*).
A fish of the Herring family that enters rivers to breed.

bottom, and the young go to sea when they are about six inches long. In the lakes of Killarney the Twaite Shad is represented by a distinct form (*A. f. killarnensis*) that never goes to the sea, and does not grow longer than eight inches ; there are also non-migratory lacustrine Shad in Northern Italy.

Allied to the Shads are *Caspialosa* of the Black and Caspian Seas, *Brevoortia*, which includes the Menhaden, found in great abundance on the Atlantic coast of America, and valued as a source of oil, and *Hilsa* of the Indian Ocean.

The Anchovies (*Engraulis*, etc.) form a large group of small fishes that abound in the warmer seas, and are distinguished by a pointed snout that projects in front of the mouth.

Salmonidae. Salmonid fishes have an adipose fin, and no oviducts ; they are marine fishes of arctic and northern seas that enter rivers to breed, and often form permanent freshwater colonies, that in time may become species, in rivers or lakes.

Salmon and Trout form a genus, *Salmo*, characterized by a fairly large mouth with conical teeth in the jaws, a double or zig-zag series of teeth along the vomer, in the middle of the roof of the mouth, and a rather short dorsal fin, placed above the pelvics.

The Salmon (*Salmo salar*) ranges from Iceland and the northern coasts of Europe south to the Bay of Biscay, and from Canada to Cape Cod. It is a graceful fish, silvery, with scattered blackish spots, that feeds on herring, sand-eels, and other fishes. Salmon enter rivers throughout the year, and make their way up stream, showing great strength and activity in the falls and rapids ; they spawn in the autumn, and by that time are very different from the fresh-run fish, being dull in colour, with numerous spots of black and red ; their skin is thick and soft, and their flesh pale and watery, instead of red and firm ; the males have the jaws prolonged, and the lower hooked up at the tip. These changes may be due to the fact that salmon rarely feed after entering the rivers, but develop their sexual glands at the expense of the other tissues, an abnormal way of living that may result in abnormalities of structure.

Salmon spawn on gravelly shallows ; the female scoops out a trough with her tail, deposits the eggs in it, and covers them over. The eggs are about as large as peas ; they hatch out at the beginning of spring, and the little fish emerge from the gravel when they are about an inch long, swim about in shoals, and feed on little crustaceans, insects, etc. ; they have a series of dark bars along each side of the body, and are known as parr, but after about two years, when they are six inches long, they lose the bars, become silvery, and go to the sea as smolts, generally about May. In the sea they grow rapidly, and in a year may weigh from four to ten pounds, and in three or four years from forty to fifty pounds or more. Many salmon breed only once, the kelts, or spent fish, dying after spawning ; none breed more than three or four times. Those that enter rivers after only one winter in the sea are termed grilse, but many salmon do not breed as grilse, and grow quite large before they breed.

Freshwater races of salmon inhabit Lakes Wenern and Ladoga, and many lakes and rivers of eastern North America ; the Ouananiche of the Saguenay River is a small non-migratory salmon, famous for its gameness and activity.

The Trout (*S. trutta*) of Europe is closely related to the Salmon, but has a larger mouth, and is less graceful in form : it forms freshwater

[*Arthur Brook.*

Salmon (*Salmo salar*) leaping a weir on its way to the spawning beds.

colonies in every lake and river that it enters. Sea-trout are silvery, with scattered blackish spots, but the trout of lakes and rivers may be covered with round black or red spots, that are often ocellated. In the sea, the Trout ranges from Iceland to the Bay of Biscay ; as a freshwater fish it extends along the north of the Mediterranean, and is found in the mountain streams of Algeria. The Trout of the Black and Caspian Seas and their tributaries have smaller scales, and there is another race in the Aral Sea and the Oxus.

The Salmon and Trout of the North Pacific form a group apart, with head more pointed, scales smaller, and anal fin longer, than in the Atlantic species. The Rainbow Trout (*S. irideus*), with a red band along the side

213

of the body, has numerous races in the rivers of California and the region to the north. The Quinnat ascends rivers for long distances, and the parr live two years in fresh water, but other Pacific Salmon do not go so far to breed, and the young fish quickly seek the sea. In some species the jaws of the breeding males are very long and strongly hooked. All these Pacific salmon are said to breed once only, and to die after breeding.

The Char (*Salvelinus*) have the teeth on the vomer restricted to a group on the head of the bone. The Northern Char (*S. alpinus*) inhabits the Arctic Ocean, but is represented by numerous different forms, relics of the Glacial Epoch, in lakes to as far south as Ireland, the Lake District, the Alps, and Maine. These are beautiful fishes, trout-like, but with orange spots and no black ones. In North America there are two other species of Char, both with dark markings on the dorsal and caudal fins, namely the Great Lake Trout (*S. namaycush*), which reaches a weight of one hundred pounds, and the smaller Brook-trout (*S. fontinalis*). The Huchen, a large black-spotted predacious fish of the Danube, belongs to an allied genus.

Reproduced by permission from]   [*Day's British Fishes.*
GRAYLING (*Thymallus vulgaris*).
In these fishes the scales are larger, the dorsal fin longer, and the mouth smaller than in Trout.

The White-fish (*Coregonus*) are silvery fishes, with larger scales than Trout, and with a small, toothless or feebly-toothed mouth. There are numerous species, some migratory, but most restricted to lakes, where they feed on minute Crustacea. British species are the Vendaces (*C. vandesius*) of Lochmaben and of Derwentwater, the Pollan (*C. pollan*) of Ireland, and the closely-related forms known as Powan (*C. clupeoides*) in Loch Lomond, Schelly in Ullswater and Haweswater, and Gwyniad in Bala. The Graylings (*Thymallus*), with smaller mouth and longer dorsal fin than Salmon or Trout, are beautiful fishes of northern rivers.

The Argentines, large-eyed, silvery fishes of the North Atlantic, live at the bottom in deep water, down to five hundred fathoms or more; they produce eggs that float in the sea.

Closely allied to the Salmonidae also is the family that includes the Smelts, the Capelin of the Arctic seas, the Surf-Smelts and Eulachon of the North Pacific, and the Ayu of Japan. These are small fishes, all with rich flesh of delicate flavour. The Capelin and the Surf-Smelts crowd into the surf to spawn in the sand, but the others breed in estuaries or rivers. The Ayu is fished for with cormorants by the Japanese.

214

The southern Salmonoids are related to the Smelts, but belong to separate families, the largest of which is the Galaxiidae, which have the dorsal fin above the anal, and no adipose fin. *Galaxias attenuatus* is a small, slender fish of Patagonia, New Zealand, and southern Australia and Tasmania ; it abounds in the rivers, but descends

[*Paul Unger.*

WHITE-FISH (*Coregonus maraena*).
The species of Coregonus are silvery, small-mouthed fishes, most of which live in lakes.

to the sea to breed. There are a number of strictly freshwater species in the same regions, some of which are prettily spotted and trout-like. *Neochanna* of New Zealand burrows in damp clay, and has been dug out with a spade at some distance from the water.

Stomiatoids. These are oceanic fishes, with a double row of luminous organs along each side of the lower part of the body ; many of them also have a large glandular organ behind the eye, with a luminous surface that can be turned downwards into a pocket and so be concealed. Some have an adipose fin, but in others the dorsal fin is above the anal, and the adipose fin is absent. About three hundred species are known.

[*Central Press.*

Opisthoproctus soleatus.
A curious oceanic fish related to the Argentines ; the eyes are directed upwards, and the body has a flat, sole-like under surface.

FISH (ISOSPONDYLI)

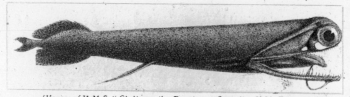

[*Voyage of H.M.S. " Challenger"; Permission, Controller, H.M. Stationery Office.*
Malacosteus indicus.
This fish lives at considerable depths; its mouth is capable of great distension, the jaws
being large, and the lower connected with the tongue by an elastic cord.

The Stern-optychiidae are silvery Stomiatoids, deep and strongly compressed, with large eyes and a small, feebly-toothed mouth. Another family includes *Chauliodus*, which swims at no great distance below the surface; it is a slender fish, with pointed teeth of extraordinary length. The Stomiatidae are blackish; they have strong teeth, and, like other piscivorous fishes of the middle depths of the ocean, are able to swallow fishes larger than themselves; they have a barbel below the mouth, which in some is very long, in others much branched; frequently it bears luminous organs, and may serve as a lure. *Eustomias* is a remarkable genus; the jaws are protractile, the front part of the backbone is unossified, and the notochord is curved into the shape of an S, the loops opening out or closing up as the mouth is thrust forward or drawn back.

In the Malacosteidae the jaws extend back behind the head; there is no floor to the mouth, but an elastic cord runs back to the tongue from the symphysis of the lower jaw; the eyes are large. *Malacosteus* lives deep down; as it opens its mouth by a downward movement of the lower jaw it throws its head right back to bring the mouth in front; it can do this without dislocating its neck, as the front part of the backbone consists merely of the notochord within a fibrous sheath.

The Osteoglossidae, with large, bony scales, are an ancient and widely-distributed group, the few living species inhabiting the rivers of Queensland, New Guinea, Borneo, Sumatra, Africa, and South America. *Arapaima gigas* of the Amazon reaches a length of over fifteen feet. Allied to the Osteoglossids is the little *Pantodon* of West Africa, which has large pectoral fins and is said to take short flights. Other freshwater Isospondyli are the

SMELT (*Osmerus eperlanus*).

[*Dr. F. Ward.*

Notopteridae of Africa and India, the Hiodontidae, or Moon-eyes, silvery shad-like fishes of North America, and the Mormyridae.

The Mormyridae, with about one hundred and twenty species from the lakes and rivers of Africa, are distinguished by a small mouth with few teeth, small eyes, and restricted gill-openings; some have the mouth at the end of a long, curved snout, which somewhat resembles an elephant's trunk. On each side of the skull is a large hole, covered on the outside by a thin, bony plate, and containing a vesicle detached from the air-

PIKE (*Esox lucius*).
The most voracious of the British freshwater fishes; it reaches a weight of over 40 lbs.

bladder; by means of this apparatus vibrations are transmitted to the internal ear. Mormyrs feed on small prey, weeds, or mud; they are nocturnal in their habits, and have the senses of smell and hearing well developed.

Order 4. HAPLOMI (Pikes, Mud-minnows)

This order contains a few northern freshwater fishes. It scarcely differs from the Isospondyli, the most important diagnostic character being the presence of a pair of large dermal bones on top of the snout, in place of the median ethmoid of other fishes.

The Umbridae, or Mud-minnows, are little carnivorous fishes of ponds,

217

ditches and swamps; they often burrow in the mud. One species of *Umbra* is known from Austria, the other from North America; in this genus the mouth is of moderate size, with bands of small teeth, the snout is short, and the dorsal fin is somewhat in advance of the anal.

The Dalliidae include the Black-fish (*Dallia pectoralis*) of Alaska and Siberia, a fish very similar to the Mud-minnows, but with the dorsal fin above the anal. It grows to about eight inches, twice as long as a Mud-minnow; it is very abundant in bogs and ponds, and is greatly valued as food by the natives. It will remain alive for weeks when frozen.

The Esocidae or Pikes (*Esox*) are larger fishes, with the snout long and flat, the mouth large, with bands of small, pointed, movable teeth, and a series of strong, fixed, erect teeth on each side of the lower jaw; the dorsal fin is above the anal. The Pikes are fierce and greedy; they feed mainly on other fishes, and often lie concealed among the weeds, and then dash out to catch their prey. The British species (*Esox lucius*) ranges through Europe and Siberia to North America. Specimens four feet long weigh forty pounds; but these are rare, although records of much larger fish seem well authenticated. In the spring the pike retire to ditches and quiet backwaters to spawn among the weeds; almost from the first the little fish are solitary.

There is another species in the Amur, and in North America three small species known as Pickerel, and a very large one, the Muskallunge of the Great Lakes, which reaches a length of eight feet and a weight of over one hundred pounds. It has been described as " A long, slim, strong, and swift fish, in every way fitted to the life it leads, that of a dauntless marauder."

Order 5. INIOMI (Lantern-fishes, etc.)

This is a group of carnivorous marine fishes, allied to the Isospondyli, but with the praemaxillaries forming the upper border of the mouth. An adipose fin is generally present. The Aulopidae (*Aulopus*), with two species respectively from the Mediterranean and the coasts of Australia, have bands of conical teeth in the jaws, and widely-separated pelvic fins placed not far behind the pectorals. The Australian species grows to over two feet, and is valued as food.

The Synodontidae include the voracious Lizard-fishes (*Synodus*, etc.) of the coasts of tropical seas, with a large mouth, and bands of curved, pointed, depressible teeth. The Indian *Harpodon*, with strong, barbed teeth, when dried and salted is known as "Bombay Duck."

The Sudidae are oceanic fishes, some of which live at the surface, others at considerable depths. *Bathypterois* includes deep-water fishes with

218

small eyes, broad, flat snout, and the uppermost rays of the pectoral fin isolated and produced as long, bifid feelers. *Ipnops* is similar in form;

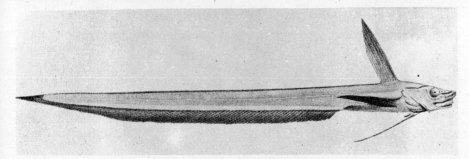

Ateleopus japonicus.

Nannobrachium nigrum.

Omosudis lowii.

[*Illusts. Voyage of H.M.S. " Challenger " ; Permission, Controller, H.M. Stationery Office.*
Bathysaurus ferox.
Fishes of the order Iniomi ; which includes a great diversity of forms.

it has no eyes, but possesses a large luminous organ that covers the flat upper surface of the head, and may serve as a lure.

The Myctophidae, or Lantern-fishes, swim in the ocean, from the surface

Bathypterois longifilis.

down to about three hundred fathoms. They are little, silvery fishes, with large eyes, and with rows or groups of pearl-like phosphorescent organs on the lower part of the body.

The remaining families of Iniomi are oceanic fishes with a large mouth, with strong canine teeth above and below, and with the pectoral fins placed low and the pelvics far back. The Scopelarchidae have slender barbed canines, the Omosudidae a pointed snout and compressed teeth ; these are small fishes of normal form. The Alepidosauridae are elongate naked fishes, with a long sharp snout, compressed and pointed teeth, and a very long and high dorsal fin. These are predacious fishes that may descend to considerable depths ; they grow to a length of about four feet. According to Dr. Günther, " From the stomach of one example have been taken several octopods, crustaceans, ascidians, a *Brama*, twelve young Boar-fishes (*Capros*), a horse-mackerel, and one young of its own species."

The Ateleopidae are elongate, naked fishes, with a small subterminal mouth protractile downwards, a short dorsal fin behind the head, a long anal fin joined to the caudal, and pelvic fins in advance of the pectorals, wide apart, each reduced to a single long, simple or bifid ray. Half-a-dozen species are known from the Indo-Pacific, living at the bottom in the deeper off-shore waters. In these fishes the skeleton is in great part cartilaginous, but they show many resemblances to the Aulopidae.

[*Illusts. Voyage of H.M.S. " Challenger " ; Permission, Controller, H.M. Stationery Office.*
Chlorophthalmus gracilis.

The Giganturidae (*Gigantura*) are highly-specialized fishes, perhaps related to the Iniomi. Four species are known from the Atlantic and Indian Oceans, naked, silvery fishes with short snout, large, cylindrical eyes placed close together and directed forwards, wide mouth extending back behind the head, bordered above by the praemaxillaries, and with sharp, slender, depressible teeth in the jaws. There are no pelvic fins ; the pectoral fins, many-rayed and with long bases, are placed high up, above the small gill-openings ; the lower lobe of the caudal is produced into a long filament. The small gills, and the pectoral arch, are far behind the skull.

These are voracious fishes that live at moderate depths below the surface. One captured in the Atlantic was distended with another fish, a *Chauliodus*, nearly twice its own length. As *Chauliodus* is itself piscivorous, and has strong, sharp teeth of great length, the capture of one by a *Gigantura* is extraordinary. The *Gigantura*, perhaps peering into the dim light one hundred fathoms down, had quietly stalked its formidable prey,

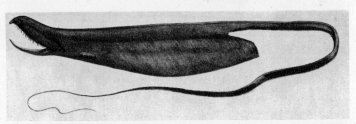

had seized it in the middle, the only safe place, had swallowed it doubled, and had then turned in the ends so that the victim was folded in four in its stomach.

[*Voyage of H.M.S. " Challenger " ; Permission, Controller, H.M. Stationery Office.*
GULPER-EEL (*Saccopharynx ampullaceus*).
This deep-sea fish, taken by the " Challenger," has its stomach distended by a fish that it has swallowed.

Order 6. LYOMERI (Gulper-eels)

This order includes some naked fishes with long dorsal and anal fins and a long, slender tail, a very large mouth bordered above by a single slender pair of bones, no pelvic fins, and small pectorals just behind the small gill-openings, which are far behind the head.

These are blackish fishes that live in the ocean at considerable depths. *Saccopharynx* grows to a length of six feet ; it has curved, pointed teeth, and feeds on other fishes : it has a very distensible stomach. *Eurypharynx*, with enormous mouth and minute teeth, probably takes in small prey in gulps.

Order 7. OSTARIOPHYSI (Carps, Cat-fishes, etc.)

The Ostariophysi are distinguished by having a chain of bones, elements of the first four vertebrae, forming a mechanism that transmits vibration from the air-bladder to the internal ear, and increases the sense of hearing.

Except the Percomorphi this is the largest order of fishes, including some five thousand species, nearly all restricted to fresh water: The more generalized forms approach in their structure primitive Isospondyli, such as the Elopidae, but many are widely divergent from these. The main groups are as follows :

Suborder **Cyprinoidea**
    Division *Characiformes* (Characins)
       ,,   *Gymnotiformes* (Electric Eel, etc.)
       ,,   *Cypriniformes* (Carps, Loaches, etc.)
Suborder **Siluroidea** (Cat-fishes).

Suborder Cyprinoidea

The Cyprinoids generally have the body covered with scales.

Copeina guttata.
A small Characin from South America.

[W. S. Pitt.

Characiformes. The Characins,, which are freshwater fishes of Africa and tropical America, have teeth in the jaws, and toothed upper and lower pharyngeals opposed to each other. They vary in form from deep, nearly circular, to slender ; they have the fins normally developed, and generally an adipose fin like that of the Salmonidae.

The Characinidae, the only family common to Africa and South America, includes several hundred American species, and about fifty from Africa. Many of these are silvery fishes, often with a black spot on the tail, with powerful jaws, and stout teeth with several-pointed cusps. *Brycon* and *Astyanax* of tropical America, and *Alestes* of Africa, include fishes of this kind. The Tiger-fishes (*Hydrocyon*) are large African fishes, with dark longitudinal stripes on the sides, and with large sharp-edged triangular teeth ; they are very voracious.

Of the South American Characinidae we may mention especially the Dorado, a large orange-coloured fish of the La Plata, the genus *Cynodon*, with a large mouth and a pair of pointed teeth in the front of the lower jaw, so long that they pierce the roof of the mouth when it is closed, and the Pirayas (*Serrasalmo*), deep, plump fishes with a serrated abdomen, a blunt snout, short but very massive jaws, and strong, sharp-edged teeth. The Pirayas grow to a length of a foot or more ; they hunt in packs, and will attack larger fishes, and any animal swimming in the water, quickly biting them to pieces, and leaving only the skeletons : even men and horses have been victims of their ferocity.

In addition to the carnivorous Characinidae, there are other South American Characins, for example, the Anostomidae, including herbivorous fishes with incisor-like teeth, and mud-eaters with none, the Xiphostomatidae, slender fishes with prolonged jaws, piscivorous, and somewhat pike-like, and the Gastropelecidae.

[W. S. Pitt.

Myletes maculatus.
A South American Characin nearly related to the Pirayas.

The Gastropelecidae have the body deep and compressed, expanded below into a large, sharp-edged semicircular disc, that contains a fan-shaped bony plate to which are attached the enormous muscles of the long pectoral fins. These fishes skim along the surface, with their keel cutting the water, by rapid beats of the pectoral fins, and then leave the water in a true flight. They are unique in this respect, for other fishes that fly have small pectoral muscles, and plane with the fins spread out flat.

The *Citharinidae* of Africa are a varied family. The Moon-fishes (*Citharinus*) are large, deep-bodied fishes, with minute teeth ; they probably feed on mud. The species of *Distichodus* are rather similar in form, but have a small mouth, and compressed, notched teeth ; these fishes are

223

herbivorous. The lower jaw of *Distichodus* has a peculiar structure, the dentaries being firmly united in a long symphysis, and movably articulated with the angulars. Other genera with this arrangement have massive, beak-like jaws, with the dentaries united by a long, wavy suture ; in some of these (*Phago*, etc.) the teeth are small and bicuspid, in others (*Ichthyoborus*, etc.) they are pointed, with strong canines in front.

Gymnotiformes. These are found in tropical America, and have small gill-openings, no dorsal or pelvic fins, and a long, tapering tail, with the anal fin long, and the caudal small or absent. In most species the mouth

[*Paul Unger.*

BLEAK (*Alburnus lucidus*).
A little silvery fish, the scales of which are used in making artificial pearls.

is small and the teeth are notched and compressed ; in some the head is blunt, in others the snout is produced into a tube, with the mouth at the end. These fishes are herbivorous, but the Electric Eel (*Electrophorus electricus*) which has a rather wide mouth, and conical teeth, is carnivorous ; it grows to a length of eight feet, and the whole of the lower part of the long tail is occupied by the paired electric organs. The shocks are very powerful, and can be continued for some time ; by means of them fishes may be stunned or killed, and animals fording a stream may be knocked down.

Cypriniformes. These differ from the Characins in having the mouth toothless, and in the structure of the lower pharyngeals, which are sickle-shaped, and bear teeth t h a t bite against a projection from the skull. This division includes four families.

In the family Cyprinidae t h e pharyngeal teeth are few in number, arranged in one to three series ; the bony process to which they are opposed is covered

DACE (*Leuciscus leuciscus*).
A graceful silvery fish, common to British rivers.

by a horny pad. The protractile praemaxillaries form the upper border of the mouth. This very large family inhabits the fresh waters of Europe, Asia, Africa and North America ; it includes a number of British species, Roach, Rudd, Chub, Dace, Minnow, Bream, Bleak, Carp, Barbel, Gudgeon and Tench, mostly fishes that swim in shoals, feed on weeds, insects, worms, etc., and breed in shallows in the spring or early summer, the eggs often adhering to weeds or stones.

All the British Cyprinids are found in the rivers of Europe, north of the Pyrenees and Alps, and many range through Siberia.

The Roach (*Rutilus rutilus*) is a silvery-white fish, with the lower fins tinged with red, w i t h a s m a l l m o u t h , rather large scales, and a dorsal fin that begins above the pelvics, and has a concave edge. It swims in shoals in lakes, ponds, and rivers, and occurs in Europe, except the Mediterranean countries, and in Turkestan a n d Siberia. The Rudd (*Scardinius erythrophthalmus*), tinged with bronze

Photos] [*W. S. Berridge.*

RUDD OR RED-EYE (*Scardinius erythrophthalmus*).
A British freshwater fish allied to the Roach.

[Dr. F. Ward.

BREAM (*Abramis brama*).
A deep-bodied fish that frequents lakes and slow-running rivers.

and with reddish fins, is a somewhat deeper fish, with the dorsal fin further back. It has the same distribution as the Roach, as has the Dace (*Leuciscus leuciscus*), a graceful and lively fish of the rivers, but the Chub (*L. cephalus*) is absent from Siberia. The Chub, which reaches a length of two feet and a weight of eight pounds, is a river-fish distinguished by a broad head, a rather large mouth, and a rounded anal fin ; it is a voracious fish, that often eats Minnows and Gudgeon. The Minnow (*Phoxinus phoxinus*), a pretty little fish, three or four inches long, is allied to the Chub and Dace, but has small scales.

The Bleak and the Breams are distinguished by a keeled abdomen and a long anal fin. The Bleak (*Alburnus lucidus*) is a little silvery fish that sports at the surface. The Common Bream (*Abramis brama*) has a deep and compressed body, and is greenish or brownish, with black fins. It reaches a weight of over ten pounds. The shoals frequent sluggish waters, feeding at the bottom on weeds, mud, and small prey, and often basking at the surface on warm days. The White Bream is a smaller species. The Barbel (*Barbus barbus*) is distinguished by a rounded mouth on the under side of the snout, with thick lips, with two barbels on each side ; it grows to more than three feet and over twenty pounds. It roots about at the bottom, using the barbels as feelers in the search for food. It spawns on gravel, and covers over the eggs with it. The Gudgeon (*Gobio gobio*) is a small fish, with only one pair of barbels, at the corner of the mouth ; it is speckled with brown, and has a lateral row of black spots. The shoals frequent quiet sandy or gravelly shallows.

The Tench (*Tinca tinca*) is a plump, greenish fish, with small scales, a broad head, and a small barbel at each corner of the mouth ; it is a sluggish fish of still waters. The Carp (*Cyprinus carpio*) has two pairs of barbels, and is distinguished by a long dorsal fin and large scales ; on the Continent it is said to reach a weight of one hundred pounds. It is a native of China, but has been introduced into many countries. It lives in lakes, ponds, or slow streams, particularly muddy and weedy places ; it eats mud, weeds, and small prey.   The Crucian Carp (*Carassius carassius*), without barbels, is a native of Europe, and is closely allied to the eastern species known as the Goldfish (*C. auratus*), a greenish-brown fish, with many cultivated varieties that lack the brown pigment, and are gold or silver in colour.

The North American Cyprinidae belong to the same group as the Roach and Dace, and are termed minnows, dace, chub, etc., according to their appearance and size.   Some Californian species grow to four or five feet.

Barbus and allied genera have hundreds of species in Africa and southern Asia.   The Mahseer (*B. mosal*) of India reaches a weight of one hundred pounds, fish of this size having scales as large as the palm of the hand. The largest species, however, are some small-scaled Barbels of the Tigris, which grow to three hundred pounds. In the highlands of Central Asia are a number of species of a peculiar group of barbels (*Oreinus*, etc.), small scaled, and with a sheath at the base of the anal fin. In Africa some little blind barbels have recently been discovered in underground waters.

In the *Bitterling*, a little fish of Central Europe, the breeding female is provided with a long tube, by means of which she lays her eggs in the

[*Paul Unger.*

GOLDFISH (*Carassius auratus*).
One of the many cultivated varieties from Japan.

FISH (OSTARIOPHYSI)

[*Sport & General.*

BITTERLING (*Rhodeus amarus*).
In this European freshwater fish the breeding female has a long tube by means of which the eggs are laid in the gills of mussels.

gills of mussels; when the little fish are hatched, and leave their shelter, they carry in their skin the encysted embryos of the mussel, which after a time become free.

Tropical Asia is the headquarters of the Cyprinidae and here occur a number of curious types. *Gyrinochilus* of the hill streams of Borneo is specially noteworthy; this is a fish in which the lips form a funnel-shaped sucker, the pharyngeals are small and toothless, the intestine is of enormous length and coiled, the gill-opening is divided into an upper inhalent and lower exhalent part, and the upper edges of the gills bear series of gill-rakers inside the inhalent opening. These peculiarities are to enable the fish to hold on to stones, to breathe while doing so, and to get sufficient nourishment from a diet of mud.

The Catostomidae, or Suckers, of North America, have small prae-maxillaries, thick lips, the pharyngeal teeth in a single series and often numerous, and no horny pad in the roof of the pharynx. Some are carp-like fishes with a long dorsal fin, others resemble chub in form and structure of fins; these fishes, of which some seventy species are known, feed on small aquatic animals and mud, sucking their food into their mouths. In the spring they run up the small streams in large shoals to spawn.

The Cobitidae, or Loaches, are rather slender, small-scaled fishes with at least six barbels round the mouth, uniserial pharyngeal teeth, and no horny pad in the pharynx. The posterior part of the air-bladder is reduced, and the anterior part is enclosed in a bony capsule, transversely expanded, with an opening on each side from which a duct runs to the skin above the pectoral fin. This apparatus, placing the skin in communication with the internal ear, renders Loaches particularly sensitive to barometric changes; hence the German name "Wetterfisch."

The Loaches are particularly numerous in the mountain streams of central and southern Asia. There are three European species, one of which is the Stone Loach (*Nemachilus barbatulus*), a greyish fish, with darker

228

spots and marbling, that grows to four or five inches long. It has small eyes, a blunt snout projecting in front of the transverse mouth, two pairs of barbels in front of the mouth, and a pair at the corners. It lies under stones in small streams, but at night goes in search of small aquatic animals. The second British species is the Spined Loach (*Cobitis taenia*), a smaller fish with similar habits. It takes its name from the spine that lies on each side of the head in a groove below the eye, but can be everted and used as a weapon. *Misgurnus fossilis* is the largest of the European Loaches, reaching a length of ten inches ; it has twelve barbels round the mouth. It is not found west of Germany.

The Homalopteridae are Loach-like fishes of the hill-streams of tropical Asia. They have numerous barbels, the lower surface of the body is flat, and the paired fins are horizontal. The air-bladder is encapsuled as in the Loaches, but the capsule is divided into two cylinders, each with an opening directly under the skin. By their form and the arrangement of their fins, these fishes are suited to hold on in swift currents ; in some the paired fins are broad-based and many-rayed, margining the flat lower surface from the mouth to the beginning of the tail.

W. S. Pitt.

Rasbora heteromorpha.
A little Indian Cyprinid.

FISH (OSTARIOPHYSI)

Suborder Siluroidae (Cat-fishes)

The Siluroids are named Cat-fishes from the resemblance of their barbels to the whiskers of a cat. They are scaleless, but may be covered with bony plates; the front part of the air-bladder is often encapsuled, as in the Loaches, and generally extends to the skin above the pectoral fin. These are carnivorous fishes that live at the bottom, many of them in stagnant water or muddy rivers; the eyes are often small, but these fishes find food by means of their barbels, which are generally six or eight in number, and may be very long.

The Cat-fishes are a very large group, including seventeen families. The most primitive Cat-fish is *Diplomystes* of Chile, which has a toothed maxillary, and only one pair of barbels. In the rest of the group the maxillary is toothless and is very small, serving only as the base of a barbel.

The Pimelodidae of tropical America are naked fishes, moderately elongate in form, with bands of small, pointed teeth, fixed praemaxillaries, and six barbels, a maxillary pair and two pairs under the chin. They have a short dorsal fin near the head, with the first ray spinous and often strong and serrated, an adipose fin, an anal of moderate length, and the outermost pectoral rays spiny. Some Pimelodidae grow to a large size, the species of *Platystoma*, for example, reaching six feet.

Other families peculiar to the fresh waters of tropical America are the Doradidae, Trichomycteridae, Bunocephalidae, Callichthyidae and Loricariidae. The Doradidae have a general resemblance to the Pimelodidae, but are distinguished by the restricted gill-openings, and by their power of making noises by means of an elastic spring mechanism; from each side of the back-bone projects a slender blade, ending in an expanded plate that is fixed in the wall of the air-bladder, and is made to vibrate by means of a special muscle. *Doras* and allied genera have a series of bony plates along the side of the body. These fishes construct nests of leaves, and guard them; they make long overland journeys when the ponds dry up.

The Trichomycteridae are slender Loach-like fishes with small eyes, without dorsal spine or adipose fin; many have the gill-covers armed with bundles of spines. Some very small ones (*Stegophilus*, *Vandellia*) live in the gill-chambers of other fishes. The Bunocephalidae, with a broad, flat head and very small gill-openings, include *Aspredo*, which is remarkable for the manner in which the female carries her young. When the eggs are laid, she lies on them so that they sink into the skin, at this time soft and spongy, of the lower parts of the body; thus the lower surface of the head and belly becomes covered with eggs; later a number of stalked cups develop, each carrying an egg; these egg-cups are rich in blood-vessels, and may supply nutriment to the developing eggs until they hatch. The Callichthyidae are armoured, a double series of bony shields covering each

230

side of the body. The Loricariidae, a family of some three hundred species, includes Cat-fishes enclosed in an armour of five series of bony plates ; they have a small mouth on the underside of the head, surrounded by the broad lips, which unite to form a sucker, used for holding on to stones ; the membraneous adipose fin is supported by a movable spine. These fishes feed on mud or minute prey, and have a very long intestine, coiled like a watch-spring. Their gill-openings are modified, inhalent above and exhalent below, so that they can breathe when holding on to stones. There are remarkable differences between the sexes, the males of some species having long, bristly " whiskers " at the sides of the head, of others, fleshy tentacles on the snout.

In the mountain streams of the Andes are a number of little Loricariids ; these are naked, as a protective armour is not needed where there are no other fishes ; but some still retain the spine of the adipose fin. The presence of these little fishes, known as Prenadillas, in mountain torrents at great heights is explained by the fact that they can crawl up vertical walls of rock, holding on alternately by the oral sucker and the rough pelvic fins ; they keep the body straight when climbing, the pelvic fins being drawn backwards when holding, and forwards when free, by special muscles attached to the pelvis.

The Bagridae, generally distinguished from the Pimelodidae by the presence of a nasal barbel, represent this family in Africa and in southern and eastern Asia. The Mochochidae of Africa, although unrelated to the Doradidae, are rather like them, and even have a somewhat similar apparatus for the production of sounds—*Synodontis* is the principal genus. Some of the species, particularly the *Batensoda* of the Nile, have the habit of floating at the surface upside down, and are coloured black below and pale above, a reversal of the usual arrangement.

A curious African fish, the type of a separate family, is the Electric Cat-fish (*Malopterurus electricus*), a naked fish without dorsal fin, and with an electric organ that has the form of a layer of jelly underneath the skin of the whole body. This is a sluggish fish that gives powerful shocks ; it grows to a length of three feet.

The Clariidae of Africa and India are large fishes, more or less eel-shaped, with eight barbels, a flat head covered by a bony shield, and a long anal fin. *Saccobranchus*, with a short dorsal fin, is an Indian genus, distinguished by a pair of long air-breathing sacs, that extend backwards from the gill-chambers into the tail. *Clarias* and its allies, with a long dorsal fin, have on each side above the gills a chamber containing a fleshy, tree-like air-breathing organ. These fishes live in swamps and stagnant pools, coming to the surface to breathe air ; in the dry season they may take to burrows, emerging at night to look for food, or may crawl overland to find water.

Of the Indian Cat-fishes *Chaca* has a large, flat head and a wide

CAT-FISH (*Arius fuerthii*).
The Ariidae are marine Cat-fishes, with six barbels ; they carry their eggs, which may be as large as marbles, in their mouths.

terminal mouth like the Angler (*Lophius*). The Sisoridae are interesting, having a flat under surface, and horizontal paired fins, adaptations to life in mountain streams. Some Sisoridae (e.g. *Pseudecheneis*) have the chest plaited, others have the lips expanded to form a sucker (*Exostoma*, etc.).

The Siluridae, elongate fishes with a small dorsal, no adipose, and a long anal fin, are mostly Asiatic. This family includes the Wels (*Silurus glanis*) of eastern Europe, a large and voracious fish that grows to a length of ten feet. *Parasilurus aristotelis* of Greece has the historic interest that it is the fish of which Aristotle recorded that the male guarded the eggs. These two species are the only European Cat-fishes.

The Amiuridae, or Cat-fishes of North America, resemble the Bagridae of Asia and Africa in external characters, and can be distinguished only by slight peculiarities of the skeleton. They are naked fishes, with bands of small teeth in the jaws, and four pairs of barbels. The spines of the dorsal and pectoral fins are often serrated, and in some species there is a poison-gland at the base of the pectoral spine. The Channel Cats (*Ictalurus*) are slender, silvery fishes with a forked caudal fin ; these are large and active fishes of the rivers. The other Amiurids, stouter in form, with broad head, transverse mouth, and rounded or truncate caudal fin, are sluggish fishes that frequent quieter waters ; the largest is the Cat-fish of the Great Lakes (*Amiurus lacustris*), which grows to over one hundred and fifty pounds ; many small kinds, some only three or four inches long, occur in ponds and brooks.

All the Ostariophysi so far described are true freshwater fishes, of which each continent has its characteristic forms. There are, however, two families of Cat-fishes that differ from the rest of the order in being marine, one, the Ariidae, containing many kinds of fishes that are found on the coasts and in the estuaries of all tropical countries, the other, Plotosidae restricted to the tropical Indo-Pacific. These two families are not closely related, and there can be no doubt that their marine habit is secondary ; but it has enabled both to reach and to enter the rivers of New

Guinea and tropical Australia, and to give rise in them to a number of freshwater genera and species.

The Ariidae are similar to the Pimelodidae and Bagridae in form, and in the structure of the fins. They produce large eggs, sometimes as large as marbles, which they may carry in their mouths. The Plotosidae are eel-like, with a very long anal fin, and with strong conical or blunt teeth ; in some genera the caudal fin extends forward along the back, simulating a second dorsal.

Finally, it may be mentioned that various blind Cat-fishes from underground waters are known, some of them hardly differing from those of the neighbouring rivers, except for the absence of eyes, others more distinct, but nevertheless related to genera of the same regions. The blind Cat-fishes of North America are Amiuridae ; of South America, Pimelodidae ; and of Africa, Clariidae.

Order 8. APODES (Eels)

The Eels are soft-rayed fishes with an open duct to the air-bladder, with an elongate body, long dorsal and anal fins, continued to the small caudal, small pectoral fins, and no pelvics. The mouth is bordered at the sides by the toothed maxillaries, and in front by a single tooth-bearing bone that is fused with the skull. The long gill-chambers extend back far behind the skull and push back the pectoral arch ; the gill-openings are small.

Most eels are marine and carnivorous. They swim by undulating movements of the body, and of the long dorsal and anal fins. Some are oceanic, but the majority live near the coasts and burrow in the mud, or hide in crevices of rocks.

A peculiarity of eels is that the larvae, which are transparent and com-pressed, may swim near the surface of the sea until they reach a length of two or three inches, or in some species much more, and then undergo a re-duction in size and a change in struc-ture, being trans-formed into little eels. This large group of fishes includes about twenty families.

[Neville Kingston.
CAT-FISH (Clarias).
There are numerous species in Africa and India ; they live in stagnant water.

FISH (APODES)

The Anguillidae include the Common Eel (*Anguilla anguilla*) found on the coasts and in rivers from Iceland and Scandinavia to the Nile. It is distinguished by bands of small, pointed teeth, and by little oblong scales embedded in the slimy skin, arranged in a parquet pattern. Eels live in ditches, ponds, lakes and rivers, and in inlets or estuaries; in the day they often lie under stones, or buried in the mud, but at night they become active, and feed on any sort of animal food. Male eels grow to a length of twenty inches, but females may reach five feet, and a weight of fifteen pounds or more. While they are feeding and growing, eels are generally yellowish on the sides, and have small eyes and thick lips; in the autumn some of them cease feeding and become silvery; the lips get thinner, the snout sharper, and the eyes larger. These silver eels migrate to the sea and make their way across the Atlantic to an area south of Bermuda, where they breed, probably at about two hundred and fifty fathoms below the surface. The breeding eels have quite large eyes, like many other fishes that live at this depth; they have accomplished a journey of perhaps three thousand miles, and developed their sexual glands, without feeding; it cannot be wondered at that all die after spawning. The eggs float in the sea, and hatch into little larvae, leaf-shaped and transparent, with long, needle-like teeth; these swim near the surface of the ocean, feeding on plankton, and spread across the Atlantic, in about two and a half years arriving in European waters. During the journey they have grown in length from two-fifths of an inch to three inches, and at this size they lose their teeth, shrink in depth and in length, become pigmented, get a new set of small teeth, and so are transformed into the little cylindrical elvers, which make for the inshore waters in the spring, enter the Severn and other rivers in large swarms, and may travel up them for long distances to inland waters. In about a year the little eels grow from two and a half inches to about four inches, and in about four to eight years, or for the larger female eels in twelve years or more, they reach their full size, turn from yellow eels into silver eels, and commence the long journey to their breeding place on the other side of the Atlantic, which may take about a year to complete, and from which they do not return. The silver eels are very fat, and in the best condition for the table; the principal eel fisheries are by means of traps and nets that catch these eels on their way to the sea. There are important fisheries in Denmark, where the Baltic eels are intercepted, and on the Bann, which flows out of Lough Neagh. At Comacchio, in the north of the Adriatic, eels are farmed in a number of large brackish lagoons; the stock is kept up by the natural run of elvers.

The breeding place of the Common Eel was discovered, and its life history described by a Danish naturalist, Dr. Johannes Schmidt. In the Western Atlantic he caught numbers of larvae of the American Eel, a distinct species, in the same hauls as those of the European Eel. He

234

found that the American Eel bred in nearly the same place, but had a shorter larval history, the elvers being only one year old, instead of three, this difference being related to the distance to be travelled.

The breeding area of the eels is a place where the water, at a depth of two hundred and fifty fathoms below the surface, has a higher temperature and a higher salinity than in any other part of the Atlantic. Schmidt has explained the distribution of the species of *Anguilla* throughout the world, their absence from the South Atlantic and from the Pacific coast of America, their presence from South Africa to Japan, in the islands of the South

[*Raoul Barba.*

CONGERS (*Conger conger*) AND MORAY (*Muraena*).
The Conger lives on rocky ground in rather deep water. The Morays hide in crevices in reefs, and are feared for their savage bites.

Seas, and New Zealand, by the accessibility or otherwise of places in the ocean where the water at this depth has a similar salinity and temperature.

The Conger (*Conger conger*) is a naked fish, with larger eyes and deeper gill-openings than the Common Eel, and with sharp-edged teeth in the jaws. It frequents rocky ground in rather deep water ; the females have been known to reach a length of nine feet and a weight of one hundred and sixty pounds, but the males do not exceed two feet. The Conger spawns out in the Atlantic and the larvae travel towards the coasts ; they are compressed, but are more slender than the eel larvae, and grow to five inches before they shrink, and change into eel-shaped congers about three inches long.

The large family Congridae includes numerous genera from tropical and temperate seas. An allied family, the Ophichthyidae, or Snake-eels, differs in having the nostrils in the upper lip, and the pointed naked end of the tail projecting beyond the dorsal and anal fin. The Snake-eels abound

235

[Voyage of H.M.S. " Challenger " ; Permission, Controller, H.M. Stationery Office.
Halosaurus macrochir.
The Halosauridae are oceanic fishes that live at considerable depths.

in tropical seas, many frequenting the coral reefs ; they are generally brightly coloured, banded or with large spots.

Another large tropical family is that of the Muraenidae or Morays, robust eels with strong jaws that are often armed with knife-like teeth ; in addition the pharyngeal bones are long and parallel, and each bears a double series of strong teeth ; these paired bones, above and below, are supported by the much-enlarged bones of the fourth gill-arch, so that these eels are provided with powerful jaws in the throat. The large Morays, that hide in the crevices of reefs and strike at their prey, are feared for their savage bites. A Mediterranean species (*Muraena helena*), brown mottled with yellow, is a rare visitor to the Channel.

Of the other families of Eels we may mention the Thread-eels, very long and slender eels that swim in the upper layers of the ocean, silvery, large-eyed, with the jaws produced into long needles that curve away from each other at the ends, and with small teeth set in quincunx.

Order 9. HETEROMI

The fishes of this order have a closed air-bladder, but in other respects are allied to primitive Isospondyli. They are oceanic fishes that live at considerable depths. They have a long, tapering tail, with a long anal fin below it, and no caudal fin.

In the Halosauridae the dorsal fin is short, there are no spinous fin-rays, and the maxillaries form part of the upper border of the mouth. In the Lipogenyidae the front rays of the dorsal and anal fins, and the outer of the pelvics, are spines ; the mouth is small and rounded, thick-lipped, and toothless. The Notacanthidae differ from the last family in having a series of isolated spines along the back, and a normal mouth, toothed, bordered above by the praemaxillaries.

Order 10. SYNENTOGNATHI (Gar-fish, Flying-fishes, etc.)

This order contains soft-rayed fishes with abdominal pelvic fins, with closed air-bladder, non-protractile mouth, and the lower pharyngeals united to form a single bone. The dorsal fin is far back, above the anal, the pectoral fins are placed high, and the lateral line runs near the lower edge of the body.

There are four families: Belonidae (Gar-fish or Needle-fish), Scombresocidae (Saury Pike or Skipper), Hemirhamphidae (Half-beaks), and Exocoetidae (Flying-fish).

The Belonidae, Gar-fishes or Needle-fishes, are slender, small-scaled fishes, with the jaws produced, long and pointed, and armed with sharp, erect teeth. They are voracious fishes, some of which grow to a length of six feet; they are found near the coasts in all warm seas, generally swimming near the surface. In the Malay Archipelago are some small freshwater species.

The Gar-fish (*Belone*) that appears on the coasts of England in the spring, is a silvery fish, blue-green above, that grows to about three feet long; it feeds on other fishes, catching them so that they are at first held cross-ways by the piercing teeth. The eggs are provided with filaments, by which they adhere together, or to weeds or stones; the young fish have at first short jaws; then the lower grows forward, and afterwards the upper jaw.

The Scombresocidae include the Saury Pike or Skipper (*Scombresox saurus*), an oceanic fish, with slender pointed jaws, minute teeth, and finlets behind the dorsal and anal fins, as in the Mackerel. Shoals of this fish visit British seas in the summer.

[*W. S. Pitt.*

BLACK-BANDED SUN-FISH (*Mesogonistius chaetodon*).
A handsome little fish found in sluggish streams from New Jersey to Maryland, U.S.A. (See also page 254.)

The Hemirhamphidae or Half-beaks have rather large scales, and a small mouth, with little, compressed, tricuspid teeth. The upper jaw is flat and triangular; the lower is produced in front of the mouth into a slender, pointed bill. The upper pharyngeals form a very large, rounded plate, slightly convex, fitting the concavity of the broad lower pharyngeal. These fishes live near the coasts in tropical seas; the shoals swim at the surface, and feed mainly on green weeds.

The Exocoetidae or Flying-fishes also have large scales, and pharyngeal plates like those of the Half-beaks. They have a small mouth, and minute teeth; the pectoral fins are very large, and the lower lobe of the forked caudal fin is long and strong. There are numerous kinds of flying-fishes in the warmer parts of the oceans, some of which grow to a length of eighteen inches. They leave the water with a rush, aided by the powerful caudal fin, and spreading out their wings, plane at a high speed for long distances, the larger ones up to a quarter of a mile. At the end of their flight some kinds, with small pelvic fins, fall into the water with a splash, others, with large pelvic fins, use these to check their progress, and glide smoothly into the water. By their powers of flight these fishes are able to escape, or at least to make the attempt, the attacks of swift predacious fishes such as the Albacores, and others of the mackerel tribe.

Order 11. MICROCYPRINI (Cyprinodonts)

This order, like the preceding, includes soft-rayed fishes with abdominal pelvic fins, and with a closed air-bladder; but the lower pharyngeals are separate, and there is no lateral line on the body. There are two families, the Amblyopsidae, including the blind cave-fishes of North America, and the Poeciliidae, or Cyprinodonts.

The Amblyopsidae of North America have a rather wide mouth, bordered above by the non-protractile praemaxillaries. The little fishes of the genus *Chologaster*, with small eyes, and with black stripes on the body, live in swamps in the southern States. The other Amblyopsids are blind fishes, with vestigial eyes concealed under the skin, with rows of sensory papillae on the head, and with unpigmented, white skin. They live in the subterranean waters of limestone regions, sometimes swimming at the surface; at others, hiding at the bottom. They feed on the little crustaceans that also inhabit the caves. Blind-fishes grow to about six inches long.

The Poeciliidae or Cyprinodonts, a group of several hundred species, have a small, somewhat protractile mouth. They are small fishes, some of which swim in shoals along the coast, or frequent brackish lagoons and estuaries; the majority, however, are restricted to fresh water. They are pretty little fishes, and are great favourites in aquaria. They pair for breeding, and may show remarkable sexual differences, the males having larger fins, and being handsomely ornamented with patterns of bright

[Paul Unger.

ROUND SUN-FISH (*Centrarchus macropterus*).
A pretty little fish from the fresh waters of the United States. (See also page 254.)

colours; often the males display before the females after the manner of birds.

Some Cyprinodonts, with tricuspid teeth, and with a rather long dorsal fin, have the appearance of diminutive carp; these are mainly found in brackish water, in the countries round the Mediterranean (*Lebias*), and in North America (*Cyprinodon*).

The oviparous Cyprinodonts with conical teeth are widely distributed in America, Africa, and southern Asia; they are carnivorous, feeding on worms, insects, etc. The Killifishes (*Fundulus*) include about fifty species from the United States and Central America, several of which grow to about six inches. Some swim in shoals in bays along the coast, such as the May-Fish (*F. majalis*); others may bury themselves in the sand of lagoons or estuaries, like the Mud-fish (*F. heteroclitus*), and others, known as Top-minnows, swim at the surface of rivers and feed on insects. Of the South American genera of this group, *Cynolebias* is noteworthy, the males having the dorsal and anal fins

[W. S. Pitt.
An oviparous Cyprinodont from West Africa.

not only much larger, but formed of many more rays than in the females. In Lake Titicaca, and other elevated lakes of the Andes, occur the species of *Orestias*, distinguished by the absence of pelvic fins.

The remaining groups of Cyprinodonts are viviparous. The Characodontinae, with a score of species from the Valley of Mexico and the adjacent region, include some carnivorous species with strong jaws and conical teeth, and others that are herbivorous, with feeble jaws and small bicuspid teeth; in this group the males have the first five or six anal rays short and stiff, separated by a notch from the rest of the fin.

The species of *Anableps*, Four-eyed Fish, are the largest Cyprinodonts, reaching a length of a foot. These fishes swim at the surface of streams in tropical America, and have the eyes divided by a black horizontal bar into two parts; the upper, projecting above the flat upper surface of the head, is used for vision in the air; the lower is in the water. These fishes swim or lie with head up-stream, and feed on floating food ; when a l a r m e d, they scatter, skipping over the surface in a series of leaps. In the male *Anableps* the anal fin is a conical intromittent organ, covered with scales.

The Poeciliidae of tropical America have the anal fin of

Mollienisia latipinna.
In this Poeciliine the dorsal fin of the male is much longer and more ornamental than that of the female.

the male further forward than in the female, with three of its rays prolonged to form a groove or tube that transmits the sperm. This group includes the Millions-fish (*Lebistes reticulatus*) of the Antilles, which swarms in any piece of water, and is very prolific ; it produces a brood every few weeks, and a few weeks after they are born, the young become mature, and breed. The females, about an inch long, are pale brown, with a dark network outlining the scales ; the males, about half as long, but often more numerous than the females, are ornamented with spots of black, red and blue. These fishes eat mosquito larvae, and their presence in Barbados is said to account for the a b s e n c e o f malaria.

The Sword-tails (*Xiphophorus*) are found in Mexico and C e n t r a l America ; in the male the lower part of the caudal fin is produced into a l o n g p o i n t e d "sword," yellow, with black edges. *Belonesox*, w i t h

Photos]   [*W. S. Pitt.*
MILLIONS (*Lebistes reticulatus*).
A viviparous Cyprinodont from the Antilles. The female reaches a length of only an inch, but is much larger than the male.

pike-like head, and bands of slender, pointed teeth in the jaws, is also Central American.

The Phallostethidae, of which six species are known in fresh and brackish water from Singapore to the Philippines, are not more than an inch long. They have no pelvic fins, and the male has a large, fleshy organ below the head and chest, bearing one or more movable bony appendages, either curved and pointed, or straight and with serrated edges. Nothing has been recorded of the habits of these fishes, but it is probable that these appendages are used to hold the female.

Order 12. SALMOPERCAE (Trout-perches)

The Percopsidae, or Trout-perches of North America, are Gudgeon-like in appearance ; they have a closed air-bladder, a small, feebly-toothed mouth bordered above by the praemaxillaries, dorsal and anal fins with one or two spinous rays, an adipose fin, and seven or eight-rayed pelvic fins nearer to the pectorals than to the anal. There are two species, the Sand-roller of the Great Lakes (*Percopsis guttatus*) and the Oregon Trout-perch (*Columbia transmontana*).

The Aphredoderidae, with two to four spines, and without an adipose fin, include only the Pirate-perch (*Aphredoderus sayanus*) found in slow muddy streams of the eastern United States.

All these fishes are small, not exceeding six inches in length ; they feed on insects, worms, and other small prey.

Order 13. ANACANTHINI (Cod, etc.)

This is an important group of marine fishes, distinguished by having soft-rayed fins, with the pelvics, which are often many-rayed, below or in advance of the pectorals, but the pelvic bones not directly attached to the pectoral arch. The protractile praemaxillaries form the upper border of the mouth. There are three families, Merlucciidae, Gadidae, and Macruridae.

The Merlucciidae and Gadidae have a caudal fin, the structure of which can be understood by supposing that the original Anacanthines were fishes in which the long dorsal and anal fins were united with a very small caudal at the end of a long tapering tail ; then the tail became shorter, the fins were sub-divided, and a new caudal was formed, consisting mainly of dorsal and anal rays, with only a few rays in the middle attached to the hypural bones, and representing the true caudal fin.

. **Merlucciidae.** The Hake (*Merluccius vulgaris*), is a long silver-grey fish, with a short first dorsal fin, and a long second dorsal and anal. The Hake has a large mouth, and strong, sharp teeth ; it feeds on other fishes. It ranges from Norway to the Mediterranean, generally in deep water ; like other members of the order it produces minute eggs in enormous numbers, which float, and hatch into little

[*Paul Unger.*

SWORD-TAIL (*Xiphophorus helleri*).
A viviparous Cyprinodont from Mexico; the male bears the "sword."

243

Reproduced by permission from]   [Day's British Fishes.
WHITING (Gadus merlangus).
A valuable British food fish.

surface - swimming larvae. The Hake reaches a weight of over t w e n t y pounds; it is c a p t u r e d by trawlers in great n u m b e r s to the south of I r e l a n d. Other species of *Merluccius* occur on the other side of the North Atlantic, in the North Pacific, and in similar latitudes in southern seas.

Gadidae. These include many valuable food fishes of northern seas, but those from deep water in other parts of the world are of little importance. The Cod (*Gadus morrhua*) has three dorsal and two anal fins; the snout is blunt and the lower jaw is shorter than the upper, with a barbel below the chin; the teeth are conical. The colour is greenish or brownish, with darker spots and a white lateral line. The Cod attains a weight of one hundred pounds; it lives at the bottom of the sea, from the inshore waters to depths of over one hundred fathoms; it feeds on shell-fish of various kinds, small fishes, etc. The principal fisheries are in the North Sea, off Norway, round Iceland, and on the Newfoundland Banks. The Haddock (*Gadus aeglefinus*) is a smaller fish than the Cod, and is easily distinguished from it by the blackish lateral line; it is particularly abundant in the North Sea. Other British species with three dorsal and two anal fins are the Whiting (*G. merlangus*), the Coal-fish, and the Pollack (*G. pollachius*).

Of the species with two dorsal fins and one anal, the most important is the Ling (*Molva*), a long fish with large, pointed teeth. The Ling lives in deep water, and is piscivorous; it grows to over seven feet. Related to the Ling is the Burbot (*Lota*), the only freshwater fish of the order; it ranges from the eastern rivers of England through E u r o p e a n d Siberia to North A m e r i c a. T h e Rocklings (*O n o s*) have barbels on the snout as well as on the chin; they are

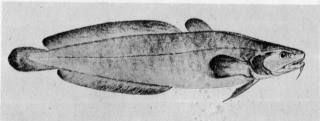

Reproduced by permission from]   [Day's British Fishes.
BURBOT (Lota vulgaris).
This is the only freshwater fish of the Cod family.

244

more southerly in their distribution than other British Gadidae, reaching the Mediterranean.

The Torsk (*Brosmius brosme*) is a rather large northern deep-water fish that differs from other species of the Cod family in having a single long dorsal fin.

Macruridae. These have a long, tapering tail, without caudal fin. They are rough-scaled, large-eyed fishes that live near the bottom in deep water, mostly in from two hundred to one thousand fathoms. In some species the mouth is terminal, but in many the snout is produced, and the mouth is on the under-side of the head, and can be protruded downwards; a barbel is generally present on the chin. There are about two hundred species; none is of any great size; they occur in all the oceans.

Chalinura Whitsoni.
An example of the Macruridae, deep-sea relatives of the Cod family, with large eyes and long, tapering tail.

Order 14. ALLOTRIOGNATHI (Opah, Oar-fish, etc.)

The fishes of this order are distinguished by the structure of the mouth, the maxillaries being protractile, carrying the praemaxillaries forward when the mouth is opened by a downward movement of the lower jaw. Except for the first one or two rays of the dorsal fin, there are no spinous fin-rays; the dorsal fin is long, the pectorals have a horizontal base, and the pelvics, often many-rayed, are placed below the pectorals. This is an isolated group, but is perhaps more nearly related to the Berycomorphi than to any other fishes.

The Opah or Moon-fish (*Lampris luna*) is a large, plump fish, nearly circular in form; it has long dorsal and anal fins, and pelvics of fifteen to seventeen rays; the mouth is small and toothless. It is a beautiful fish, bluish above, rose-red below, with silvery spots on the body, and scarlet fins. It swims near the surface in warm seas, and feeds on small prey.

The two species of *Velifer*, from the seas of Japan and Australia, are relatively small fishes, less deep and more compressed than the Opah, and with very high, sail-like dorsal and anal fins.

The Trachypteridae, or Ribbon-fishes, are elongate and strongly compressed, with a dorsal fin along the back, but the anal fin small or absent. These are silvery, large-eyed fishes, with a small mouth, toothless or feebly toothed. They live in the upper layers of the oceans, probably down to two hundred fathoms below the surface. *Trachypterus*, with pelvic fins of several rays, includes a number of species, one of which is the Deal-fish (*T. arcticus*), found in the seas from Iceland to Norway and Scotland; it reaches a length of eight feet. *Regalecus*, with each pelvic fin of a single long ray expanded at the end, includes a few species known as Oar-fishes, from the oar-shaped pelvic fins. These fishes grow to over thirty feet in length; the head, narrowing to the small mouth, is somewhat horse-like; the fins are red, and the rays of the front part of the dorsal fin are long, and free towards the end; there can be little doubt that some sea-serpents described as " with a horse's head and a long red mane," are large Oar-fishes.

The Lophotidae are very similar to the Ribbon-fishes, but have a high crest on the head, bearing the front part of the dorsal fin, which commences with a strong spine.

Stylophorus, a small, slender, silvery fish of the Atlantic, has the lower lobe of the caudal fin produced into a filament which is twice as long as the fish. It is further distinguished by large eyes of cylindrical form, close together, parallel, and directed forwards. The small, toothless mouth is extremely protractile; the lower jaw is very long, extending back far behind the head, and can move from a horizontal to a nearly vertical position, pulling down the upper jaw, so that the mouth opening is at the end of a long funnel-shaped pouch, below the head. As this downward protrusion of the mouth would not avail to catch prey sighted by the forwardly-directed eyes, the fish throws its head right back as it thrusts its mouth out, losing sight of its prey in the act of catching it. In relation to these peculiar habits, the front part of the backbone is modified, the vertebrae having strong, interlocking processes, to stand the strain of the sudden jerking back of the head.

Order 15. SOLENICHTHYES (Tube-fishes)

All the members of this order have the mouth at the end of a long, tube-like snout, hence the names Flute-mouth, Snipe-fish, Trumpet-fish, and Pipe-fish given to various kinds. A spinous dorsal fin may be present, but there are no other spinous fin-rays, and the pelvic fins are abdominal.

The Aulostomidae (*Aulostoma*) are elongate fishes, with small scales, a series of isolated dorsal spines, and toothed jaws, with a barbel at the chin. The two species are tropical, one from the Indian Ocean, the other from the Caribbean Sea.

The Fistulariidae (*Fistularia*) are slender, naked fishes, with a very long snout, no spines, and the middle caudal rays produced into a long filament. There are half-a-dozen species, coastal fishes of tropical seas; some grow to a length of six feet.

[James's Press.

THE SNIPE-FISH (*Macrorhamphosus scolopax*).
An occasional visitor to British waters.

The Macrorhamphosidae, or Snipe-fishes, have the body rather deep, covered with rough scales and bony scutes; the mouth is toothless, and there is a spinous dorsal fin. A dozen species are known from tropical and temperate seas, one (*M. scolopax*) named Snipe-fish, or Trumpet-fish, from the long snout, or Bellows-fish from its shape, occasionally arrives in British waters. The Indo-Pacific Centriscidae are a related family, but the body is very strongly compressed, sharp-edged below, and is enclosed in thin, bony shields; the spinous dorsal is terminal, at the hind end of the fish, and the soft dorsal, caudal, and anal are close together on the lower side of the tail. These fishes sometimes swim with the body in a vertical position.

The remaining families are sometimes termed Lophobranchii, a name referring to the structure of the gills, which are in the form of short thick lobes, instead of the usual filaments. *Solenostomus*, an Indo-Pacific genus with a few species, is the type of a family distinguished by a toothless mouth, stellate ossifications on the body, a spinous dorsal of a few flexible spines, and large seven-rayed

OAR-FISH (*Regalecus*).
An oceanic fish, silvery with red fins, that may reach a length of forty feet. Sea-serpents, described as with a horse's head and a red mane, are examples of this fish.

[From Jordan, after Day.

247

pelvic fins. The pelvic fins of the female form a pouch in which she carries the eggs until they hatch.

The Syngnathidae (Pipe-fishes and Sea-horses) differ in having no spinous dorsal and no pelvic fins, and the body enclosed in a series of bony rings. The dorsal and pectoral fins are small, but are formed of many rays, and are capable of very rapid vibrating or undulating movements; the caudal is small or absent. The males carry the eggs in a groove or pouch on the underside of the body, in some on the abdomen, in others on the tail. This is a large family, containing a number of marine species, mostly living among seaweeds in warm seas: some inhabit

[Douglas P. Wilson.

PIPE-FISHES.
These curious fishes swim about slowly amongst the blades of eel-grass (*Zostera*).

fresh water. The fishes of this family are remarkable for their power of changing their colour to harmonize with that of the weeds; they are of two types, the long and slender Pipe-fishes and the Sea-horses.

There are several British Pipe-fishes to be found among seaweeds, and among the eel-grass (*Zostera*), the long blades of which they resemble in form, and in their green or brown colour; here they swim about slowly, often in an upright position, bending and curving their graceful bodies, and sucking in little crustaceans and other minute prey.

The Sea-horses (*Hippocampus*), of which many kinds are known from warm seas, have a horse-like head set at an angle to the curved neck, and a long, tapering tail that can be curled round weeds or other objects. These curious little fishes swim about slowly in an upright position, moving their heads up and down and curling and uncurling their tails, and progressing by means of their fins, a series of waves passing in rapid succession along the dorsal, and the pectorals vibrating. The males have a large pouch, open at the front end, under the fore part of the tail; into this the eggs are received, and here the young are hatched. The walls

[Paul Unger.

SEA-HORSES (*Hippocampus*).

These little fishes are in many ways unique; for example, in having a tail that can be curled and also in having a distinct neck and a head that moves.

249

of the pouch are of n a k e d skin, which, at first, is thick and soft, and is said to exude a milky secretion for the nourishment of the young ; eventually it becomes thin and flaccid, after which the brood escapes.

[*Voyage of H.M.S. " Challenger " ; Permission, Controller, H.M. Stationery Office.*
Polymyxia nobilis.
The species of Polymyxia are large-eyed deep-water Berycoids, with a pair of barbels below the chin.

The Sea-horses, like the Pipe-fishes, are coloured to resemble the weeds that they inhabit ; they have bony spines or knobs on top of the head, and often bear little skinny tags or filaments. In *Phyllopteryx* of the seas of Australia these tags are excessively developed, resembling the branched fronds of seaweeds.

Order 16. BERYCOMORPHI

This order includes fishes that are related on the one hand to the Herrings, and on the other to the Perches. The scales generally bear spinules, the anterior rays of the dorsal and anal fins are spiny, the pelvic fins are placed below or not far behind the pectorals, the pelvic bones may be directly attached to the pectoral arch, and the mouth is bordered above by the protractile praemaxillaries. But the pelvics are often many-rayed, the forked caudal fin generally has nineteen principal rays, as in the Herring and Salmon, and there are other primitive f e a t u r e s. Fossil Berycoids are abundant in Cretaceous strata ; t h e l i v i n g m e m b e r s o f the group are marine, carnivorous fishes, with bands of small, pointed teeth in

Reproduced by permission from]   *[Day's British Fishes.*
BOAR-FISH (*Capros aper*).
A small, reddish fish with a very protractile mouth ; it ranges from the Mediterranean to Southern Britain.

250

the jaws, and with rather large eyes ; except the Holocentridae, all live in deep water.

Polymyxia, with four species from the warmer parts of the Atlantic and Pacific, is distinguished by a pair of barbels below the chin ; the dorsal and anal fins are long, with a few graduated spines ; the pelvic fins, seven or eight-rayed, are well behind the pectorals. In the remaining Berycoids the pelvic fins have a spinous ray and are further forward, and the pelvic bones are attached to the pectoral arch, as in the Perches. The species of *Beryx*, from the warmer parts of the North Atlantic and Japan, are deep-bodied red fishes, with a long anal fin. *Beryx splendens* is one of the fishes taken on long lines by the fishermen of Madeira. *Hoplopteryx* is a southern genus, with a longer dorsal fin preceded by strong, s p a c e d s p i n e s. T h e species in which t h e a b d o m e n bears a median series of ridged scales belong to three families, of which the Trach-ichthyidae are the more normal, the Monocentridae have the body en-closed in a firm box of bony plates, and the Anomalo-pidae have a large luminous o r g a n

[James's Press.
Monocentris japonicus.
A Berycoid from the seas of Japan, in which the body is enclosed in a bony box.

which can be withdrawn into a cavity below the eye, and the luminous surface so be concealed. *Monocentris* is known from the seas of Japan and Australia, the Anomalopids are from the Malay Archipelago.

The Holocentridae have a long, spinous dorsal fin ; there are some seventy species, shore fishes of the tropics, abundant on coral reefs. They are red, often striped with silver or gold.

Order 17. ZEOMORPHI (Dory, Boar-fish, etc.)

These fishes resemble the Berycoids in having many-rayed pelvic fins, but have a rounded or truncate caudal fin, with only twelve or thirteen rays. They are marine fishes, generally living in rather deep water ; they have large eyes, and a very protractile mouth. About fifty species are known from tropical and temperate seas.

The John Dory (*Zeus faber*) is common in the Mediterranean and

Reproduced by permission from]   [Day's British Fishes.
BASS (*Morone labrax*).
A large silvery fish of the Sea-perch family, that reaches the south coast of Britain.

northward to England. It grows to a length of two feet, and has a deep, strongly-compressed body, small, smooth scales, and a row of spiny plates along the bases of the dorsal and anal fins. The spinous dorsal fin has long spines, between which the membrane is produced into filaments; the anal is preceded by a separate fin of four spines; the soft dorsal and anal are low and rounded. The coloration is olive, with golden bands, and there is a large round black spot, edged with yellow, on each side of the body. The Dory swims about slowly, quietly stalking small fishes, and suddenly protruding its mouth to catch them.

Other species more or less closely allied to the Dory belong to a number of genera that show great diversity in scaling, from spiny scales to bony tubercles or bosses.

The Boar-fish (*Capros aper*) is a small red fish with rough scales, and a protractile mouth like that of the Dory. It ranges from the Mediterranean to the Western Channel. *Antigonia* includes fishes with a deep body, red in colour, that live in deep water in the warmer parts of the Atlantic and the seas of Japan.

Order 18. PERCOMORPHI (Perches, Bass, Sun-fishes, Blennies, etc.)

This large order, which contains several thousand species, is difficult to define. It includes the typical Perches, which originated from the Berycoids at the end of the Cretaceous period. They are fishes of normal form, with a spinous

Reproduced by permission from]   [Day's British Fishes.
WRECK-FISH (*Polyprium cernium*).
A large Sea-perch, which takes its name from the habits of the young, which accompany ships or floating timber.

dorsal fin, thoracic pelvic fins, each of a spine and five branched rays, pelvic bones directly attached to the pectoral arch, a caudal with seventeen principal rays, and the mouth bordered above by the protractile praemaxillaries. But other fishes of the order may be of various shapes, may have no spinous fin-rays, may have the pelvic fins farther back and their bones unconnected with the pectoral arch, or placed on the throat, or reduced or absent ; some have no caudal fin, some a non-protractile mouth, etc. etc. In other words, many diverse types are included, either because they resemble the typical perches in many of their characters, or are connected with them by transition-forms.

The Sea-perches, Serranidae, several hundred in number, are carnivorous fishes mostly with small, sharp teeth, that live at the bottom near the coasts in warm seas. This family is characterized by an exposed maxillary, no scaly process in the axil of the pelvic fin, and three anal spines. It includes some very large species, for example, the Californian Jew-fish (*Stereolepis gigas*), which attains a weight of six hun-

[*Neville Kingston.*

JOHN DORY (*Zeus faber*).
A marine fish that ranges from the Mediterranean to England. The spot on the side has been ascribed to St. Peter's thumb, hence the German name " Peterfisch."

dred pounds. The Wreck-fish (*Polyprion cernium*) of the Mediterranean and Madeira takes it name from the habit smaller fish have of accompanying ships or floating timber, perhaps to feed on barnacles ; the larger ones, up to six feet in length, live at the bottom at depths of three to four hundred fathoms. The Groupers (*Epinephelus*, etc.) are large, showy tropical and subtropical fishes, remarkable for their instantaneous colour-changes, changing from red to yellow, green, or brown, and turning on or off bars, stripes or spots.

The Bass (*Morone labrax*) reaches the south coast of Britain ; it is a silvery fish, rather like a salmon in appearance ; it attains a length of three feet and is active and cunning ; the shoals swim along the coast and often enter rivers in pursuit of prey.

Two tropical marine families closely related to the Serranidae are the

Priacanthidae, red, large-eyed fishes with a nearly-vertical mouth, and the Chilodipteridae, with only two anal spines, including the large genus *Apogon*, pretty little fishes, brightly coloured, and often striped or banded.

[*Otho Webb.*

GROUPER (*Promicrops lanceolatus*).
The name Grouper is a corruption of the Portuguese "Garrupa." It is applied to many
kinds of Sea-perch, some of which grow to a very large size.

Three important families of fresh-water perches may next be considered, the Centrarchidae, Percidae and Cichlidae.

The North American family Centrarchidae is closely related to the Serranidae. The Black Bass (*Micropterus*) are predacious fishes. The Small-mouthed Black Bass frequents cool streams, and is a celebrated sporting fish. The Large-mouthed Black Bass, which grows to eighteen inches long, prefers slow rivers or ponds; it is very voracious, and will eat frogs and rats, as well as fishes. The Sun-fishes are small, deep-bodied Centrarchids, prettily coloured, and favourites in aquaria; some have a large eye-spot, black edged with red or blue, on a flap behind the gill-cover. These fishes pair, and the male hollows out a saucer-shaped nest in the sand, and guards it until the eggs are hatched. (See illustrations on pages 237 and 239.)

The Perch family, with only two anal spines, includes the Perch (*Perca fluviatilis*) of our lakes and rivers, which ranges through Europe and Northern Asia, and is represented in North America by the closely - related Yellow Perch. The Perch is greenish above, yellow below, with dark bars; it reaches a length of eighteen inches, and a weight of five pounds. It is a bold fish, that swims in companies, and feeds on small fishes, worms, shrimps, etc. In the spring it spawns in shallows, when the eggs, connected by a membrane, form long, floating bands, attached at one end to reeds.

[*W. S. Pitt.*

MANY-SPINED PERCH (*Polycentrus Schomburgkii*).
This little fish from Trinidad changes colour in a few seconds, from pale grey to black. It represents a distinct family, Polycentridae.

The Pope or Ruffe (*Acerina cernua*) is a little speckled fish of quiet waters, common in the Norfolk Broads. The Pike-perches (*Lucioperca*) are large, active, predacious fishes, more slender and with a larger mouth than the Perch. The Sander of Eastern Europe reaches a length of four feet, and like the Wall-eyed Pike of the Great Lakes of North America, is a valuable food fish.

The Darters (*Etheostoma*, etc.) are dwarfed Perches of the swift,

[*Raoul Barba.*

Epinephelus gigas.
A large Sea-perch of the Mediterranean.

Reproduced by permission from]   [Day's British Fishes.
POPE OR RUFFE (*Acerina cernua*).
This little fish of the Perch family is common in the Broads.

clear streams of eastern North America; they lurk among stones or weeds, or may burrow in the sand, and then dart about, swimming by means of the large pectoral fins. Some species pair, the breeding males being brilliantly coloured; the female makes a trough in the gravel after the manner of a salmon; in this the eggs are laid, and stick to the stones.

Cichlidae. This is a large family, with over two hundred species from Central and South America, six hundred from Africa, and a few from Syria, Madagascar and India; some frequent brackish lagoons and estuaries, but the majority live in fresh water. The lower pharyngeal bones form a tooth-bearing plate that is opposed to the toothed upper pharyngeals. In the breeding season the males are generally more brilliant than the females, and have larger fins, and often a hump on the forehead. In some species the male hollows out a nest in the sand or mud, which is guarded by the parents until the eggs hatch, when the mother takes the little ones, sometimes a hundred in number, into her mouth; in other species no nest is made, and the mother puts the eggs in her mouth, where they hatch. The parents swim with their brood, and at any sign of danger the mother opens her mouth, and the little fish swim in; she also houses them every night, until they become too big for her.

Many South American Cichlids are small oval fishes, large-scaled, with a small

[*Neville Kingston*.
BLUE-SPOTTED CICHLID (*Herichthys cyanoguttatus*).
This Mexican species is profusely spotted with bright blue.

ANGEL-CICHLID (*Pterophyllum scalare*)

This fish of the Amazon is nearly circular and very strongly compressed, with high, pointed dorsal and anal, and long, thread-like pelvic fins ; the body is crossed with broad, dark bands that tend to conceal the fish as it floats among the stems of weeds.

mouth and small conical teeth; they often have dark crossbars, that can be seen to fade out and reappear if the fishes are watched in aquaria, and gleaming blue spots on the head. *Herichthys cyanoguttatus* of Mexico (generally labelled *Neetroplus carpintis* in aquaria) reaches a length of a foot, and is covered with bright blue spots. In the lakes of Central America are some predacious species (*Parapetenia*) with large, protractile mouth, and strong, piercing teeth at the front of the jaws, and others with blunt teeth and lips produced into fleshy lobes, organs of touch used for finding food at the bottom.

[*Paul Unger.*

ANGEL-FISH (*Pterophyllum scalare*).
A Brazilian Cichlid remarkable for its deep form and high fins.

The South American *Crenicichla* includes a number of slender fishes with pike-like heads. *Pterophyllum scalare* of the Amazon is nearly circular and very strongly compressed, with high, pointed dorsal and anal, and long, thread-like pelvic fins; the body is crossed with broad dark bands that tend to conceal the fish as it floats among the stems of weeds.

The African Cichlids show great diversity, particularly in the great lakes, each of which possesses numerous genera and species that have evolved in them, and are found nowhere else. Tanganyika and Nyasa, for example, have each over one hundred Cichlid species; but none is common to the two lakes. They include large predacious pike-like fishes, others that feed on various kinds of invertebrates, and others that eat weeds; they show many types of teeth, acute, conical, compressed and incisor-like or bi- or tricuspid, bristle-like and movable, etc.; those that feed on molluscs have massive pharyngeals, the lower united by an interlocking suture, provided with blunt, crushing teeth. The largest genus of the African rivers is *Tilapia*, which includes heavily-built, oval, large-scaled herbivorous fishes, with broad head, and rounded mouth, furnished with bands of small bi- or tricuspid teeth. *Tilapia nilotica* is the Bolti of the Nile.

The Centropomidae, with maxillary exposed, but with a scaly process in the axil of each pelvic fin, include the Robalos (*Centropomus*), silvery fishes found on both coasts of Tropical America, that enter rivers. These have the interest, which is shared by many genera of this region, that the species fall into pairs, each Pacific species having its nearest ally on the Atlantic side. *Ambassis* includes small silvery fishes, found on the coasts of West Africa, and throughout the Indo-Pacific. *Lates* of the rivers of Africa includes the Nile Perch (*L. niloticus*), which reaches a weight of nearly three hundred pounds.

A number of Percoids, that occur near the coasts in warm seas, differ from the Serranidae in having the maxillary sheathed by the prae-orbital, and in the presence of a pointed scaly process in the axil of each pelvic fin. The principal families with these characters are the Lutianidae, Pomadasidae, Liognathidae, Mullidae, Sparidae and Sciaenidae.

The Lutianidae, or Snappers, are tropical carnivorous fishes with sharp teeth. *Lutianus aya* is the Red Snapper of the Gulf of Mexico, a valued food fish and the object of an important line-fishery; it is a crimson fish, up to thirty pounds in weight, that haunts rocky

[*W. S. Pitt.*

Heros spurius.
A South American Cichlid of the usual ovate form.

gullies, where it feeds on crabs, prawns, and fishes.

The Pomadasidae, with small conical teeth, are also widely distributed in the tropics. The species of *Haemulon*, an American genus, are known as " grunts," from the noises they make when taken from the water. Many of the grunts are marked with undulating stripes of blue ; the inside of the mouth is bright scarlet.

The Liognathidae are tropical fishes, silvery, with a scaly sheath at the base of the dorsal and anal fins, a forked caudal, and a small, very protractile mouth.

The Mullidae, or Red Mullets, of which there are numerous species in all warm seas,

[*W. S. Pitt.*
Ghost-fish (*Ambassis*), so called because it is almost transparent. (*Life size.*)

are small fishes, generally red or yellow in colour, with the dorsal fins short and well-separated, and a pair of barbels below the chin, with which they probe for the small animals on which they feed. *Mullus barbatus* of the Mediterranean reaches the British coast ; it attains a length of about a foot. It is a fish of delicate flavour, and was valued highly by the Romans.

The Sparidae, or Sea-breams, are mostly tropical and sub-tropical. Two species, common in the Mediterranean, are found in southern British waters, particularly in the summer. These are the Black Sea-bream (*Cantharus lineatus*) and the Common Sea-bream (*Pagellus centrodontus*). The Black Sea-bream, ovate, and dusky in colour, has bands of small teeth in the jaws, with an outer series of cutting teeth ; it feeds on seaweeds. The Common Sea-bream is a plump, large-eyed fish, silvery, with red back and a black spot on the shoulder ; it has strong, blunt teeth at the sides of the jaws ; it haunts rocky ground, and feeds on mussels and other shell fish.

Another Mediterranean Sea-bream is the Gilt-head (*Pagrus auratus*), with a golden band between the eyes ; the Romans used to keep it in salt-water ponds, and fed it on oysters. *Sargus* includes species with incisors at the front of the mouth, and molars at the sides ; the Sheepshead, of the Atlantic coast of the United States, is a valuable fish of this genus.

The Sciaenidae, known as Drums or Croakers, are a large family, with

259

Reproduced by permission from]   [Day's British Fishes.
RED MULLET (*Mullus*).
These fishes probe with their barbels to find small prey.

short spinous and long soft dorsal fins, and two anal spines. These are silvery fishes of sandy shores and estuaries in warm seas ; many of them make drumming or purring sounds by the rapid vibration of the air-bladder, which has a number of hollow appendages ; these noises are said to be a call for the assembling of the shoals for breeding.

The Meagre (*Sciaena aquila*) is a widely-distributed fish that visits the coasts of Britain ; in South Africa it is known as Salmon, a fish that it resembles in form and colour. It is large and active, and preys on Grey Mullet and other fishes that swim in shoals. Still more voracious are the species of *Cynoscion*, slender fishes, with large mouth, and strong, piercing teeth. In many Sciaenids, however, the snout is blunt, over-hanging the rather small, feebly-toothed mouth ; these kinds feed on worms, shellfish, etc., that they find in the sand. The Drum (*Pogonias chromis*) of the Gulf of Mexico is a large, heavily-built fish of this type, with a fringe of little barbels along the lower jaw, and with powerful, blunt pharyngeal teeth, with which it crushes the shells of oysters.

The Chaetodontidae are little fishes that swim about slowly, and frequent the pools of coral reefs. They are deep and compressed, with high fins covered with little scales, and a small mouth, with a brush of slender teeth in each jaw. They are brightly coloured, and show fantastic patterns of bands, stripes and spots. *Chelmo* has the mouth at the end of a long tube-like snout, and probes into crevices for food.

The Archer-fishes comprise the genus *Toxotes* of India and Poly-nesia. They have a pointed head, and an oblique mouth with the lower jaw promi-

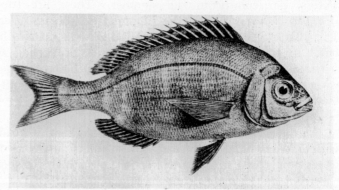

Reproduced by permission from]   [Day's British Fishes.
BLACK SEA-BREAM (*Cantharus lineatus*).
A British species that feeds on seaweeds.

260

nent ; they swim near the surface in lagoons and backwaters, and shoot drops of water from the mouth at insects, which fall when hit, and are eaten.

The Latilidae are fishes with a long dorsal fin, with a few slender spines in front, a decurved snout, and a horizontal mouth. The Tile-fish (*Lopholatilus*),

CORBEAU-DE-MER (*Corvina nigra*).
A Mediterranean Sciaenid belonging to the group with blunt snout and small mouth.

bluish with golden spots, and with a crest on the head, was discovered in 1879 on the Nantucket Shoals, at depths of eighty to two hundred and fifty fathoms. A fishery with long lines developed, and many fish, up to fifty pounds in weight, were caught for the market. But in 1882 they were destroyed, probably by an influx of cold water ; millions were seen floating dead at the surface, over an area of three hundred by fifty miles. For many years the species seemed to be extinct, but it is now re-established.

The Pomatomidae are closely related to the Serranidae, but have

Photos]   [*Raoul Barba.*
Dentex vulgaris.
A Mediterranean fish, distinguished from other members of the Sea-bream family by its sharp-pointed teeth.

the spinous dorsal of a few slender spines, and the soft dorsal and anal long, with pointed lobes in front. The Blue-fish (*Pomatomus saltatrix*) is a silvery fish, blue-backed, with strong, sharp-edged teeth ; it attains a weight of fifteen pounds. These voracious and wasteful fishes swim in companies near the surface in the warmer parts of the Atlantic, pursuing other fishes, and cutting them to pieces. The Blue-fish abounds on the coast of the United States, and is esteemed as food.

The Carangidae are a large and varied group of fishes, some slender, some deep in form, mostly tropical ; many swim in shoals at the surface at no great distance from the coasts. They have long, soft dorsal and anal fins, produced and pointed in front, and a widely-forked caudal ; the teeth are generally small and conical. The Scad or Horse-mackerel (*Trachurus*) visits Britain. It is a slender fish, silvery and blue-backed, with a series of keeled scutes along each side ; it swims in shoals near the surface, feeding on the fry of other fishes. The Pilot Fish (*Naucrates ductor*) is oceanic ; it associates with sharks, and often accompanies ships. The Yellow-tails (*Seriola*) are large active fishes, liked by anglers.

The Coryphaenidae, or Dolphins, are swift piscivorous oceanic fishes, with a single long dorsal fin, forked caudal, and a deep head with a sharp, nearly vertical edge in front. *Coryphaena hippurus*, blue, with deeper spots, and gleaming with gold, is famous for the beauty of its changing colours while it is dying.

Next may be considered three unrelated groups of marine Percoids in which the lower pharyngeals are completely united, bearing conical, molariform, or flat teeth that meet those of the upper pharyngeals. The largest of these groups is that of the Wrasses, including the families Labridae, Odacidae and Scaridae.

The Labridae have a protractile mouth, thick lips, conical teeth, and a triangular lower pharyngeal plate. They live near the coasts, in rocky or weedy places, or in the pools of coral reefs, and feed mainly on s h e l l-f i s h. The tropical species are numerous, mostly small and gaily coloured. There are a few British species, including the Ballan Wrasse

[*Raoul Barba.*
BALLAN WRASSE [MALE] (*Labrus maculatus*).
A handsome fish with blue spots enclosed in an orange network.

[Paul Unger.

ARGUS FISH (*Scatophagus argus*).
A fish of the Indian Seas related to the Chaetodonts.

and the Striped Wrasse, the former growing to eighteen inches, the latter to twelve. These fishes pair, and make nests of seaweed in crevices of the rocks ; they show remarkable sexual differences. The male Ballan Wrasse (*Labrus maculatus*) is blue, with an orange network ; the female is yellow-brown, with darker spots. The male Striped Wrasse (*Labrus mixtus*) is green, with blue stripes ; the belly is yellow, and the fins yellow with blue spots and edges ; the female is reddish, with three large blackish spots on the upper part of the body.

The Odacidae of Southern Australia, small scaled, and with fixed upper jaw, include the curious *Siphonognathus*, with a snout like that of a Pipe-fish.

The Scaridae, or Parrot Wrasses, are large scaled, plump, oval fishes, beautifully coloured, from the shores of warm seas, and particularly the coral reefs of the Pacific. They have short, powerful jaws, with sharp-edged plates formed by the union of numerous series of little teeth : the pharyngeal teeth form a pavement, and the upper pharyngeals are united to form a bone that slides backwards and forwards over the somewhat hollowed surface of the lower. These fishes are mainly, but not exclusively, herbivorous, biting off pieces of seaweed, and chewing them in the throat.

The other Perches with united lower pharyngeals are the Pomacentridae, beautiful little fishes, many of which frequent the pools of coral reefs, and

263

the Embiotocidae, or Surf-fishes, of California and Japan, silvery fishes of sandy bays, and viviparous.

The Teuthididae and Siganidae are herbivorous fishes with a small non-protractile mouth, and with a single series of cutting teeth in the jaws. *Teuthis* is the name of the Surgeon-fishes, which have a movable lancet, sharp-edged and pointed, on each side of the tail ; these fishes live near the coast in the tropics. A related genus, *Naseus*, includes the Unicorn-fishes of the Indo-Pacific, with a long, bony horn projecting forward from above the eyes.

Kurtus of the Indo-Pacific is an isolated genus, with a deep body, short dorsal fin, and long anal. The male has a bony hook on the forehead ; the eggs are in two bunches connected by a string, and he carries them about, the string on the hook and a bunch of eggs on each side of him.

The Stromateoids have a large muscular gullet, with little teeth on the inside ;

[*W. S. Pitt.*

CORAL FISH (*Amphiprion melanopus*).
A Pomacentrid from the Indo-Pacific. This little fish is red, with cross bands of creamy-blue.

the mouth is small, with a single series of small teeth in each jaw ; the spinous dorsal, when present, is formed of short or slender spines ; the soft dorsal and anal are long. Many of these fishes swim near the surface of the sea, and feed on little crustacea, and other small prey. The group includes the Black-fish (*Centrolophus niger*), elongate in form, and the more oval Rudder-fish (*Lirus perciformis*) ; both these North Atlantic species are of a deep purple colour. They like floating timber and if a ship is becalmed, shoals of Rudder-fishes may appear. Some of the smaller kinds shelter under large jelly-fishes, which do not sting them. The Butter-fishes (*Stromateus*, etc.) are rounded or oval, with high, pointed dorsal and anal fins ; they are valued as food in Italy and in the United States.

The Anabantidae, freshwater fishes of Africa and southern Asia, have an air-breathing chamber, containing a labyrinthic organ, above the gills ; they rise to the surface of the water to breathe air, and suffocate if they be prevented. The air-breathing habits enable them to live in swamps and stagnant pools, and to migrate overland. The Climbing Perch (*Anabas scandens*) of India walks about on land, getting alternate holds with the spines on the gill-covers and those of the anal fin. Also Asiatic are the little Paradise Fish (*Macropodus opercularis*) and the Gourami (*Osphromenus olfax*), a large fish valued as food. *Betta splendens* is the Fighting-fish of Siam ; the breeding males are brilliantly coloured and are very pugnacious, and are kept by the Malays and Siamese to fight. These fishes pair, and the male blows bubbles that form a floating

[*W. S. Pitt.*

SIAMESE FIGHTING-FISH (*Betta splendens*).
The large fins characterize the male, which is brilliantly coloured.

mass of foam ; he catches the eggs in his mouth, sticks them on to the under side of the nest, and guards it.

The Ophiocephalidae of Africa and Southern Asia have a simple air-breathing chamber above the gills. These are elongate fishes, with a flat head covered by large scales, sharp teeth, long soft-rayed dorsal and anal fins without any spines, and six-rayed pelvics well behind the pectorals, and unconnected with the pectoral arch. They may grow to a length of

265

[*Paul Unger.*
PARADISE FISH (*Macropodus opercularis*) [MALE].
Like the Fighting-fish, the breeding male is brilliant, large-finned, and pugnacious.

two feet or over, and feed on fishes, frogs, mice, etc. When the ponds dry up, they may burrow in the mud, or may wriggle along overland in search of water. The Murrul of India has been observed breeding; the male clears a space in the reeds at the edge of a pond, in which the eggs are laid, and float at the surface; he stays on guard until they hatch.

The Sphyraenidae, Mugilidae, Atherinidae and Polynemidae are fishes with the short spinous dorsal well separated from the soft fin, and pelvic fins, of a spine and five-branched rays, far behind the pectorals and unconnected with the clavicles.

The Sphyraenidae, or Barracudas, are large pike-like piscivorous fishes of tropical seas, with strong, sharp-edged, pointed teeth; some kinds grow to over eight feet in length. They are bold and voracious, and are feared by bathers, as they may inflict fatal injuries; on one occasion a man's leg was bitten right through at the knee with a single bite.

The Mugilidae, or Grey Mullets, are found on the coasts in all tropical and temperate seas, especially in bays and estuaries. *Mugil* includes over a hundred species; these are elongate, silvery fishes, often with dark longitudinal stripes, with a broad, scaly head, small mouth, and teeth scarcely visible. They swim in large shoals, and feed on mud, or on minute creatures. There are three British species of *Mugil*.

The Atherinidae, or Sand Smelts, are mostly small fishes, often bluish with a silvery lateral band ; they have conical teeth, and are carnivorous. They frequent inlets and estuaries, and occur as freshwater species in places where true freshwater fishes are scarce, such as Australia and Madagascar. In the lakes of the Valley of Mexico are some twenty species of *Chirostoma* ; they grow to a length of a foot or more, and are highly valued as food.

The Polynemidae have the five lower rays of the pectoral fin detached to form long filaments, used as feelers. The eyes are large, and the blunt snout projects beyond the mouth. Some species grow to a large size, six feet or more. The shoals frequent sandy bays and estuaries in the tropics.

The Gempylidae have the maxillaries attached to the fixed, beak-like praemaxillaries. They are predacious marine fishes, with a large mouth, and strong, compressed, pointed teeth. *Thyrsites atun*, known as Snoek in South Africa and Barracuta in Australia, is an elongate fish, with long, spinous dorsal, short, pointed soft dorsal and anal followed by a series of finlets, and forked caudal ; it is caught in numbers by line fisheries, and is valued as food. *Ruvettus pretiosus*, a somewhat similar fish, but more heavily built, is purple-black in colour and is covered with prickles ; it grows to six feet, and is caught on long lines in deep water off Cuba and

[*F. Schensky, Helgoland.*

MACKEREL (*Scomber scombrus*).
The Mackerel swims in large schools and is a valued food fish.

Madeira. *Lepidopus caudatus*, slender, and with a small caudal fin, swims at the surface; it is very susceptible to cold, and is named Frost-fish in New Zealand, where numbers come ashore on cold nights.

[*By courtesy of the High Commissioner for New Zealand.*
SWORD-FISH (*Xiphias gladius*).
These large and swift fishes have the snout produced into a long, flat blade. In the western North Atlantic they are fished for regularly with harpoons.

The Trichiuridae resemble the preceding, but have a long, tapering tail and no caudal fin; they are silvery, and swim near the surface in tropical seas.

The Scombridae also have the maxillaries attached to the fixed, beak-like praemaxillaries, and may be characterized as swift fishes that swim near the surface, silvery and blue-backed, with a conical head, spindle-shaped body, and caudal fin with pointed lobes diverging from a narrow base; the spinous dorsal fin is formed of slender spines, and is depressible in a groove; the soft dorsal and anal are triangular, each followed by a series of isolated and much-branched little rays, or finlets. All the Scombridae have rich oily flesh. There are several kinds of Mackerel in tropical and temperate seas. The British species (*Scomber scombrus*) is found on both sides of the North Atlantic; it has small teeth, and feeds on little crustaceans, and the fry of other fishes. It swims in large schools, which come near land during the summer.

The oceanic fishes of this family are larger and plumper than the mackerel, and have a crescentic caudal fin. The largest of all is the Tunny (*Thynnus*), which reaches a length of twelve feet ; it has a large mouth, and conical teeth, and lives on other fishes. It is found in all warm seas, and in British waters during the summer. The Bonitos and Albacores resemble the Tunny in their habits, but do not grow so large.

Closely related to the Scombridae is the fish named *Luvarus imperialis*, which is distinguished by a blunt head and a very small mouth, without teeth ; it grows to a length of six feet, and feeds on plankton in the warmer parts of the oceans.

Also related to the Scombridae are the Xiphiidae and Histiophoridae, distinguished by a long sword-like or spear-shaped snout, projecting beyond the mouth.

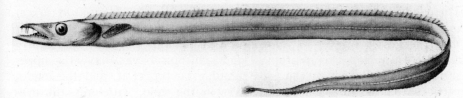

[*Voyage of H.M.S. " Challenger " ; Permission, Controller, H.M. Stationery Office.*
Lepidopus tenuis.
A slender, silvery fish, with sharp teeth.

The Sword-fish (*Xiphias gladius*) has a long, flat, pointed blade with which it strikes right and left among the shoals of fishes that form its prey ; it is also said to attack whales, and certainly does on occasions attack ships, as do the Spear-fishes. If the ship has thick wooden sides, the sword or spear may be driven in so hard that the fish can escape only by breaking it off short. The Sword-fish reaches a length of twenty feet ; it is one of the swiftest swimmers, and occurs in all warm seas. In the United States it is esteemed as food, and is caught off the Atlantic coast by harpooning. Young Sword-fish have both jaws prolonged, and a high dorsal fin along the back ; in the adult, the dorsal fin is divided into two widely-separated parts, a high-pointed fin in front, and a little one on the tail.

The Histiophoridae have a rounded spear. They are large fishes, similar in their habits to the Sword-fish. Half-a-dozen species are known. Those with a divided dorsal fin (*Tetrapturus*) are named Spear-fishes, those with a single long and high dorsal fin (*Histiophorus*) are named Sail-fishes. In some Sail-fishes the dorsal fin is beautifully coloured, bright blue, with numerous round black spots ; it may be used as a sail when these fishes float at the surface, but when they are swimming, it is folded into a groove on the back.

We now come to the Percomorphi that have the pelvic fins placed in advance of the

Reproduced by permission from]   *[Day's British Fishes.*

WEEVER (*Trachinus draco*).
These fishes live on the bottom, often partly buried ; their poisonous spines make them dangerous to bathers.

pectorals, generally on the throat ; Weevers, Dragonets, Blennies, etc.

The Weevers (Trachinidae) are elongate fishes, with long soft dorsal and anal fins, and an oblique mouth. The spines of the short spinous dorsal fin, and a strong one projecting from the operculum, are grooved or channelled to transmit poison. These fishes live at the bottom, often partly buried in the sand ; they feed on small fishes and crustaceans. There are two British species ; the Greater Weever (*Trachinus draco*) reaches a length of eighteen inches, and is larger, and lives in deeper water than the Lesser Weever (*T. vipera*), which abounds on sandy shores.

The Uranoscopidae, of tropical and subtropical seas, have the upper surface of the head flat, the eyes standing on top of it, and the mouth vertical. These fishes bury themselves in the sand, with only the eyes projecting, and protrude from the mouth a membraneous appendage, in one species a broad white flap, in another a red filament, which is moved about as a lure for other fishes.

The Dragonets (Callionymidae) are naked fishes, with large eyes close together on top of the triangular head, a strong praeopercular spine, often serrated or with divergent points, and a small mouth ; the short, spinous dorsal fin has four flexible rays. These fishes live at the bottom and feed on small invertebrates ; they are found in tropical and temperate seas near the coasts, but sometimes in rather deep water. They pair for breeding, and the males are ornamented with bright colours and have large showy fins ; but they take no care of the eggs,

Histiodraco.
A Nototheniid from the Antarctic, remarkable for its high dorsal fin.

which float in the
sea. *Callionymus
lyra* is a British
species ; the male
grows to a foot
long, and is yellow,
striped and spotted
with green and
blue ; the female
is brown, with
greenish spots.

[W. S. Berridge.

GUNNEL OR BUTTERFISH (*Pholis gunnellus*).
The Gunnel occurs all round Britain ; its breeding habits are interesting ; when the eggs are laid, the female rolls them up into a ball, which is guarded by the parent fish.

The Nototheni-
iidae and allied
families, carnivor-
ous fishes with a
short spinous dorsal of a few flexible spines, and long, soft dorsal and
anal, form the predominant element in the Antarctic fish-fauna ; they are
very diverse in size and in form.

The Ammodytidae are elongate fishes with a single long dorsal fin, and
with a pointed lower jaw ; some tropical species have small pelvic fins on
the throat, but in *Ammodytes* of the North Atlantic and Mediterranean
there are no pelvic fins. There are two British species of *Ammodytes*,
known as Sand-launces or Sand-eels ; they swim in large shoals, and feed
on small prey ; they burrow in the sand, and may remain buried while
the tide is out.

[M. H. Crawford.

TOMPOT (*Blennius gattorugine*).
This Blenny ranges from the Mediterranean to the Channel. It differs from the Shanny in having a tentacle above each eye.

The remaining
Percomorphi are
Blennioids, a large
group of marine
fishes in which the
pelvic fins are jug-
ular and have fewer
than five soft-rays.

The Clinidae
are the most
perch-like of the
Blennies, having a
scaly body, a dor-
sal fin with several
sharp spines, and
a protractile
mouth with coni-
cal teeth. These
are known as

271

Kelp-fishes in America, and Klip-fishes in South Africa ; they live near the coasts, often among rocks or weeds. The mimic combats between the males of certain kinds, which take place at the breeding season, have the interest that they appear to be conducted according to different rules in the different species.

The Gunnels (Pholidae) are northern fishes, elongate in form, with the dorsal fin formed of spines only.

The Bleniidae, like the Clinidae, have pelvic fins formed of a spine and two to four simple rays, that may be thickened and partly free for use as tactile organs. But the body is naked, the dorsal spines are

[Dr. F. Ward.
Sand-eel (*Ammodytes lanceolatus*) showing the mouth closed and open.

flexible, the mouth is non-protractile, and the teeth are slender and close-set in a single series, with a pair of strong, curved canines posteriorly. The large family includes small fishes of the shores of tropical and temperate seas, often found between tide-marks. There are several British species of *Blennius*, including the Shanny (*B. pholis*), a greenish fish of the rock pools. The male Shanny guards the eggs, which are attached to the roof of a hole in a rock. *Salarias* is a tropical genus with numerous species, known as Rock-skippers ; when the tide is out, they leap about on shore by strokes of the tail, or rest on the rocks.

The Anarrhichadidae are large northern fishes with powerful jaws, with conical teeth in front and molars at the sides ; they feed mainly on shell-fish. The Wolf-fish (*Anarrhichas lupus*) ranges from Iceland to the North Sea, in rather deep water. It is a long fish, blue-grey, with darker cross-bars ; it reaches a length of over four feet. Many are caught by trawlers, and when skinned, are sold under the name of rock-salmon.

The Zoarcidae, without spinous dorsal, and with long dorsal and anal fins joined to the caudal, include the Viviparous Blenny (*Zoarces viviparus*), an eel-like fish that ranges from Scandinavia to Sussex, frequents inlets and estuaries, and feeds on small shell-fish ; the young are born when about two inches long.

The Brotulidae, with a strong opercular spine, without spinous fin-rays, with many-rayed dorsal and anal fins joined to the caudal, and with the

pelvics reduced
to a pair of fila-
ments, include
a number of
strange types
that live in the
depths of the
ocean, and also

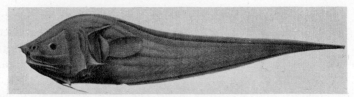

[*Voyage of H.M.S. "Challenger"*; *Permission, Controller, H.M. Stationery Office.*
Acanthonus armatus.
One of the strange Brotulids that live in the depths of the ocean.

the Blind-fishes of the underground rivers of Cuba. Blind-fishes are viviparous : when first born, the young have eyes, but these soon degenerate
and become covered by the skin.

The Ophidiidae, or Cusk-eels, differ from the Brotulids in having the
pelvic fins placed below the chin, where they form a pair of feelers. These
are carnivorous fishes that live near the coasts. *Genypterus* is a southern
genus, with some large species that are caught for the market, known as
" Rockling " in Australia and " Ling " in New Zealand.

The Fierasferidae are little, eel-shaped fishes, without pelvic fins, found
in warm seas. They have the curious habit of hiding inside the bodies
of sea-cucumbers, or sometimes within the shells of living bivalve
molluscs.

Order 19. GOBIOMORPHI (Gobies)

The Gobies form a large group, well defined by skeletal characters,
and recognizable by a spinous dorsal of a few flexible spines, a longer
soft dorsal similar to the anal, and typically a rounded caudal ; the gill-
openings are lateral, in front of the broad vertical bases of the pectoral
fins ; the thoracic pelvic fins, of a spine and four or five branched rays,
have the inner rays longest, close together or united.

The Eleotridae, with separate pelvic fins, are found on the shores of
all warm seas, and in tropical rivers. They are carnivorous, with protractile mouth and conical teeth ; they vary in shape from ovate to rather
elongate ; those of the rivers of Australia are known as " Gudgeons."
One of the largest species is the Guavina (*Philypnus dormitator*) of the rivers
of Central America, which reaches a length of two feet ; it has a rather
large, oblique mouth, and is somewhat perch-like. The species of *Eviota*,
not more than half - an - inch long, frequent crevices in coral reefs.

GUAVINA (*Philypnus*).
The Guavinas are large Gobies of the rivers of Central America.

The Gobiidae, with the pelvic fins united to form a cup-shaped sucker, used for holding on to rocks, include some five hundred species, mostly small. A few occur in deep water and a few swim at the surface of the sea ; but the majority live between tide-marks ; there are also a number of freshwater species.

Gobius and its allies have the body moderately elongate, the eyes close together, and the mouth small, with conical teeth. Fishes of this type are widely distributed, and there are several British species ; they feed on small worms, shrimps, etc. The Common Goby (*Gobius microps*) is abundant on sandy shores, and in estuaries ; it is sandy in colour, and speckled with brown. In the summer, the male acquires a series of dark bands on the body ; he hollows out a space under a shell, to the under surface of which the eggs adhere, and he stays on guard until they hatch. The Rock Goby (*G. paganellus*) is larger, growing to four inches ; it has a yellow band along the top of the spinous dorsal fin ; it frequents rock pools, and lays its eggs on the underside of a projecting rock. The Black Goby (*G. niger*) is an allied species, grey or black in colour.

There are also to be found in British seas some little transparent Gobies that swim in shoals near the surface of the sea, and feed on small crustaceans. These are the White Goby (*Aphya pellucida*) and the Crystal Goby (*Crystallogobius nilssoni*) ; they live for one year only, all dying after spawning.

The Blind Goby (*Typhlogobius*) of California is a naked, pale pink fish, with eyes reduced to vestiges hidden under the skin ; it lives where the waves beat directly on the rocks, and it crawls about in the crevices or sticks on to the undersides of the rocks.

Some tropical Gobies are eel-shaped, for example the species of *Gobioides*, fishes with a large, oblique mouth and strong teeth, that enter rivers, and grow to a length of two feet.

The Mud-skippers (*Periophthalmus*) frequent mud-flats from West Africa to Australia ; they grow to nearly a foot in length, and are blue-grey in colour. The eyes are prominent, close together on top of the head, and can be turned backwards or forwards ; the rays of the pectoral fins are set at the end of

Reproduced by permission from]   [*Day's British Fishes.*
NORWAY HADDOCK (*Sebastes norwegicus*).
A reddish fish of the North Atlantic ; it is not related to the Haddock, but sometimes
has a blackish shoulder spot as in that fish.

long muscular lobes, and the lower rays of the caudal fin are thick. At low tide these fishes walk about on the mud in search of food, progressing by means of their arm-like pectoral fins ; they can also make long leaps by strokes of the tail, and may be seen jumping about

[James's Press.

RED GURNARD (*Trigla pini*).

in company, apparently playing ; sometimes they rest on a rock, with the tail hanging in the water, the caudal fin serving as an organ of respiration ; they will often skip across the surface of a pool in a series of jumps, in preference to swimming.

Order 20. SCLEROPAREI (Mail-cheeked Fishes)

The Scleroparei, or Mail-cheeked Fishes, have the second suborbital bone produced across the cheek to support the praeoperculum, which is generally armed with spines. This is a large group of carnivorous marine fishes ; most live at the bottom near the coasts.

There are eighteen families, of which the Scorpaenidae are the most primitive, resembling the more generalized sea-perches, such as the Serranidae, in structure. The Scorpaenidae include the Norway Haddock (*Sebastes norwegicus*), a red perch-like fish with large eyes, that reaches a length of three feet. It lives in rather deep water, on both sides of the Atlantic, in the east from Iceland to the North Sea ; an inshore form is smaller and darker. This fish is viviparous, but the young are numerous and are born when quite small. Many species of genera allied to *Sebastes* occur in the North Pacific, but in warmer seas *Scorpaena* and its allies are prevalent, with strong spines on the head, little skinny tags on the body, and the lower rays of the pectoral fins thickened and free at the end. These Scorpion-fishes are spotted and marbled, and are to be found among rocks and weeds.

The Zebra-fishes (*Pterois*) of the Indo-Pacific have very long and slender dorsal spines and very large pectoral fins ; the body is crossed by broad and narrow bands that can change in colour from brown and red to pale and dark blue.

The Triglidae include the Gurnards (*Trigla*). They are widely distributed, mostly in warm seas, and there are several British species. Gurnards have a bony head, and large pectoral fins, the three lowest rays

Reproduced by permission from]   *[Day's British Fishes.*

GURNARD (*Trigla*).
The three finger-like rays of the pectoral fin are used for walking on the bottom, or to probe for small prey.

of which are detached to form long and slender " fingers," used for walking about on the bottom, or for probing for shrimps, worms, and other small animals.

Of the British species the commonest are the Grey Gurnard (*Trigla gurnardus*), the Tub (*T. hirundo*) and the Red Gurnard (*T. pini*). The Grey Gurnard, grey with pearly spots, ranges from Scandinavia to the Mediterranean ; but the other kinds are rare north of the Channel. The Tub, reddish, with the inside of the pectoral fins bright blue, is the largest British Gurnard, growing to over two feet long. The Red Gurnard is bright red, with pink fins. *Peristedion cataphractum*, of the Mediterranean and adjacent parts of the Atlantic, is one of a group of deep-water Gurnards that are covered with bony plates, and have two free pectoral rays only.

The Synanciidae are naked fishes, with a large head and nearly vertical mouth, and with the dorsal spines channelled for the passage of the poison that is contained in sacs at their base. These fish lie in hollows in the coral reefs, concealed by their colour and protected by their poisonous spines, waiting to pounce on little fishes and other prey.

The Pataecidae (*Pataecus*) of southern Australia are curious-looking fishes, naked, with a deep, compressed head, vertical in front ; the long and high dorsal fin extends from the front of the head to the caudal fin.

The Hexagrammidae and Anoplopomatidae of the North Pacific are rather slender fishes, with a smooth head, small scales, and many-rayed dorsal and anal fins; some have several lateral lines. The names given to some

FLATHEAD (*Platycephalus*).
These fishes lie on the bottom, or bury themselves in the sand or mud, with only the eyes uncovered.

species, Black Cod, Blue Cod, Rock-trout, and Greenling are evidence of their appearance. They are valued as food.

The Congiopodidae of southern seas have a small mouth at the end of a tubular snout, the head resembling that of the sea-horses ; the dorsal fin begins on the head, like a mane The naked skin of these fishes grows thick and dull, and is shed in patches, revealing the bright new skin.

The Platycephalidae of the Indo-Pacific have a broad, flat head that bears several spines. There are numerous species ; they lie on the sand or mud, and often bury themselves until only the eyes show.

The Cottidae, a family of some three hundred species, may be recognized, as a rule, by a spinous dorsal with feeble, generally flexible spines, broad pectoral fins, and small pelvics with the rays reduced in number.

These are northern fishes, mostly marine, and of small size. There are some freshwater species, including several peculiar to Lake Baikal. The Cottids of the North Pacific are very numerous, and show great diversity.

The British species include the Bull-head, or Miller's Thumb (*Cottus gobio*)

[*John J. Ward.*

THE BULL-HEAD OR MILLER'S THUMB (*Cottus gobio*).
It rests on the bed of a stream, where its colours simulate its surroundings almost perfectly.

and the Sea-scorpions. The Bull-head is a little freshwater fish, with a broad, flat head, and a pair of strong praeopercular spines. It generally lies at the bottom in shallow water, and feeds on little fishes, and other small prey. The eggs are laid in a hole scooped out under a stone, and are guarded by the father. The largest of the Sea-scorpions is the Father-lasher (*Myoxocephalus scorpius*), which grows to three feet long off Greenland. It has spines on top of the head, and two diverging praeopercular spines on each side of it ; it is brown, mottled with darker colour, and with the fins spotted or barred. The eggs are rather large, and red ; they form a cluster, which the male clasps between his pectoral fins, guarding them until they hatch.

The Agonidae are closely related to the Cottidae, but have the body enclosed in series of bony plates. Like the Cottids, they are small fishes of northern seas, and are particularly characteristic of the North Pacific. The Pogge (*Agonus cataphractus*) ranges from the Arctic Ocean to the seas of Britain ; it has a slender tail, a prominent snout projecting in front of the small, feebly-toothed mouth, and several barbels on the under side of the head; it lives on a sandy bottom, and feeds on little crustaceans.

The Cyclopteridae include the Lump-suckers and Sea-snails, and are distinguished by a large, circular sucking-disc formed by the united pelvic fins, used for holding on to rocks or stones.

The Lump-sucker (*Cyclopterus lumpus*) is a deep, plump fish, growing to two feet in length, that is found on both sides of the North Atlantic. The skin is covered with bony tubercles, some of which are enlarged and conical, forming a series along the back and three on each side; there is no spinous dorsal fin in the adult. The Lump-sucker occurs on rocky ground in deep water, and feeds on worms and shell-fish; it breeds in inshore waters in the spring, at which season the male is blue above and red below, the female bluish grey. The fishes pair, and the eggs are laid in a clump, which is guarded by the male.

The Sea-snails (*Liparis*) have a broad head, a long, slender tail, and long, soft-rayed dorsal and anal fins; the skin is smooth and naked. Several kinds are known from deep water in northern seas, but the two British species live in inshore waters and estuaries, sometimes hiding between stones, or resting attached to rocks; they grow to about six inches long.

[*Paul Unger*.

THREE-SPINED STICKLEBACK (*Gasterosteus aculeatus*).
Male building a nest.

The Dactylopter-
idae, or Flying Gur-
nards, are an isolated
family, characterized
externally by a bony
head, and a very long
praeopercular spine,
firm keeled scales,
and rounded pectoral
fins, even larger than
those of the Flying-
fishes, that are orna-
mented with black,
red, and blue spots
or markings. Four

[M. H. Crawford.
FIFTEEN-SPINED STICKLEBACK (*Spinachia spinachia*).
A marine British species that grows to six inches in length.

species are known from tropical seas; they make fairly long flights, but
in spite of their spread of wing, are not such good fliers as the true Flying-
fishes, the small caudal fin not being constructed to give them such a good
lift from the water.

Order 21. THORACOSTEI (Sticklebacks)

The Sticklebacks have the second suborbital produced across the
cheek, as in the Scleroparei, but the praeoperculum is unarmed, and there
is a pair of large bony plates on the chest, behind which are the pelvic
fins, each formed of a strong spine that can be fixed when everted, with
or without two to four small soft-rays.

The Three-spined Stickleback (*Gasterosteus aculeatus*) is a widely-
distributed northern fish, not more than four inches long, found both
in the sea and in fresh water, in rivers, ponds, and even ditches. It has a
conical head, a small mouth with sharp teeth, and a spinous dorsal fin
of three isolated spines. There are no scales, but along each side of the
body is a series of keeled, bony plates, either complete, or interrupted
in the middle, or reduced to a few plates behind the head; the last
condition is generally found in British Sticklebacks from inland localities,
fully-armoured specimens occurring in the sea.

This pugnacious and greedy little fish breeds in the spring or summer,
when the males become bright red on the belly. Each male builds a
barrel-shaped nest of bits of roots and stalks, stuck together by a mucous
secretion; in this the eggs are laid, and are guarded by the father, who
pulls down the upper part of the nest to make a cradle when the young
are hatched. The males will fight for their wives, and in defence of their
nests, trying to rip each other with their sharp spines.

The Ten-spined Stickleback, or Tinker (*Pygosteus pungitius*), of which
there are several races in Europe, Northern Asia, and North America, has

279

nine to thirteen dorsal spines. It is a smaller fish than its relative, and builds nests that are attached to stems. The Fifteen-spined Stickleback (*Spinachia spinachia*) has a long tube-like snout ; it is a marine species of inshore waters ; it reaches a length of about six inches, and nests in seaweeds. *Aulorhynchus* of the North Pacific is rather similar to *Spinachia*.

Order 22. HYPOSTOMIDES (Dragon-fishes)

The Pegasidae, or Sea-dragons, are quaint little fishes of the Indian Ocean and the seas of China and Japan. The head is bony, with the snout produced into a flat blade ; the trunk is enclosed in a broad, bony box, and the tail in a series of bony rings. The mouth is very peculiar, placed in a cavity underneath the head ; it is small, toothless, and protractile downwards ; the praemaxillaries can be retracted within the maxillaries, which meet in front, and are attached by a ligament to the roof of the cavity. The dorsal and anal fins are small ; the pectorals are large, horizontal, supported by strong, unbranched rays ; the pelvic fins are a pair of long feelers on the under surface of the body.

The position of this order is quite obscure, and little has been recorded of the habits of these fishes, although they have been seen skimming over the surface of the sea, like flying-fishes. Probably, they stir up sand or mud with their blade-like snout, and probe it with their pelvic feelers, to find food.

Order 23. HETEROSOMATA (Flat-fishes)

The Heterosomata, or Flat-fishes, have strongly-compressed bodies, and long dorsal and anal fins ; they are distinguished from all other fishes by having both eyes on the same side of the head. They live at the bottom of the sea, with the eyeless, or blind, side underneath, and the eyed side uppermost. When first hatched, the little transparent larvae have an eye on each side of the head, and they swim near the surface of the sea in the same manner as the larvae of other fishes ; but after a time one eye moves round the top of the head on to the other side, the dorsal fin grows forward on to the head, and the little fish seeks the bottom and thereafter lives there, resting or swimming on one side.

It is often stated that this migration of the eye produces, or is produced by, the twisting of the orbital region of the cartilaginous skull of the larva. This, however, is untrue ; when the fish is hatched, it has a bar of cartilage above each eye, but almost at once the bar above the eye that is going to migrate begins to be absorbed ; eventually a wide gap is formed, through which the eye passes to reach the other supra-orbital bar ; this now separates the eyes, and may be bent as the eyes move downwards to their final position. As a result of these processes the skull, when it ossifies, is very peculiar, with a curved bar between the eyes formed mainly by the frontal bone of the eyed side, and on top, above the eyes, a broad bone which is the chief part of the frontal of the blind side.

The Flat-fishes are an off-shoot of the Percomorphi, and probably took their origin from sea-perches that were in the habit of resting on one side at the bottom of the sea, and found it profitable to remain in this position habitually, lying in wait for fishes that came near enough to be caught. Their efforts to use the eye that was underneath have finally resulted in its migration, as described above. The habit of resting or swimming at the bottom has produced further asymmetry; the eyed side is coloured, the blind side generally white; the muscles of the eyed side are more developed, and this side is more rounded, whereas the blind side is flat; the scales of the two sides may differ in structure, on the eyed side they are often spiny, on the blind side thin and smooth. The paired fins are frequently asymmetrical, the pectoral of the blind side being reduced, and one pelvic sometimes being extended along the edge of the body. Finally, those Flat-fishes that feed habitually on creatures that they find on the bottom, or in the sand or mud, have an asymmetrical mouth, with the jaws stronger and the teeth more developed on the blind side.

Very remarkable is the power that most Flat-fishes possess of imitating the ground on which they lie, whether sand, gravel, or mud On passing from one type of bottom

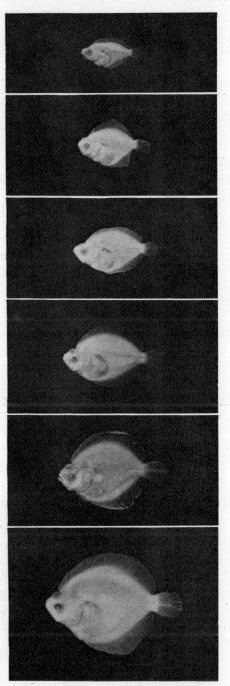

[*James's Press.*

Turbot, showing the migration of the right eye to the left side of the head.

281

to another they change almost instantaneously. In an aquarium a little Mediterranean species of *Bothus* was placed on a variety of backgrounds, such as black and white chess-board pattern, a black ground with round white spots, etc. Its attempts to

Bothus podas.
A Mediterranean Flat-fish [see below].

imitate these were quite successful. Experiments in America with species of *Paralichthys* produced even more remarkable results, these fishes being able to change from brown to red, blue, etc. These changes of colour and pattern are produced by the spreading out or concentration of pigment granules in the pigment-cells of the skin; in order to effect them the fish must be able to see the ground on which it lies, which it can do easily, as the eyes project upwards and look sideways, and can be turned independently either backwards or forwards; as soon as the ground is seen, nervous impulses proceed from the brain to the pigment-cells, and produce the appropriate response.

In many species specimens with spots or patches of colour on the blind side are fairly common, but those in which the whole blind side is coloured like the other are much rarer. Such complete ambicoloration—as it is termed—is a variation towards symmetry, which is always accompanied by others of the same nature, the scales of the blind side assuming the structure of those of the eyed side, and the migration of the eye being delayed, so that it often gets no further than the top of the head and interrupts the forward growth of the dorsal fin, the front part of which projects, forming a hook above the eye. Plaice, Flounder, and Turbot are among the species in which varieties of this kind are known.

The order Heterosomata includes some eight hundred species, most of which are

Photos]   [*Prof. F. B. Sumner.*
Bothus podas.
A Mediterranean Flat-fish. The same specimen as the one shown above but on a different ground.

FLAT-FISH

marine. All produce minute floating eggs in great numbers, sometimes millions from a single fish. Many are the objects of important fisheries. Five families may be recognized, Psettodidae, Pleuronectidae, Bothidae, Soleidae, and Cynoglossidae.

Reproduced by permission from]   [Day's British Fishes.
PLAICE (*Pleuronectus platessa*).
A valuable British Flat-fish, easily distinguished by its red spots.

The most primitive Flat-fish is *Psettodes*, a genus with one species from West Africa and another from the Indian Ocean. Structurally *Psettodes* is very like the sea-perches, except that the body is compressed, and the dorsal and anal fins are long and many-rayed. The dorsal fin does not extend on to the head, and its anterior rays are slender spines; the mouth is large, with strong, sharp teeth. *Psettodes* probably lies in wait until other fishes come near enough to be caught, and then makes short dashes after them.

Psettodes is indifferently dextral or sinistral, but the other Flat-fishes belong to groups in which the eyes are definitely on one side of the head or the other, although reversed examples, that is with eyes on the wrong side, may occur in certain species. In all Flat-fishes but *Psettodes*, the dorsal fin extends forward on to the head and is formed of flexible, jointed rays; these fishes swim by undulating movements of the body and of the fins that margin it.

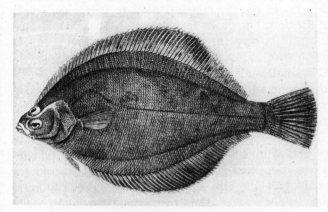

Reproduced by permission from]   [Day's British Fishes.
DAB (*Limanda limanda*).
A common British Flat-fish, greyish in colour.

The Pleuronectidae are Flat-fishes with the eyes on the right side, and with a prominent lower jaw; this family includes many important food-fishes of Northern Seas. The Halibut (*Hippo-*

283

glossus hippoglossus) is a northern species, found in both the Atlantic and Pacific Oceans. It is a powerful swimmer, with the body thicker than that of other Flat-fishes. The mouth is rather large, and the teeth are strong and sharp. The Halibut feeds mainly on other fishes ; it may reach a length of eight feet and a weight of four hundred pounds.

The Plaice (*Pleuronectus platessa*), distinguished by its red spots, has a small mouth, with the teeth in the jaws chisel-shaped, and more developed on the blind side ; it feeds mainly on bivalve molluscs, the shells of which are crushed by the strong, blunt, pharyngeal teeth. In Iceland waters plaice reach a weight of fifteen pounds.

Other British species that resemble the Plaice in having a small mouth, with the teeth more developed on the blind side, are the Flounder (*Platessa flesus*), the Dab (*Limanda limanda*), the Lemon Sole (*Microstomus microstomus*), and the Witch (*Glyptocephalus cynoglossus*) ; all feed mainly on small invertebrates.

The Pleuronectids of Australia and New Zealand form a distinct group (Rhombosoleinae) ; they have the jaws of the eyed side toothless, those of the blind side curved and toothed. and one pelvic fin elongate, continuing the anal forward.

The Bothidae have the eyes on the left side ; the lower jaw is prominent, and the teeth are generally equally well developed on both sides of the mouth. This family includes numerous species from tropical seas in which both pelvic fins are small ; some of them reach a large size and are valued as food ; the Summer Flounder (*Paralichthys dentatus*) of the Atlantic coast of the United States is an example.

Bothids in which the pelvic fin of the eyed side has a long base include the genera *Bothus* and *Arnoglossus*, with numerous species in warm seas. *Bothus* shows marked sexual differences, the males having spines on the snout, and the eyes wider apart than in the females. In this genus the young swim at the surface and are symmetrical until they reach a length of an inch or more, and the dorsal fin grows forward before the eye migrates, so that the eye has to push its way through under the fin, and seems to go through the head. *Arnoglossus* includes one British species, the Scald-fish (*A. laterna*), a small and worthless fish.

The most important group of the Bothidae, characterized by having both pelvic fins long-based, is restricted to the North Atlantic. There are several British species. The Turbot (*Scophthalmus maximus*) is a deep fish, naked, but with scattered, bony tubercles on the eyed side. It feeds on other fishes, and attains a weight of more than twenty pounds. The Brill (*S. laevis*) is less deep, and is normally scaled ; it also feeds on fishes, but grows to only half the size of the Turbot. The Top-knots (*Zeugopterus*) have small, spiny scales ; they live among the rocks. The Megrim (*Lepidorhombus megastoma*) is a thin, pale, large-eyed fish that lives in deep water ; in appearance it resembles the Witch.

SUCKER-FISHES (DISCOCEPHALI)

The Soleidae, or true Soles, have the small eyes close together on the right side ; the rounded snout projects beyond the small, curved mouth, which is toothed on the blind side only ; tactile filaments are generally present on the underside of the head, and the under nostril may be enlarged. There are more than one hundred species belonging to *Solea*, *Synaptura*, and allied genera, which extend from Europe and Africa to the Indo-Pacific, living mainly in sandy places. The Common Sole (*Solea vulgaris*) of Britain and the Mediterranean reaches a length of two feet ; it lives at depths down to fifty fathoms, and generally hides in the sand during the day ; but at night it goes in search of the worms, shell-fish, etc., on which it feeds, finding them in the sand by smell and touch.

The American Soles (*Achirus*) are small fishes of no value.

The Cynoglossidae, or Tongue-soles, are somewhat similar to the Soles, but have the eyes on the left side. The numerous species of *Cynoglossus* occur on sandy shores from West Africa to Japan ; they have a rounded head, and a long, tapering tail.

[*Otho Webb.*
TOP OF THE HEAD OF THE SHARK-SUCKER (*Echeneis naucrates*). The plates of the adhesive disc are depressible backwards ; when it is applied to a surface, the plates are raised, making a series of vacuum chambers and effecting adhesion.

Order 24. DISCOCEPHALI (Sucker-fishes)

This order includes a single family, the Echeneididae, or Sucker-fishes, of tropical seas. They have the spinous dorsal fin transformed into a large oval adhesive disc placed on top of the flat head, bearing a series of transverse narrow plates, each of which is a modified fin-ray. When the disc is applied to the skin of a shark, turtle, or other marine animal, the edges of the plates are raised, a series of vacuum chambers is created, and adhesion is effected.

These fishes, of which about a dozen species are known, stick on to other fishes or marine animals, or even to ships, and so are carried about ; when they are hungry, particularly if they find themselves in the neighbourhood of a shoal of small fishes, they leave go and search for food ; after a meal they look out for something on which to hold.

285

The largest species is the Shark-sucker (*Echeneis naucrates*), which grows to a length of four feet. This is a slender fish, with a long sucking disc. In the tropics large sharks are often caught with two or three shark-suckers on them, which drop off as the shark is taken from the water. The Remoras are more robust in form, and have a broader adhesive disc.

In many parts of the world the natives use the shark-sucker to catch turtles. In East Africa, the canoes put out carrying the fish in buckets : a long line is attached to a ring round the tail, and when a turtle is seen the fish is cast towards it and fastens on ; then the turtle is played carefully until it is captured. The Torres Straits islanders bore a hole through the tail for the line, and the fish are allowed to swim with the canoes or to attach themselves to them, being held by another line passed through the mouth and out of the gill-opening. The turtle, after being played, may in the end be secured by a diver, or may be harpooned.

It may be noted that in these methods of fishing, the sucking-fish is pulled backwards, and that a backward pull raises the laminae of the sucking-disc, so that the harder the fish is pulled the tighter it sticks ; indeed, it is easier to pull the ring off the tail, or the tail off the fish, than the fish off the turtle. The head-lines used by the Torres Straits natives to secure their fish make it easy to get them off, by means of a forward pull, when they are sticking on to their canoes.

Order 25. PLECTOGNATHI (Trigger-fishes, File-fishes, Globe-fishes, Porcupine-fishes and Sun-fishes)

The Plectognathi are distinguished from the Percomorphi by certain peculiarities of the skeleton. The order includes a large number of fishes from tropical and subtropical seas, with bony or spiny scales, small gill-openings, and short but powerful jaws, with the teeth few and generally strong. Except in the Triacanthidae the maxillaries are firmly attached to the non-protractile praemaxillaries. The Plectognathi are of no value as food, and many of them are poisonous.

The principal genus of the Triacanthidae is *Triacanthus* of the Indo-Pacific, which includes fishes with a deep, compressed body, covered with small, rough scales. The first ray of the short spinous dorsal fin is a long spine ; the pelvic fins are represented by similar spines. The small protractile mouth is provided with a few strong teeth arranged in two series, the outer incisive, the inner molar. These little silvery, blue-backed fishes live on sandy ground, and feed on shell-fish.

The Balistidae include over one hundred species from warm seas. The spinous dorsal fin consists of two or three spines, the first of which is strong, and when erected can be fixed by means of a knob at the base of the second ; the pelvic fins, if present, are represented by a small spine at the end of the long, movable pelvic bone, which helps to expand an abdominal air-sac. The mouth is small, with strong incisors in the jaws.

In *Balistes* and allied genera (Trigger-fishes) the body is covered with rather large, bony scales set edge to edge. Many of the species exhibit striking patterns of contrasting colours; they are tropical shore fishes, often found in the pools of coral reefs. They are able to make holes in the shells of molluscs with their powerful teeth, and to devour these animals. *Monacanthus* (File-fishes or Leather-jackets) differs from *Balistes* in having the body covered with small close-set spines.

The Triodontidae include only one species from the Indian Ocean, which differs from the Balistidae in having no spinous dorsal fin, and in

[*Raoul Barba.*

TRIGGER-FISH (*Balistes capriscus*).
A Mediterranean species. When the strong dorsal spine is erected, it is held firm by a knob on the basal part of the small spine behind it.

having the teeth represented by sharp-edged beak-like plates, that of the upper jaw being divided in the middle.

The Ostraciontidae, or Trunk-fishes, have the head and body enclosed in a firm, bony box, made up of six-sided plates. The small mouth protrudes at one end, and the short, naked tail at the other. There is no spinous dorsal fin, these fishes relying on their bony armour for protection. About twenty-five species are known from the shores of tropical seas; the box differs in shape, having three, four or five sides; in some species two long bony spines project forward from the head, in others two spines are also present at the hind-end of the box. Most Trunk-fishes are prettily marked with bright colours.

The Tetrodon-tidae, known as Globe - fishes or Puffers, have no spinous dorsal and no pelvic fins; the naked skin is studded with l i t t l e spines; the teeth form strong, sharp-edged plates, which are divided in the middle. Over a hundred s p e c i e s are known from warm seas, and a few from tropical rivers. They are

[*W. S. Pitt.*

PUFFER OR GLOBE-FISH (*Tetrodon cutcutia*).

carnivorous fishes, remarkable for their capacity for blowing themselves out like a balloon until they are spherical in shape ; this they accomplish by distending a large sac, connected with the gullet, either with air or water. When inflated with air, they may float upside-down at the surface of the sea.

The Diodontidae, or Porcupine-fishes, differ from the Tetrodonts in having undivided tooth-plates, with broad crushing surfaces inside the sharp edges. They have a short snout, a broad head, and strong spines in the skin, which in some species are very long, two-rooted, and erectile, and in others stout, three-rooted, and immovable. These tropical fishes inflate themselves in the same manner as the Tetrodonts ; they feed on corals and molluscs.

The Molidae, or Sun-fishes, are the most eccentric in form of all the Plectognaths. The two species of *Mola* have a deep and thick body ; the dorsal and anal fins are elevated, and immediately behind them the body is cut off short, the vertical hind-end being margined by a low caudal fin. The mouth is small, with sharp-edged tooth-plates ; the skin is rough. These fishes reach a length of over eight feet ; they inhabit the warmer parts of the oceans and may often be seen basking at the surface, or swimming about among shoals of fishes, and feeding on them. They may descend to considerable depths ; one caught in a trawl in deep water to the south of Ireland had in its stomach a Silver Ling (*Molva elongata*), a bottom-living fish rarely found in less than one hundred fathoms of water. The food of *Mola* is varied, and includes larval eels ; it is surprising that a fish of so clumsy a shape, and with so small a mouth, should ever be able to catch other fishes.

The Oblong Sun-fish (*Ranzania truncata*) is a smaller fish, growing to about two feet long ; it is longer and more compressed than *Mola*, and has the skin smooth, tessellated, containing little hexagonal plates. It is silvery, with a purple back, and with stripes and spots on the sides. It is widely distributed in the tropics.

Recently Dr. Johannes Schmidt has described the early stages of the Molidae. When first hatched, the larvae are very small, but are not peculiar in structure ; soon, however, a number of stout spines develop on the body ; next the caudal fin disappears, and five of the spines grow out into long horns, namely one on each side and three median ones, respectively on the back, snout, and chest ; next the fish changes its shape, becoming deeper ; now all the spines become small, the dorsal and anal fins become pointed, and a new caudal fin develops, connecting them along the hind end of the body. All these changes occur while the fish increases in length from about one-fifteenth to one-half inch, at which size it is not very different in structure from the adult.

Order 26. MALACICHTHYES (Rag-fishes)

This order includes the Icosteidae, or Rag-fishes, a family of uncertain position, that comprises two species known from deep-water off the Pacific coast of North America. They have a rather broad head and a strongly-compressed body, a terminal mouth with a single series of small teeth, long, many-rayed dorsal and anal fins without spines, a fan-like caudal with the rays spreading out from a narrow base, and pelvics, when present, behind the pectorals and unconnected with the pectoral arch. The skeleton is in great part cartilaginous, and "the entire body is characterized by a want of firmness, as it can be doubled up as readily as a piece of soft thick rag."

[*W. S. Pitt.*

PUFFER-FISH (*Tetrodon cutcutia*).
When annoyed, the Puffer inflates itself with air and floats upside-down, head below the water.

Order 27. XENOPTERYGII (Cling-fishes)

The Gobiesocidae, Suckers or Cling-fishes, have a large sucking disc on the flat under-surface of the body, formed in part by the widely-separated pelvic fins, and in part by pads of thickened skin. They are naked, with a broad head, a pointed snout, and a small mouth with conical or incisor-like teeth. There are no spines, and the few-rayed dorsal and anal fins are opposed.

These are little fishes, rarely more than three to four inches long; they are generally red in colour. They live near the coasts in tropical and temperate seas, clinging to stones or shells, and feeding on small prey. There are three British species, all belonging to the genus *Lepadogaster.*

[James's Press.

PORCUPINE-FISH.
The skin is covered with long, erectile spines.

The Two-spotted Sucker (*L. bimaculatus*) is reddish, with yellow spots and stripes, and a conspicuous spot, black encircled with white, on each side of the body; it grows to about two and a half inches. The shoals occur on a sandy or pebbly bottom down to about twenty fathoms; sometimes a fish will settle on a stone, and rest, turning its eyes about. The eggs are laid in empty shells, to which they adhere, forming a patch; the male clings to the shell and coils up, guarding the eggs until they hatch.

The Cornish Sucker (*L. gouanii*) grows to four inches. It varies in colour from brown to red, green, or blue; it lives between tide-marks, as does the Red Sucker (*L. descandolii*).

Order 28. HAPLODOCI (Toad-fishes)

The Toad-fishes have a flat head, a wide mouth with sharp teeth, a spinous dorsal fin of a few sharp spines, long soft dorsal and anal, broad pectorals, and jugular pelvics. A score of species, mostly American, are known from tropical and subtropical seas; they live near the coasts and feed on small fishes, molluscs, and crustaceans. They lie on the ground, often concealed by their mottled coloration, but dart out quickly to capture prey.

Porichthys is an American genus, naked, with rows of little silvery spots along the body ; it makes a humming or singing sound by vibrating the air-bladder. *Thalassophryne*, also American, has spines hollowed to transmit the poison that is contained in little bags at their bases.

These fishes guard the eggs and young ; the breeding habits of *Opsanus pardus*, the Leopard Toad - fish of the Atlantic coast of America, are as follows : mud is cleared away from beneath a stone or shell, to the underside of which the eggs adhere ; these are nearly a quarter of an inch across, and may number about two hundred ; when they hatch, the little fish remain attached by their tails ; the father guards them and fans water into their retreat, and later on, when they become free, he swims with the brood.

[*James's Press.*

SUN-FISH (*Mola*).
A fish of eccentric shape, the body being cut short immediately behind the dorsal and anal fins.

Order 29. PEDICULATI (Anglers)

The Angler-fishes are distinguished by a spinous dorsal fin of a few flexible rays, the first of which is placed on top of the head, above or a little behind the mouth, and is used as a line and bait ; the pectoral fins have the rays inserted on lobes that are often long and narrow, so that the fins may resemble arms, with many-fingered hands ; the pelvic fins, when present, are jugular. The gill-openings are small.

The Angler or Fishing-frog (*Lophius piscatorius*) of the North Atlantic is a naked fish, with an enormous, flattened head, and a wide terminal mouth, with rows of sharp, depressible teeth in the jaws. It reaches a length of five feet, and lies on the bottom, from the inshore waters down to depths of two hundred fathoms; the bait, or lure, is a skinny flap, sometimes white in colour, at the end of the slender line, and it is moved about to attract other fishes, which are seized when they come near enough. Sometimes the Angler swims up and takes birds at the surface of the water.

The eggs of the Angler float at the surface of the sea, enclosed in a band of mucus about ten yards long, known as a purple veil. The young have very large fins, and swim at the surface until they are two or three inches long. About twenty other species of Lophiidae are known, from tropical and temperate seas. *Chirolophius naresii* is remarkable for the long, branching tags that fringe the body and project from the dorsal rays; these have the appearance of weeds and help to conceal the fish.

The Sea-toads and Frog-fishes (Antennariidae) are small Anglers of tropical seas, compressed in form, and with oblique mouth. The species of *Antennarius* are numerous; they have a prickly skin, and are brightly coloured, with patterns of spots or bands; they frequent the coral reefs, crawling about or hanging on by means of their pectoral fins. *Pterophryne histrio* inhabits the floating *Sargassum* weed of the Atlantic; it is naked; yellow marbled with brown and dotted with white is a coloration that makes it inconspicuous among the weed, on the smaller inhabitants of which it preys.

Related to the Antennariidae are the Chaunacidae, oceanic fishes, red in colour, with the lure fleshy, on the upper surface of the broad snout, and the Oncocephalidae, or Bat-fishes.

The Bat-fishes, of which some forty species are known, live at the bottom in warm seas, some at considerable depths. They are flattened, with the arm-like pectoral fins at the hind-end of a large triangular or circular disc, covered with bony tubercles or spines; the lure is fleshy, and is placed in a cavity at the front of the head, above the small mouth.

The Ceratioids, or Sea-devils, are a large and varied group well distinguished from other Anglers by characters related to their habitat and manner of life. They live in the middle depths of the ocean, mostly from about two hundred to one thousand fathoms below the surface. As there is little or no light at these depths, they are uniformly blackish in colour.

The Sea-devils exhibit a remarkable sexual dimorphism. The females are much larger than the males, and generally have a large mouth, strong, sharp teeth, and a very distensible stomach; they float about in the darkness of the depths, attracting prey by means of a luminous lure. The males have a small, feebly-toothed mouth, and large olfactory sacs and nostrils, but they have no lure, and swim actively in search of small prey, or to find the females.

In some families the males become mature as free-swimming fishes;

292

the largest known males of this kind are about one and a half inches long. In other families the males seek the females, and do not become mature until they have found one, when they hold on to her with their mouths, become grown to her, and remain with her for the rest of their lives, living as parasites. As a rule a female has only one male, but wives possessing two, and even three husbands, are known, and when this occurs the males are of the same size, are attached close together, and are evidently brothers that were swimming in company when they first met their future wife. These parasitic males are dwarfs, mostly measuring from one-third of an inch to an inch in length. The largest known males, three to four inches long, were carried by very large females, over three feet long, and had evidently grown considerably since they first began

their parasitic existence. The males are generally attached to the abdomen of the female, but may occupy other positions, even the top of the head. The union of the two fishes is so perfect that it is difficult to say where one ends and the other begins; at their junction

[*James's Press.*

ANGLER OR FISHING-FROG (*Lophius piscatorius*).
The first dorsal fin is slender, and ends in a flap which is moved about to lure other fishes near to the capacious mouth.

the tissue connecting them is fibrous, and full of small blood-vessels. The male, without lure, toothless, and otherwise degenerate, appears to be nourished solely through the continuity of his blood-system with that of the female.

These differences between the sexes appear to be a consequence of the habits and conditions of life of these fishes; if the fish of both sexes lived a solitary life, were inactive, and waited in the dark for their prey to come to them, it would be difficult for them to know in what direction to seek a mate, or to have much chance of finding one. The problem has been solved by the males ceasing to be Anglers, and becoming small active fishes, searching for the females, and perhaps able to find them in the dark by an increased sense of smell. Some males appear to be content to find a female and perhaps keep near her, but others ensure that they will have a mate for life by first holding on and then growing on to her.

Some female Ceratioids, such as *Melanocetus* and *Linophryne*, have an enormous mouth, with very long, sharp, depressible teeth in the jaws;

293

these are able to swallow fishes much larger than themselves until they are distended like balloons. Two in this condition, that had only just begun to digest the swallowed fish, took baits, and were caught on long lines off Madeira. Others have been found alive, but helpless, at the surface of the ocean, to which they had been brought by the efforts of their victim, before it was completely engulfed. These Sea-devils are so constructed that once they have seized a fish, they cannot release it ; the victim may dash away, carrying its attacker with it, but it is held by the sharp teeth, and the minute it tires, it begins to be swallowed by its captor, whose teeth are depressible inwards ; when the struggles are resumed, the teeth again become erect and hold the captured fish.

[Brit. Mus. (Nat. Hist.).
An oceanic Angler-fish (*Melanocetus johnsoni*).

There are many curious types. *Gigantactis macronema* has a fishing line four times as long as itself, with a little lure at the end. The line is a fin-ray, and is articulated to the front end of a basal bone that generally lies in a trough on the top of the skull ; but this bone may project and may increase in length, and in some species forms a long rod. *Lasiognathus* has such a rod, and its line is prolonged beyond the lure to end in a triangle of hooks ; this complete angler has a curious mouth ; the slender praemaxillaries project forwards and are connected with the head by a broad membrane, that forms the walls of a pouch when the upper jaw moves down to enclose the prey ; the teeth are long bristles, of no use for piercing, but meeting across the opening in front of the lower jaw to close the trap.

Order 30. OPISTHOMI (Spiny Eels)

This order includes eel-like fishes of the fresh waters of Africa and Southern Asia.

The majority of the numerous species belong to the genus *Mastacembelus*, in which the body is covered with small scales, the dorsal and anal fins are long, the caudal is small, there is a series of isolated spines along the back, and pelvic fins are absent. There is a fleshy tentacle at the end of the snout, on each side of which is a tubular nostril ; the posterior

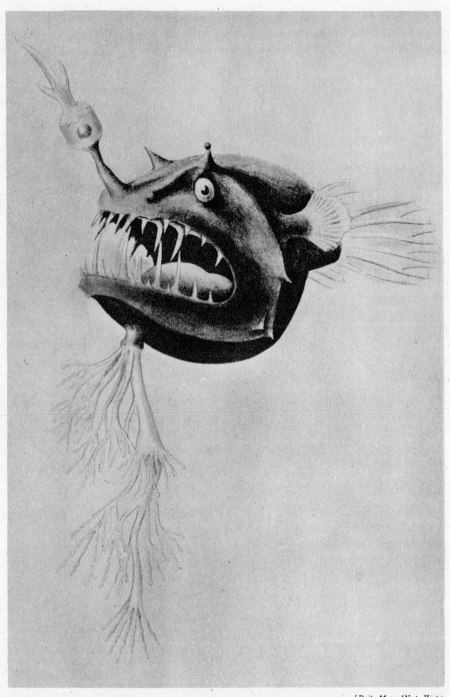

[Brit. Mus. (Nat. Hist.).

ANOTHER OCEANIC ANGLER-FISH (*Linophryne arborifera*).

nostrils are in front of the small eyes. These fishes are generally ornamented with spots or bars ; they are carnivorous, and probably burrow during the day and seek their food at night.

Order 31. SYMBRANCHII (Symbranchoid Eels)

These are eel-like fishes, without pectoral fins, and with the dorsal and anal fins membraneous, rayless, and continuous with the small caudal ; the gill-openings form a single transverse ventral slit.

The little Shore-eels (*Alabes*) of the coast of Australia have a broad, flat head and a small mouth, with blunt, compressed teeth ; the dorsal and anal fins are well-developed and the minute two-rayed pelvic fins are placed just behind the gill-opening.

The other members of the group are larger, growing to two feet or more ; they have a long head, a large mouth with strong, sharp teeth, very low dorsal and anal fins and no pelvics.

Symbranchus has three species, respectively from Tropical America, West Africa, and India to Western Australia and New Guinea ; they are found in fresh or brackish water, particularly in marshes and estuaries, and sometimes in the sea ; they burrow in the mud like true eels.

The Cuchia (*Amphipnous*) of tropical Asia has a pair of air-breathing sacs above the gill-chambers ; it spends most of its life out of water, wriggling along the banks, and making burrows in them in which it rests during the dry season ; it goes into the water to find the worms and small shell-fish on which it feeds.

[*Brit. Mus. (Nat. Hist.).*]

OCEANIC ANGLER-FISH (*Gigantactis macronema*).

CLASS BATRACHIA (or Amphibia)

BY

E. G. BOULENGER, F.Z.S.

Director of the Zoological Society's Aquarium, London.

INTRODUCTION

The name " Batrachian " is here used to embrace the frogs, toads, newts and salamanders in preference to the name " Amphibian " given to the group by Linnaeus, since this term might equally apply to the many widely-diverse creatures—birds and mammals that are equally at home on land or in the water. Batrachians bridge the gulf between the fish and the reptiles, living examples being the degenerate survivals of a once mighty race. The group is of primary importance to the evolutionist, since it marks that epoch-making step, the vertebrate's conquest of the land. The batrachians had their inception in the Devonian age when much of the northern hemisphere was clothed with swampy forest, now represented by the coal measures. In the succeeding Carboniferous age, huge jungles of giant club mosses extended even to the sea-shore. The earlier batrachians often reached vast proportions, resembling such heavily-armoured reptiles as the much later crocodiles ; others shared many features in common with the Crossopterygian fishes.

The batrachians known to-day, though frequently reptilian in form when adult, evince their affinity with the fishes by first passing through a gill-breathing larval stage. This may endure for years or be hurried through in a few weeks, according to the exigencies of the circumstances. Usually the eggs are enclosed in a more or less gelatinous envelope—a provision against frost. Though abundantly represented in the tropics, few batrachians are tolerant of excessive heat. With few exceptions their skin is naked, and is studded with numerous glands. Some of these, especially the parotids, give off secretions noxious to foes and sometimes of a highly toxic nature. The skin of some adult batrachians, and of all whilst in the larval stage, possesses sense organs analogous to those seen in the lateral lines of fishes. A reptilian feature is a tendency to shed the skin, which first ruptures near the head and is pulled off inside-out. The skeleton presents most of the general characteristics seen in the higher vertebrates ; ribs, however, are usually wanting, and in the tailless species the terminal vertebrae are fused together into one elongate process— the urostyle. The skull is articulated by two condyles ; the teeth, when present, are usually minute. The alimentary system is simple, and the lungs are not developed until the gills are in process of absorption. As in most aquatic or semi-aquatic creatures, the eyes and nostrils are set high up on the head. The eyes are usually large and show great diversity in the shape of the pupil, which may be rounded, vertical, or elliptical.

297

The ear, when present, is represented externally by a round or oval membrane, the tympanum, which is situated just behind the eye. The mouth is large and the palate is pierced by two choanae—the internal openings to the nasal cavity. A tongue, except in the case of certain entirely aquatic forms, is always present. It may be united with the floor of the mouth, or be attached by one end and capable of great and rapid extension. Limbs, which may be altogether wanting, reach their highest development in the strictly terrestrial species. In some forms small discs are present on the tips of the digits, and these by pressure and suction serve the same function as the suctorial pads of certain Gecko lizards.

As a class, batrachians affect moist situations, terrestrial species lying concealed in times of drought and issuing forth in force when the rain returns—a phenomenon which accounts for the tales of "showers of frogs" still accredited by some people. Though the courtship and incubatory habits of many batrachians are sufficiently picturesque, their general intelligence cannot be considered to be of a high order. They do not appear to appreciate objects unless in motion, and will snap indifferently at a passing fly or a brandished pencil. Vocal efforts play a part in bringing the sexes together. The well-known songs of frogs and toads are usually produced by an inflation of large sacs on the sides of the head or throat, which when in action may occasionally rival the animal's entire bulk. Save in the early larval stages, all batrachians are purely carnivorous.

Living batrachians are usually divided into the following three orders :—

1. The *Apoda*—limbless batrachians (Coecilians).
2. The *Urodela*—tailed batrachians (Newts, Salamanders, etc.).
3. The *Anura*—tailless batrachians (Frogs and Toads).

Order APODA (Limbless Batrachians)

The Apoda are degraded wormlike creatures adapted to a subterranean life. The cylindrical body is marked with ring-like grooves, there are no limbs, and the tail is absent or but rudimentary. The skin is smooth, and the eyes, which are minute, are in most forms covered with skin. There are no ear openings, but a pair of short retractile tentacles—sensory organs—are situated between the eyes and the tip of the snout. The mouth is well developed, and is furnished with small or large teeth.

The Apoda are represented by a single family—the *Coeciliidae*, of which there are twenty-two genera and over fifty species. The members of the Order inhabit Tropical Africa, America, South-eastern Asia, and the Seychelles. They are usually found in damp situations, where they feed nearly entirely on worms. Some species lay eggs, whilst others bring forth their young alive.

The development of *Icthyophis glutinosa* of Ceylon and South-eastern

Asia has been described by P. and F. Sarasin. The large eggs form a rosary-like string and are deposited in the earth close to a river or pond. They adhere together, forming a mass round which the female coils herself. The embryos are provided with very long external gills and are liberated at an advanced stage in their development, after the gills have been lost, when they are provided with an opening on each side of the head—the spiraculum. The metamorphosis is completed in the water, and at this stage they are furnished with well-developed eyes, and a tail—crested above and below.

In *Hypogeophis* of the Seychelles the young leave the egg in the perfect form.

Typhlonectes and *Siphonops* of South America and *Dermophis* of West Africa do not lay eggs, the young being born alive—exact replicas of their parents in the American species, and at an advanced stage in their development in the case of the African.

[*D. Seth-Smith.*
TIGER SALAMANDER (*Amblystoma tigrinum*) [ADULT STAGE].
A common North American species which is now known to be specifically the same as the Axolotl.

Order URODELA
(Tailed Batrachians)

The tailed batrachians are divided into the following four families : 1. The *Salamandridae*, with well-developed eyelids, four limbs, toothed jaws, and no gills in the perfect form ; 2. The *Amphiumidae*, which resemble the members of the previous family, but have no eyelids ; 3. The *Proteidae*, with toothed jaws, no eyelids, well-developed limbs, and gills which persist throughout life ; 4. The *Sirenidae*, which also retain their gills, but have no hind limbs, toothless jaws, and no eyelids.

Family Salamandridae

This family comprises the salamanders and newts, and is distributed over nearly the whole of the northern hemisphere. The eyelids are well developed, although in *Typhlotriton* they are concealed under the skin.

In the genus *Salamandra*, represented by two species in Europe and two in South-western Asia, the tail is rounded and the tongue is short.

The Spotted Salamander (*Salamandra salamandra*) extends over Southern and Central Europe, ascending to an altitude of 3,000 feet. The broad, flat head has large parotid glands, and there is a row of pores extending along each side of the body. The striking livery of black and yellow markings is subject to great variation. The young, ten to forty in number, are born in a larval state with well-developed limbs and large external gills. They are deposited in brooks and streams in the spring and seek land when they are about six months old.

The Black or Alpine Salamander (*S. atra*) is an Alpine species not found below 2,500 feet. It is smaller than the preceding, uniform black in colour, and produces two young only, which are born in the perfect form, having passed through their larval stage within the parent.

The Newts (genus *Molge*) have the tail, which is often crested, compressed vertically. All resort to water at least during the breeding season, when the males of many kinds develop ornate crests and bright colours,

[*Paul Unger.*

SPOTTED SALAMANDER (*Salamandra salamandra*).
A European species strikingly marked with black and yellow.

and indulge in grotesque evolutions with the apparent object of attracting the females.

Of the twenty species known, three—the Smooth Newt (*M. vulgaris*), the Crested Newt (*M. cristata*), and the Palmated Newt (*M. palmata*), are indigenous to Great Britain. The male Crested Newt courts the female with an elaborate ritual.

The Alpine Newt (*M. alpestris*), of Central Europe, is by no means restricted to mountainous regions, being common in the lowlands of Holland. It is dark above, with an orange or red waistcoat.

The olive or black Pleurodele Newt (*M. waltli*), of Portugal, Spain and Morocco, is unique in having long, pointed ribs, which may actually pierce the skin. It carries no crest on tail or body.

Amblystoma is known by twenty species, all of which, with a single exception from Siam, live in Northern or Central America. In appearance and habits they closely resemble Salamanders.

Amblystoma tigrinum, of Northern America and South-west to C e n t r a l

CRESTED NEWT (*Molge cristata*).
Breeding male and females, the former distinguished by the large crest.

Mexico, is a common species, the larval form being the famous Axolotl. The Axolotl is furnished with enormous external gills, and well-developed fins on the back and tail. It may attain to nearly a foot in length and unless forced to take to land through drought, spends its whole life submerged, breeding freely whilst in the larval condition. Although for long known to scientists, the true relations between the *Amblystoma* and the Axolotl were not established until 1865, when at Freiburg University it was demonstrated that the creatures could be forced to metamorphose when placed under conditions which rendered the function of the gills difficult and that of the lungs easy. It is now known that the change can always be produced by a single meal of t h y r o i d or pituitary gland.

The salamander-like creatures of the E u r o p e a n a n d Central and South A m e r i c a n genus *Spelerpes* are remarkable for their extensile tongue, which can be shot out with great suddenness and to a very considerable distance.

Photos]   *[W. J. Clarke.*
PLEURODELE NEWT (*Molge waltli*).
This Spanish newt has no crests and is peculiar in that its ribs sometimes project through the skin.

301

[H. Bastin.

SMOOTH NEWT (*Molge vulgaris*).
A British species. In all newts the tail is compressed for use in swimming.

Family Amphiumidae

The largest member of this family is the Giant Salamander of Japan—
Megalobatrachus maximus, which inhabits mountain streams, and reaches
nearly six feet in length. The head is large, very broad and much
flattened, and the minute eyes are scarcely discernible amid the numerous
tubercles. The grey or brown skin harmonizes well with a rocky habitat.
The eggs of the creature are laid in strings, and are incubated by the male,
who aerates them by heaving the mass up and down with his body. The
young on hatching have external gills and rudimentary limbs.

An allied species, *M. sligoi*, is known by a single three-and-a-half-foot-
long specimen discovered by chance in the Hong Kong Botanical Gardens.
It is now lodged in the Aquarium of the London Zoological Society. It
resembles the Japanese species, but has a longer and more flattened
head.

Cryptobranchus, of the Eastern United States, is represented by a single
species, known as the Hell-bender, which attains a length of eighteen
inches. It hides by day in rock fissures under water, where it waylays
fish, crayfish, frogs, and sometimes members of its own species. As in
the Giant Salamander, the eggs are tended by the male.

The Amphiuma or Blind-eel (*A. means*), the sole representative of its
genus, is an eel-shaped relative of the Giant Salamanders, inhabiting the

South-eastern United States. It reaches about a yard in length and owes much of its fish-like appearance to the very rudimentary limbs, which possess only two or three fingers and toes. It has a small, pointed head with minute eyes, and is exceptionally slimy. The eggs, laid in strings, are deposited on land, where the female coils round them and protects them. They hatch in about three months and for the first six weeks of their existence the young are provided with external gills.

Family Proteidae

This family is represented by two genera—*Proteus* of Yugo-Slavia, and *Necturus* of North America.

Necturus has minute but serviceable eyes, fairly well-formed limbs and a long tail, with high fins above and below. The general colour is chocolate, with large, fringed gills crimson in colour. Like many Urodeles, it is strangely indifferent to injury, specimens deprived of their gills continuing to respire through their skin. It reaches about two feet in length, is nocturnal, and feeds on small frogs, worms and crustaceans.

The slender and elongate Proteus (*P. anguineus*) is confined to the subterranean lakes and mountain cavities east of the Adriatic, where it lives in complete darkness. It is a completely blind batrachian whose life spent in darkness has resulted in the almost total loss of its eyes.

[*Paul Unger.*

AXOLOTL (white variety).
In the lakes of the Valley of Mexico Axolotls become sexually mature as gilled aquatic animals.

The skin is pale pink or whitish, but the dormant pigment cells become assertive on exposure to light. It attains a maximum length of about eighteen inches. It lays some fifty eggs, which hatch in ten weeks, the issuing young having two fingers only and but slightly-developed eyes.

[*W. S. Berridge.*

THE MENOBRANCH (*Necturus maculatus*).
The Menobranch of North America is one of the Urodeles that retain gills throughout their lives.

It is an extremely hardy creature and in captivity has been known to thrive without taking any food for a period of over five years. In its native haunts, Proteus feeds entirely on small crustaceans.

[*F. W. Bond.*

PROTEUS (*Proteus anguineus*).
A blind salamander of subterranean waters.

Family Sirenidae

The family Sirenidae of the south-eastern regions of the United States includes two genera — *Siren* and *Pseudobranchus*, each of these having but a single species. In the genus Siren the digits are four in number, but, on the other hand, in the genus Pseudobranchus there are only three. The Siren (*Siren lacertina*) is snake-like in appearance, and inhabits marshes, where it digs burrows in the mud. This batrachian grows to a length of three feet, of which length about one-third is taken up by the tail. When swimming, the limbs of Siren are folded back against the sides of the body.

[*W. S. Berridge.*

Amphiuma means.
An eel-shaped salamander with vestigial limbs.

304

Order ANURA (Frogs and Toads)

This Order embraces nearly fifteen hundred species and is divided into two Suborders : the *Phaneroglossa* — the tongued batrachians, a n d t h e *Aglossa* — the tongueless batrachians. The Order is characterized by its representatives being entirely without a tail in the adult stage, by the more or less rounded and com-

By courtesy of]   [*Carl Hagenbeck's Tierpark, Stellingen.*
AFRICAN BULL FROG (*Rana adspersa*).

pact body, and by the absence of a discernible neck. The transverse processes of the sacral vertebra, as a rule the ninth, may be either dilated or cylindrical. The jaws may be either finely toothed or entirely toothless. The tympanum may be large or scarcely discernible. Each fore limb bears four toes, and each hind limb five. Anura are almost as abundant in the temperate as in the tropical and sub-tropical regions.

Suborder Phaneroglossa

This Suborder is divided into two divisions—(*a*) the *Firmisternia*, in which the two halves of the shoulder girdle are united; (*b*) the *Arcifera*, in which the two halves of the shoulder girdle are movable and may overlap.

Division Firmisternia.

[*James's Press.*
EDIBLE FROG (*Rana esculenta*).
The edible frog is found in eastern England, where it was probably introduced from Italy.

This division includes the typical frogs. *Family Ranidae (Frogs)*.

This family is distributed throughout the world, with the exception o f t h e southern - most parts of South America, the greater part of Australia and New Zealand. The upper jaw is toothed, and the transverse processes of the sacral vertebra are not dilated. The genus *Rana* comprises more than a hundred and fifty species.

BATRACHIA (ORDER ANURA)

The Common Frog (*Rana temporaria*) is found throughout the greater part of the temperate Old World, from England to Japan. Although its range of coloration is great, the sexes are easily distinguished in the breeding season, when the males show slightly larger webs between the hind toes, and the inner fingers of the front limbs develop swollen pads, covered with small, dark, horny spinules which serve to clasp the female. The males may be further distinguished by the presence of two internal

[Chase (Dorien Leigh).
BULL FROG (*Rana catesbiana*).
The largest American frog takes its name from the bellowing noise it makes.

vocal sacs. In this frog the skin is perfectly smooth with a dorso-lateral glandular fold. The snout is rounded and only slightly projecting beyond the mouth. Though a terrestrial species, the Common Frog is much addicted to water during the summer months, and not infrequently hibernates in the mud at the bottom of a pond. In Central Europe the breeding season begins in February, later in the north, when the well-known masses of spawn appear wherever there is standing water. Even a water-filled cart-rut may serve, though drought may prevent the eggs hatching, or, if hatched, the tadpoles from metamorphosing. The eggs (from one thousand five hundred to four thousand in number) are laid in the bottom of the pond but soon float to the surface and hatch in a few weeks. The length of time taken by the tadpoles to develop limbs, absorb their tails and take to the land depends much on the temperature. In the extreme north they may even be obliged to hibernate. At first vegetarians, the growing tadpoles soon become carnivorous, eating smaller animals and any chance carrion. The perfect frog lives almost exclusively on insects and worms, which it catches with a rapid flick of its adhesive tongue.

The Edible Frog (*R. esculenta*), abundant throughout Europe, Western Asia and North-west Africa, is in England confined to the fens of Norfolk and Cambridgeshire, where it was probably introduced in the Middle Ages by Italian monks, since the British specimens agree with an Italian variety. The male Edible Frog is the possessor of a pair of large inflatable vocal sacs situated on each side of the head. Its croak is extremely loud and may be heard not only during the breeding season, but throughout the summer months. The eggs, from five thousand to ten thousand in number, are slightly smaller than those of the Common Frog, and are laid in the late spring. Unlike those of the

[*W. S. Berridge.*

FLYING FROG (*Rhacophorus pardalis*).
The web between the digits is said to enable this frog to parachute down from trees to earth.

commoner species, they do not float but remain submerged. The Edible Frog is usually greenish or dark olive in colour mottled with black.

The Agile Frog (*R. agilis*) occurs in Sweden, Denmark, France, Italy, Germany, Austria and south-western Europe. By means of its greatly-developed hind limbs it can jump a couple of yards. Its colouring closely approximates to the dry woodland leaves amongst which it lives. It enters water only during the breeding season, when the eggs, similar

PICKEREL FROG (*Rana palustris*).
A handsomely-marked North American relative of the common frog.
[*Topical.*

both in size and shape to those of the Common Frog, are laid amongst submerged leaves.

The Bull Frog (*R. catesbiana*), the largest of the New World frogs, is found throughout the greater part of the eastern United States, where it grows to over eight inches in length. The tympanum almost exceeds the eye in size. The toes are completely webbed, the species being purely aquatic. The voice fully justifies the popular name, since it resembles the bellowing of a bull. The tadpoles need two or three years to transform.

The Giant Frog (*R. goliath*) of the Cameroons, which is the largest member of the Order, attaining a foot in length, is capable of capturing and swallowing a full-grown rat. Few specimens are known. The first was discovered by a former Zoo keeper who confined his capture in a ten-gallon spirit drum filled with water, from which the frog escaped after forcing off the heavy metal cover.

The Solomon Island Frog (*R. opisthodon*) is noteworthy in that its globular eggs are placed in rock crannies near running water. The young, about four inches in length, undergo their entire metamorphosis within the egg, and as soon as liberated, leap about with astonishing agility.

The Skating Frog (*R. cyanophlyctis*), a very aquatic species inhabiting India, literally jumps on the water, covering the surface in big leaps, alighting on all fours and leaping off again as it would on land.

The genus *Arthroleptis* includes a dozen diminutive forms from Africa with horizontal pupils, and the digits almost without webs.

The Seychelles Frog (*A. seychellensis*) carries its very large tadpoles—about a dozen in number—on its back, where they cling by means of their adhesive bellies. In this position they are believed to undergo their entire metamorphosis.

The genus *Hylambates* includes arboreal species from Tropical Africa, with large adhesive discs on the tips of the digits.

308

The female of *H. breviceps*, from the Cameroons, incubates her few but bulky eggs in her mouth.

Rhacophorus is a genus represented by some fifty species from the East Indies, China, Japan and Madagascar. The digits are tipped with large adhesive discs and in many species they are joined by extensive webs.

In the so-called "Flying" Frog (*R. pardalis*) the membranes between the toes are so extensive that they serve to support the creature in the air during its leaps to the ground from the branches of trees.

In *R. schlegelii*, from Japan, the sexes combine to build an underground chamber in damp earth; here the eggs are deposited in a frothy mass, formed by a secretion exuded and beaten up by the female.

R. malabaricus, from India, places its eggs in frothy nests attached to vegetation overhanging the water, into which the tadpoles eventually fall.

The female of *R. reticulatus*, from Ceylon, carries about a dozen young attached to her under-surface.

Family Dendrobatidae (Poison Frogs).

The family Dendrobatidae contains three genera from South America, West Africa and Madagascar, all the members of which are distinguished by the absence of teeth.

The genus *Dendrobates* is represented in tropical America by seven small, tree-dwelling species with horizontal pupils, and digits with adhesive discs but no webs.

D. tinctorius, from Brazil, owes its specific name to its toxic secretion, which is used by the natives to poison their arrows. It is also employed by the Indians to dye the green feathers of parrots. On some of the feathers being removed and the bare patches rubbed with a live frog, the new feathers emerge as bright yellow.

The tadpoles of *D. trivittatus* are transported from one

[*James's Press.*

MOORISH TOAD (*Bufo mauritanicus*).
A North African toad.

309

shallow pool to another, since the nurseries continually dry up, thus the larvae enjoy a protracted tour whilst clinging to the parental back by their adhesive lips.

Family Engystomatidae.

This family includes a score of genera characterized by the dilated transverse processes of the sacral vertebra. Most are narrow-mouthed, ant-eating species, terrestrial, aquatic, or burrowing. The members of the family have no teeth, and the nocturnal species are distinguished by vertical pupils.

Darwin's Frog (*Rhinoderma darwinii*), the only member of its genus, is a diminutive form from Chili, with a triangular snout surmounted by a fleshy knob. The vocal sac of the male covers almost the entire under-

[*D. Seth-Smith.*

BARKING TOAD (*Ceratophrys ornata*).
A South American burrowing toad.

surface, and serves as a nursery for the larvae, which do not develop gills and have from the first very insignificant tails. The eggs are placed in the sac by the male parent, who forces them into his mouth with his hands.

The members of the African burrowing genus *Breviceps* are almost globular in shape. The hind limbs bear shovel-shaped tubercles which are employed in digging.

Division Arcifera.

In this division the two halves of the shoulder girdle are free, but overlapping.

Family Cystignathidae.

In the frogs of this family the upper jaw is toothed, and the transverse processes of the sacral vertebra are not dilated. It is represented by arboreal, aquatic, terrestrial, and burrowing forms.

310

The Barking Toad (*Ceratophrys ornata*) of Brazil and the Argentine has bright saffron-yellow jaws, and a vivid green skin bearing black-edged gold or chestnut markings. A small, triangular horn surmounts each eye, and the hind feet bear large, bony tubercles, which are employed in digging. This toad spends most of its time wholly or partially hidden in the ground,

[W. J. Clarke.
NATTERJACK TOAD (*Bufo calamita*).
The Natterjack occurs in Europe in dry, sandy places; it is local in Britain.

where it waylays small birds, mice and other frogs. When handled it often evinces its annoyance by loud cries, strikingly suggestive of a peevish pet dog.

Chiroleptes, of Australia, is another burrowing genus, with the first finger opposable to its fellows.

C. platycephalus weathers long droughts by storing water—as much as a wineglassful—in its body cavity, a peculiarity that thirsty natives sometimes find useful.

Family Bufonidae (True Toads).

The True Toads number over a hundred species. They are of world-wide distribution, occurring in all countries, with the exception of Madagascar and some of the Pacific islands. The sacral vertebrae are dilated, and teeth are absent. The fingers are free, and the toes are usually webbed. The tongue is oval or pear-shaped, and rooted to the front of the mouth.

The genus *Bufo* includes the bulk of the group and is represented throughout Europe

[W. S. Berridge.
GREEN TOAD (*Bufo viridis*).
This European toad is smaller than the common toad; it is variable in colour.

and North-west Africa by the common species *Bufo vulgaris*. The general appearance is well-known, the most distinct features being the absence of a vocal sac, the prominently wrinkled skin, and the large parotid glands measuring half the length of the entire head. The female is much larger than the male. The Common Toad is the most intelligent of all the batrachians, being easily tamed. It is nocturnal in its habits, and lives principally upon worms and slugs. This Toad is a staunch conservative in the choice of a breeding ground, journeying, in late March or early April, long distances to some chosen pond, where all the toads in the neighbourhood congregate in great numbers. The eggs, from four thousand to seven thousand in number, are laid in long, gelatinous strings and are twined round submerged vegetation.

The Green Toad (*B. viridis*) varies much in colour, and may be grey, green, yellow or pinkish, with irregular blotches. It is smaller than the Common Toad, seldom exceeding four inches in length. It is found in Central and Southern Europe, Northern Africa and South-western and Central Asia eastwards to the Himalayas, where it ascends to a height of fifteen thousand feet, a record altitude for any batrachian. The eggs resemble those of *B. vulgaris*, but the larvae are much larger in proportion.

The Natterjack Toad (*B. calamita*) occurs in dry, sandy localities

[*W. S. Pitt.*

MIDWIFE TOAD (*Alytes obstetricans*).
Male carrying eggs.

312

James's Press.

Hyla aurea.
An Australian Tree-frog, golden in colour.

throughout Northern and Western Europe. In the British Isles it is very local. The feet are webbed only at the base, consistent with a burrowing habit, and the hind limbs are so short that the creature does not hop like most toads, but progresses by means of short runs. It is brown or yellowish in colour with a pale vertebral line, which always distinguishes it from the other British species. The eggs are laid in strings composed of two rows, and where the toad frequents sandhills by the sea, these may be laid in decidedly brackish water.

The Giant Toad (*B. marinus*), which abounds in Southern and Central America and the West Indies, grows to over six inches in length. Bony ridges surmount the head, and the enormous parotid glands discharge their fluid in jets when danger threatens.

Family Hylidae (*Tree-frogs*).

This family comprises some two hundred arboreal species with dilated sacral vertebrae. The teeth are present only in the upper jaw and the tips of the digits usually bear adhesive discs.

In *Hyla*, the type genus, the fingers are sometimes webbed, the toes always so. The pupil is horizontal, the tongue is entire or slightly cleft. The family is cosmopolitan, but is absent from the Ethiopian and the greater part of the Indian regions. *H. maxima*, of British Guiana, attains a length of five inches, but the majority of the representatives of the genus are much smaller.

The Common Tree-frog (*H. arborea*), of Western Europe, North-west Africa, Madeira, the Canary Islands, China and Japan, is a neat, compact frog, rarely reaching two inches in length. It is usually a vivid emerald green in colour above, but is capable of great colour changes, and may pass from white to yellow or dark brown in a few seconds. Blue specimens are not uncommon. The skin is smooth above, granular on the under-surface. The male can distend its throat sac until it exceeds the head in size, and the ensuing voice is worthy of a very much larger creature. The eggs, eight hundred to a thousand in number, are laid on submerged weeds in clumps, each the size of a walnut.

H. goeldii, from Brazil, has strange breeding habits, the female carrying the score or so of eggs upon her back, the emerging young being fully-fledged frogs, save for the presence of a tail.

The members of the genus *Phyllomedusa* of Tropical America are unique in that the inner digits of all four limbs are opposable. With these it wraps its egg-masses in leaves overhanging the water, into which the larvae fall when fully formed. These frogs frequent tree-tops, only descending to the ground level during the breeding season.

The genus *Nototrema*, also of Tropical America, differs from other Tree-frogs in that the females are provided with a brood-pouch on the back, formed by a horse-shoe-shaped fold of the skin. Herein lie the eggs until they develop, the precise stage at which the larvae escape varying with the different species.

Family Pelobatidae (Spade-foot Toads).

The members of this family have strongly-dilated sacral vertebrae, vertically elliptic pupils, and teeth in the upper jaw only. The seven genera are almost world-wide, though absent from Africa and Australia.

The Common Spade-foot (*Pelobates fuscus*) occurs in sandy districts in North-eastern and Central Europe. The head is very broad and the eyes are large and prominent. The Spade-foot is a burrower, employing its short, massive hind limbs as shovels. When molested it utters shrill cries, like those of an infant, and the skin gives off an exudation which smells of garlic ; at the same time, its body becomes swollen like a balloon. The eggs are expelled in a thick band, and are deposited round water plants ; they develop into remarkably large tadpoles, exceeding four inches in length.

Family Discoglossidae (Bell-toads).

The family Discoglossidae, of Europe, Asia, and New Zealand, is characterized by having short ribs on the anterior vertebrae. The circular tongue is almost entirely fixed to the mouth-floor, and the sacral vertebrae are much dilated.

314

BELL-TOADS (DISCOGLOSSIDAE)

The genus *Bombinator* is represented by two species from Europe, one from North-eastern Asia, and a fourth from Southern China.

The European Fire-bellied Toad (*B. igneus*) and Yellow-bellied Toad (*B. pachypus*) seldom attain a length of more than two inches. Both are very aquatic, but whereas the former frequents ponds or pools of clear water, the latter is found in small sheets of water, clear or dirty, even in rain puddles formed by cart-ruts. Both species when freshly captured may feign death. At first they will seek to scare away the foe by grotesque antics, finally twisting the limbs so that the vivid underparts are largely exposed. They will thus remain motionless until they judge all danger is passed. Further protection is afforded by a frothy acrid secretion exuded from their skin, which causes sneezing and watery eyes.

Alytes is a European genus represented by two species—*A. obstetricans* of France, Spain, Portugal, Switzerland, West of Germany and South-eastern Holland, and *A. cisternasi* of Spain and Portugal —a somewhat stouter form with a larger head. The skin in these toads is very tuberculate, the pupil is vertical, the

[W. S. Pitt.

CLAWED TOAD (*Xenopus laevis*).
A thoroughly aquatic South African toad.

sacral vertebrae much dilated; the fingers are free and the toes feebly webbed.

The Midwife Toad (*A. obstetricans*) is remarkable for the fact that the nursing duties devolve upon the father. Pairing commences in April, when about fifty eggs are laid in a rosary-like string. These are taken charge of by the male, who pushes his legs through the masses of eggs as they are expelled. Eventually the strings settle round his hind legs, where they form a living life-belt. Thus encumbered he crawls off to some secure retreat, venturing forth only on rare occasions with the object of taking a hip bath in an adjacent pool in order to moisten his precious burden. At the end of a month, when the eggs are about to hatch, he betakes himself to the water, where the family wriggles away in the form of large tadpoles.

BATRACHIA (ORDER ANURA)

Suborder Aglossa

The tongueless frogs belong to the family *Pipidae*, which is divided into the following three genera—*Xenopus* of Tropical and South Africa, *Hymenochirus* of Tropical Africa, and *Pipa* of Tropical America. In all these thoroughly-aquatic animals the eyelids and the tympanum are absent, and the toes are very broadly webbed. The sacral vertebrae are much dilated.

The Clawed Toad (*Xenopus laevis*) of South Africa has the tips of the three inner toes tipped with horny sheaths. The fingers are free, but the webs between the toes are so enormously developed that they resemble half-opened umbrellas. The skin bears numerous sense organs similar to those seen in fishes. About a hundred eggs are laid singly, attached to aquatic plants. The tadpoles bear long feelers, which attain a length equal to that of the head and body, at the angles of the mouth; these are believed to serve as balancing organs.

The Surinam Toad (*Pipa pipa*) is a grotesque creature, with a much-compressed triangular head, toothless jaws and a star-shaped appendage on each finger tip. A large, fleshy flap is situated at the angle of the mouth and sometimes on the snout. The eggs, about fifty in number, are laid in the spring, when the male presses them from the extensile oviduct into the back of the female, which at this time of the year becomes spongy and yielding. The cavities so formed become, after a few days, covered with a horny lid. About three months later, the infants lift the lid and emerge as fully-formed replicas of their grotesque-looking parents.

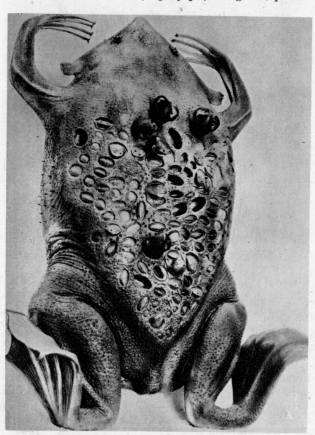

[*Sport & General.*

SURINAM TOAD (*Pipa pipa*).
Female with young on the back.

CLASS REPTILIA (Reptiles)

BY

E. G. BOULENGER, F.Z.S.,

Director of the Zoological Society's Aquarium, London.

Living reptiles—Tortoises, Crocodiles, Lizards, and Snakes—agree with the Amphibians and Fishes and differ from Birds and Mammals in being cold-blooded vertebrate animals, the temperature of their blood rising and falling according to that of their surroundings. The skull articulates with the vertebral column by a single rounded knob—occipital condyle—as in Birds. Some Reptiles lay eggs, either hard- or soft-shelled ; others are viviparous. Reptiles differ from Amphibians in never undergoing metamorphosis, being born or hatched from the egg in the perfect condition, which they will retain for the whole of their lives. In most Reptiles the skin is covered with scales or shields. In short, Reptiles may be defined as cold-blooded vertebrates, unprovided with feathers or hairs, breathing by means of lungs, and not undergoing any transformation.

In the majority of living Reptiles, the teeth are either inserted on the edges of the jaws, or are applied on the inner side to the wall of a groove, but in the Crocodiles they are implanted in sockets. In Snakes, the teeth may be solid, grooved, or tubular, and in the poisonous species the grooves or canals may be connected with a gland from which an active poison may be ejected. In Tortoises and Turtles the jaws are devoid of teeth, but are covered with horn and form a cutting beak.

Ribs are usually present, and may be single- or double-headed. In the Snakes, they often extend the whole length of the trunk, with the exception of the atlas. In *Sphenodon* and the Crocodiles, there are present certain supplementary bones—abdominal ribs, which foreshadow the plastron of the Tortoises and Turtles. All Reptiles had originally four well-developed feet, with five toes on each, but in the modern groups there is a tendency to reduction in the size of the limbs, which in certain Lizards and Snakes are represented by mere vestiges. In the true Turtles, the limbs are modified to form paddles adapted for swimming purposes. Nearly all Reptiles have long and well-developed tails. With regard to the soft internal parts, the alimentary canal is remarkable, especially in the Snakes, for the wide oesophagus, which allows for the swallowing of the prey entire.

When compared to the huge bulk of many of the extinct forms, modern Reptiles are of comparatively small dimensions. The largest of the Crocodiles and the giant Snakes—Pythons and Anacondas—which may attain a length of thirty feet, are midgets in comparison with the extinct Dinosaurs, some of which were nearly one hundred feet long.

Reptiles came into being in the Carboniferous epoch. The earliest ancestral Reptiles were probably medium-sized species, resembling salamanders. Presently this generalized type branched out in many directions, developing all kinds of exaggerations—specializations of certain particular features.

Characteristic of the Secondary Period were the Plesiosaurs and Ichthyosaurs, marine fish-eating Reptiles with paddle-shaped hands and feet, the Pterosaurs, which developed one finger on each hand to support wing-like membranes that enabled them to soar aloft, and in some forms had a span of eighteen feet, and the Dinosaurs, a large and varied order. Climatic changes at the close of this period may have been amongst the causes which led to the sudden end of the Reptilian epoch, one relic of which, the Tuatera, survives in New Zealand, and owes its continued existence to its unobtrusive habits and to Government protection.

The existing representatives of the Class Reptilia number about four thousand different species and may be divided into the following five orders :

1. The *Rhynchocephalia*—the Tuatera Lizard of New Zealand, the sole survivor of this Order.
2. The *Chelonia*—Turtles, Terrapins, and Tortoises.
3. The *Crocodilia*—Crocodiles, Alligators, and Caimans.
4. The *Lacertilia*—Lizards and Chameleons.
5. The *Ophidia*—Snakes.

Order RHYNCHOCEPHALIA

The Tuatera Lizard (*Sphenodon punctatus*), once common on the mainland of New Zealand, but now restricted to a few small islands off the North Island, is a notable example of a " living fossil." It is the only representative of a group of Reptiles otherwise known from fossil representatives only, and survives to-day as a result of the most rigorous protection. In its external appearance the Tuatera resembles an Iguana, but it differs from all other living Reptiles in a number of important anatomical features. For instance, the temporal region is bridged over by two bony arches—a lower and an upper, the former of which is absent in all true Lizards. It is also, as already mentioned, provided with certain abdominal ribs, which form a bony armour corresponding to the plastron of the Tortoises and Turtles. In the structure of its bony palate it likewise differs from Lizards. The front end of the downwardly curved upper jaw is hooked, and terminates in a chisel-shaped tooth, which, with a similar tooth in the lower jaw, gives this part of the skull the appearance of a beak. The teeth are of the *acrodont* type, being inserted on the edge of the jaw.

The Tuatera Lizard displays to great advantage a vestigial organ which can be traced in the brain of most vertebrates—including Man. This is the pineal, or median, eye, holding a central position in the upper surface of the cranium. The Reptile, which may measure over two feet in length, is stoutly built, and is dark olive-green in colour, with a few whitish specks on the sides. A ridge of large spines extends from the base of the head to the short, thick and slightly-compressed tail, on which the crest is repeated by similar spines. The eye is large, with a vertical pupil. On the upper part of the body the scales are granular, but on the abdomen they are large and arranged in transverse series.

The Tuatera is clumsy and lazy in its movements, and unable to jump the smallest obstacle; its normal mode of progression is by means of a slow crawl, the abdomen and tail seldom leaving the ground. But, when spurred on by the sight of a dinner, it will show more activity and may lift the whole trunk off the ground in the pursuit of its prey, which consists of rodents, frogs, lizards and insects. Its eggs are white and hard-shelled; they are laid in holes in the sand and take thirteen months to hatch.

Van Haalst, in the Transactions of the New Zealand Institute, has given an interesting account of the home life of this Reptile. It excavates its own burrows, in which it lives on amicable terms with various species of petrel. The entrance to the burrow, which termi-

[*James's Press.*

TUATERA (*Sphenodon punctatus*).
Although lizard-like in appearance, this New Zealand animal differs widely in structure from lizards, and is the only survivor of an ancient group.

nates in a chamber one and a half feet long by a foot wide and six inches high, is four or five inches in diameter. This habitation is lined with grass and leaves, and the petrel almost invariably lives on the left side of the inner chamber and the Tuatera on the right side. Although showing the greatest solicitude for the bird and its young, the Tuatera will not allow another of its own kind to invade its home. Tuateras are nocturnal in habit, and seldom leave their burrows before sunset. Captive specimens seldom become tame, and if handled, are liable to inflict a very painful bite.

Order CHELONIA (Turtles, Terrapins and Tortoises)

The members of this Order—the Turtles, Terrapins and Tortoises, present comparatively little variation in form, and are sharply distinguished from all other Reptiles. They may be strictly aquatic, semi-aquatic, or entirely terrestrial. In the permanently aquatic forms, the limbs are paddle-shaped; in the entirely terrestrial forms they are club-shaped; in those that are at home both on land and in the water, they are intermediate in structure between the two extreme types. The body is short and stout, and is protected both above and below by a bony framework, usually covered with horny shields, into which the head, neck, limbs, and tail may be withdrawn. The upper shell, or carapace, is composed of bones which, except in the Leathery Turtle, include expansions of the vertebrae and ribs. Those of the under-surface, or plastron, are generally free from the internal skeleton. The carapace and plastron are usually connected by a bridge. The bony plates and the superficial horny shields are important characters in the classification of these Reptiles. In certain Tortoises, known as Box Tortoises (*Kistudo*), the anterior or posterior lobes of the plastron may be divided by transverse hinges of elastic ligament, rendering them movable and enabling the animals to retire within their shells, closing them completely. The genus *Kinixys* is remarkable for the fact that the posterior portion of its carapace is similarly movable, permitting the posterior half of the shell to open and close. The bones of the head are firmly attached to each other. The orbits are separated by a bony septum. Although regeneration of lost parts does not take place, as in certain other Reptiles, injuries to the shell may be made good by a new growth of bony and horny tissue. The jaws, which are toothless, are covered with cutting, horny sheaths. A tympanum, or external ear drum, like that of Frogs, is usually situated on each side of the head. In certain aquatic forms, however, there is no exposed ear drum. A tail is always present, but differs much in size. The eye is well developed, and is protected not only by an upper and lower lid, but also by a third transparent lid—a nictitating membrane, which moves laterally. The pupil is always round. The neck varies greatly in length and may be completely or incompletely withdrawn into the shell—(*a*) by means of an S-shaped curve in a vertical plane (*Cryptodira*) ; or (*b*) simply sideways (*Pleurodira*). All the members of the Order are oviparous, the land and freshwater forms laying hard-shelled eggs. The marine Turtles, however, lay eggs with imperfectly-calcified shells. In the land Tortoises the eggs are buried in the ground, but in the aquatic species they are laid at the bottom of the ponds or rivers that they frequent, or out of the water in the mud on the banks, or, in the marine Turtles, in the sand on the shore some distance away from the sea. The food of these animals varies. Most land forms are firm vegetarians, whilst those frequenting the water either enjoy a mixed diet or are strictly carnivorous.

As regards distribution, the members of the Order are specially plentiful in the warmer parts of the world. A few species only inhabit Southern Europe. The giant land forms, which formerly occurred on the mainland both in the Old and New Worlds, are now on the verge of extinction, occurring in small numbers only on a few oceanic islands.

The *Chelonia* may be divided into two Suborders—(1) the *Athecae*, and (2) the *Thecophora*.

SNAPPING OR ALLIGATOR TURTLES (CHELYDRIDAE)

Suborder Athecae

In this suborder the vertebrae and ribs are not fused with the carapace, as in all other members of the order, but are entirely free.

Dermochelys coriacea, the Leathery Turtle, the sole representative of the Suborder, is the largest living Chelonian, attaining a length of nine feet and a weight of over fifteen hundred pounds. It has a world-wide range, being generally distributed in tropical seas, and is an occasional visitor to Southern European coasts. Like all other marine Turtles, it comes ashore during the breeding season with the object of depositing its eggs, of which each female lays some three or four hundred. In spite of its huge bulk it is extremely active, and by using its four flippers can turn almost instantly from side to side whilst travelling at a high speed. It is capable of emitting sounds which have been compared to the grunts of a wild boar. By some authorities the Leathery Turtle is believed to represent a very primitive type, out of which all other Chelonians have been evolved, the ossifications underlying the skin becoming fused with the bones of the skeleton to form the carapace of other Tortoises and Turtles.

Suborder Thecophora

The Suborder Thecophora, in which the vertebrae and ribs are united with the carapace, is divided into three Super-families—(1) the *Cryptodira*, in which the neck bends in an S-shaped curve in a vertical plane, (2) the *Pleurodira*, in which it simply bends sideways, and (3) the *Trionychoidea*—soft-shelled turtles, which agree with the first-mentioned Super-family in the movement of the neck.

Super-family Cryptodira.

Family Chelydridae (Snapping or Alligator Turtles).

This family is represented by a number of large forms inhabiting the fresh waters of Central and North America and New Guinea. They are popularly known as Snapping Turtles, or Alligator Turtles, and are characterized by very large heads, thick necks, strongly-hooked jaws, broadly-webbed feet, and small cruciform plastrons.

The Common Snapper (*Chelydra serpentina*), of the United States and Mexico, derives its name from its habit of snapping at everything within reach. The adult, whose shell is rough and often overgrown with aquatic weeds, spends the greater portion of its life lying motionless at the bottom of some pond or river, giving no sign of life, but with its mouth wide open awaiting any fish that may approach. At times it will rise to the surface with the object of attacking a water-fowl, which it will drag below and drown before devouring. Its hard-shelled eggs, which are perfectly spherical, have been laid and hatched in the Zoological Society's Reptile House.

The Alligator Snapper (*Macroclemmys temminckii*), of the South-eastern

United States, is the largest member of the Family, attaining a length of two feet and a weight of over one hundred pounds. It differs from the Common Snapper in the absence of plates under the tail, in the higher carapace, and in having white, fleshy appendages attached to the mucous membrane of the mouth. These move about in the water, where they resemble living worms, and are said to attract the fish upon which the Reptile lives.

Family Dermatemydidae.

A short tail and a series of shields on the body separates the Family Dermatemyidae from all others. The Family is divided into three genera, *Dermatemys*, *Staurotypus* and *Claudius*, all inhabitants of central America.

In Maw's Terrapin (*Dermatemys mawii*), of Honduras, which grows to a length of over two feet, the plastron is well developed and not cross-shaped, as it is in the other members of the Family. It differs from most other aquatic Turtles and Terrapins in being a strict vegetarian.

Family Kinosternidae (Mud Terrapins).

In the small, partially, or thoroughly, aquatic Mud Terrapins of the Eastern United States and Central America, the anterior and posterior lobes of the plastron are hinged and movable, the mobility varying considerably according to the species.

Family Platysternidae.

Platysternum megacephalum, a native of the rivers of South-eastern Asia, attains a length of nearly a foot. It is specially remarkable for its much-flattened carapace, its very long tail (longer than the carapace) and its enormous head—out of all proportion to the size of the body.

Family Testudinidae.

This family, which except for Australia and Papuasia, is represented in nearly all the temperate and tropical parts of the world, embraces about one hundred and fifty species, amongst which are aquatic, semi-aquatic, and terrestrial forms.

The uniformly-brown Royal River Turtle (*Batagur baska*), of Bengal, Burma, Siam and the Malay Peninsula, is a thoroughly-aquatic species, occasionally venturing out to sea, where it is caught in fishing nets. It is omnivorous, and in our Zoological Gardens develops a liking for the buns and biscuits thrown into its tank by visitors. The collecting of its eggs, which are laid on sandy banks above tidal influence, is a royal prerogative in many of the Malay States.

The members of the North American genus *Chrysemys* are semi-aquatic in their habits. They are generally known as Ornamented Terrapins from the bright markings with which their soft parts as well as their carapaces are adorned. These markings are specially well defined in young specimens. Most species are regarded in the States as excellent eating, and support a profitable industry. Mr. Hugh Smith has described the breeding habits of *Chrysemys scripta*. The nest, which is shaped like a bottle, is excavated by the female some distance away from the water. When the eggs, some thirty-five in number, have been laid, earth is scraped into and over the hole, and this is then packed, the packing being accomplished by the mother terrapin raising herself as high as possible on her hind legs and then dropping heavily. The young hatch in the nest in the late autumn, and remain there until the following spring.

In *Emys* the plastron is united to the carapace by ligaments and is divided into two lobes, slightly movable upon a central transverse hinge. The limbs are fairly extensively webbed, and are provided with well-developed claws. The genus is represented by two species, *Emys orbicularis* of Southern Europe, North Africa and South-western Asia, and *E. blandingii* of North America, which resemble each other not only in their semi-aquatic habits, but in having carapaces of a similar colour — brown or black with bright yellow markings. In pre-historic times the European species was abundant throughout Northern Europe, including the British Isles. In this genus, the tail, which is

[W. S. Pitt.

ORNAMENTED TERRAPIN (*Chrysemys elegans*).
The members of this North American genus are adorned with bright markings.

almost as long as the shell in the young, becomes relatively shorter with age. The skin covering the head is smooth. The European Pond Tortoise (*E. orbicularis*), which seldom attains a length of more than six inches, lives in both stagnant and running waters, feeding on such aquatic animals as fish and small frogs. On land it is more active than any terrestrial species. Blanding's Terrapin (*E. blandingii*) differs from its Old World cousin in having a slightly more elongated and higher carapace. Its head is dark above, bright-yellow below. It spends much time on land and feeds on a mixed diet of frogs, fish, insects, worms and berries. Both members of the genus hibernate in the mud below water during the winter months, but they are less lethargic than most hibernating species, and on a sunny day wake from their slumber.

In the genus *Clemmys*, represented in Europe, Asia and North America, the plastron is firmly united to the carapace by bone and not by ligament. There are two European species: *C. caspica*, the so-called Caspian Terrapin, inhabiting South-eastern Europe and Asia, from the borders of the Caspian Sea to the Persian Gulf; and *C. leprosa*, the so-called Iberian Terrapin, which inhabits running water, and is a native of Spain, Morocco, Algeria and Tunisia. Neither attain a length of more than five inches. *C. leprosa*, which derives its specific name from the fact that it is subject to a peculiar disease giving the shell a leprous appearance, is dark olive above, yellow below, the sides of the head being adorned with red or orange markings. *C. caspica* differs in having the cutting edges of the upper jaw finely denticulated, and in its carapace being ornamented with yellow, black-edged, wavy markings.

The American members of the genus are very terrestrial in their habits and feed mainly on insects and vegetable matter.

In the true Box Tortoises (genus *Kistudo*) the plastron is connected with the carapace by ligament and is divided by a hinge into two movable lobes by means of which the openings of the shell can be closed after the head, tail and limbs of the animal have been withdrawn. Box Tortoises, although possessors of slightly-webbed feet, are so entirely terrestrial in their habits that they will speedily drown when thrown into the water. They are the possessors, as are most land tortoises, of a high, globular shell. The genus is represented by several species, all natives of North America and Mexico. The Common Box Tortoise (*K. carolina*) varies much in colour, no two specimens being quite alike. The six-inch-long shell is usually light brown in colour, with spots or stripes of bright-yellow or orange, disposed without symmetry. The head is likewise brown, ornamented with yellow spots, or transverse bands. A few yellow and red markings are present on the neck.

The typical land-tortoises with club-shaped feet and web-less digits are embraced within the genera *Kinixys*, *Pyxis*, *Homopus* and

[*W. S. Berridge.*
WEST AFRICAN HINGED-BACK TORTOISE (*Kinixys erosa*).
The posterior part of the carapace is hinged and can be closed against the plastron.

Testudo. In *Kinixys*, of Tropical Africa, represented by three species, the posterior portion of the carapace, being hinged and consequently movable, may be closed tightly against the plastron, protecting the soft hinder portion of the animal from possible aggressors. In the West African Hinged-back Tortoise (*K. erosa*), the margins

[*M. H. Crawford.*
REEVE'S TORTOISE (*Geoclemys reevesi*).
This tortoise from China and Japan has a highly-arched carapace.

of the carapace are much serrated and strongly reverted, and the plastron is forked in front and projects considerably beyond the anterior border of the upper portion of the shell.

In *Pyxis*, represented by a single species, *P. arachnoides* from Mexico, a small tortoise measuring three to four inches in length, the front lobe of the plastron is hinged.

The typical land tortoises of the genus *Testudo*, with unhinged, dome-shaped shells and club-shaped feet, are represented by nearly fifty species, and are distributed over Southern Europe, Asia, Africa and North and South America. The yellow and black Greek Tortoise (*Testudo graeca*) and the similarly-coloured Mediterranean Land Tortoise (*T. hermanni*) are the two species which are most commonly kept in captivity in this country. The Greek Tortoise may be distinguished from the Mediterranean Tortoise by being the possessor of a large, bony tubercle situated on the back of the thigh, and by the supra-caudal shield being single and not divided into two. Both are inhabitants of the Mediterranean region. The former likewise occurs in Asia Minor, Syria, Palestine, Persia, Morocco, Algeria and Tunisia.

The Margined Tortoise (*Testudo marginata*), also of Southern Europe, is a rarer form and is to be distinguished from the two other European species by its more elongated shell, the posterior margin of which is very broad.

These land tortoises, if properly looked after, may flourish for many years in this country. Gilbert White kept a Greek Tortoise for fifty-four years, and another with which I was acquainted spent ninety-six years in a garden in Cornwall. In the wild state these tortoises hibernate during the winter months, burying themselves in the ground until the warm weather returns. In England it is probably best to allow them to do this rather than keep them active in a greenhouse, and they should be buried about a foot deep as soon as the cold weather comes. Should they emerge from their winter quarters on a sunny day, they should be reburied until all risk of frost has passed. If they refuse to hibernate completely in a cold, though frost-proof, place, they should be taken indoors and kept warm and fed, for if allowed to spend the winter in a state of semi-torpidity, they are almost certain to die in the following spring. These tortoises frequently lay white, oval eggs about two inches in length, but it is seldom possible to incubate them. Three or four is the average clutch, and they are usually buried in the ground. The incubation period is about four months. Although the eggs of tropical tortoises have occasionally been hatched in our Zoological Gardens, I know of but a single authenticated case of the egg of the European land tortoise being hatched in this country, which is remarkable considering the fact that for the last century at least a hundred thousand of these reptiles have been annually imported to Great Britain, and that quite a large percentage lay eggs in captivity. The egg in question was laid in a garden in Dulwich and was artificially incubated by being placed in a box with straw and cotton wool and kept at a temperature of about 90°F. These tortoises are often brought over, usually in the early spring, as ship's ballast, being consigned in barrels. As a result a large percentage are so severely injured in transport that they die before reaching England. The survivors are then sold by dealers and hawked through the streets on barrows. The householder is told that these reptiles, in reality vegetarians, will eat black-beetles in the kitchen, and as a result by early winter only about one in every thousand of those imported in the spring is still alive. If the importation of these tortoises is allowed to continue under the present conditions they will probably be on the verge of extinction within a very few years.

Giant Tortoises. The interest in Giant Tortoises grows annually, since these monster reptiles constitute a race which one can literally watch fading into extinction. For many centuries they have lived in colonies on small island groups enjoying immunity from foes. In the remote past tortoises of gigantic size inhabited the mainland, but to-day they occur as indigenous forms in two groups of islands only—the Galapagos, off the coast of South America, and the Island of Aldabra adjacent to Madagascar. One need only walk round the Zoo Tortoise House to understand how easily the largest of these witless monsters may have fallen a prey to all kinds of foes upon the mainland. A small island escapes the fierce competition of the centres of civilisation. The Giant Tortoises that once abounded on the mainland and escaped predaceous animals, fell to man, and eventually not even the survivors on remote islands, inhospitable and dangerous of approach, can be called safe. The accounts of some of the early voyagers show all too clearly how the now treasured pets of private parks and zoos once abounded and were abused.

The explorer Leguat wrote of Rodrigues Island in 1691: "Sometimes you see two or three thousands of them (i.e. giant tortoises) in a flock so that it is possible to walk a hundred paces on their backs." Grant described the conditions in Mauritius in 1740 : "We possess a great abundance of fowl, beside both land and sea

[James's Press.
GIANT TORTOISE (*Testudo elephantina*).
This species is indigenous in the Island of Aldabra.

turtles, which are not only a great supply of our wants but serve to barter with the crews of ships which put in here for refreshment on their voyage." By the beginning of 1870 neither Rodrigues nor Mauritius had retained a single giant tortoise—not even a keepsake. What happened to these helpless monsters whose vast dome-like shells must have once blackened the islands of the Indian Ocean was repeated in the far distant Galapagos group. Dampier in his " Voyage Round the World " in 1697 declares : " The land turtle are here so numerous that five or six hundred men might subsist on them alone for several months without any sort of provision. No poulet tastes more pleasantly." Volumes could not explain more satisfactorily why the last survivors are only to be found in zoos and museums. These monsters swarmed in all the larger islands of the more isolated island groups. Some specimens weighed four hundred pounds. Even under the greatest provocation, their steps were heavy and slow, the body being with difficulty raised more than nine inches from the ground. Their capacity for existing for a long time (fifteen months or more) without food, yet suffering no diminution in edible qualities, went far to commend them to the early travellers. Further, the Giant Tor-

[W. J. Clarke.
STARRED TORTOISE (*Testudo elegans*).

327

toises carry reserves of water amounting to about two gallons, and every part of the meat is excellent. The females, distinguished by their longer tails descend from the mountain centres of the islands to the coastal plateaux to lay their eggs, which are large, seven to eight inches in circumference and almost globular, with a hard white shell. The largest giant tortoises measure some five and a half feet long by four and a half feet wide. Such monsters might be plentiful to-day if left alone in their island fastnesses, when they would die only from old age, disease, or accidents such as falling over a precipice.

The ages of some of these giant forms from Aldabra and Galapagos Islands have been faithfully recorded. A giant tortoise (*Testudo gigantea*) that lived on the Island of St. Helena at the time of the sojourn there of the great Napoleon was still alive in 1933. Another that died only recently (1928) in the garden of the Royal Artillery Mess at Mauritius was taken from the French in 1820. Both these veterans were, when last measured, much smaller in size than one that arrived recently in Regent's Park, and was saved from the pot by a Fellow of the Society who bought him from a restaurant pro-

[*James's Press.*

CHARLES ISLAND TORTOISE.
One of the Giant Tortoises of the Galapagos Islands.

prietor in Valparaiso. This patriarch has developed a plebeian taste for buns, and, raising himself upon his hind legs, will appeal to the generosity of the public with as much zest, if less dignity, than a bear. Its exact age none can say, and the same may be said of most of its kind. In 1928 an American expedition visited the Galapagos Islands. One hundred and eighty giant tortoises were collected in the mountain districts and are now in safe keeping in various United States zoological gardens. At a conservative estimate about ten million tortoises have been taken from the Galapagos group in a little over three centuries. On these desolate islands the giant reptiles have thriven on a large, spineless cactus which supplied them with food and water at the same time. Growth upon such a diet is slow, but it is known that these tortoises increase in bulk rapidly during their first years. A youngster from Albemarle Island kept in captivity increased from twenty-nine to three hundred and fifty pounds in seven years, and was " going strong " when it died suddenly as the result of a chill.

The Spurred Tortoise (*T. sulcata*) of Tropical Africa is characterized by a somewhat flattened light or dark brown carapace. It is the largest existing land tortoise inhabiting the mainland, and attains a length of three feet and a weight of over a hundred pounds. The popular name is derived from the presence of a pair of large, spur-like tubercles on the limbs. The natives sometimes call it the " Six-footed Tortoise " referring to these spurs.

The Gopher Tortoise (*T. polyphemus*) of Florida excavates deep burrows by means of the spade-shaped projection of its plastron and its large claws. These burrows are said to afford a refuge for various other animals. including opossums, racoons, owls and rattlesnakes.

In the Soft-shelled Tortoise (*T. tornieri*) of East Africa, some of the bones of the carapace and plastron are missing, the so-called shell being consequently soft and springy in places and capable of being slightly inflated. The tortoise looks as if it had been crushed, the " shell " reacting to pressure when handled in a manner that is almost uncanny. In order to remedy the defect of being nearly devoid of armour, this tortoise has taken to living in holes and rocks after the manner of certain lizards.

Family Chelonidae (True Turtles).

In the turtles of the genera *Chelone* and *Thalassochelys*, the shell is covered with horny epidermal shields, the neck is incompletely retractile, the jaws of the large head are provided with cutting edges, the lower being hooked in front, and the limbs are paddle-shaped and form powerful swimming organs. These turtles are entirely marine in their habits, resorting to land only during the breeding season.

Chelone mydas, the Green Turtle, the animal from which the greatly-prized turtle soup, inseparable from the civic banquet, is obtained, has a very wide distribution, occurring in all tropical and sub-tropical seas. During the summer months specimens may wander as far north as the Southern European coasts. The shields of the carapace are smooth, olive or brown in colour. The Green Turtle may attain a weight of four hundred pounds, the shell of such specimens measuring nearly four feet. Its food consists of fishes and marine vegetation.

The eggs are laid on sandy shores, and in the process the reptiles show surprising cunning. Each female may bury some hundreds of eggs about two feet deep in the sand well above high-water mark, and, so neatly is the excavation accomplished, that the site can be detected only by " sounding " with a probe. Moreover, she makes her way back to the sea by so devious a route that the location of the family-to-be is rendered very difficult. The sun's warmth hatches out the eggs in a few weeks, when the young turtles fight their way to the surface and make seawards, running the gauntlet of numerous foes, from crabs and racoons to hungry gulls.

Zoo turtles sometimes share their tank with various fish to mutual satisfaction, but not always, as the following curious incident which occurred in the Amsterdam Aquarium goes to show. During a period when the capacity of the tanks was put to considerable strain it was decided to risk introducing some mullet into the tank inhabited by a number of large green turtles. The reptiles apparently associated the uproar and splashing made by the staff when introducing the fish with the fish themselves, and at first left them severely alone, but later appeared to conceive a queer kind of attachment for them. This proved to be the case, for when some more mullet identical with those already installed were put into their tank the turtles at once attacked the new-comers and killed them, though leaving their original tank-mates unharmed. Plenty of accommodation was available at this period, so the original mullet were given a tank to themselves. At once the turtles showed unmistakable signs of moping and loss of appetite, nor did they recover until their old tank-mates were restored to them, when all was again well.

The majority of turtles brought to market are caught by turning them upon their backs whilst they are making for the sea after having come ashore to lay their eggs. Other methods of capture are harpooning, grappling with the turtle as it basks on the sea surface, or employing the Remora or Sucking-fish. This fish has a powerful sucking disc on the top of its head, and if a tethered specimen is cast near a basking turtle, it will quickly attach itself with such tenacity that both may be drawn aboard. Owing to the thin and pliant nature of its undershell, a green turtle lives longer out of water when on its back than it would otherwise. If allowed to rest " right-side-up," its great weight would put such pressure on the lungs and other internal organs as to cause a speedy death.

The closely-related but somewhat smaller Hawksbill Turtle (*Chelone imbricata*), which derives its name from its very hooked snout, is another inhabitant of all the tropical and sub-tropical seas, venturing inland only during the breeding season. Its carapace is marbled yellow and brown, the horny shields affording the valuable " tortoise-shell " of commerce. From a single specimen as much as ten pounds of tortoise-shell may be obtained.

The members of the genus *Thalassochelys* inhabit all the warmer seas, and are popularly known as Loggerhead Turtles ; they may be differentiated from all other marine turtles by their larger heads, and by the presence of a pair of nails on each flipper. The common Loggerhead Turtle (*T. caretta*) is the giant of the family, attaining a weight of five hundred pounds.

TRUE TURTLES (CHELONIDAE)

Super-family Pleurodira.

In the members of this super-family, the neck when retracted bends simply sideways.

Family Pelomedusidae.

In this family, represented in Southern and Tropical Africa, Madagascar, and South America by the genera *Sternothaerus*, *Pelomedusa* and *Podocnemis*, the neck is completely retractile. The front lobe of the plastron is movable in *Sternothaerus*, but not in *Pelomedusa* and *Podocnemis*. With the exception of *Pelomedusa galeata*, which spends the greater part of

[*Dorien Leigh.*

GREEN TURTLE (*Chelone mydas*).
This large turtle of tropical seas comes ashore to lay its eggs.

its existence on land, these tortoises are aquatic, seldom leaving the water.

Family Chelydidae.

In this family, the neck is long and is always exposed.

The Matamata (*Chelys fimbriata*) of the rivers of the Guianas and Brazil has a grotesque appearance and strange feeding habits. Its head is triangular and much flattened and its nose is produced into a long, soft tube. The shell, which almost invariably carries a mass of aquatic weeds, is very rough, and is divided into a number of protuberances, each of which simulates a boulder covered with algae. The chin, however, forms the most remarkable of many strange features, being provided with a number of movable fleshy appendages, which in the water resemble worms, and serve the purpose of attracting the fish upon which the reptiles feed.

331

REPTILIA (ORDER CHELONIA)

The jaws, being very weak and covered with soft skin, are not used in seizing the fish, which are sucked into the large cavernous mouth by the inrush of water upon their approaching the bait.

The representatives of the genera *Chelodina* of Australia and *Hydromedusa* of South America are popularly known as the Long-necked Terrapins, from the fact that their long, slender, and snake-like necks almost exceed the length of their shells.

Super-family Trionychoidea.

In these thoroughly aquatic turtles the neck bends as in the Cryptodira. There are no epidermal shields, and the roughish and flat carapace is covered with soft skin. The snout ends in a tube-shaped appendage, and the jaws are covered by fleshy lips. The feet are partly webbed, and are provided with three claws. The group is represented in both the Old and the New World by a number of species. In these reptiles the rounded head is almost completely retractile, but may be suddenly shot forth with lightning-like rapidity. The powerful jaws are provided with cutting edges, and the turtle is capable of amputating a man's finger or even hand.

Trionyx gangeticus is the largest species and attains a length of nearly three feet. According to Theobold, so tenacious of life is this creature that its head will bite vigorously after being completely severed from the body.

Order CROCODILIA (Crocodiles and Alligators)

Crocodiles, Alligators, etc., are the largest of existing limbed Reptiles, and are abundant throughout the tropical and sub-tropical regions of the world. In the prehistoric past, when many countries enjoyed a more congenial climate than they do to-day, Crocodiles were far more widely distributed. Fossil remains of these creatures have been found in this country, and Alligators that must have been almost identical with those occurring in modern Tropical America are known to have existed throughout Europe during the Miocene period. The Gharial, now confined to the Far East, has left its bones in Sussex. In

[*W. S. Berridge.*]

HAWKSBILL TURTLE (*Chelone imbricata*).
The marbled shields are the tortoise-shell of commerce.

early times, the Crocodiles presented a far greater range of size and form than those that have survived to recent times. Some were apparently wholly aquatic, and many eclipsed all modern records as regards size.

Crocodiles and their allies are elongate, four-limbed

[W. S. Berridge.

MATAMATA (*Chelys fimbriata*).
This inhabitant of the rivers of Brazil and Guiana has a grotesque appearance and strange habits.

animals with the body covered with large scales, sometimes with underlying bony plates, those of the back being elevated and forming longitudinal ridges, those of the ventral surface being smooth. The snout varies very much in shape and may be broad and rounded, or narrow and pointed. Since these animals spend most of their time in the water their limbs are short, although capable of raising the creatures clear of the ground. Each fore limb bears five toes and the hind limbs four. These are strongly webbed and the three inner digits of both limbs bear strong claws. The tail is enormously powerful and propels the creature swiftly through the water by lateral movements, the limbs being held close to the sides. The skull is large. The quadrate bone, movable in most Reptiles, is firmly wedged in position. The palate is formed of a solid roof of bone, and at the hinder end are the two openings of the internal nostrils. The upper extremity of the wind-pipe opens well into the mouth. The eyes, nostrils and external ears are situated on the upper surface of the head so that when the animal is swimming with the head raised above the surface of the water, its breathing, seeing, and hearing are unimpaired. The nostrils and ears are valvular, and are kept shut when the animal is under water. The eyes are provided with a lower and an upper eyelid and a nictitating membrane. The short, thick tongue has at its base a ridge or floor which can entirely close the entrance to the throat, thus ensuring free play with the jaws when the animal is submerged, and making it an easy matter for it to hold and drown an animal once it has been seized. The vertebrae carry transverse processes which render the neck rigid. Thus, although the vertebrae are connected by ball and socket joints, only the body and tail can be flexed, and the creature's power of turning in a small space is consequently feebly developed. The ribs resemble those of birds. The heart and vascular system is more highly developed than in any other Reptile. The slit-like pupil of the eye denotes a largely nocturnal mode of life.

333

REPTILIA (ORDER CROCODILIA)

About a score of species have been recorded and the majority show considerable similarity in habits. All live in close proximity to water, infesting rivers and lakes, and one species is largely marine. Crocodiles, etc., spend much of their time resting upon land, where they escape observation by the often remarkable likeness that they bear to moss-grown boulders or stranded logs. When disturbed, they take quickly to the water, where they can move with great ease and rapidity. Some seek their prey in the water, others drag their prey to it, or when submerged suddenly rise and seize by the muzzle such creatures as come to the water's edge. Some species are dangerous to man and annually take a heavy toll of native lives. Most Crocodiles crush their prey before swallowing, and this is effected by the sharp teeth, which are set in a single row upon the summit of the jaw. These teeth vary in size and beneath the conical hollow base of each is a reserve tooth which in time pushes out the old one above it. There is, therefore, always a fair proportion of teeth which are thoroughly sharp. " Shed " teeth are frequently found at the Zoo when cleaning out the Reptiles' tanks. Like many other creatures, Crocodiles lend themselves to exaggeration, and many of the recorded giants have lived only in the traveller's imagination. About four species are known to attain twenty to thirty feet, the latter measurement being extremely rare. The majority seldom exceed fifteen feet. Since Crocodiles, like most other Reptiles, grow continuously throughout life, size is not always a criterion of age, but it is fairly certain that many of the giants have lived for over fifty years, if not considerably longer. Their growth is very quick in the early stages, healthy specimens growing about a foot in length for each of the first five or six years of their lives.

The Crocodilians lay eggs, usually about twenty in number, which may be compared to very elongate duck's eggs. They have a white, glossy and hard shell, and are deposited in holes dug by the females in some convenient sandbank or heap of decaying vegetable matter. A few Crocodiles show parental care and assist in the incubation of the eggs, sleeping upon the top of the nest. The young announce their entry to the world by noises audible through some two feet of sand, when they are dug out by the mother, who conducts them to the water. The egg shells are broken by means of a horny spike on the snout of the infant Crocodile, an arrangement very like that which is universal amongst birds. It is very questionable whether the mating is preceded by any particular display of courtship. Crocodiles, however, have a voice and the male can emit a large roaring note, which can be uttered with the mouth closed and the throat greatly dilated. They emit a powerful musky odour from certain glands, which possibly aids in the bringing together of the sexes.

Despite the universal detestation in which Crocodiles are held by the majority of mankind, they have from early times played a prominent part in the folk-lore and religious beliefs of the peoples whose countries they infest. The Crocodile figures extensively in early Egyptian paintings and sculptures and is to-day held in reverence by millions of devout Buddhists, besides receiving the homage of countless savage tribes. Crocodile skin has, of course, a high commercial value and in several parts of the United States Alligators are farmed to meet the demands of the leather market.

[*James's Press.*

ALLIGATORS.
Alligators differ from Crocodiles in that the fourth tooth in the lower jaw is concealed when the mouth is closed.

The Order is represented by the single family *Crocodilidae*, which embraces the genera *Alligator, Caiman, Crocodilus, Osteolaemus, Gavialis* and *Tomistoma*.

The so-called Alligators (genus *Alligator*) may be distinguished from the Crocodiles by the fact that the largest tooth in the lower jaw—the fourth—fits into a pit in the upper jaw and is thus hidden when the mouth is closed. The upper and lower teeth of Crocodiles interlock, and the fourth, or canine, fits into a notch, where it plainly shows in a sinister fashion when the mouth is tightly shut. Further, the thinness or absence of certain bony plates underlying the skin on the under-surface of the body is a characteristic feature of Alligators.

There are two living species of Alligator— *Alligator mississippiensis*, which inhabits the South-eastern United States, and *Alligator sinensis* from the Yangtse-kiang River in China. The American Alligator, though fast disappearing as a result of systematic slaughter, is still tolerably abundant in certain swamps in Florida and Georgia. There it makes rude nests of twigs and rushes, in which it lays some thirty eggs. A single egg measures three and a quarter inches long, and the nest may be five feet across and two feet high. The eggs are placed in two layers, and hatch in about six weeks. At night the Reptiles are very vocal, and large specimens can be heard bellowing from a distance of a mile or more. The American Alligator attains a length of fourteen feet. An Alligator hatched under observation has been recorded as gaining eight ounces in the first year. In the second year it increased from eighteen inches and a weight of nine and a quarter ounces to twenty-three inches and a weight of three pounds. At the end of six years it measured exactly six feet and weighed seventy-two pounds.

The Chinese Alligator closely resembles its American namesake in general appearance. Apart from being smaller, it has a very pronounced development of bone over the upper eyelids, and thin, bony plates on the under-surface of the body. The upper-surface is a greenish black, speckled or streaked with pale yellow, the under-parts are grey. Alligators, though often violent enough when handled, are in the main less dangerous than Crocodiles, which are at all times vicious, sullen and treacherous.

A group of New World Crocodilians very closely allied to the Alligators go by the generic name of *Caiman*. There are eight species restricted to Central and South America, and they are characterized by relatively short and broad snouts. The canine teeth of the lower jaw are received by special pits in the upper. The most widely-distributed species is the Spectacled Caiman (*Caiman sclerops*), which ranges from Southern Mexico to Central America, and from Tropical South America to the Argentine. In this form ridges are present above the upper eyelids, which, being puffed up and wrinkled, suggest the popular name. Large specimens measure eight feet in length. In a near relative (*C. latirostris*) the eyelids are produced to form short horns. The largest member of the genus is the Black Caiman (*C. niger*), which attains a length of nearly twenty feet.

The genus *Osteolaemus* is represented by a single species—*O. tetraspis*, an inhabitant of the rivers of West Africa. Superficially it resembles the Caiman, but the fourth tooth of the lower jaw fits into a niche in the upper as in the Crocodiles proper, from which it differs in certain cranial characters.

The distribution of the true Crocodiles (genus *Crocodilus*) embraces

Africa, Asia, North Australia and Tropical America. One of the best-known species is the Nile Crocodile (*Crocodilus niloticus*), which abounds throughout tropical and semi-tropical Africa. It is also very common in Madagascar. It is worshipped by many savage tribes and the ancient Egyptians mummified its remains on a grand scale. It is a notorious man-eater, still accounting for hundreds of natives annually, as they go to the river to bathe, or to wash clothes at the water's edge. Its snout is one and two-thirds to twice as long as broad at the base. It grows to a length of eighteen feet and is dark brown or olive, lighter on the sides. The Nile Crocodile, like most other Crocodiles, is much infested by

[*Keystone.*

CROCODILES IN AN AMAZONIAN SWAMP.
The American Crocodile preys on large fish off the coast of Florida.

parasites and welcomes the attention of the small birds that volunteer to rid it of its pests. It is stated on reliable authority that it opens its mouth and freely admits the entry of the black-headed plover, who picks leeches and other undesirables from the monster's gums.

The American Crocodile (*C. americanus*) may be recognized by the presence of a longitudinal ridge along the middle of the tapering snout. It is similar in colour to *C. niloticus*. It has a wide distribution, ranging along the Central and South American coasts to the West Indies. It is abundant off the coast of Florida, where it attacks such active fish as Bass, Mullet, and Tarpon. Its size limit appears to be about fifteen feet.

A justly famous Crocodile is the Mugger or Great Indian Crocodile (*C. palustris*), which grows to a length of about sixteen feet, and is known practically throughout the whole of India, Ceylon and Burma, and the Malay Peninsula and Archipelago. Its snout is shorter and broader than that of any other members of the Order. When threatened by drought, it will make long journeys overland in search of more congenial surroundings. Its claim to fame lies in the veneration it has been accorded for countless centuries by devout Hindoos and others. The famous Mugger Pit at Karachi, a noted sight to Western tourists, harbours some score of large specimens. They are so well fed by the faithful that they are too generously-developed to offer any violence, even if they were so inclined. A special staff of priests attends to their wants and some of the most bloated specimens will even feed from the hand.

The Estuarine or Salt-water Crocodile (*C. porosus*) is one of the largest species, growing to over twenty feet. It is also one of the most dangerous,

[W. S. Berridge.

MUSKY CAIMAN (*Caiman palpebrosus*).
The Caimans are closely related to the Alligators; they live in Central and South America.

being a man-eater, and much dreaded throughout its habitat, which covers India, Ceylon, Southern China, Malay Archipelago and Northern Australia. Its wide range is explained by its sea-going habits, the Reptile frequently making long excursions from one shore to another. It seldom wanders far inland, keeping closely to coastal regions, swamps and the lower reaches of tidal rivers. It is occasionally seen travelling far out at sea. In the breeding season it is exceptionally savage, and will upset small boats that chance to cross its path, and the gold and silver ornaments that are frequently found in its interior bear testimony to its man-eating qualities. It is to be differentiated from the Mugger by the presence of a very prominent ridge which extends in front of each eye.

The Australian Crocodile (*C. johnstoni*) and the West African Crocodile (*C. cataphractus*) have slender snouts which are three times as long as

[*James's Press.*

BROAD-FRONTED CROCODILE (*Osteolaemus tetraspis*).
This species inhabits the rivers of West Africa ; the fourth lower tooth is exposed when the mouth is shut, as in the Crocodiles.

broad at the base. Their snouts, however, are nothing like as slender as that of the Gharial of India and Malaya, the largest of all the Crocodilians.

The Indian Gharial (*Gavialis gangeticus*) is confined to Northern India, infesting the Ganges and Indus. It grows to thirty feet and may at once be recognized by its peculiarly slender snout. The body of large

[*W. S. Berridge.*

MUGGER OR GREAT INDIAN CROCODILE (*Crocodilus palustris*).
A famous crocodile regarded as sacred by Hindoos.

339

specimens may measure three feet in diameter. The long, narrow jaws are closely set with an unusual number of sharp teeth, which alternate so that upper and lower fit tightly against each other when the mouth is closed. As one might expect from such teeth, the Gharial feeds almost entirely upon fish. In accordance with its diet, it is very aquatic, the female frequenting land for any length of time only during the nesting season. About forty eggs are deposited in two layers covered with a considerable depth of sand, and the young, on hatching, have the snout even longer in proportion than have the adults. A curious feature of large males is the big box-like hollow excrescence on the end of the snout

[*W. S. Berridge.*

GHARIAL (*Gavialis gangeticus*).
The Gharial of Northern India has long, narrow jaws and sharp teeth ; it feeds on fish.

containing a chamber for the reception of air, which enables them to remain submerged for much longer periods than the females. Two specimens that have lived for over twenty years in the London Zoological Gardens are just as savage to-day as they were on the day that they arrived at Regent's Park.

The Malay Gharial, or False Gharial (*Tomistoma schlegelii*), which attains a length of fifteen feet, has a shorter snout, the length being only three and a half times the basal width. It is rarer than the Indian species, and, like it, is held sacred by certain religious sects. It is said to be less thoroughly aquatic than its Indian relative, favouring swamps on the river banks. Gharials represent one of the oldest branches of the Crocodile family, specimens identical with those now living having been found in association with the bones of animals long since extinct.

340

Order LACERTILIA (Lizards)

The Order *Lacertilia* comprises some fifteen hundred species represented in all temperate and tropical climes and varying greatly in size, form and habits. It is evident that Lizards at one time enjoyed a far wider distribution than at the present day—large Iguanas being represented by fossils in Hampshire and France. The largest true Lizard known is an extinct Monitor that could not have measured less than thirty feet.

Modern Lizards are covered with scales, and usually possess two well-developed pairs of limbs. A few, however, are snake-like in form, but in these the pectoral and pelvic girdles are always present. The presence of a movable tongue and the horizontal cleft of the vent are characters which separate them from the crocodiles. From snakes they differ in the structure of the lower jaw, the mouth being non-extensible, the two halves of the lower jaw being united by suture and not connected by an elastic ligament. In the majority of Lizards, eyelids and ear-openings are present, and the senses of sight and hearing are usually well developed. The tongue is an important organ and differs much in shape. It may be broad and short and merely an organ of taste, long and forked, acting as a probe with which to explore the immediate surroundings, or exsertile and sticky and adapted for catching insect prey. When the teeth are set along the inner edges of the jaws, they are said to be *acrodont*, but when they are rooted in a deeply-cleft socket running the entire length of the jaw, they are termed *pleurodont*. In one genus the teeth are developed into poison fangs, being grooved and connected with a poison gland. The tail in some Lizards may be cast off and by its reflex movements hold the attention of the enemy whilst the Lizard makes good its escape. When it is cast off, the tail is not disjointed, but one of the vertebrae is snapped clean across; the broken end at once begins to grow and in time gives rise to a new tail; injury to the tip may result in the tail becoming forked. The tail may be heavily armoured with spikes and knobs and form a formidable weapon, or be ornamented with a fin and serve as a useful means of propulsion through water; in one family it is highly prehensile. Many Lizards change colour with their surroundings, but even the far-famed chameleons cannot compete in this respect with certain fish. Most Lizards reproduce by laying a moderate number of oval, soft-shelled eggs, which are usually buried in the earth or sand, and hatch in a few weeks. A few forms are viviparous. The voice is generally a mere hiss, but some Lizards are more vocal, and utter cries of varying pitch and volume. Voice and colour may both play an important part in courtship; at the breeding season males of many species may fight fiercely for their brides, and seek to attract them with a dazzling display of colour. Lizards are less abundant in the more temperate climes than are snakes. Their presence in isolated island

341

groups has in many instances been effected by man's agency, the reptilian c o l o n i s t s having made voyages as stowaways amongst merchandise.

Family GECKONIDAE

The Geckos have a very wide distribution, occurring in nearly all the tropical and semi-tropical parts of the, world. The typical Geckos have flattened heads, bulky bodies, and stumpy tails. The skin is rough and the digits are expanded.

[*W. S. Berridge.*

TOKAY (*Gecko verticillatus*).
This Gecko is pale blue with red spots; the expanded digits enable Geckos to run on walls and ceilings.

As a result, these Lizards can scramble over vertical surfaces or even run about the house ceilings like flies. They have no eyelids, and the vertical pupil bespeaks the night walker. The tongue is thick and viscid, and is used to pick up insect prey. The popular name is derived from the characteristic cry of " Yeko " or " Gekko," but some can utter bird-like sounds or emit cat-like " mews." Scouting over walls and ceiling in search of flies and insects, the Geckos do much to enliven the night-life of bungalow dwellers in the tropics. Male Geckos usually exceed the females in size. The eggs are round or oblong, and have hard, white shells. Geckos are perfectly harmless, indeed beneficial, since they keep a steady check on noxious insects, but in many parts of the world are regarded as being poisonous and even capable of poisoning any surface they may happen to cross.

Delalande's Gecko (*Tarentola delalandii*) of the Canary Islands and West Africa is a typical form, with strongly-dilated digits. Its grey-brown body is covered with granules and tubercular scales of unequal size. It is a frequent stowaway in banana crates, and specimens have often been received at the Zoological Gardens from the Canary Islands *via* Covent Garden Market.

The Tokay (*Gecko verticillatus*) is a large form, attaining a length of over a foot. It is common in South-eastern Asia, frequenting the jungle, where it feeds on small rodents, fledglings and insects. It is a peculiarly handsome animal, being light blue in colour above with large, round orange or red spots. Its popular name is expressive of its call.

GECKOS (GECKONIDAE)

In the so-called Flying Geckos (genus *Ptychozoon*) of the Malay region, the limbs and sides of the head and body are provided with a much-developed membraneous expansion of skin, which is believed to enable the creatures to parachute from one tree trunk to another.

In the Madagascar Bark Geckos (genus *Uroplates*) peculiar coloured flaps of skin render these Lizards so like bark covered with lichenous growths that the animals are indistinguishable when resting on some ancient tree trunk.

Family PYGOPODIDAE

The members of this family inhabit Australia, Tasmania and New Guinea ; they are related to the Geckos, although they bear a striking superficial resemblance to snakes. The fore limbs are entirely absent, and the hind ones are represented by scaly flaps ; the body is scaled, and the head is plated like a serpent's. The commonest species is the slate-coloured *Pygopus lepidopus*, which attains a length of about two feet. It crawls along in a serpentine fashion, and makes no use of its atrophied hind limbs.

Family AGAMIDAE

The Agamas are members of a strictly Old-World family characterized by their acrodont dentition. The limbs are sturdy, the tongue is short and fleshy, and the eyes have rounded pupils and movable lids. About two hundred of these lively diurnal Lizards are known from Africa, Asia and Malay, Australia and Polynesia. They are wholly absent from Madagascar. Those living on the ground have flattened bodies, but the tree-dwellers are more or less compressed vertically.

A remarkable group is constituted by the members of the small genus *Draco*—the "Flying Dragons." These number some

[James's Press.
MADAGASCAR BARK GECKO (*Uroplates fimbriatus*).
When resting on a tree trunk, these Geckos are almost invisible.

343

twenty species and are confined to the Malay Peninsula and Archipelago. They are slightly - b u i l t creatures w i t h long, slender tails, measuring n o t more than a foot over all.

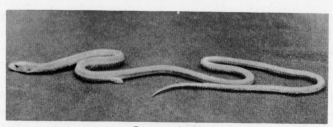

Pygopus lepidopus.
These snake-like Lizards have no fore limbs, and their hind limbs are reduced to scaly fingers.

Their most striking feature is the curious expansion of the ribs to support wide membranes which can be either folded close to the sides or spread to form two planes with which they take long, flying leaps from one tree to another. The colours are brilliant in the extreme, and when in flight these Lizards are far more suggestive of gaudy butterflies than of reptiles.

Draco volans bears on the throat three brightly-tinted dewlaps; in *D. quinquefasciatus* the central dewlap is nearly a third the length of the body and resembles a pendulous comb.

The Blood-sucker (*Calotes versicolor*) is one of the most abundant Lizards inhabiting Eastern Asia, and is much less harmful than its name would suggest. Its popular appellation is derived from the fact that when agitated the normal drab body turns bright yellow and the sides of the head, neck and throat take on a vivid red hue. During the breeding season the males fight fiercely together, and register their emotions by many striking changes of colour, turning from brown to yellow striped with black. When courting they perform curious dances before the females, who appear quite unmoved by these undignified proceedings. The oval soft-shelled eggs, each about half an inch long, are laid to the number of

Photos]   [*W. S. Berridge.*
FLYING GECKO
(*Ptychozoon homalocephalum*).
These Malay Geckos are said to glide through the air.

344

about a dozen in some rotten log, where the young emerge in about two months' time. Nineteen species of *Calotes* are recorded ; in some the head and shoulders bear a crest of sharp spines. The largest form attains a length of two feet.

In *Agama* the somewhat depressed body is sometimes furnished w i t h a feebly - developed crest. A group of spines may be present on the hinder part of the head.

A very common species in Egypt and Asia Minor is *Agama stellio*. This little reptile has incurred the hatred o f devout Mohammedans b y its habit of nodding i t s head t o w a r d s the ground, w h i c h gesture the faithful regard as a travesty of their o w n f o r m o f worship.

FRILLED LIZARD (*Chlamydosaurus kingii*).
This Lizard, from Northern Australia, spreads its frill to intimidate its enemies.

The West African Agama (*A. colonorum*) is remarkable for the rapid changes of colour which it undergoes. Mr. W. A. Lamman has described how it is found in groups of six or seven females headed by a male. As the females so greatly outnumber the males, they are forced to various artifices to secure their share of his attention, and will run up and perform the most peculiar antics in front of him. The males will always fight any of their brethren that presume to inflict themselves upon their harems.

345

A remarkable type of Agamid Lizard is the Frilled Lizard (*Chlamydosaurus kingii*) of Northern Australia. It measures about a yard in length and has a very slender tail. At rest it looks particularly meek, having a big cape, the cleft wings of which droop from just behind the head over the shoulders; when the Lizard is roused to anger, however, this cape spreads stiffly on either side of the head like an

[W. S. Berridge.

MALAY FLYING-DRAGON (*Draco volans*).
The ribs support a membrane that can be spread, enabling the Lizard to take flying leaps from tree to tree.

Elizabethan ruff; this, combined with an open mouth, glaring eyes, and a trick the reptile has of rising on its front legs, is usually sufficient to intimidate its enemies. This warlike display is, however, merely a piece of bluff, for at the first opportunity the reptile closes its frill, turns about, and makes off at a great pace on its hind legs, holding itself semi-upright with its tail clear of the ground. In captivity the Frilled Lizard often becomes so tame and gains such confidence that it cannot be induced to display, even when teased.

The Bearded Lizard (*Amphibolurus barbatus*) of Australia has an enormous frill of spiky scales on the under-surface of the neck; when angry it distends this, and opens its mouth with terrifying effect.

The Mastigures (genus *Uromastix*), or Spiny-tailed Lizards, inhabiting the sandy wastes

[W. J. Clarke.

STARRED LIZARD (*Agama stellio*).
A common species in Egypt and Asia Minor.

of South-western Asia and Northern Africa, attain a length of from twelve to fifteen inches. The moderately long but stout tail is ringed with sharp hard spines. In colour these Lizards match their desert surroundings, amid

[*James's Press.*
HISPID LIZARD (*Agama hispida*).
A South African species.

which they wander at a clumsy, lumbering gait. They live in burrows or rocky crannies, the entrances to which are closed by the spiny tails.

The Australian Spiny Lizard (*Moloch horridus*) of Southern and Western Australia, is the most highly armoured of all Lizards, its toadlike body,

[*W. S. Pitt.*
AUSTRALIAN SPINY LIZARD (*Moloch horridus*).
The " Thorny Devil " bristles with spines that serve to protect it.

short tail, and small head bristling with spines of all sizes, the largest rising like horns over the eyes and between the shoulders. The " Thorny Devil," as it is often called, inhabits barren ground ; its motto is defence rather than defiance, since few creatures care to meddle with it.

[*Otho Webb.*
AUSTRALIAN BEARDED LIZARD (*Amphibolurus barbatus*).
The " beard " of spiky scales is distended when the Lizard is angry.

CUBAN ANOLIS.
The Anoles of tropical America are arboreal Lizards with adhesive digits.

Family IGUANIDAE

The Iguanas may be distinguished from the members of the previous family by their pleurodont teeth. They are, with the exception of two genera which are found in Madagascar and the Fiji Islands, confined to the New World.

The Anoles (*Anolis*) are small arboreal Lizards, distinguished by having toes with adhesive pads. The scales are minute and granular. The head is big in proportion, and somewhat crocodilian in shape. The tail, which may be compressed or rounded, is long and slender, and serves as a balancing pole in the creature's swift progress over all kinds of vertical and horizontal surfaces. The males are in many species distinguished by a large gular pouch which can be distended fanwise across the throat, and is often resplendent with flashing tints of gold and scarlet. These Lizards are common in Southern North America, throughout the whole of Mexico, Central America, tropical South America and the West Indies. The males are inveterate fighters.

The Common American Anole (*Anolis carolinensis*) is typical of the genus; it stalks flies with the stealth of a cat, and runs along walls and tree branches with remarkable rapidity. Light, temperature, or passing emotions produce a sudden change of coloration, ranging from brown to grey, and ashen-blue to emerald-green. The males, when fighting each other, bob their heads violently, at the same time distending the throat pouch, that becomes a deep salmon-pink. Anoles sip the dew from leaves. They have no notion of regular drinking, and caged specimens may die of thirst, though a tank of water be within their reach.

The Basilisks (*Basiliscus*) are arboreal inhabitants of South America that spend much

Photos]   *[James's Press.*
SPINY-TAILED LIZARD (*Uromastix spinifer*).
The Mastigures inhabit desert regions of South-Western Asia and Northern Africa.
When they enter burrows, their spiny tails close the entrances.

of their time in the water. The males are very striking, having high dorsal crests, cockscomb appendages at the back of the head, and extremely long, finned tails. In females and young males these ornaments are but feebly developed. The largest species, *Basiliscus americanus*, is typical of the group, climbing, swimming, and leaping with great agility. The general attitude of these Lizards is distinctly " spry," the creatures sitting bolt upright with head cocked, making a perfect picture of intelligent alertness. The hind legs are very long and the Lizards can travel " on the flat " so swiftly as to be almost invisible. They will suddenly stop dead when in full stride, so that to the pursuer they seem to vanish as if by magic. *B. americanus*, *B. vittatus*, and *B. plumifrons* are kept

[*Wide World Photos.*

BASILISK (*Basiliscus*).
These American Lizards are very alert and climb, swim and leap with great agility.

in the Zoological Gardens and are fed on an insectivorous and vegetarian diet.

The Swifts (*Sceloporus*) are smallish Lizards, four to twelve inches in length, from Northern and Central America. The body carries no crest, but the scales, which are very finely keeled, are sometimes pointed and directed upwards, producing a prickly effect. These Lizards live up to their popular name, being amongst the fleetest of reptiles, traversing rocky ground with lightning speed.

The largest member of the genus is the Collared Swift (*Sceloporus torquatus*), whose bristling scales have earned for it the name of " Porcupine." It is often to be found playing hide-and-seek amongst rotten timber, where it hunts for the larvae of wood-boring beetles.

The true Iguanas (*Iguana*) are large Lizards characterized by high,

349

compressed bodies, ornamented with dewlaps and spiny crests. They occur from the south-western limit of the United States, through tropical South America, the West Indies and the Galapagos Islands. One species is confined to the Fiji and Friendly groups.

The Common Iguana (*Iguana iguana*) is abundant over a large part of tropical America and numbers are imported to the New York market, where they are sold for food, the flesh rivalling that of the choicest chicken. This is an essentially arboreal Lizard, and makes a striking object as it gathers in small communities that perch upon each other, forming a dense mass poised upon some topmost branch. In coloration it is grass-green

[*Sport & General.*

FIN-TAILED LIZARD OR PARARANG (*Hydrosaurus [Lophura] amboinensis*).
A curious Agamid from the Malay Archipelago.

striped with white and black, with a large, vivid eye-spot of pearly hue situated close to the tympanic membrane. It lives largely on fruit and vegetables, but is not averse to worms and insects. A specimen at the Zoo developed a partiality for bread and marmalade.

The West Indian Ground Iguanas (genus *Cyclura*) are massively-built Lizards that hide in burrows at night, and hunt birds and rodents by day.

The Rhinoceros Iguana (*Metopocerus cornutus*), which grows to some four or five feet in length, has three conical horns on the snout, the longest being nearly half-an-inch high. It makes a striking object as it sits up, exposing its great, swollen jaw muscles and voluminous, painted dewlap. It is a savage and powerful creature, killing birds as large as a fowl. This Lizard is found only in Porto Rico and Haiti, where the natives hunt it for food with specially-trained dogs. These reptiles abound on the shores of a certain dead sea lake, one hundred and thirty feet below sea-level in the desert of Santo Domingo. Here the Rhinoceros Iguana and the allied spike-tailed species *M. ricardii* use their powerful claws to dig burrows, forty feet long, through hard rock consisting of the fossil remains of extinct corals. The eggs, which are larger than a hen's, are buried about two feet deep in sand. Four or five females may use a common nest, depositing between them over one hundred and twenty eggs.

Two very large species of Iguana inhabit the Galapagos Islands. The Marine Iguana (*Amblyrhynchus cristatus*) is almost unique amongst

[Carl Hagenbeck's Tierpark, Stellingen.
IGUANA (*Iguana tuberculata*).
The true Iguanas are characterized by a dewlap and a crest of spines.

reptiles in being unusually sociable. It gathers in vast quantities on the barren rocks of the Galapagos group, and like the nearly-related land species is in demand for food. It grows to about three feet and feeds upon seaweeds, browsing upon them both in and out of the water. Its flattened tail stamps it as a powerful swimmer.

The nearly-related Land Iguana (*Conolophus subcristatus*) is somewhat larger and more massively built.

The so-called Horned Toads (*Phrynosoma*) are broad toad-like creatures encased in spiny coats, the spines round the head being specially large. The arrangement of the armature has largely determined the separation of the genus into about fifteen species. Horned Toads are common throughout the desert regions of the United States and Mexico.

The largest species (*Phrynosoma regale*) reaches seven inches in length. In spite of their impressive armature these reptiles are quite harmless. If molested, a Horned Toad will swell to make the most of himself, and at the same time open his mouth wide and will do all possible to

[*D. Seth-Smith.*
COLLARED LIZARD (*Crotaphytus collaris*).
A North-American Iguanid.

intimidate the foe. The creature's trump card, however, is the faculty which it possesses of being able to squirt a thin stream of blood, fine as a hair, from the inner corner of each eye to a distance of about five feet ; this performance may be counted upon effectually to embarrass an opponent, especially as it is resorted to with extraordinary suddenness.

Family Zonuridae

This family forms a connecting link between the Iguanas and the Lizards next to be considered—the *Anguidae*. It is confined to South Africa and Madagascar. All the species carry large, bony plates on the back and tail, the latter fairly bristling with sharp, double-plated scales.

The Giant Zonure (*Zonurus giganteus*) of South Africa is the largest member of the family, and attains a length of nearly two feet. It lives in rocky districts, retreating into underground burrows at night and during cold weather.

[*James's Press.*
HORNED "TOAD" (*Phrynosoma cornutum*).
Horned Toads inhabit the desert regions of Mexico and the United States.

The members of the genus *Chamaesaura*, though wearing the characteristic spiky scales, have the limbs reduced to mere rudiments. In *Chamaesaura aenea* both pairs of limbs are present and are

352

half-an-inch long, but in *Ch. macrolepis* the fore limbs are entirely absent

[*L.E.A.*

A MARINE IGUANA.

(*Reproduced from " Galápagos : World's End," by courtesy of the author, Mr. William Beebe ; of the New York Zoological Society and of the Publishers, Messrs. G. P. Putnam's Sons.*)

and the hind ones are represented by mere rudiments, almost invisible to the naked eye.

REPTILIA (ORDER LACERTILIA)

GIANT ZONURA (*Zonurus giganteus*).
This South African Lizard lives in rocky districts.

Family Anguidae

Some members of this family are of the t y p i c a l Lacertilian form, but in others the limbs are either reduced, o r a r e r e tained as mere vestiges completely h i d d e n under the skin. All A n g u i d a e are thoroughly terrestrial. The headquarters of the family is in Mexico, Central America and the New World, generally, but a few kinds inhabit Europe, and a single species is found in Asia. The teeth are of the pleurodont type and the new teeth, instead of forcing out the old and worn fangs from beneath, push in between them. Throughout the family (about forty-five species) the scales are underlaid with bony plates arranged in rings, completely encasing the animal.

The Slow-worm (*Anguis fragilis*) of England should be known to every country walker, as it often obtrudes itself upon one's notice by calmly basking in the middle of the foot-path, relying upon its likeness to a twisted fern stump to defy detection. Its scales gleam in bright sunlight, but although wholly limbless, it can dart under brush with considerable speed. It is perfectly harmless, living entirely upon small insects, but is nevertheless the object of superstitious dread. Its tail is extremely brittle and often remains in the hand of its would-be captor. In the late autumn the female brings forth from six to twenty silvery-white young, which are born alive.

The Glass Snake (*Ophiosaurus a p u s*) o f S o u t h - eastern Europe, North Africa, a n d South-western A s i a, is one of the largest members of the family, reaching a length of f o u r feet and a girth of four-and-a-half inches ; it is a c o m m o n item in the live-stock d e a l e r ' s

Photos]   [*James's Press.*
BLUE LIZARD (*Gerrhonotus coeruleus*).
A Californian Lizard related to the Slow-worm, but of normal form and with well-developed limbs.

354

[*W. S. Berridge.*

GLASS SNAKE (*Ophiosaurus apus*).

The Glass Snake, like its relative the Slow-worm, when seized by the tail discards it, leaving it thrashing in the hand of the would-be captor.

catalogues. The animal, which is provided with minute rudiments of hind limbs, looks and feels as if made of polished metal. Although very snake-like in form, the large head, with its big ear membranes, and eyes with lids, is obviously that of a Lizard. The stiff, unyielding armour renders its movements somewhat ungainly, yet it is very active and can kill mice and rats as well as insects. It is fond, also, of eggs, breaking the shell with its powerful jaws and lapping up the yolk. Like the Slow-worm, it will discard its tail if seized by that organ, leaving it thrashing furiously in the hands of the would-be captor.

[*W. S. Pitt.*

SLOW-WORM OR BLIND-WORM (*Anguis fragilis*).

This legless Lizard is quite harmless, but is often mistaken for a snake.

REPTILIA (ORDER LACERTILIA)

Family Helodermatidae (*Beaded Lizards or Gila Monsters*)

The Beaded Lizards or Gila Monsters of the desert regions of Mexico and Arizona are known by two species only. They are characterized by the beadlike formation of their scales, and by their grooved teeth. The teeth are curved as in poisonous snakes, and those of the lower jaw have each two deep channels for the conveyance of poison from a chain of glands at their bases. The venom is reported to be powerful enough to kill a person. This was proved some time ago at the Pasteur Institute in Paris, where one of these Lizards bit a member of the staff who was experimenting on its venom. The victim—a lady—in spite of receiving immediate treatment, only just escaped with her life, and was seriously ill for over six months. These Lizards are heavy, bulky animals, with broad tails holding large reservoirs of fat upon which they can draw for sustenance in lean times. The colouring of the warty surface is striking, consisting of picturesque black markings on a vivid terra-cotta or Indian-red background. Gila Monsters are heavy, sluggish creatures, crawling slowly and seldom raising the body clear of the ground. When

[W. J. Clarke.

NILE MONITOR (*Varanus niloticus*).
Monitors are large, active and predaceous Lizards.

provoked, however, they can leap or dart with surprising activity, and if given an opportunity to strike, will plunge their fangs into the victim and hold on with tenacity. In captivity, they are very fond of hen's eggs. In the wild, they probably subsist on the soft-shelled eggs of Lizards and Snakes, digging them out of the sand with their powerful claws. Of the two known species, *Heloderma suspectum* inhabits Arizona and New Mexico, and *H. horridum* is confined to the Southern United States.

Family Varanidae (*Monitors*)

The Monitors, of which there are twenty-eight species, are the largest of living Lizards—the giant of the tribe (*Varanus komodoensis*) attaining a length of twelve feet. All are fleet of foot and powerful of limb, as befits such highly predaceous animals. The general conformation is not unlike that of our Common Lizard, but the neck is exceptionally long in proportion. The tongue, which is retractile into a basal sheath, is long and deeply forked, and restlessly probes the

By courtesy of]   *[Carl Hagenbeck's Tierpark, Stellingen.*
GILA MONSTER (*Heloderma suspectum*).
The Gila Monsters of the deserts of Mexico and Arizona are venomous.

ground as the animal progresses. The eyes and ear openings are well-developed. The body is covered with small scales, which are arranged in cross rows on the lower surface. The long, laterally compressed tail is used with effect, not only in swimming, but as a weapon, being swung from side to side with a scythe-like action. In desert forms the tail is rounded, but in those that frequent water it is compressed. The vestigeal structure known as the pineal eye is better developed in the Monitors than in most other Lizards. The teeth are pleurodont, long, slightly curved, and swollen at the base. The name Monitor has arisen from the corruption of the Arabic ' *ouran* ' a Lizard, which has become in some way confused with the German '*varen*' to warn, and refers to the ancients' belief that these reptiles acted as scouts and heralds to the crocodiles.

Varanus salvator, which grows to eight feet in length, is common throughout Ceylon and the Malay Peninsula, and in most of the Islands of the Malay Archipelago. It is a jungle-dwelling form, keeping to dense undergrowth, where it kills such creatures as it can overpower. Its table-manners are typical of its tribe. Rushing upon a bird or mammal with great suddenness, it shakes it violently from side to side, like a terrier with a rat. When it is quite dead, the " morsel " is seized by the head and bolted whole in a series of gulps. This Monitor is very unpopular in many parts of India, not only because of its raids on poultry yards, but owing to its reputation for being very venomous. In captivity it soon becomes very tame, and its fondness for eggs is such that it will bolt eight or a dozen at a single meal, and with such greed that they may be heard bumping against each other in their rapid passage

[Otho Webb.
INDIAN MONITOR (*Varanus indicus*).
The long, compressed tail of the Monitor is used in swimming and also as a weapon.

down the throat. These Monitors fight furiously in the breeding season, rearing upon their hind legs and grappling each other's necks firmly with their jaws. The female lays about twenty-four white, soft-shelled eggs about two inches long.

This Monitor is much addicted to water, remaining submerged for long periods ; it has large nasal cavities which can be closed and retain considerable supplies of air. Like most of the tribe, it is soberly coloured, brown or blackish above with numerous rings and bands of both lighter and darker shades.

The largest member of the genus is the so-called Komodo Dragon (*Varanus komodoensis*). In 1926 eight-foot-long specimens of this animal, which was discovered as recently as 1912, were obtained for the London and New York Zoos from the Island of Komodo, which lies between Flores and Sumbawa. To capture the dragons special traps were built, were baited with dead pigs, and were so arranged that a Lizard on seizing the food was hoisted into the air by a noose attached to a sapling. Numerous specimens were thus obtained, but even when, as was thought, they were securely caged, a few contrived to escape, exerting enormous strength. These animals, which grow to over twelve feet in length, are able to dismember a fair-sized hog, and one was reported to have attacked and severely injured a pony. Like most Lizards, however, they usually make off when disturbed, either into the jungle or the sea, in which they show themselves powerful, if clumsy, swimmers. In captivity they may become very tame.

Not long ago the presence of a living eight-foot-long dragon at the Zoological Society's Scientific Meeting caused a sensation, as it was allowed to walk about the floor of the Meeting Room. " Sumbawa," as this giant Lizard had been named, did not give a moment's anxiety, and entertained its audience by devouring a large chicken, a pigeon and half a dozen eggs, whilst its Curator was discoursing on its temperament and habits. " Sumbawa " not only follows its keepers about the Reptile House, but has been taken for walks in the Gardens during the summer months.

The Desert Monitor (*V. griseus*), of North Africa, South-west Asia and Arabia, does not exceed four-and-a-half feet. It is coloured to match its arid surroundings.

The slightly larger Gould's Monitor (*V. gouldii*) is strikingly marked with bright-yellow rings or bars on a black ground. It is a common species inhabiting Australia.

In many parts of the world inhabited by Monitor Lizards, these reptiles are regarded with such aversion that, should one enter a house or even walk over the roof, it is regarded as an omen of ill-fortune and a priest is sent for to go through an incantation in order to avert the evil.

[W. S. Pitt.

KOMODO DRAGON (*Varanus komodoensis*).
The largest of the Monitors, attaining a length of twelve feet; it inhabits the small island of Komodo.

REPTILIA (ORDER LACERTILIA)

Family Lacertidae

The family Lacertidae includes all the typical Lizards in the Old World. They are provided with well-developed limbs, cleft tongues, and efficient organs of sight and hearing. The scales are usually small, and the dentition is pleurodont. Most of these Lizards are insectivorous. A few are viviparous, but the majority lay soft oval eggs, which are buried in the ground, and are hatched by the sun.

[Heinrich Fischer.

SAND LIZARD (*Lacerta agilis*).
This Lizard is locally distributed in England. The example was photographed when basking in the sun.

Two species are native to England, the C o m m o n or Viviparous Lizard (*Lacerta vivipara*) and the Sand Lizard (*L. a g i l i s*). The Common Lizard has a wide European range north of the Alps, and abounds on all heathy wastes. It is brownish or dark fawn in colour, and grows to a length of e i g h t inches. About nine to a dozen young, less than an inch in length, are produced at a time; t h e y are either born free, or enclosed in a membraneous capsule. For the first fortnight or so they subsist upon the remains of the yolk attached to their abdomen.

The Sand Lizard, which reaches a length of nearly a foot, is common throughout Northern and Central Europe, but in England it is peculiarly local in its distribution. It is very abundant in the south on the sandy heaths near Bournemouth and Poole, near Frensham, and between Farnham and Hindhead; in the north it frequents the sand-dunes in the neighbourhood of Southport in Lancashire. The female of this species is brown,

LIZARDS (LACERTIDAE)

GREEN LIZARD (*Lacerta viridis*).
This handsome species is a native of Europe.

with black-and-white eye-spots on the back and sides, but the male is bright emerald-green above.

The handsome Green Lizard (*Lacerta viridis*), so popular with vivarium keepers, reaches a length of nearly fourteen inches, and inhabits the Channel Islands, Central and Southern Europe and Asia Minor. Both sexes are green above; in the typical form the throat of the males is of a deep blue hue.

The Eyed Lizard (*L. ocellata*) is a much bulkier creature, which may attain a length of over two feet. It is a native of the South of France, North-west Italy, Spain, and North-west Africa. The dull green background is relieved by a dark network, and by large blue spots edged with brown. If kept in captivity these Lizards take readily to a diet of minced beef, eggs, mice, and young birds, but sometimes develop a liking for smaller members of their own species.

The vividly-coloured Wall Lizard (*L. muralis*) is one of the most abundant continental species. It scampers up and down walls with wonderful agility and presents an almost infinite variety of harlequin-like patterns of great intricacy. The Wall Lizards inhabiting some of the smaller islands of the Mediterranean and the Adriatic are either entirely black, or black above and lapis-blue beneath.

Photos] [*W. J. Clarke.*
COMMON LIZARD (*Lacerta vivipara*).
One of the two British species of Lizard. It is viviparous.

Family Teiidae
(*Tegus or Teguexins*)

The Tegus, or Teguexins, are an exclusively American group. The teeth are remarkable in c o m b i n i n g both acrodont and pleurodont features, and some species have flattened crushing teeth at the back of the jaws. S o m e forms are arboreal, b u t others a r e strictly terrestrial.

[W. S. Berridge.
RED TEGUEXIN (*Tupinambis rufescens*).
The Teguexins are handsomely-marked Lizards with lacey patterns.

In a few species the limbs have become entirely rudimentary.

The Common Teguexin (*Tupinambis teguixin*) grows to four feet in length and is typical of the genus. It abounds in South America, where it frequents open ground, chasing and devouring small mammals and birds. It is a great nuisance to farmers, breaking into fowl runs and carrying off birds, besides cracking large numbers of eggs with its powerful jaws. Teguexins are handsomely-marked animals with intricate, lacey patterns ; brown, black, yellow, and pearly-white being the prevailing colours. Old specimens develop heavy crocodile-like pouches on the sides of the powerful jaws, which are capable of crushing a man's hand. T h e s e Lizards a r e vicious b y n a t u r e though capable of becoming tame in confinement.

[W. J. Clarke.
WALL LIZARD (*Lacerta muralis*).
This European Lizard scampers up and down walls with great agility.

Family Gerrhosauridae

This family is an African one, its members being most abundant in South Africa and in Madagascar. The family presents much variatior., some forms having well-developed limbs, others

Photos] *[W. J. Clarke.*

EYED LIZARD (*Lacerta ocellata*).
The Eyed Lizard takes its name from the large blue spots, margined with brown, on its side.

FRINGE-TOED LIZARD (*Acanthodactylus vulgaris*).
This Lizard from Spain and North Africa lives in sandy places, and has the toes broadened by a fringe of scales.

363

[W. S. Berridge.
SPINY-TAILED SCINKS (*Egernia depressa*).
This Australian species is remarkable for the strongly-spinate tail.

lacking them entirely. There is a deep fold down each side of the body. The family is intermediate between the typical L i z a r d s (*Lacertidae*) and the Scinks (*Scincidae*), agreeing with the f o r m e r in t h e structure of t h e skull and with the latter in having the body protected by bony plates underlying the scales.

Family Scincidae (*Scinks*)

The Scinks are pleurodont Lizards occurring throughout the greater part of Southern Europe, Australia, Southern Asia, and Africa. The majority are inhabitants of desert districts, and live in the sand, but some live in grass, and a few are arboreal. The head, body, and tail are less distinctly marked than in most Lizards, and in the many limbless forms, are all but indistinguishable. The entire creature is covered with fairly uniform scales, overlying bony plates arranged in the usual formation and not in rings as in the Anguidae. The tongue is short, thick, and feebly bifurcated, and is often of a bluish tint. The teeth show great variety in the size and shape of their crowns. The limbs are at best but feebly developed. The lower eyelid is provided with a transparent shutter ; this, combined with the cylindrical form and exceeding smoothness of these lizards, greatly facilitates a subterranean life.

The Common Scink (*Scincus scincus*) inhabits the Sahara and the shores of the Red Sea, where it grows to a length of about nine inches. At one time it was used in Egypt for medicinal purposes, and was regarded as a panacea for almost every ill. By the Arabs its flesh is still valued, both as a food, and as a drug.

The Giant Scink (*Tiliqua gigas*) attains a length of two feet. It comes from New Guinea, the Moluccas, and Java, where it stalks small birds, mice, a n d insects. Like most of the members of

[Otho Webb.
BLUE-TONGUED SCINK (*Tiliqua scincoides*).
A Lizard remarkable for its bright blue mouth and tongue.

the genus *Tiliqua*, it is dull-brown in colour, with a blue or purple tongue.

The Stump - tailed Scink (*Trachysaurus rugosus*) of Australia is the only representative of its genus. So short a n d thick is its tail t h a t at a distance the creature appears

[*W. S. Pitt.*
OCELLATED SAND SCINK (*Chalcides ocellatus*).
The species of Chalcides differ in the degree of reduction of the limbs, and number of the digits.

to have a head at either end. The elongate and thick body is covered with large, rough scales suggestive of the cone of a fir tree. This Scink is viviparous, and is the only Lizard that brings forth but a single young at birth, the newly-born reptile being half the size of its parent.

The diversity of the limbs of the members of this family is remarkable ; for example, some members of the genus *Lygosoma* are provided with well-developed limbs, but others are without any at all.

The Seps (*Chalcides tridactylus*) has the limbs so degraded as to be almost invisible. Twelve known species of the genus vary much in the number of the digits, some having five, others three ; in one they are mere knobs.

Family Amphisbaenidae

The Amphisbaenas have been not inaptly named after a mythical monster that possessed a head where its tail should have been, and progressed either backwards or forwards with equal facility. The small and harmless namesakes of this nightmare beast inhabit both hemispheres, and though true Lizards, have no limbs. Scales are represented merely

[*D. Seth-Smith.*
STUMP-TAILED SCINK (*Trachysaurus rugosus*).
This Australian Scink has such a short and thick tail that it appears to have a head at each end.

by a series of horny rings, giving these creatures a remarkably wormlike appearance. The top of the head and chin bear shields, and the " rings " are divided into minute squares, which enable these animals to maintain a tolerable grip of whatever surface they may be traversing.

By a series of slow, vertical undulations the reptile can progress equally well either forwards or backwards. Amphisbaenas are specially adapted for raiding ant-hills, in which they find their principal sustenance. The broad rounded-off tail resembles the equally blunt head, and natives believe Amphisbaenas to be two-headed snakes, and affirm that not only 'does each end feed in turn, but that one end sleeps while the other watches. It must be admitted that there is some small excuse for the belief, as superficially the two extremities are strikingly similar in shape, and as the eyes are rudimentary and nearly invisible, it is only after careful examination that one is able to tell one end from the other. The reptile, it would appear, is well aware of this remarkable resemblance, as when attacked, it will lift its tail in such a manner that it looks like a head in an aggressive attitude ; meanwhile the head remains motionless on the ground, and then is suddenly swung round with lightning rapidity to inflict a painful bite, the jaws being endowed with great muscular power.

The genus *Amphisbaena* is divided into about thirty species, inhabiting Europe, South America, and Africa. The largest species reaches two feet in length and about an inch in diameter, displaying remarkable uniformity in girth from nose to tail.

Blanus cinereus of Spain and Portugal resembles a big earthworm.

Family Chamaeleontidae (*Chameleons*)

The Chameleons are by some authorities placed in a special Suborder—

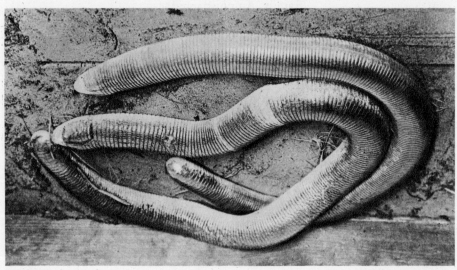

[*Wide World Photos.*

WHITE AMPHISBAENA (*Amphisbaena alba*).
A South American species. The Amphisbaenas are Lizards of worm-like appearance.

[F. W. Bond.

CHAMELEON WITH TONGUE EXTENDED TO RECEIVE FOOD.

the *Rhiptoglossa*. All the species are comparatively small, the largest not exceeding a length of eighteen inches, including the tail. The leading characteristics of the group are unmistakable. The body is deeply compressed laterally, with a rather short and very prehensile tail. The head juts out at the back into a large flange or crest, and the males of several species wear upon the snout or forehead grotesque protuberances. The feet, both fore and hind, bear five toes, so divided that three of them are opposable to the remaining two, forming a very efficient grasping organ. The huge eyes are set in deep cavities, the eye-balls being covered with skin, leaving only a minute opening for vision. Each eye moves independently, and can be turned in any direction. The scales are small and granular. The tongue, which is furnished with a viscid, club-like tip, can be shot forth and back with surprising rapidity, and to a distance often exceeding the length of its owner's body. Chameleons are slow and lethargic to a degree, relying upon their protective coloration and Job-like patience to admit of insect quarry venturing within striking distance of the tongue. The dentition is acrodont. Most members of the family are oviparous, but the Pygmy Chameleon (*Chamaeleon pumilus*) of South Africa, and a few related species, bring forth their young alive, a dozen or so at birth.

Of the fifty species of Chameleons known, forty-five inhabit Africa, Madagascar, Southern Spain, India and Ceylon.

[L.E.A.(G.P.A.).
RHINOCEROS-HORNED CHAMELEON (*Chamaeleon bifurcatus*).
A curious Chameleon from Madagascar, the long horns characterize the male.

The Common Chameleon (*Chamaeleon chamaeleon*) is found in countries bordering the Mediterranean. Like most of its relatives, this species is soberly tinted brown, fawn, or green, only assuming other tints very gradually, and with no great degree of certainty.

In the mating season these Chameleons fight violently, enjoying long rests between the bouts.

The male of *Chamaeleon bifurcatus* of Madagascar has the front portion of the skull developed into two enormous horn-like projections, as long as the entire skull and covered with scales. The female presents only a rudiment of this structure. Even more striking are the three large horns, one on the snout and one over each eye, of *C. oweni* of West Africa, a Chameleon that bears a remarkable superficial resemblance to the extinct Dinosaur (*Triceratops*).

[*Paul Unger.*
AFRICAN CHAMELEON.
This figure shows well the crested head, grasping digits, and prehensile tail characteristic of Chameleons.

368

Order OPHIDIA (*Snakes*)

Structure. Snakes, of which some two thousand living species are known, are reptiles closely related to the Lizards and to certain extinct forms, notably the huge aquatic reptiles known as Mosasaurs. Characteristics of the suborder are the absence of limbs, the great elongation of the body, the absence of ear openings and movable eyelids, the long, neatly-cleft tongue, which can be withdrawn into a sheath, the paired generative organ, and the connection of the two halves of the lower jaw by ligament, allowing each portion considerable independent action. Snakes progress by lateral undulation, the formation and arrangement of the scales covering the under-surface enabling them to grip earth, branch, or whatever else they may be traversing. Some snakes are arboreal, some burrowing, and a few are entirely aquatic; most, however, are ground dwellers. The tail usually occupies about one-fourth the entire length, and may be flattened to form a paddle, or be rounded and highly prehensile. In a few snakes, such as the Boas, hind limbs are represented by vestiges, each being reduced to an ilium, sometimes supporting a rudimentary femur, and terminating in a claw. The entire body is covered with scales. Large shields are usually present on the head, and these are often of great importance in classification. The outer scale-covered portion of the skin is cast periodically, usually in a single piece, although this depends greatly on the creature's state of health. The structure of the jaws, coupled with the absence of a breast bone and the peculiar attachment of the ribs, makes it possible for most snakes to assimilate masses of food entire, which any other creature would have to bite or tear to pieces before swallowing. The eye is covered by a transparent membrane, which is cast with the rest of the outer skin. The eye may be minute, as in the Worm-snakes, or very large, as in many arboreal species. The pupil may be round, or horizontally or vertically elliptical. There is a deep cleft in the snout of most snakes, allowing the free passage of the tongue, a tactile organ, even when the mouth is closed. The teeth are, in most species, numerous and not situated on the four jaw bones only, but distributed also in two rows on the palate.

Poison Glands. Less than one-third of living snakes are known to be venomous. These have grooved, or tubular, teeth for the injection of venom from the poison glands, which are connected with them by special ducts. The poison is secreted by two modified salivary glands, one on either side and situated just behind the eyes. Although usually a single tooth—sometimes a pair, on either side, connect with the poison glands. Several reserve teeth may lie behind it, and when the first tooth is worn out, broken, or otherwise discarded, the second moves forward to take its place. In the Vipers the fangs, situated in the front of the upper jaw, are attached to a maxillary bone, by the movement of which they can be folded back when not in use. The poison consists of a solution of modified proteids, its toxic nature, and its rate of action, varying greatly in different species. Anti-toxins are now produced for distribution in several institutions in various parts of the world. A few animals, such as the dormouse, hedgehog, and secretary bird are immune to small injections of the poison of such snakes as they habitually meet. The old belief that poisonous snakes have a flattened, diamond-shaped head may be discarded, as there is no golden rule for identification of the poisonous or harmless, save examination of teeth and head shields—a procedure that is seldom practicable. Neither is the size of the fangs any criterion, some of the smallest fangs being possessed by the deadliest of snakes. Most snakes seem to be immune to their own poison, and some harmless and cannibalistic species are immune to and actually prey upon poisonous snakes sharing their habitat. As may be supposed, the snake's internal organs are enormously elongated. The liver occupies about one-fourth the entire length, and the lungs are similarly attenuated.

Reproduction. In the majority of cases there is apparently little, if any, attempt at courtship preceding mating and reproduction, although scent glands are usually present, and probably play a part in bringing the sexes together. Apart from the almost universal " hissing," a few snakes produce sounds by friction of the scales, and the well-known Rattle-snakes vibrate their strange caudal appendages when disturbed. Reproduction is effected either by laying comparatively soft-shelled eggs, which may in some species be incubated, or by hatching the eggs within the body of the parent. The young on hatching fracture the shell by means of a complex egg-tooth, a sharp-edged projection of the infant snout, which is discarded soon after they emerge. Freak embryos are not infrequent ; a three-foot long Milk Snake (*Lampropeltis triangulum*) hatched in the New York Zoo possessed two heads which fought each other so savagely at mealtimes that when food was introduced into the cage, each had to be hidden from the other's sight by a cardboard screen.

Feeding. Snakes, when feeding, take their food whole, and usually head first. Since a snake's teeth are recurved, food once taken cannot easily be regurgitated and swallowing proceeds more or less mechanically. Both in the wild and in captivity long fasts can be survived by these reptiles, a Boa in the Paris Jardin des Plantes having been known to fast for a period of over four years. Drinking is accomplished not by lapping, but by placing the whole of the muzzle in the water.

Size and Age. The size and age to which snakes attain have been greatly exaggerated. The largest living snakes—Pythons and Anacondas, which may attain over thirty feet in length, are probably less than fifty years old. Size and longevity, however, do not always go together, since a specimen of the smallest known snake (*Glauconia decimum*), kept for many years in captivity, never exceeded its length when caught—namely four inches. Snakes are found chiefly in the tropics, diminishing in numbers as they approach the north and south. A species of *Tropidonotus* occurs in the Himalayas at a height of fourteen thousand feet. Fossil remains are rare and fragmentary, but Sea-snake remains have been dug up in the London clay off Sheppey. The largest known snake is *Python gigantodius*, from the Middle Eocene deposits of the Fayum Desert of Egypt, which attained to a length of over fifty feet.

Coloration and Markings. Environment and coloration are, naturally, closely associated, and in the majority of snakes both colour and markings would appear to be largely protective. The arboreal Boas and the other Tree-snakes, desert-dwelling Vipers and the Sea-snakes of mid-ocean, all blend very effectually with their several habitats. In the Coral-snakes, however, the colouring is such that it is conspicuous against almost any background. A p a r t from the demand for snake-skins, these reptiles cannot be said to have any great economic importance for man although they may be of service in destroying vermin. In legend and religion snakes h a v e played an important part, and many examples might be quoted. The toll some species take of human

[*W. S. Berridge.*

BURROWING SNAKE (*Typhlops punctatus*).
The Burrowing Snakes are degenerate and worm-like ; they live in all warm countries.

life is large in spite of all precautions. In India alone, the annual mortality from snake-bite still exceeds twenty thousand. In the small Island of Martinique the Fer-de-lance (*Bothrops atrox*) is annually responsible for the death of over a hundred human beings. At one time handsome rewards were offered for the suppression of this snake in the West Indies, with the result that the enterprising natives bred the snakes in secret, and retired upon the proceeds. So-called "snake-stones" still have a ready market East of Suez ; these stones are composed of limey concretions from the stomachs of various mammals, and are regarded as infallible specifics against snake-poison.

Families Typhlopidae and Glauconiidae (*Blind or Worm-snakes*)

The members of these families are degenerate worm-like snakes, the head, with its minute eyes, being scarcely distinguishable from the tail, which may end in a small spine. In the Typhlopidae the teeth are situated in the upper jaw only, but in the Glauconiidae they are restricted to the lower jaw. The scales are small, and are more or less uniform over the entire animal. Worm-snakes show their affinity with the largest known serpents in the possession of a vestigeal pelvis. These snakes are found in all the warmer countries. They are essentially burrowers, closely resembling the earth in coloration, and feeding principally upon the eggs of white ants, their hard scales rendering them immune to the jaws of these insects.

Family Boidae (*Boas and Pythons*)

The Constrictors have from early time been famous not only for their gorgeous colouring and intricate patterns, but for their often enormous size. The jaws entirely lack poison fangs, but are capable of great expansion, and the teeth are exceedingly long, curving backwards towards the throat. The teeth maintain a firm grip of the prey whilst the snake coils its body round it and crushes it to death by the vigorous contraction of the dorsal and intercostal muscles. Many of the larger species are capable of overpowering large animals such as deer. A twenty-foot Python will have no difficulty in making a meal off a forty-pound hog.

The true Boas occur in Central and Tropical America, the West Indies and Madagascar. The commonest species, *Boa constrictor*, of Central and South America, enjoys a quite false reputation for being a giant amongst snakes, as it seldom exceeds twelve feet in length. The colour is a rich, ruddy chestnut, with a chain of big tan-coloured saddle markings, margined with lighter tints, down the back. As in many large snakes, the skin gives rise to a brilliant bloom of rainbow hues when seen in a certain light, and this is specially evident when the skin has just been cast. This Boa, like most, rests fairly high up amongst the tree branches, and descends at intervals to secure small mammals or birds. An eight-foot long Zoo specimen in the course of a single year devoured twenty-three rabbits, thirteen pigeons and three rats. A few years ago, two Zoo Boas, the one measuring eleven feet in length and the other eight feet, shared the same enclosure, and attacked the same dead pigeon. The two met in the middle of the prey and both pigeon and smaller Boa were swallowed by the larger. On another occasion an eleven-foot-long Boa completely swallowed another, nine feet long, with which it had lived on friendly terms for several years; for weeks after its swallowing feat this snake had no longer the power of curling itself round, but it digested its companion and eventually regained its normal size, and its appetite. Boas do not lay eggs, but bring forth their young alive.

The Tree Boas (*Corallus*) are graceful serpents, often of a bright green colour that harmonizes with the foliage of the trees they frequent. They have very slender necks and prominent eyes set in very large heads, which

in young specimens look quite disproportionate. The genus is represented in Tropical South America and Madagascar.

The Sand Boas (*Eryx*) are degenerate species inhabiting the desert
regions of North Africa, and Central and Southern Asia. All are flattened
burrowing forms with stumpy heads and thick, rounded tails. These
creatures, like the Amphisbaenas, are sometimes named two-headed
snakes. The Indian and Egyptian snake-charmers, indeed, doctor the
tail end so as to make it resemble the head. The Indian species, *E. johnii*,
is of a dark sandy colour when adult, but passes through flesh-pink and
coral-red before arriving at this tint.

[*Paul Unger.*

BOA (*Boa constrictor*).
This handsome snake inhabits Central and South America; it feeds on small mammals and birds.

The Anaconda (*Eunectes murinus*) of the Guianas, Brazil and Peru
is one of the largest of living snakes, attaining a length of over thirty
feet. It matures early, seventeen-foot specimens being not more than
ten years of age, but able to bring forth more than thirty young. The
colouring is dark olive-green, with a dorsal chain of large, round, dark
blotches, and a broken line of smaller blotches parallel to it on either
side. This snake is largely aquatic, and in conformity with its mode of
life the nostrils are directed upwards. Normally it preys upon birds,
which are constricted and swallowed under water, but small mammals
and fish also figure on its menu. Although there is only one authentic

373

record of it attacking a man, this huge water Boa is disliked by natives on account of the raids it makes upon their poultry. A smaller and lighter-coloured species, *E. noteus*, inhabits the Argentine and Paraguay.

The Pythons (*Python*) differ from the Boas in the presence of a supra-orbital bone above the eye. They may further be distinguished from true Boas by having large and irregular shields on the anterior half of the head, the head-shields in the Boas being usually small and broken up into scales. Pythons are oviparous, the female coiling herself round the eggs, fifty to a hundred in number, and incubating them until they hatch, a period of about two months. The temperature within the massive coils of the mother during the incubation period increases steadily, rising from about 80° to 90°. Pythons are abundant in the tropical areas of Africa, Asia, the East Indian Archipelago, and Australia. All are expert swimmers and climbers, frequenting, with few exceptions, dense jungle overhanging water-ways.

The Reticulated Python (*P. reticulatus*) is, perhaps, the largest living snake, many well-authenticated specimens of thirty-two feet and over being recorded. This snake is a vigorous feeder, and in a zoo has been known to take more than thirty meals in a year. Small deer and birds appear to be the chief food. In early life growth is rapid, a length of ten feet being reached at the age of four years ; by the time the snake is twenty another ten feet have been added. Thirty-foot specimens are probably not far short of fifty years old. No description can do the colours of this snake full justice ; they are richer and deeper than in most Boas, and the iridescent tints reach a splendour seen in no other serpent. The Reticulated Python is savage in disposition, and often temperamental in captivity ; one kept in the Jardin des Plantes in Paris was persuaded to break a year's fast when tempted with a goose, after all other offers of food had failed ; from that time onwards the snake would not touch any food save geese, refusing ducks, chickens, etc., and geese it ate throughout the rest of its life.

The Indian Python (*P. molurus*), abundant throughout India and

[*W. J. Clarke.*]

AFRICAN PYTHON (*Python sebae*).
This Python reaches a length of twenty feet ; it is common throughout tropical Africa.

Ceylon, and less common in Malaya and Java, is a smaller but heavier species. The colour is dark brown or yellowish, with irregular dark blotches. The newly-hatched young, which are two feet long, have been known in captivity to retire to rest in their broken egg-shells, when tired of perambulating their quarters.

[W. J. Clarke.

DIAMOND-BACK WATER SNAKE (*Natrix rhombifer*).
A North American relative of the British Grass Snake.

The common African Python (*P. sebae*) occurs over the whole of tropical Africa. It is brown in colour, with markings in the form of wavy cross-bands, connected by a dark band along each side of the body. It attains a length of twenty feet.

The Diamond Python (*P. spilotes*) is the largest snake of Australia, attaining a length of nine feet. It is bluish-black in colour, each scale bearing a central yellow spot. A variety of this species, known as the Carpet Python, is greenish-brown with patches of yellow.

The West African Burrowing Python (*Calabaria rhinhardi*), the only member of its genus, is a dwarf form not exceeding a yard in length. It frequents farmsteads and chicken runs, where it is largely tolerated for the ceaseless war it wages upon vermin.

Family Colubridae

This family, which embraces the great majority of snakes, is divided into over two hundred genera. Most of the species are ground dwellers, though others have invaded every possible sphere accessible within their peculiar limitations. The family is divided into three Divisions—(*a*) The *Aglypha*—harmless species with solid teeth ; (*b*) The *Ophisthoglypha*—more or less venomous forms with the hinder maxillary teeth grooved ; and (*c*) The *Proteroglypha*—all deadly, having the anterior maxillary teeth grooved or channelled.

Division Aglypha. The division *Aglypha* is further divided into three Sub-families : (i) The *Acrochordinae*, aquatic snakes with nostrils situated on the top of the head, and with small, wedge-like, tubercular scales ; (ii) *Colubrinae*, the typical snakes ; and (iii) *Elachistodontinae*, egg-eating snakes, with rudimentary teeth.

375

REPTILIA (ORDER OPHIDIA)

Sub-family Acrochordinae. The members of the Sub-family *Acrochordinae* live in fresh or brackish water. The Elephant-trunk Snake (*Acrochordus javanicus*), of Siam and the Malay Peninsula, frequents canal and irrigation ditches. The head and neck are almost as thick as the body, which is covered with uniform scales, there being no large shields running across the under-surface. The skin recalls an elephant's trunk, and is much in demand amongst natives for drum-heads. This snake is strictly aquatic, and is usually of savage temperament, throwing itself out of the water if attacked. Its young, about thirty in number, are born alive.

Sub-family Colubrinae. A typical example of the extensive Sub-family *Colubrinae* is the common Grass Snake *Natrix* (syn. *Tropidonotus*) *natrix*, which is abundant over the greater part of Europe, Algeria and West and Central Asia. In Great Britain the snake is restricted to England, and is commonest in the southern counties. In England it is easily distinguished by the white or orange collar on the nape, with two conspicuous black patches just behind it; the general colour ranges from grey-green to olive-brown, with black patches on the sides. The number

[*Will F. Taylor.*
GARTER SNAKE (*Tropidonotus ordinatus*).
Garter Snakes frequent swamps in North America, where they prey on insects, frogs and fish.

of scales round the body is invariably nineteen. The Grass Snake is a good swimmer, and often frequents small ponds or ditches, where it catches frogs and fishes. The young make their first meals of earthworms and dragon-fly larvae. In the spring the female deposits a string of twenty to forty eggs; these are hidden among vegetable debris or in manure heaps, and incubate in about eight weeks. In the autumn the snake hibernates underground, waking about the middle of April. The size limit of this snake in England is about four feet, though nearly half as much again may be attained in Southern Europe.

The Garter Snake (*Tropidonotus ordinatus*) is abundant throughout North and Central America and is on sale in every livestock dealer's shop. It is very variable in colour, the species being divisible into about twenty varieties. The typical form is olive-green above, either plain or with black spots. The variety *sirtalis* of eastern North America is olive or dark brown above, with three yellow or red stripes. Garter Snakes frequent swampy land, where they hunt for insects, frogs, toads and fish.

376

Mr. J. L. Workman has recounted how a large Garter Snake lay hidden behind him whilst he was fishing and swallowed six large chub in succession, seizing them as fast as they were thrown upon the bank. This New World relative of the British Grass Snake is viviparous, and has broods of over eighty young.

Pseudaspis cana of South Africa is the only species of its genus. The head is but slightly defined from the neck ; the posterior teeth of the upper jaw are larger than those in front, but this curious arrangement is reversed in the lower jaw. The Mole Snake, as it is sometimes called, is dark brown or blackish, measuring up to six feet in length ; it shares with the Garter Snake the distinction of being the most prolific snake known, bearing upwards of eighty young at a time.

The snakes of the genus *Zamenis* are terrestrial or semi-arboreal and inhabit Europe, Asia, North Africa, and North and Central America. The head is usually elongate, and distinct from the neck. The eye is large, with a round pupil. The Indian Rat Snake (*Z. mucosus*) is the giant of the genus, specimens over nine feet in length being frequently recorded. It is slender, almost emaciated in

[Chase (Dorien Leigh).
BLACK SNAKE (*Coluber constrictor*).
A North American constricting snake. Young emerging from the eggs.

appearance, and pale brown in colour. Exceedingly nervous and irritable in captivity, it will raise the anterior portion of its body clear of the ground, at the same time flattening the back of the neck vertically and striking out with its snout in such a violent manner as to injure itself seriously if a sheet of glass intervenes between the snake and the observer. At such times, it may give out a mysterious musical sound like that of a lightly-struck tuning fork. In India, where it helps bungalow dwellers by waging war upon rats, it is the subject of numerous legends, one being to the effect that it mates with the cobra, another that it sucks the udders of cows. The eggs, ten to twenty per clutch, are laid in holes in the ground and the emerging young display all the parental irascibility.

The genus *Coluber* of Europe, Asia, and North and Tropical America, embraces some fifty species of constricting snakes. The head is distinct from the neck, and the teeth in the upper jaw are all equal in length. The body and tail are usually elongate.

The Aesculapian Snake (*C. longissimus*), common throughout Italy and South-eastern Europe, and found in parts of Central Europe as far north as Denmark, is one of the few snakes dedicated to Aesculapius, and it is supposed to have been introduced into many widely-scattered localities by the Romans. More probably, however, it is a species which once enjoyed a much wider range and is now in course of extermination. It is yellowish or dark olive when adult, the young having yellow or white collars like those of the Grass Snake. The snake frequents woods and meadows, where it captures mice and voles. It hibernates for an unusually long period, retiring early in October and not venturing forth again until the middle of May. Its average length is about four feet, and it lays not more than half-a-dozen eggs at a time, these being deposited in hollow trees and similar shelters.

The Four-lined Snake (*C. quatuorlineatus*) of Southern Italy, Dalmatia, Greece, Hungary and Southern Russia, is the largest European snake, attaining a length of eight feet. Adults are light or dark brown, with four black longitudinal bands. The young are spotted, the spots gradually giving place to long streaks. In its habits this resembles the Aesculapian Snake, but it is a more efficient climber, ascending trees and robbing the nests of small birds. It may be commended as a pet, being one of the hardiest and most docile of all snakes, quickly becoming tame, and taking food from the hand. It lays about a dozen eggs in midsummer.

The Bull or Pine Snake (*C. melanoleuca*) of North America and Mexico, is a massively-built snake with strongly-keeled scales on the back. Individuals in different parts of the United States vary much both in colour and markings, though all agree in frequenting dry pine forests, where they secrete themselves amongst the fallen needles. The name of "Bull" refers to a bellowing sound audible at some distance; the snake produces this by expelling air from the lungs, so that it vibrates a movable plate—the epiglossus—in the lower jaw. The Bull Snake is a hearty feeder, four Zoo specimens consuming between them two hundred and twenty mice, forty rats and a guinea pig in the course of a year.

In the snakes of the genus *Coronella*, the maxillary teeth increase in size posteriorly; the head is not distinct from the neck, and the eye is very small. All are constrictors. The Smooth Snake (*C. austriaca*), so named from its keelless scales, is common throughout most of Europe, including Scandinavia. In this country it occurs in Hampshire and Dorset, in places frequented by the Sand Lizard, which forms its staple diet. It is sometimes mistaken for the Viper, being greyish above, with chains of dark spots down the back and sides. It may always be distinguished, however, from the poisonous species by its rounded and not vertical pupil. The Smooth Snake reaches a length of two feet. It grows at a great rate, and a captive specimen kept by the writer added seven inches to its length in only nine months. It produces broods of from six to a dozen young in August and September.

The North American King Snakes (*C. getulus*) attain a length of six feet. They are blackish, with yellowish spots or bands. Although a most active and greedy cannibal, which readily attacks and devours Rattlesnakes and Moccasins, to whose poison it is immune, it is docile and intelligent, making an interesting and easily-tamed pet. It must possess a sanguine and resilient temperament, since a Zoo specimen that had

[*Will F. Taylor.*

BULL OR PINE SNAKE (*Coluber melanoleuca*) AND ITS EGGS.

been almost entirely engulfed by a larger cage-mate, so far recovered its spirits as to devour two rats within five minutes of being rescued by its keeper. The King Snake is oviparous.

The Viper-like snakes of the genus *Heterodon* have turned-up snouts, very short and stout bodies, and flat, triangular heads. On account of their raised snouts, which are capped with a strong triangular shield enabling them to excavate in the sand, they are popularly known as Hognosed Snakes. Their colour varies greatly with the locality, the usual design consisting of dark blotches with lighter interstices on a greyish background. A striking characteristic of these snakes is their power to feign death. When first molested, they may assume a threatening cobra-like attitude, and expand the back of the neck into a hood. Should this fail to intimidate, they will try the effect of violent convulsions, throwing themselves upon their backs and twisting their coils into knots. This failing also, they play their last card and become so limp and helpless that they may well be taken for dead. Mr. Raymond Ditmars, Curator of Reptiles in the New York Zoo, has recounted how, whilst collecting in Georgia, he demonstrated the snake's power of shamming death to his negro porters, giving them to understand that he had by occult means brought about the death of the reptile, which they regarded with great aversion. To further increase his prestige with his credulous followers, he pretended by mesmeric passes to restore the dead snake to life. The result was altogether too much for negro nerves and the whole of his entourage decamped, leaving the collector stranded in a wild and lawless region. These snakes lay about twenty-five eggs in holes in the ground, the emerging young showing from the first all their parents' histrionic powers when confronted with an enemy. At the back of the upper jaw of these snakes are a number of long, fang-like teeth which come into play when the snake secures its exclusive diet of toads. Despite their sharp teeth and dramatic powers of bluff, Hog-nosed Snakes cannot be induced to bite the most persistent tormentor.

Sub-family Elachistodontinae. This Sub-family is represented by a single species—the Egg-eating Snake *Dasypeltis scabra* of Tropical and South Africa, which attains a length of about two feet. This particular snake, as its name suggests, feeds entirely on eggs, being nearly toothless. The eggs reach the gullet unbroken, but there they come into contact with large, enamel-capped projections of the vertebrae, the object of which is to crack the shell, which is ejected after a short interval in the form of pellets. The snake may, in fact, be stated to have its teeth situated on its backbone. The expanding power of the creature's jaws is even more amazing than in other snakes, as a snake with a head no larger than a man's little finger is capable of swallowing a hen's egg. Egg-eating Snakes have a very acute sense of smell, and will immediately reject an egg if it is not quite fresh. At the Zoo they have been observed to eat some of the eggs offered them and reject others, which when broken open were invariably found to be slightly addled. The general colour is pale brown, with three longitudinal rows of dark brown blotches. The scales are very strongly keeled, more strongly than in any other non-poisonous species.

Division Opisthoglypha (Back-fanged Snakes). The members of this Division are known as Back-fanged Snakes, and include many forms which have been within recent years recognized as being more or less poisonous. About three hundred species are scattered throughout the tropical and sub-tropical regions. They are sub-divided into the following Sub-families: (i) the *Homalopsinae,* with valvular nostrils directed upwards; they are all aquatic; (ii) the *Dipsadomorphinae*, w i t h the nostrils placed laterally, and the teeth highly developed.

Sub-family Homalopsinae (Freshwater Snakes). The members of the first sub-family frequent rivers, though

[F. W. Bond.
SOUTH AFRICAN EGG-EATING SNAKE (*Dasypeltis scabra*).
These snakes feed exclusively on eggs; the one photographed has just swallowed an egg.

some also enter salt-water. They feed upon fishes and crustaceans; as their nostrils have valves like those of a crocodile, they are able to spend long periods under water in search of food. The body is often compressed, the head but slightly defined, and the tail either flattened for swimming, or more or less prehensile. These snakes seize their prey with a chewing action, the venom quickly overpowering the most active fish, which is swallowed head first. Some twenty-three species are recorded from Eastern Asia.

Sub-family Dipsadomorphinae. These are typical back-fanged snakes of world-wide distribution, classified into over eighty genera. The species are principally arboreal, feeding on lizards and birds. The Boomslang (*Dispholidus typus*) is a typical representative of the sub-family, slenderly built, and with large eyes. It inhabits tropical and South Africa, where it attains a length of six feet, and was until comparatively recently regarded as harmless. Its bite is now known, however, to produce serious if not fatal symptoms in human beings.

Dryophis is an Old World arboreal genus remarkable for the slender whip-like form, the long neck, and the graceful lanceolate head, which, like the body, is much compressed. The Green W h i p S n a k e (*D. mycterizans*) is a typical species from the Malay Peninsula and Archipelago. It has large, golden eyes with horizontal pupils, and the poison fangs and several teeth in both jaws are g r e a t l y developed. Its snout is long and

[W. J. Clarke.
KING SNAKE (*Coronella getulus*).
An active North American snake. It feeds on other snakes.

pointed, with a fleshly appendage at the end; when the long tongue is extended, the whole head appears to lengthen and shorten alternately in a telescopic fashion. Its native name of " Eye-poking " snake refers to the belief that it deliberately strikes at its enemies' eyes. This species is a brilliant uniform green, but in some other members of the sub-family, the tongue bears markings which are continuous with those of the head and it has been suggested by some authorities that the sudden shooting back and forth of the tongue has a fascinating effect upon the lizards which form the principal diet of these reptiles. All these tree-snakes blend with their surroundings, being almost indistinguishable from the tangled twigs or creeping forest vines.

In the genus *Leptodira* the head is very distinct from the neck, the body is compressed, and the eye is very large, with a vertical pupil. The maxillary teeth are followed after an empty space by a pair of enlarged fangs. The genus has a wide distribution throughout Tropical and South Africa, Tropical America and the West Indies.

The Annulated Snake (*L. annulata*) from the West Indies and Tropical South America, often arrives in England as a stowaway amongst bunches of bananas. It is an arboreal species, reddish-brown in colour, and grows to a length of about a yard. It feeds exclusively on fish and frogs.

The genus *Chrysopelea* of South-eastern Asia is represented by three species. The head is distinct from the neck, the eye is large with a round pupil, and the body and tail are compressed. The plates on the belly and tail are keeled, and notched laterally. The fangs are only feebly enlarged.

The so-called " Flying " Snake, *Chrysopelea ornata*, occurs in Ceylon and Southern India and eastwards to Malaya and Southern China. It is very variable in colour, being sometimes green or black, and strikingly marked with yellow, orange or red. The head is invariably black with yellow spots or cross bars. The snake is able to parachute to the ground from considerable heights, hollowing-in the ventral surface in the process. It is recorded as having, whilst planing, covered a distance of twenty feet. By constriction it kills small mammals and lizards, showing a marked predilection for geckos.

Division Proteroglypha. This division, in which the anterior teeth of the upper jaw are grooved, have the fangs connected with very large poison glands. These snakes are usually extremely venomous.

The division is sub-divided into two sub-families: (1) the *Hydrophiinae*; and (2) the *Elapinae*.

Sub-family Hydrophiinae (Sea-snakes). The first Sub-family is wholly maritime, its members having vertically-compressed tails, which serve as powerful swimming organs. The nostrils are placed on the upper surface of the head, and are furnished with internal valves, which open when the snake is at the surface and close when it dives. The scales do not overlap and are uniform in size all over, save in the semi-terrestrial genus *Platurus*, in which the usual transverse ventral plates are present. The eye is small, with a round pupil that dilates greatly when submerged, but contracts above water, when the snake is partially blind. The skin, unlike that of most snakes, is cast in fragments. The food consists almost exclusively of fish and crustaceans, which quickly succumb to the virulent poison. The majority of Sea-snakes measure little more than two-and-a-half feet in length. They are usually brightly coloured, their banded liveries often breaking up the outline so as to render them almost invisible. About sixty species are known, all except one being viviparous. The female usually brings forth her young on the rocks of some unfrequented islet, protecting her offspring amongst her coils until they are able to shift for themselves. Sea-snakes inhabit the tropical parts of the Indian and Pacific Oceans, and swim near the surface, where they frequently fall victims to various kinds of sea-birds.

Sub-family Elapinae. The members of this sub-family range extensively throughout the Tropics. The *Elapinae* include most of the world's deadliest serpents, which frequently are not easily distinguished from quite harmless species. None illustrate this more convincingly than the Coral Snakes (genus *Elaps*). Two

[*W. S. Berridge.*

CAT SNAKE (*Tarbophis fallax*).
An opisthoglyphous snake from South-east Europe and Western Asia.

species are found in the United States and about twenty-four are scattered over Mexico, Central America and Tropical South America. The majority are strikingly banded with black, yellow, and coral red, arranged in alternating bands, the precise arrangement of these bands frequently, but not invariably, giving a clue to the harmlessness or otherwise of the species. However, many fatalities have resulted from mistaken identity as certain entirely harmless serpents imitate the deadly Coral Snakes, just as some harmless flies are almost indistinguishable from wasps and hornets. The Harlequin Snake (*Elaps fulvius*) of the south-eastern United States is one of the most deadly of the group. It is common in potato fields, and is frequently exposed by the plough. It grows to about a yard in length, and as in most members of the genus, the head and tail are very much of the same calibre as the body. Though sometimes seen abroad after heavy rains, it is a secretive burrowing creature, subsisting largely upon small lizards and the young of other snakes. Coral Snakes do not strike with their fangs, but bite with a chewing action, and frequently hold on with grim tenacity. The fangs are much smaller than in most poisonous species.

The Kraits (*Bungarus*) of India and the countries as far east as Southern China, are unobtrusive creatures preying principally upon serpents, often devouring others as large as themselves. They are very quiet in their habits, hiding their heads between their coils when attacked, rather than seeking safety in retreat. Kraits show a strange liking for human dwellings, where they sometimes cause loss of life through being trodden on accidentally. Should the snake bite, the result is usually fatal unless proper measures are taken immediately.

The Common species *Bungarus candidus* grows to over four feet in the more northern part of its habitat. It has a row of prominent scales down the centre of the back, and is purplish-black or brown in colour, with lighter cross bands.

The Banded Krait, *Bungarus fasciatus*, is somewhat larger, and is vividly marked with bright yellow and black rings. Its poison is rather less virulent than that of the Common Krait. Kraits are oviparous, laying eight to a dozen eggs, the female wrapping her coils about them, making some attempt at incubation.

The Cobras (genus *Naja*) are represented by ten species, of which seven come from Africa, the remaining three from India, China, the Malay Archipelago and the Philippine Islands. Cobras play an important part in legend and religious beliefs, the common species being deified as the snake which sheltered Buddha from the sun by spreading its hood above his head. The Egyptian species was sacred to the gods and goddesses associated with the sun, and is seen worn as a head ornament in innumerable ancient Egyptian monuments and mural paintings. Characteristics of the group are a cylindrical body, a moderately long tail, smooth scales, and comparatively small fangs. A striking feature is the hood, an expansion of skin supported by long ribs, which can open out to distend the skin covering them into a shape like the bowl of a spoon. The head is often strikingly marked.

The Indian Cobra (*Naja naja*) presents considerable variation in colour and in the typical form is distinguished by the head markings, which suggest a pair of spectacles. The Common Cobra is one of the most deadly of serpents, yet, despite the heavy annual death rate for which it is still responsible, many natives refuse to kill it and regard its presence in the house as a beneficent omen. It is a great favourite with native charmers, who seem to enjoy tolerable immunity from its bite, due, it is said, to their inoculating themselves with small but steadily increasing doses of the venom. Since the snake is virtually without a hearing apparatus, the gourd flute which usually accompanies the charmer's display may be

384

regarded as a piece of professional bluff, the so-called dancing being usually independent of the orchestral accompaniment. Despite its virulent poison, which may induce death in human beings within six hours, this snake is useful in removing large quantities of vermin. One Zoo specimen ate one hundred and thirty mice in a year, sometimes taking as many as eight at a single meal. Cobras are oviparous, laying about a dozen eggs in vegetable debris, the heat generated in the course of decomposition hatching them.

The King Cobra, or Hamadryad (*Naja hannah*) is the largest species, attaining a length of over sixteen feet. It is an exceedingly bold and poisonous snake, its poison producing death in man in less than six hours. Its greatest danger lies in its complete fearlessness, for it will attack on sight, and even pursue its foe with great speed and persistency. The colour is yellowish-brown or blackish above, sometimes crossed with darker striations. The King Cobra has a wide distribution

[*Paul Unger.*

INDIAN COBRA (*Naja naja*).
The markings on the hood in some varieties of this species resemble a pair of spectacles.

over India and all the oriental lands eastwards to Sumatra. It feeds almost exclusively upon other snakes, devouring not only small pythons and rat-snakes, but such venomous species as kraits and common cobras. The first King Cobra to be exhibited in the Zoo arrived some forty years ago, and was placed in a cage along with a number of other rare snakes by an inexperienced keeper. Being specially hungry after a prolonged fast, it devoured in the course of its first night in its new quarters all its cage mates, which happened to be the property of a dealer who had deposited them at the Zoo. The meal proved an expensive one, costing the Society about twenty-five pounds.

Three species of African Cobra are able to eject their poison to some distance. The efforts of *Naja melanoleuca* and *N. nigricollis* of Tropical Africa are, in this direction, eclipsed, however, by the Ringhals, or Spitting Cobra (*Sepedon haemachaetes*) of South Africa. This last-named snake grows to about five feet and is sooty-black in colour with greyish bands. When defending itself, it habitually ejects its venom, sometimes to a distance of eight feet. Whether intentionally or otherwise, it spits with deadly accuracy at its victim's eyes. When thus in action, it expands its hood and throws the head well back so as to bring the fangs into a horizontal position. Specimens newly introduced to the Zoo cover the glass front of the cage with their poison in an endeavour to bespatter the visitors, and when the door of their cage has to be opened in order to introduce food, the attendants always protect their eyes with motor-goggles.

The Mambas (*Dendraspis*) constitute a small group of semi-arboreal snakes from Tropical and Southern Africa. The body and tail are very long and slender, and are covered with elongate, narrow, and smooth scales. The fangs are much larger than those of Cobras. The commonest species, *Dendraspis angusticeps*, is uniform black, olive or green above. It feeds on birds, which it catches amongst the branches of trees. Like the King Cobra, it is justly dreaded, not only for its bite, which is deadly, but because it almost invariably pursues when molested.

Family Viperidae (*Vipers and Rattlesnakes*)

The Vipers are distinguished by the fact that the short maxillary bones which bear the fangs are not firmly fixed to the skull, but are capable of vertical movement, thus bringing into play the very long fangs, which, when not in use, are folded back horizontally against the palate. The group contains two sub-families—the True Vipers (*Viperinae*), distributed over Europe, Asia and Africa ; and the Pit-vipers (*Crotalinae*) of Asia and America.

Viperinae (True Vipers). The genus *Vipera* is confined to Europe, Africa and Asia. The well-defined head bears scales or small shields, the short, stout body is covered with keeled scales, and the tail is more or less abrupt.

The Common Viper or Adder (*Vipera berus*) is the only poisonous snake found in Great Britain. It may be recognized by the dark zig-zag band which runs along the centre of the back, and usually also by its initial—a V-shaped marking on the back of the head. Sometimes, but rarely, specimens are uniformly black, due, in the male, to an extension of the dark zig-zag bands, but in the female, to the darkness of the ground-colour. An average length for this snake is twenty inches, but a record specimen in the Natural History Museum measures exactly twenty-eight inches. At one time this Viper played an important part in the pharmacopoeia of our forebears, and until quite recently a certain rustic charlatan drove a thriving trade in Viper Oil, obtained from the reptile's fat, which he purveyed amongst the inhabitants of the New Forest and an extensive clientele beyond. Normally the Viper feeds upon lizards, field mice, and young birds nesting on the ground. In early autumn the Viper retires underground, venturing forth in the following March. In the late summer about a score of young are brought forth alive. From the first they are very active, keeping in the parental vicinity for some time, and quickly vanishing upon the slightest alarm. This habit is,

[*Stanley Crook.*

ADDER (*Vipera berus*).
The only poisonous British snake.

no doubt, responsible for the rustic legend that the female Viper swallows her young when danger threatens. About twenty years ago the *Field* newspaper offered a tempting reward for satisfactory evidence of this interesting phenomenon ; but the money has not been claimed to date. On the other hand, the Vipers killed in summer are very likely to disclose on post mortem examination a brood of young *in situ*.

The Long-nosed Viper (*Vipera ammodytes*) is abundant in Southern Australia, Hungary and the Balkan Peninsula. It may at once be recognized by its prominent up-turned snout.

In Orsini's Viper (*Vipera orsinii*) of the mountains of Italy, Yugoslavia, Austria, and Hungary, the snout is pointed but not raised. Its diet is mainly insectivorous.

Russell's Viper (*Vipera russellii*)—the "Tic Polonga" of Ceylon—abounds in all types of country throughout India, Ceylon, Burma, Siam, and Sumatra. It is a large and handsome snake, measuring five feet in length, and is pale brown in colour with three rows of black rings, edged with yellow, and encircling terra-cotta coloured spots. Though slow to wrath, this snake, when finally roused, will emit a hissing sound audible at a great distance, and will at the same time launch itself at its foe with such energy as actually to leave the ground. Its venom is probably only superseded in virulence by that of the Hamadryad and Mamba. It produces about twenty-five young at birth.

The Night Adder (*Causus rhombeatus*) of Southern Africa reaches a yard in length. It is pale brown or olive above, with a central chain of large, rectangular, dark brown blotches. A dark V-shaped marking crosses the nape. It is less nocturnal than its name implies, and wanders about by day catching frogs. The genus to which it belongs is unique in that the two poison glands are situated on the side of the neck between the skin and the body muscles, extending backwards for almost a third of the snake's entire length.

The Puff Adder (*Bitis arietans*) is one of a genus noted for its large head, which is covered with scales, and is very distinct from the neck. The fangs are enormous, and the rather big eye has, as in most Vipers, a vertical pupil. The body is squat and covered with keeled scales. The Puff Adder extends over the greater part of Tropical Africa. It grows to more than a yard in length and is of greyish or yellowish colour, with dark brown or blackish bands set at regular intervals. Its popular name refers to the spasmodic hissing sounds which it produces when disturbed. It usually lies hidden amongst sand or dead grass by day, stealing forth at night to stalk small mammals, for which it will lie in wait with its anterior portion bent into an S-shaped loop that can be released suddenly, when striking with lightning-like rapidity.

The Gaboon Viper (*B. gabonica*), which grows to five feet in length with a girth of twelve inches, is found throughout all Tropical Africa from Damara Land to Liberia and to the east coast. Like many Vipers with the nostrils placed high up on the snout, it is given to lying buried in the sand. A pair of blunt horns ornaments the snout. The pattern of its back recalls a Persian carpet.

The Nose-horned or Rhinoceros Viper (*B. nasicornis*) is a slightly smaller species from the same localities. The squat, purplish-coloured body bears a central chain of rectangular white patches with bars of gold. The snout bears two long, and sometimes several smaller, horns formed of compressed head-shields, and the scales, especially in old specimens, are so strongly keeled that the snake when moving may be fairly said to bristle.

The two species composing the genus *Cerastes* are small snakes, not exceeding two feet in length, and inhabiting Northern Africa, Arabia and Palestine. The head is very distinct, and the eyes are small with elliptical pupils. The scales on the cylindrical body have pronounced keels, and are arranged in longitudinal series, the side scales being smaller than those above, and directed backwards. These snakes harmonize with the sandy and stony wastes which they affect, often lying concealed in the sand with the head, which might easily escape notice as a mere piece of stone, alone showing. They bury themselves by flattening the body until the lower edges act as scoops, the sand being heaped over the back by a series of wave-like movements. When disturbed, they make loud rustling sounds by rubbing the serrated lateral scales against each other. Their food consists of small mammals, such as mice and jerboas, whose holes they frequent and who

may be attracted, it has been suggested, within striking distance by the projecting heads. Although capable of k i l l i n g fair - sized animals, these snakes seldom prove deadly to human beings.

[*Wide World Photos*.

PUFF ADDER (*Bitis arietans*).
This African snake takes its name from the loud hisses it produces when disturbed.

The genus *Atractaspis* comprises fifteen species from Tropical and Southern Africa. Few exceed thirty inches, and all are highly poisonous, the fangs being larger in proportion than in any other snake, so large that only one is able to function at a time.

Crotalinae (Pit-vipers). A deep pit is situated on each side of the head. This sub-family is divided into the following four genera :

A. No rattle.

    Upper surface of head covered with nine symmetrical shields—*Ancistrodon*.

    Upper surface of head covered with scales or small shields—*Lachesis*.

B. Tail ending in a rattle.

    Upper surface of head covered with nine symmetrical shields—*Sistrurus*.

    Upper surface of head covered with scales or small shields—*Crotalus*.

In all forms the fangs are very large, and the pupil of the eyes vertical.

The Water Viper, or Moccasin (*Ancistrodon piscivorus*) inhabits the greater part of the Eastern United States. It is a heavily-built snake about four feet long, dull olive or brown above, with wide blackish bars on the sides that sometimes unite to form a central dorsal line. It is one of the most deadly of the North American snakes, and frequents the banks of lagoons, where it devours almost anything not too large for it to swallow—small mammals, birds, fish, frogs, and other snakes. It is remarkably hardy in captivity and produces a brood of a dozen or more, the young being bright pink, with white-margined transverse bands and vivid yellow tails. Its white gums have earned for it the popular name of " Cotton-mouth." That of " Moccasin " refers to a common use made of its skin by the natives. It is a conservative snake, selecting some particular spot and returning to it regularly to roost. Specimens kept in captivity have lived for over twenty years.

The Copperhead (*A. contortrix*) has a similar distribution, but is more showily marked and less aquatic than the Moccasin. It is yellowish or pale reddish above, with broad dark-brown or brick-red cross bars.

The Temple Viper *Trimeresurus wagleri* of the Malay Peninsula reaches about four feet in length, and presents considerable variation in colour, from brown to green, and from green to blue. The species is of interest, since in the country of its origin it is regarded as sacred and is treated with considerable respect. It is an arboreal species, and is worshipped by the natives and encouraged to reside in their gardens. In the Snake Temples hundreds of these poisonous reptiles are guarded and fed by the priests ; the pampered vipers cover the altar, and even the altar steps where the natives offer up gifts and prayers. At night the snakes steal forth to hunt for rats and geckos. The priests, however, represent them as being ardent egg-eaters, exhibiting blown shells alleged to have been sucked by the serpents, and, by this adroit explanation, induce devotees and tourists to benefit the Temple funds. These serpents have not been known to inflict bites upon their worshippers, and it may be assumed that they have either been doped, or have had their fangs removed by their holy guardians.

The genus *Lachesis* is confined to South-eastern Asia, and to Central and South America ; its representatives are distinguished from the Pit-vipers hitherto reviewed by the slightly longer head, and more slender body ; the scales are either keeled or smooth. The forty odd species vary greatly, some being small, others large. Many are terrestrial, and a few are arboreal. The Fer-de-lance (*Lachesis lanceolatus*), of South America and the West Indies, is highly poisonous. It grows to about six feet in length, and its colour is lead grey, with dark bands of red and dull yellow. It is a night prowler, stalking its prey, such as agoutis and other small mammals, with cat-like stealth. It is particularly abundant on the

RATTLESNAKES (CROTALUS AND SISTRURUS)

Island of Martinique, where it multiplies rapidly, producing as many as three dozen young at a birth. When disturbed amongst dry vegetation, it vibrates its tail, creating a sound suggestive of a rattlesnake.

The Bush-master (*L. mutus*) of Central and Tropical America is a large species, eight feet in length, strikingly marked with a black

RATTLESNAKE (*Crotalus*).
The Rattlesnakes of America take their name from the hollow, horny segments at the end of the tail ; these rattle when vibrated.

band of olive on a pinkish ground colour. It is believed to be the only *Crotaline* snake that lays eggs. These, about a dozen in number, are larger than those of a duck, and are incubated by the female.

The Rattlesnakes (*Crotalus* and *Sistrurus*) owe their popular name to the loosely-connected horny segments at the end of the tail, which are represented in the newly-born young by a single horny button. They are hollow, and when vibrated give out a rattling sound, which suggests a toy clock-work train in motion. When in action, the rattle is held aloft in the centre of the snake's closely-constricted coils. Although a fresh segment is uncovered at each successive shedding of the skin, the number gives little indication of the snake's age, as the terminal segments often pull off, or are detached by accident ; a dozen segments seem to be the maximum number recorded in a rattle. The object of the rattle is problematic ; it is common to both sexes and may possibly be used to bring them together or it may serve as a

Photos]   [*W. S. Berridge.*
COPPERHEAD (*Ancistrodon contortrix*).
A showily-marked viper of the Eastern United States.

warning to enemies. The members of the genus *Crotalus* frequent arid districts, and live almost exclusively on small mammals. Nineteen species have been identified and are spread over almost every portion of the United States. One species occurs in South America.

The Common Rattlesnake (*C. durissus*), of the South-eastern United States, reaches eight feet in length. It is pale or light brown above, with rhomboidal markings of a dark colour edged with yellow. Natural histories of a few decades ago widely circulated the legend that these snakes shared the warrens of prairie dogs and burrowing owls on more or less friendly terms. Although the presence of the snakes in these situations

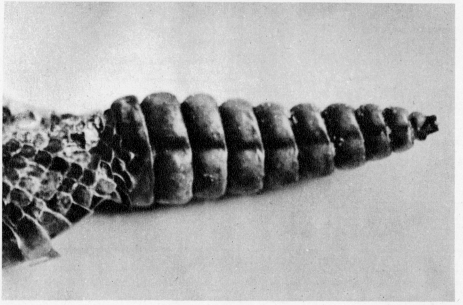

RATTLE OF RATTLESNAKE.

[*W. S. Berridge.*

is vouched for, the picture is anything but one of Arcadian bliss, the snakes devouring the young of both mammals and birds, and the owls returning the compliment with interest.

One species of Rattlesnake (*C. cerastes*) of the South-western United States exactly parallels the Horned-viper of Arabia. It inhabits similar desert country and has a blunt horn over each eye.

The three members of the genus *Sistrurus* inhabit the North American swamps east of the Rocky Mountains. None exceeds a length of more than two feet, and their rattles are so feeble that they cannot be heard more than a few feet distant. Their fangs are comparatively small and their bite is not regarded as dangerous, the effects having been compared to the sting of a hornet.

BIRDS (Aves)
BY
W. B. ALEXANDER, M.A. (Camb.), *Director of Research in Economic Ornithology, University of Oxford*

Birds (Class Aves) are warm-blooded vertebrate animals covered with feathers. The fore limbs are typically wings adapted for flying, but in the Penguins they are flippers used as paddles in swimming, and in some terrestrial birds are degenerate, and useless for flight. The hind limbs serve for progression on land, for climbing or perching in trees, or for swimming. The jaws are covered with horny sheaths forming a beak or bill, used not only for securing food, but for picking up and holding sticks and other objects, for defence, and, in some instances, as an accessory to the feet when climbing. All birds lay eggs of comparatively large size enclosed in a calcareous shell. These are deposited in a more or less elaborate nest and, except in the Mound-birds, are incubated until they hatch.

Birds exhibit a more intense vitality than that found in any other group of animals. Their temperature is maintained at a constant level from 2° F. to 14° F. higher than in Mammals. Their blood is richer than that of Mammals in red corpuscles, and the circulation is maintained by very rapid heart-beats. Their breathing also is very rapid, and the bronchial passages extend through the lungs into thin-walled air-sacs which lie among the viscera and even penetrate into the bones. Thus the air passes through the lungs both during inspiration and expiration instead of merely being drawn into the lungs and expelled again as in other vertebrate animals. The digestive processes of birds are also very rapid and perfect, almost the whole of the food being absorbed. Many forms, notably Owls and Hawks, eject the indigestible portions of their food, such as bones, hair, feathers and the wing-cases of beetles, from the mouth in the form of pellets. The faeces consist largely of nitrogenous matter excreted by the kidneys, hence bird guano has high value as a fertilizer.

Plumage. Feathers form the body-covering of all birds, and are found in no other creatures. A typical feather consists of a stem with lateral branches or barbs forming a web on each side. The quill, or lower portion of the stem, is hollow and roughly cylindrical, and the shaft, or upper portion, which bears the barbs, is somewhat quadrangular and solid. The barbs project obliquely on both sides of the shaft, approximately in one plane, and in their turn bear smaller oblique branches, or barbules, on both sides in the same plane. The barbules of adjacent barbs interlock by means of minute hooks, thus forming a practically air-tight web. Feathers of this type form an external covering to the body and are known as contour feathers. Beneath them are feathers with a soft shaft, whose barbules have no hooks, forming the down. There is a special development

393

of down in many birds of cold regions, especially those of aquatic habits, such as Penguins and Ducks.

In flying birds, specially large feathers are attached to the bones of the wings. Those attached to the bones which correspond to the hand are known as *primaries*, and are usually the largest. Those attached to the fore-arm are named *secondaries*. The bases of these wing-quills are covered by other fairly large feathers known as the *wing-coverts*. The tail of birds is very small, but specially large feathers are usually attached to it; these tail feathers serve for steering and for braking during flight; their bases are covered by smaller feathers known as *tail-coverts*.

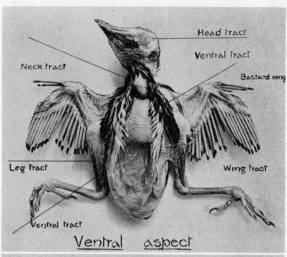

Ventral aspect

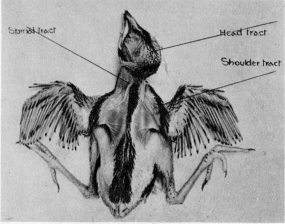

[H. Bastin.

A nestling perching-bird, showing the sprouting contour feathers developing in special tracts, not uniformly scattered over the body.

Flight. The flight of birds differs essentially from that of aeroplanes in that the wings correspond both to the propeller and the planes. By flapping its wings backwards and downwards, the bird acquires speed and lift, and when these are obtained, it can glide for a greater or less distance with its wings spread. In normal flight flapping and gliding alternate. Certain species, e.g. Humming-birds and Kestrels, can maintain a stationary position in the air by beating their wings very rapidly; this is hovering. Some other birds, notably Albatrosses and Vultures, when once they have acquired speed, can continue to circle round in the air for hours without further wing-beats. This is termed soaring, and how it is accomplished is still not completely understood.

Migration. The phenomenon of migration is met with in various

(1) Part of (2) enlarged, showing barbules springing from the barbs.

groups of animals, but, doubtless owing to their great powers of locomotion, is specially conspicuous in birds. Although some individual birds apparently never travel more than a few miles from the place where they were hatched, it is probable that there are few species in which this is true of all the members. Within recent years much information on migration has been gained by placing light, numbered rings on the legs of birds,

thereby enabling the movements of individuals to be traced. By this means it has been proved that, although Wild Ducks and Starlings bred in the British Isles are mainly stationary, many from Scandinavia and the Baltic countries are also present in Britain during the winter. In these species British birds are stationary, although Scandinavian birds are migratory. There are also a very large number of species, all of whose members are migratory. For example, the Swallows, Cuckoos and Storks, which breed in Europe in summer, spend the northern winter in tropical or southern

(2) Barbs springing from the shaft or rachis.

Photos]   [H. Bastin.
STRUCTURE OF A FEATHER.
(3) Part of (2) greatly enlarged showing the minute hooks on the barbules.

Africa. Evidence is accumulating that such migratory birds often have two quite definite homes, one in the north where they breed, and the other in the south where they winter, individuals returning annually to the same fields or gardens at both ends of their journey. In the southern hemisphere movement takes place in the opposite direction, though on a smaller scale, numerous species that breed in Patagonia, New Zealand and Tasmania migrating north into the tropics for the winter. Even within the tropics, seasonal movements take place. In most species the journey is mainly, or entirely, made during the hours of darkness, and in many it involves passage over hundreds of miles of open sea ; but how the birds find their way is not known. In some species, individuals migrate independently ; in others, flocks travel together ; frequently young birds of the year migrate independently of the adults.

Voice. The syrinx, which is the organ of voice in birds, is situated at the lower end of the windpipe (trachea), at the point where it bifurcates into the two tubes (bronchi) which lead into the lungs. The syrinx differs greatly in form in different types, but consists essentially of a cavity with membraneous walls, and containing membraneous flaps or valves. Muscles attached to the various parts can modify the form of the syrinx, and alter the tension of the valves. Most birds utter frequent notes or calls, varying according to their emotions. In many species, as the breeding season approaches, the male birds spend much of their time in singing, generally repeating a series of notes in a particular order. Songsters of the highest rank, however, vary the order of the notes almost indefinitely. Song is undoubtedly primarily the expression of emotion during a period of high vitality, but it serves also to advertize the presence of a male to rivals and to females. There can be no question that the bird is to some extent an artist capable of enjoying its own performance, and birds of many species sing at periods other than the breeding season.

Classification. The known species of birds number about twelve thousand, but although they are more numerous than in Mammals or Reptiles, the structural differences between them are comparatively small. In a recent system of classification (that of Wetmore and Miller, which is here followed) they are divided into thirty-three orders, of which six are extinct and twenty-seven have living representatives. The orders are grouped as follows :

Sub-class 1. ARCHAEORNITHES
Order 1. *Archaeopterygiformes* (Extinct).

Sub-class 2. NEORNITHES
Superorder 1. Odontognathae (Extinct).
Order 1. *Hesperornithiformes*.   Order 2. *Ichthyornithiformes*.

Superorder 2. Palaeognathae
Order 1. *Struthioniformes* (Ostriches).   Order 5. *Aepyornithiformes* (Extinct).
„ 2. *Rheiformes* (Rheas).
„ 3. *Casuariiformes* (Emus and Cassowaries).   „ 6. *Apterygiformes* (Kiwis).
„ 7. *Tinamiformes* (Tinamous).
„ 4. *Dinornithiformes* (Moas, Extinct).

396

CLASSIFICATION

Superorder 3. Neognathae

Order 1. *Sphenisciformes* (Penguins).
„ 2. *Colymbiformes* (Divers).
„ 3. *Podicipiformes* (Grebes).
„ 4. *Procellariiformes* (Petrels and Albatrosses).
„ 5. *Pelecaniformes* (Pelicans, Cormorants, etc.).
„ 6. *Ciconiiformes* (Storks, Herons, etc.).
„ 7. *Anseriformes* (Ducks, etc.).
„ 8. *Falconiformes* (Birds of Prey).
„ 9. *Galliformes* (Game-birds).
„ 10. *Gruiformes* (Cranes, Rails, Bustards, etc.).
„ 11. *Diatrymiformes* (Extinct).
„ 12. *Charadriiformes* (Plovers, Gulls, Auks, etc.).

Order 13. *Columbiformes* (Pigeons and Sand-grouse).
„ 14. *Cuculiformes* (Cuckoos, etc.).
„ 15. *Psittaciformes* (Parrots).
„ 16. *Strigiformes* (Owls).
„ 17. *Caprimulgiformes* (Night-jars, etc.).
„ 18. *Micropodiformes* (Swifts and Humming-birds).
„ 19. *Coliiformes* (Colies).
„ 20. *Trogoniformes* (Trogons).
„ 21. *Coraciiformes* (Hornbills, Kingfishers, etc.).
„ 22. *Piciformes* (Woodpeckers, Toucans, etc.).
„ 23. *Passeriformes* (Song-birds or Perching-birds).

The extinct Jurassic toothed birds present many reptilian features that entitle them to rank as a separate sub-class, named either *Archaeornithes* (Ancient Birds) or *Saururae* (Lizard-tailed), the latter name having reference to the very long tail, each vertebra of which bears a pair of feathers. The remaining birds form collectively the sub-class *Neornithes* or *Ornithurae*, distinguished by a much shorter tail, with the last five or six vertebrae united to form a bone that supports the tail-feathers, which spread out like the ribs of a fan.

The *Odontognathae* are toothed birds found fossil in the Cretaceous strata ; the other two divisions of the Neornithes take their names from the arrangement of the bones of the palate. In the *Palaeognathae* the palatine bones are well separated by the vomer, and are more or less firmly attached to the pterygoids, whereas in the Neognathae the palatines converge behind the vomer, and are movably attached to the pterygoids by a cup-and-ball joint.

Sub-class ARCHAEORNITHES

Order ARCHAEOPTERYGIFORMES (Extinct)

This order contains the single Family *Archaeopterygidae*, which includes two fossil creatures whose skeletons have been found in Jurassic strata in Bavaria. The first, discovered in 1861 in the lithographic slate of Solenhofen, is now in the Natural History Museum, South Kensington, and is known as *Archaeopteryx lithographica*. This name was originally bestowed on a feather previously discovered in the same locality. In 1877 a second individual in a much better state of preservation was found near Eichstätt and is now in the Berlin Museum. It was for long thought to be another example of the same species, but recent critical study has indicated several differences in the skeleton, and it has been named *Archaeornis siemensi*.

The fact that they were clothed with feathers has led to the inclusion of these creatures in the Class Aves, but in almost every feature of their skeleton they differed greatly from modern birds, agreeing with one or other of the orders of Reptiles, and they might aptly be termed " Feathered Reptiles." The skull is quite reptilian in character and the jaws are furnished with teeth in separate sockets. The head was probably covered with scales, the nostrils opened near the tip of the snout and there was no horny sheath or " beak " covering the jaws. The eyes were very large. The front limb had three fingers, each provided with a sharp, curved claw; along its posterior margin there was a row of strong quill feathers. The breast-bone is absent in both fossils, but the space it occupied shows that it was small, and it is possible that it has not been preserved because it was cartilaginous. In that case, the fore limbs cannot properly be regarded as wings and the creatures would have been incapable of true flight, but able only to glide through the air in the manner of " Flying Squirrels." The hind limbs were slender, and the feet had three toes in front and one behind, each with a sharp, hooked claw. Superficially these legs are the feature in which these creatures most resembled modern birds, but the bones of the foot are not reduced and fused in the manner characteristic of birds. The most obvious reptilian character is the long, slender tail, like that of a lizard, in length about equal to the body. The tail, however, was furnished with strong quill-feathers arranged in pairs. The body was also covered with softer feathers. *Archaeopteryx* had a body about the size of that of a crow ; *Archaeornis* was a little smaller.

There can be no doubt from the structure of the feet that these creatures were arboreal and they doubtless used the claws on their hands to assist them in clambering about the branches, probably, as already suggested, gliding from tree to tree by the support of the large wing and tail feathers. As a complete link between Reptiles and Birds, they form convincing evidence of the evolution of the latter group from the former.

Sub-class NEORNITHES

Superorder ODONTOGNATHAE (Extinct)

Order HESPERORNITHIFORMES

This is a group of flightless, aquatic, toothed birds found as fossils in rocks of Cretaceous age. It includes at least two, and possibly three, families: *Hesperornithidae*, *Baptornithidae* and *Enaliornithidae* (?).

Hesperornithidae. This family contains a number of species from the Niobrara beds of western Kansas, some of which are known from practically complete skeletons. They had greatly-elongated bodies and long necks. Their jaws contained sharply-pointed teeth placed in continuous grooves, though in the upper jaw the teeth were confined to the posterior portion. Their wings were rudimentary and their breast-bones without a keel. Their short, strong legs were placed far back and set at right angles to the body, whilst their paddle-like feet resembled those of Cormorants. In their general form, and probably in their habits, they resembled the Divers, except, of course, that they were flightless. *Hesperornis regalis* attained a length of six feet and *H. crassipes* was even larger.

Baptornithidae. This family contains the genus *Baptornis* from the same deposits as those in which *Hesperornis* is found, but as its jaws are not known it is not certain that it was toothed.

Enaliornithidae. This family contains *Enaliornis* from the Cambridge Greensand of England. It was much smaller than *Hesperornis*, but similar in general form of body, though its jaws are unknown, so that it may not have had teeth.

The remains of various other fossil birds from Cretaceous deposits indicate that there was already great diversity among the birds of that period. *Palaeotringa* had the form of a Wader, *Telmatornis* that of a Rail, and *Laornis* that of a Duck. But since the only Cretaceous birds whose jaws are known (*Ichthyornis* and *Hesperornis*) were toothed, though very dissimilar in other features, it seems probable that this was a characteristic of all birds at that period.

Order ICHTHYORNITHIFORMES

This order contains only one known family, the *Ichthyornithidae*, which includes several species whose remains have been found in the Niobrara beds of Cretaceous age in western Kansas. The two that are best known, *Ichthyornis victor* and *I. dispar*, had the body about as large as that of a pigeon. They had long necks; large, strong heads; and long pointed bills. In each jaw there were many small, sharply-pointed, recurved teeth set in sockets, whilst the two jaw-bones of the lower jaw were not united at the tip. In these features they agree with reptiles and differ from all modern birds, whilst the form of their vertebrae, which were biconcave, is even more primitive, being that found in fish and in some

399

amphibians.   The wings were large, long and strong and the breast-bone had a deep keel, so that there is no doubt they were powerful fliers.   Their legs and feet were comparatively weak.   They probably resembled Terns in appearance and habits.

Superorder PALAEOGNATHAE

Order STRUTHIONIFORMES (Ostriches)

By courtesy of]   [Carl Hagenbeck's Tierpark, Stellingen.
COCK OSTRICH (*Struthio camelus*).
A fine specimen of the largest living bird, showing the beautiful plumes for whose sake it is farmed in South Africa.

This order includes a single family, *Struthionidae*, containing only one existing species, viz., the Ostrich (*Struthio camelus*), the largest living bird. It occurs in most parts of Africa from the Sahara southwards, and in the Arabian and Syrian deserts, but in the settled parts of South Africa it is now found only in a domesticated state.   An adult male stands eight feet high, but females are somewhat smaller.   The Ostrich has a very wide, flat bill ;   small head with large eyes ; long neck scantily covered with down which does not hide the skin ;   enlarged, soft, ornamental plumes in the small wings and the tail ;   very long, large legs, with the lower part of the " thigh " devoid of feathers ; feet with only two large toes, padded beneath, and with broad, stunted claws, that of the outer toe being frequently absent.   The body of the adult male is covered with black feathers, whilst the ornamental plumes of the wings and tail are white. Females and young males have all the feathers grey.   The skin of the neck and " thigh " is flesh-coloured in birds from northern Africa, bluish in South African birds, and lead-coloured in those from Somaliland.

The Ostrich frequents deserts and open plains, associating in small flocks, and showing a liking for the companionship of zebras, hartebeests and other antelopes.   Its speed is very great, exceeding that of a galloping horse, but it usually runs in a curve so that it is possible to overtake it on horseback by keeping a straighter course.   When running, the head is held forward and the wings are outspread.   It defends itself with its beak and by kicking, and its kick is so powerful as to be very dangerous.   It feeds largely on herbage, but is practically omnivorous and has a propensity for swallowing stones, bones, nails, etc.   The Ostrich can exist for a long time without water, but drinks regularly when it has the opportunity, and is fond of bathing. It is generally a silent bird, but at times utters a deep roar like that of a lion. The male is polygamous and several hens lay in the same nest, a mere depression in the sand. The male incubates at night, but the hens sometimes sit in the daytime. The nest may contain thirty or more eggs, which in the northern race have a smooth shell like ivory, but in the southern race are pitted. The chicks run as soon as they are hatched, and are clothed in bristly, yellowish-white down with blackish stripes.

Order RHEIFORMES (Rheas)

The Rheiformes include only a single family, the *Rheidae*, containing two species of large flightless birds found in South America—the Common Rhea (*Rhea americana*), and Darwin's Rhea (*Pterocnemia pennata*). Rheas have wide, flat bills ; long necks ; small wings ; no specially-developed tail feathers ; long, stout legs ; and feet with three stout toes with large claws. The head and neck are covered with short feathers, as are also the legs down to, or below, the " knee." The feathers of the body are large, rounded and soft, and are largely used for making feather - dusters. In colour, the different species vary considerably, but are generally grey or greyish-brown above and whitish below.

Rheas frequent open plains and run swiftly with the wings partly spread. They feed on grass, roots, seeds and berries as well as on small reptiles, insects and molluscs. The males are polygamous

[*James's Press.*
RHEA OR SOUTH AMERICAN OSTRICH
(*Rhea americana*).
The largest American bird, an inhabitant of the "pampas."

and fight fiercely in the spring. The members of the harem all lay in the same nest, a mere hollow in the ground, or scatter their eggs round about. The eggs, which are yellowish or greenish when fresh, but soon fade to white, are incubated entirely by the male, who generally sits on from twenty to thirty. He also cares for the brood. The chicks of the smaller species are covered with soft down, but in the larger one are hatched with a covering of stiff, hair-like feathers.

Order CASUARIIFORMES (Emus and Cassowaries)

A group of large, flightless birds found in Australia, New Guinea and some of the adjacent islands. They have long necks ; rudimentary wings ; no special tail-feathers ; fairly long, stout legs ; and feet with three strong front toes. The feathers, like those of Moas, appear to be double, since the aftershaft, which in other birds is a very small branch from the main feather, is in these birds almost or quite as long as the main shaft. The order contains three families, of which two have living representatives, viz : *Dromornithidae* (Dromornis and Genyornis, extinct) ; *Dromaeidae* (Emus) ; and *Casuariidae* (Cassowaries).

Dromornithidae. This family contains two or three large extinct birds including *Dromornis australis*, found in Pleistocene or Pliocene beds in Queensland and *Genyornis newtoni* from the Pleistocene of South Australia. The latter was a gigantic bird with an enormous skull.

Dromaeidae (*Emus*). This family contains only one living species found in Australia, but two smaller species existed when Australia was first colonized, one on King Island in Bass Strait, the other on Kangaroo Island off South Australia. Both were exterminated early in the 19th century by settlers and sealers, who captured great numbers for food.

The Emu (*Dromaeus novaehollandiae*) is still common over much of the Australian continent, but has disappeared from the more settled districts and has been extinct in Tasmania since about 1860. It is second in size among living birds, being surpassed only by the Ostrich. It has a wide, flat bill ; its head and upper neck have only a sparse clothing of short, black, hair-like feathers, which do not obscure the bluish colour of the skin of the neck ; its body is clothed with brownish-black feathers, somewhat barred with yellowish and black ; and, as in Kiwis and Penguins, its rudimentary wings are entirely without quill feathers. It frequents grassy plains and open forest country, running swiftly when alarmed and feeding on grass, leaves, berries and fruit. The nest is a depression in the ground, sometimes lined with grass, sticks and leaves, and in it from seven to eighteen eggs are laid. These are from five to five and a half inches long, dark green with a granulated surface. Both sexes usually share in incubation, though sometimes it is undertaken by the male alone. The downy chicks are broadly striped with black and greyish-white, and run as soon as they are hatched.

Casuariidae (*Cassowaries*). There are about half a dozen living species of Cassowaries found in New Guinea, the Papuan Islands, Ceram and North Queensland. An extinct bird, *Hypselornis sivalensis*, from Pliocene beds of the Sivalik Hills in India, shows that the family formerly had a wider distribution.

Cassowaries range in size from that of a Turkey to a bird standing five feet high. They have strong, compressed bills, curved at the tip ; a horny helmet or casque on the top of the head, varying in form in the different species ; fairly long, thick necks, devoid of feathers on the upper part, where the skin is wrinkled and ornamented with caruncles and pendent wattles ; rudimentary wings, bearing four or five stiff quills without any webs, like the spines of porcupines ; moderately long, very robust legs ; and feet with three toes, of which the inner has a long, sharp, straight claw, which is a formidable weapon. The plumage is always black in adult birds, brown in the young. The naked skin of the head and neck is brightly coloured, often largely blue, with orange, pink, red or white patches, caruncles and wattles.

Cassowaries frequent dense jungles, through which they push their way, with the horny casque forming a protection for the head. At dusk and in the early morning they leave the denser cover and are often found near water. They can run swiftly, but heavily, and jump over obstacles of a considerable height. Their food consists of jungle fruits, berries and other vegetable matter, varied with insects and crustacea. The nest is a depression in dense cover, usually at the foot of a tree, lined with leaves and grass. The three to eight eggs are light green, with close-set granulations of dark green. The male alone is said to incubate and care for the brood. The downy chicks are pale brown with longitudinal black stripes, and run from birth.

[*James's Press.*
EMU (*Dromaeus novaehollandiae*).
The second largest of living birds, widely distributed in Australia.

Order DINORNITHIFORMES (Moas)

This order includes a single family, *Dinornithidae*, of extinct, flightless birds peculiar to New Zealand. Over twenty species of Moas are represented among the bones which have been collected in that country and two of them, *Dinornis giganteus* of the North Island and *D. maximus* of the South Island, were the largest birds known, probably standing twelve feet high. The smallest species was about the size of a Turkey. They all had long necks, rudimentary wings and long legs ; in some species the legs and feet were also extremely stout. The feet had three stout toes with strong claws and the hind toe either absent or small and elevated. The bill was wide and flattened, but differed considerably in form in the different species. In addition to bones, feathers and portions of skin with feathers attached

403

AVES (ORDER AEPYORNITHIFORMES)

[*James's Press.*
CASSOWARY (*Casuarius casuarius*).
An inhabitant of the jungles of New Guinea, Ceram, the Aru
Islands and North Queensland.

have been obtained. These show that the feathers were double, like those of Emus ; that they varied in colour—some being reddish-brown, then black with a white tip, others yellow with purplish-brown borders, and others white ; that they were sometimes as much as seven inches long ; and that the whole head and neck and the legs down to the toes were feathered. Maori tradition states that Moas had crests and tufts of longer feathers on the tail. Pitting of the skull bones indicates that some species had crests, but its absence shows that others had not. According to tradition Moas lived in the open country, ran swiftly and defended themselves by kicking ; both dogs and men are said to have been killed by a kick from a Moa. They lived on fern-roots, leaves and grass, also on fruits, to obtain which they entered forests, and on freshwater mussels, crayfish and fish, obtained in the streams. That they swallowed stones, like Ostriches, Emus, etc., is shown by the fact that little piles of these gizzard-stones, rounded pebbles of white quartz, are frequently found among their remains. Four perfect eggs and many bits of egg-shells have been discovered ; some of these had a pale green colour. The largest egg, probably that of *Dinornis maximus*, measures about ten inches by seven inches, and thus is much smaller than that of the *Aepyornis*. That some at least of the species were still living in New Zealand when the Maoris arrived there is certain, but the date of their final extermination is unknown.

Order AEPYORNITHIFORMES

This order contains a single family, *Aepyornithidae*, including the extinct species of the genus *Aepyornis*, and allied forms, found in Madagascar. About twelve kinds of these birds have been described from bones found in the island, and the largest probably stood about seven feet high. They had long, stout legs ; feet with four toes ; rudimentary wings and very small breast-bones. Large pits on the bones of the forehead indicate that they had crests. A number of their eggs have been found and exceed

404

all other known eggs in size, and it is probable that these gave rise to the legend of the gigantic *Roc*, which was said to inhabit Madagascar. If so, however, their size was enormously exaggerated, as they actually measure about thirteen inches by nine and a half inches, and hold about two gallons. Some of the bones of one of the smaller species show marks of a cutting instrument, so it is probable that the birds were exterminated by the Malagasy, perhaps surviving till the 17th century.

Order APTERYGIFORMES (Kiwis)

The *Apterygiformes* contain only the single family *Apterygidae*, which includes three species of flightless birds found in New Zealand. They have long, slender bills, slightly curved downwards, and differ from all other birds in having the nostrils situated close to the tip of the upper mandible instead of near its base. The head is small, the wings rudimentary and hidden in the feathers and the tail absent. The legs are very stout and placed far back, and the feet have three strong toes with long claws in front and a small elevated hind toe. The plumage is rufous- or greyish-brown, streaked or barred with blackish, and the feathers are long and hair-like. On the head near the base of the bill there are numerous long hairs and the eyes are small and weak.

Kiwis frequent damp forests and are nocturnal in habits, spending the day in burrows or holes under fallen trees. At dusk they become active, probing soft ground, decaying logs or beds of moss, with their bills, for the earthworms and grubs on which they chiefly feed; though they also eat berries, seeds and tender shoots of plants. Their shrill, whistling call, generally uttered in the evening, resembles the name Kiwi, bestowed on them by the Maoris. This is the note of the male, that of the female being lower and hoarser.

The nesting place is a burrow, hole or hollow log, usually lined with sticks, ferns, grass or leaves. One, two, or occasionally three, eggs are laid, white or pale greenish in colour, and remarkable for their great size compared with that of the parent; they weigh about a quarter the weight of the female. Incubation is generally, or always, performed by the male.

By courtesy of]   *[the High Commissioner for New Zealand.*
KIWI (*Apteryx australis*).
The most remarkable of the curious birds of New Zealand.

405

JACKASS PENGUIN (*Spheniscus demersus*).
The bird is here seen under water in the act of catching a fish.

[*Neville Kingston.*

Order TINAMIFORMES (Tinamous)

This Order includes only a single family, *Tinamidae*, containing about fifty species distributed throughout South America and northwards to Southern Mexico. Tinamous vary in size from that of a Quail to that of a Fowl and have a considerable general resemblance to Partridges. By Europeans in South America they are commonly called Partridges or the equivalent of that name in Spanish or Portuguese. The resemblance is, however, only superficial and in many points of their structure they agree with the primitive flightless Ratite birds (Ostriches, Rheas, Emus, Kiwis, etc.). They have small heads and rather long necks, clothed with very small feathers; the horny sheath of the bill is in several pieces; their short, rounded, concave wings have ten primaries; their tails are very short and composed of soft feathers; the small hind toe is elevated above the three anterior ones when it is present, but in some species it is absent. The plumage is generally brown, varying from rufous to slaty according to the species, often more or less barred with dark brown or black, sometimes decidedly lighter, or even white, on the throat or underparts.

Tinamous are mainly terrestrial in their habits, some frequenting forests and others open plains. They run swiftly and fly strongly and fast. Their food consists mainly of seeds, berries, roots, etc., varied with spiders and insects. The nest is a hollow on the ground beneath a bush, scantily lined with leaves or herbage. The eggs, which vary in number from four or five to sixteen, have a wonderfully smooth shell, looking as if it were of burnished metal or glazed porcelain. In colour they vary greatly according to the species, primrose-yellow, sage-green, dark-blue, wine-purple, reddish-chocolate and pinkish-orange being some of the shades displayed. The sexes are alike, but the male undertakes the incubation of the eggs. The chicks are covered with buffish or chestnut down, often with black or white markings, and run as soon as they are hatched.

NEOGNATHAE

Order SPHENISCIFORMES (Penguins)

The Order Sphenisciformes includes two families. One of these, *Family Cladornithidae*, contains only a fossil bird, *Cladornis pachypus*, from Miocene deposits in Patagonia. The other, *Family Spheniscidae* (Penguins), contains seventeen species of flightless, marine birds, peculiar to the southern

[*Central Press.*]

ADELIE PENGUINS (*Pygoscelis adeliae*).
The young bird helps itself to shrimps from the throat of its parent.

hemisphere. They are stout-bodied, short-necked birds of moderate or large size. Their bills are stout, and covered with several separate horny plates, instead of a single sheath on each mandible as in most other birds. Their wings, generally termed 'flippers,' are used only for swimming, and are covered all over with small, scale-like feathers, there being no specially-developed quill-feathers. Their tails are usually very short. Their short, stout legs are set very far back, so that they stand or walk in an upright

407

position when on land, and their three front toes are united by webs, the hind toe being very small.

Penguins are the most completely marine of all birds, travelling swiftly beneath the water by the use of their flippers, and emerging for brief periods to breathe. When at the surface, they swim very low in the water so that only the head and back are exposed. They feed almost entirely on fish, cuttle-fish and crustacea. They are sociable birds, both when at sea and when breeding. For the latter purpose they come ashore on islands or desolate coasts and hop, run, waddle or scramble over rocks, and even up steep hillsides, to their breeding grounds or " rookeries." Most of the species construct a slight nest of bits of grass or weeds in cavities between rocks, caves or burrows, but some of the larger forms select a slight hollow and line it with stones. They lay one, two, or occasionally three, eggs either nearly spherical or pear-shaped and with a white, chalky shell. The young, when hatched, are densely covered with down, which is replaced by feathers before they venture into the sea. The voices of Penguins are loud and harsh, and some species utter a bray which has earned them the name of " Jackass." They are particularly noisy when congregated on their rookeries.

All the species are bluish-grey or blackish above and white below, but they differ in the arrangement of black and white on the face and throat, and some have orange or yellow patches on the sides of the neck, whilst others have crests of long, yellow feathers on each side of the head.

The King Penguin (*Aptenodytes patagonica*) is a large species about three feet in length, with a long, rather slender bill, and with patches of orange-yellow on the sides and front of the neck. It breeds on sub-antarctic islands of the South Atlantic and Indian Oceans. It incubates its single egg whilst standing in an upright position, the egg being held in a fold of skin between the legs.

The Jackass or Cape Penguin (*Spheniscus demersus*), about two feet long, has a rather stout bill and patches of black and white on the face. It frequents the shores of South Africa, breeding on various small islands off the coast. It is of some importance as a producer of guano, and its eggs are collected for sale under Government regulation.

By courtesy of]   *[Carl Hagenbeck's Tierpark, Stellingen.*
KING PENGUINS (*Aptenodytes patagonica*).
These birds stand nearly three feet high and breed on sub-antarctic islands.

[*Arthur Brook*

BLACK-THROATED DIVER (*Colymbus arcticus*).
The larger of the two species of Diver which breed in Britain, here seen on its nest in Caithness.

Order COLYMBIFORMES (Divers)

This Order contains a single family, *Colymbidae*, including four species. They inhabit the northern portions of the northern hemisphere, frequenting sea-coasts, lakes and rivers. The bill is strong, compressed and pointed ; the head large ; the neck fairly long and the body long, large and heavy. The wing is short, narrow and pointed, having eleven primaries, and the tail is very short. The legs are placed far back and are short and remarkably flattened ; the three front toes are large and connected by webs, whilst the hind toe is small.

Divers feed almost entirely on fish, which they obtain by pursuing them under water, propelling themselves by their feet. In winter they frequent the sea near the coasts, but in the breeding season visit inland lakes and pools on moors and tundras. They lay two oily-brown eggs, spotted and blotched with grey and black, in a depression close to the water's edge ; and the downy chicks, when hatched, immediately take to the water, swimming and diving readily. When at sea, Divers are almost silent, but during the breeding season they utter extraordinary loud, laughing calls. Their flight is swift but laboured, but on land they shuffle along with difficulty and cannot stand up on their legs.

The Great Northern Diver or Loon (*Colymbus immer*) breeds in North America from the northern United States to the Arctic regions and in Greenland and Iceland. In winter it occurs on both coasts of North America and the coasts of Europe, south sometimes to Lower California, the Gulf of Mexico and the Mediterranean. It is not uncommon in winter round the British Isles. In winter the feathers of the upper parts are blackish margined with grey and the underparts are white ; but in breeding plumage, the head, neck and upper parts are glossy black, with white streaks on the throat and sides of the neck, and white spots and bars on the back, wings and sides.

The Black-throated Diver (*C. arcticus*), somewhat smaller than the preceding, breeds on lakes in arctic North America, Siberia and northern Europe, including the Highlands of Scotland. In winter plumage it closely resembles the Great Northern Diver, but in summer the crown and hind-neck are ashy-grey, the upper parts black, barred and spotted with white, the throat purplish-black, the sides of the neck striped with black and white and the underparts white.

The Red-throated Diver (*C. stellatus*) is the smallest member of the family and has a more slender bill than the other species, somewhat upturned. In breeding plumage the crown and nape are slate-grey, streaked with

[*G. K. Yeates.*

LITTLE GREBE OR DABCHICK (*Podiceps ruficollis*).
Uncovering its eggs.

white, the upper parts are brownish, there is a patch of chestnut red on the throat, and the underparts are white. In winter the brownish upper parts are spotted with white and the throat is white like the underparts. This bird breeds in the northern parts of America, Asia and Europe, including Scotland and northern Ireland, usually nesting by small moorland pools and hill-lochs. In winter it is plentiful off the coasts of the British Isles and ranges south to the Mediterranean, Caspian Sea, South China, California and Florida.

Order PODICIPIFORMES (Grebes)

The Grebes include only a single family, the *Podicipidae*, containing eighteen species of water-birds distributed over the world. They have rather long necks ; short, concave wings with twelve primaries ; no true tail-feathers ; and short legs placed very far back. The leg is extraordinarily flattened ; the three front toes are independently lobed with fringing membranes, and have broad, flat claws ; whilst the hind toe is extremely small. The sexes are similar and the plumage is usually dusky brown or blackish-grey above, silvery below, with some white in the wings. Many species have ornamental tufts of feathers on the head, and the head and neck are frequently marked with patches of chestnut, yellow and black.

Grebes frequent lakes, rivers and ponds during the breeding season, but in winter are often met with on estuaries or the sea near the coast. They feed on fish, small aquatic animals and vegetable matter, obtaining their food by diving, using their feet alone to propel them under water. The nest is a pile of aquatic plants, generally half submerged in the water, anchored by attachment to reeds or other plants. The three to six eggs are white with a smooth, chalky covering and are covered by wet weeds whenever the parent leaves the nest. The chicks are covered with down, often strikingly striped, and swim and dive freely almost directly they are hatched.

The Great Crested Grebe (*Podiceps cristatus*) is found in suitable situations in Europe, Africa, Asia, Australia and New Zealand. In the British Isles it has greatly increased in numbers in recent years and has spread northwards. It is the largest member of the

[*Arthur Brook.*

GREAT CRESTED GREBE (*Podiceps cristatus*).
This striking bird has become much commoner in Britain in recent years.

family in the eastern hemisphere and has a long, slender neck. In breeding plumage both sexes have a tuft of elongated brown feathers on each side of the head and round the neck a ruff or tippet, which is chestnut with black edges.

The Red-necked or Holboell's Grebe (*Podiceps griseigena*), somewhat smaller than the preceding species, with a stout bill, breeds in the north temperate portions of Europe, Asia and North America, though not in the British Isles. In summer the crown and back of the neck are blackish, the cheeks and throat silvery-grey and the front of the neck chestnut red; the upper parts are dark brown, except for a conspicuous white patch on the wing. In winter the birds are mostly found on sea-coasts and are not uncommon on the east coast of Britain, more rarely on inland waters and the west and south coasts.

The Horned or Slavonian Grebe (*Podiceps auritus*) is a comparatively small species which breeds in subarctic regions of North America, Siberia and Europe, including the Highlands of Scotland, migrating south in winter. In breeding plumage the head and a ruff round the upper neck are black, with a tuft of orange-chestnut feathers on each side of the crown, the neck, breast and flanks are chestnut.

[*Central Press.*
BLACK-BROWED ALBATROSS (*Diomedea melanophris*).
In the act of checking its gliding flight in order to descend to the water for food.

The Eared or Black-necked Grebe (*Podiceps nigricollis*), not much larger than the Little Grebe, breeds in many parts of Europe, western and central Asia, Africa and western North America. It has at times nested in various localities in England, Wales, Ireland and southern Scotland, sometimes in considerable colonies. In breeding plumage the head and neck are black, with a golden chestnut coloured tuft of long, hair-like feathers on each side of the head.

The Little Grebe or Dabchick (*Podiceps ruficollis*), the smallest member of the family, is found on ponds and streams in Europe, Africa, Asia and Australia. In breeding plumage it is blackish-brown above, reddish-chestnut on the cheeks, throat and neck, and greyish-white below.

412

Order PROCELLARIIFORMES (Petrels and Albatrosses)

This Order contains about one hundred species of oceanic birds distributed over all seas. Its members are characterized by the form of their external nostrils, which are more or less tubular, the tubes sometimes uniting on the upper part of the bill, sometimes opening independently at the sides. The horny covering of the bill is more or less divided into separate scutes, and the bill is usually hooked at the tip. The wings are long and have ten primaries developed. The feet have the three front toes united by webs and the hind toe small or absent. The plumage in all the species has a peculiar, strong, musky smell. All lay only a single, white egg. The chick is covered with down and remains a very long time in the nest.

Diomedeidae (*Albatrosses*). This family contains fourteen species of large sea-birds found in the southern oceans south of the tropic of Capricorn, and in the tropical and north Pacific Ocean. They have stout, hooked bills covered with a number of distinct horny plates, the nostril openings forming short tubes on each side of the middle plate of the upper mandible. They have rather large heads, somewhat elongated necks, stout bodies, and very long, narrow wings. Their legs are short and placed rather far back, their plumage is either brown, black and white, or almost completely white.

A great part of the life of an Albatross is spent in the air, gliding over the waves with its narrow, pointed wings held almost motionless, commonly many miles from land. The birds usually rise in a slanting direction against the wind, then make a turn in a large circle during which one wing points downwards, the other upwards, and finally make a rapid descent down wind. When the wind drops, they begin to flap their wings much more frequently. They feed chiefly on cuttle-fish, also eating fish and other marine animals and refuse floating on the surface. They breed in colonies on remote oceanic islands and when on land walk with a waddling gait. The nest is a depression in the ground or a hollow on the top of a mound of grass, moss and trampled earth. The single white egg, usually marked with some reddish spots or blotches, is somewhat pear-shaped. The young are fed by their parents on food regurgitated from the stomach, for many weeks, and become extremely fat. They remain in the nest for a further period while their down is being replaced by feathers, living at the expense of the accumulated fat.

The Wandering Albatross (*Diomedea exulans*), found throughout the southern ocean, chiefly between 60° S. and 30° S., is the largest ocean bird. Its body is as large as that of a Goose and the span of its wings is from ten feet to eleven feet six inches, occasionally reaching fourteen feet. Its plumage, when adult, is mainly white, with black tips to the primaries, and with some feathers on the back and sides freckled with narrow zig-zag, dark cross-bars. The immature bird is mainly brown with white face,

[*T. M. Fowler.*

FULMAR PETREL (*Fulmarus glacialis*).
Formerly only breeding in the British Isles at St. Kilda, the Fulmar now nests on cliffs throughout the northern parts of Britain.
Here it is in an unusual situation on the roof of a crofter's hut.

throat and under-surface of the wings. It breeds on various islands in the South Atlantic, South Indian Ocean and New Zealand seas.

Procellariidae (*Petrels, Shearwaters and Fulmars*). This family includes over fifty species of sea-birds distributed over all the oceans. They vary in size from the little Whale-birds or Prions, about the size of Starlings, to the Giant Petrel (*Ossifraga gigantea*), as big as a Goose, and show much diversity of plumage, though in structure and habits they are very uniform. The bill is hooked at the tip, and somewhat compressed at the base, with the nostrils opening together at the end of a double tube on the upper mandible. The wings are long, and the legs rather short. The birds have a characteristic gliding flight, alternating with periods of flapping, and often skim close over the crests of the waves. Except when breeding, they spend all their lives at sea, feeding on small fish, squids, crustacea and other floating or surface-living animals. They are more or less sociable when at sea and often congregate in vast numbers to breed. For this purpose, they resort to islands or in a few instances to cliffs on the mainland. The majority excavate a burrow or utilize a cavity under rocks or bushes, but a few nest on ledges of cliffs, and the Giant Petrel lays its egg on the ground in the open. The young are densely covered with down and become very fat, and in this stage some species are collected for food, notably the Mutton-bird of the islands of Bass Strait.

The Manx Shearwater (*Puffinus puffinus*) breeds on islets in the North Atlantic and Mediterranean, from Iceland, Bermuda and Madeira to the

Aegean, large colonies being found on various islands off the coasts of Scotland, Wales and Ireland, though it does not now occur on the Calf of Man, from which its trivial name was derived. It is sooty-brown or blackish above and white below, with dusky patches on the sides of the neck and flanks.

The Great Shearwater (*Puffinus gravis*) is only known to breed at Tristan d'Acunha, but ranges over the Atlantic Ocean, migrating in the southern winter north to the Newfoundland Banks, the British Isles and even to the Arctic Circle. It is considerably larger than the Manx Shearwater and has the crown and nape and the mantle ashy-brown, the wing-quills and tail-feathers blackish, the underparts, back of neck and some of the upper tail-coverts white.

The Sooty Shearwater (*Puffinus griseus*) has the whole plumage dusky, brownish above and greyish below. It breeds in great numbers round New Zealand and near Cape Horn and in the southern winter ranges in flocks into the North Pacific and North Atlantic, frequently appearing off the coasts of the British Isles.

The Fulmar (*Fulmarus glacialis*) is in size and appearance decidedly like a small gull, the mantle, wings and tail being brownish-grey, the rest of the plumage white. The species is, however, dimorphic, and individuals occur in which the upper parts are darker than in the normal form, whilst

[*Otho Webb.*

WEDGE-TAILED SHEARWATER (*Puffinus pacificus*).
A species widely distributed in the Indian and Pacific oceans, only coming ashore by night to its breeding hole.

the head and underparts are brownish-grey. Such dark individuals are much more abundant in some parts of its range than in others, and are very rare in British seas. The Fulmar breeds in vast numbers on ledges of cliffs in far northern latitudes on the coasts of the North Pacific and North Atlantic, and it has been suggested that it is the most numerous of all species of birds. From the earliest times until 1878, the only breeding place of the Fulmar in the British Isles was the St. Kilda group; in 1878 it colonized Foula in the Shetlands, and during the next twenty years spread throughout that group. In 1897 it first bred on the mainland of Great Britain at Cape Wrath and in 1910 colonized Horn Head, Donegal, Ireland. It now breeds as far south as Flamborough Head, Yorkshire, and the Skelligs off the coast of Kerry, South-West Ireland, and has appeared at the Stack Rocks near Pembroke, South Wales.

Hydrobatidae (*Storm-petrels*). This family includes about twenty species of small sea-birds, distributed over the oceans of both hemispheres, often known as " Mother Carey's Chickens." They have rather slender, hooked beaks, on the upper surface of which the nostrils open within a single median tube. Their wings are fairly long and their tails either square or forked. Their slender legs are frequently very long in proportion to the size of the bird. The majority have dusky plumage, but a few are grey; many have a patch of white at the base of the tail and some have white areas on the under-surface.

These little birds flit over the waves with swift but erratic flight; when feeding, or in calm weather, they frequently assist their progress by patting the water with their feet, supporting the supposed origin of their name from

St. Peter, who walked on the water. Their food consists of small organisms picked up on the surface of the sea. They breed in burrows excavated in soft soil, or beneath matted vegetation, or utilize natural cavities among rocks, almost always on small islands. The single white egg is frequently

[Dr. F. Barns.
WHITE-TAILED TROPIC BIRD (*Phaëthon lepturus*).
Tropic Birds are often called " Bo'son-birds " by sailors because they carry a marline-spike on the tail.

marked with small red, purple or black spots. The young bird is densely covered with grey or brownish down. When full-fed it is considerably larger than its parents, which then leave it, and when the feathers have replaced the down, the young fledgling follows them to sea.

The Stormy Petrel (*Hydrobates p e l a g i c u s*) breeds on islets in the eastern Atlantic from Iceland to Brittany, including many off the north and west coasts of Britain and Ireland, and also in the western Mediterranean. In winter it ranges south down both coasts of Africa. Its plumage is sooty black, except for a white patch at the base of the tail.

Leach's Fork - tailed Petrel (*Oceanodroma leuco-*

[*James's Press.*

DALMATIAN PELICAN (*Pelecanus crispus*).
The range of this bird extends from S.E. Europe to China and in winter it visits Egypt and Northern India.

rhoa) is similar in colouring but somewhat larger and with a strongly-forked tail. It breeds on various islands in the eastern North Pacific and the North Atlantic, including some in the Outer Hebrides and off the west coast of Ireland.

Pelecanoididae (*Diving-petrels*). There are five species of Diving-petrels, small sea-birds confined to the southern hemisphere. They are very similar in appearance, and superficially closely resemble the Little Auk, or Dovekie, of Arctic seas. Their bills are short and broad at the base ; their necks short and stout ; their wings comparatively small ; and their legs short and placed far back. Their plumage is mainly black above and white below, and between the diverging sides of the lower mandible, they have a small pouch partly feathered. They are generally found near the coast in small flocks and obtain their food, which consists of small fishes, crustacea, etc., by diving, using their wings under water. They excavate burrows in the soil, or under rocks on islands, in which to deposit their egg ; during the breeding season they are nocturnal in habits.

Order PELECANIFORMES (Frigate-birds, Cormorants, Darters, Gannets, Pelicans and Tropic-birds)

This group consists of aquatic birds, mostly marine, of moderate or large size. They are very diverse in appearance, but agree in various structural features and differ from all other birds in having all four toes united by webs.

Odontopteryx toliapica, an extinct bird from the London Clay (Lower Eocene) beds of Sheppey, England, may be placed in this Order. The edges of its jaws were serrated, like those of certain Tortoises.

Phaëthontidae (*Tropic-birds*). This family contains three species of sea-birds almost confined to tropical coasts. They have straight, heavy beaks; long wings; wedge-shaped tails with the two central feathers enormously elongated in adults; and short legs. Their plumage is white, frequently more or less completely suffused with rosy or salmon colour, marked with black bars, often crescentic in form. Their bills are red or yellow, and in one species (*Phaëthon rubricauda*) the long streamers in the tail are red. These streamers are valued as

[*James's Press.*
EASTERN WHITE PELICAN (*Pelecanus onocrotalus*).
This species breeds on lakes in S.E. Europe, western Asia, and tropical Africa.

ornaments by the natives of the South Sea Islands, who obtain them by pulling them out of the tail of the sitting bird, which apparently suffers little inconvenience.

Tropic-birds frequent the high seas, flying with rapid wing-beats, usually at some height above the water, and plunging down on their prey, which consists mainly of fish and squids. They breed somewhat gregariously on rocky islands, laying a single egg on the ground under a bush or in a crevice. The egg is yellowish or reddish, thickly spotted with reddish-brown and blotched and streaked with purplish-black. The young are covered with thick white down.

Pelecanidae (*Pelicans*). This family contains eight species of very large water-birds distributed throughout the tropical and temperate regions of both hemispheres, with the exception of eastern South America, New Zealand and Oceania. Their bills are extremely large and a great distensible pouch is suspended from the lower mandible. They have fairly long necks ; heavy bodies ; broad, rounded wings ; rather short, rounded tails ; short legs and large feet. Their plumage is mainly white, grey or brownish, with the primaries usually black ; the great bill and pouch, and the naked areas of the face, are commonly yellowish or fleshy-pink. Most of the species frequent large freshwater lakes, lagoons and estuaries, also visiting sea-coasts, but on the coasts of the warmer parts of the American continent a species occurs which is entirely marine in its habits. This species obtains its food like Gannets, by diving down upon it from the air, feeding almost exclusively on fish. The remaining species have a more varied diet largely obtained in shallow water. Frequently, they form in line a short distance from the shore and by flapping their wings drive shoals of small fish into the shallows, where they are scooped up into their capacious pouches.

Pelicans are sociable birds, flying in flocks or feeding together. They have difficulty in rising from the water, flapping along the surface for a considerable distance, but when once fairly launched their flight is buoyant and strong. Sometimes they rise high into the air and soar round in circles on motionless wings. In flight, their heads are carried well back on their shoulders so that the large bill rests on the front of the neck. They nest in colonies, usually on islands, either in lakes or on the sea-coast. The nests are sometimes mere hollows, more often rough structures of sticks and weed-stalks on the ground, on a low bush or in a tree. The two to four large eggs are bluish-white with a chalky coating. The young are born naked and with quite short bills, but they soon become covered with white down and their bills enlarge rapidly. They are fed on partly-digested fish, which they obtain by thrusting their bill, and often also their whole head and neck, into the capacious pouch of the parent.

Pelagornis is a very large fossil bird, allied to Gannets and Pelicans, whose remains have been found in Miocene beds near Bordeaux, France. *Cyphornis magnus*, from Tertiary beds, probably of Miocene age, of Vancouver Island, and *Palaeochenoides mioceanus* from the Miocene of South Carolina, are known only from small portions of their skeletons, which resemble those of corresponding parts of Pelicans, but show certain resemblances to Gannets and more remotely to Cormorants and Darters. *Cyphornis*, if it was capable of flight, was larger than any existing flying bird, its leg-bone being twice as large as that of the largest Pelican.

Sulidae (*Gannets and Boobies*). In this family are nine species of large sea-birds found off the coasts of all the oceans except the North Pacific. They have stout, conical, pointed beaks ; fairly short necks ; stout bodies ; long wings ; long, wedge-shaped tails and short legs. Areas of the face and a small pouch on the throat are unfeathered. In most species the plumage of the adult is mainly white with black wing-quills, and in all, the immature birds have mottled brown plumage. They feed on fish, which they obtain by diving from the air and then pursuing them under water. They commonly dive from a height of about sixty feet, sometimes from as much as a hundred feet, above the surface and have been caught in fishermen's nets at a depth of ninety feet. They breed in colonies on oceanic islands or precipitous crags. The nests of some species are merely hollows in the ground or mounds of guano with a hollow at the top ; others build rough nests of weeds or sticks either on the ground, on the ledge of a cliff or on a bush or tree. The one to three eggs have a pale blue shell,

[*Gibson & Sons.*

COMMON CORMORANT (*Phalacrocorax carbo*).
Note the large sticks used in the construction of the untidy nest.

usually completely hidden by a white, chalky, surface layer. The chick when first hatched is naked, but soon becomes covered with white down. It is fed on partly-digested fish, to obtain which it thrusts its head and bill into the throat of the parent.

The Northern Gannet or Solan Goose (*Morus bassanus*) is an inhabitant of the North Atlantic and breeds in large colonies on islands off the coasts of the British Isles, Faroe Isles, Iceland, Labrador and Newfoundland and in the Gulf of St. Lawrence. The adult is mainly white with blackish primaries and the head and neck pale straw yellow ; the young are dark greyish-brown spotted with white above, paler below.

Phalacrocoracidae (*Cormorants or Shags*). There are about thirty

420

species of Cormorants. They are large or moderate-sized aquatic birds, found on the coasts of all countries except the Central Pacific Islands. Many of the species also frequent lakes, rivers and estuaries. The bill is slender and terminates in a sharp hook ; the neck is long ; the wings and tails are rather long, the legs short and set far back, and the feet very large. The plumage is usually black, with green or purple gloss, sometimes white below; a number of species have crests in the breeding season. Parts of the face and a small pouch on the throat are devoid of feathers, and the naked skin is often brightly coloured. Cormorants feed on fish or crustacea, which they capture under water, swimming with their feet. They are frequently destructive to sporting fish in rivers and lakes, but in the sea they feed almost entirely on the slower-swimming fish that haunt rocks and weed-beds, and seldom capture the more active surface-swimming fish. After capturing a fish, a Cormorant has to bring it to the surface before swallowing it,

[T. M. Fowler.

NORTHERN GANNET (*Morus bassanus*).
The striking contrast between the white adult and the dark-plumaged young bird is here visible.

and this has probably led to their being trained by fishermen in India, China and Japan for the purpose of catching fish. A leather collar is put round the neck to prevent the bird from swallowing the fish.

Cormorants are sociable birds and mostly breed in colonies, placing their nests on the ground on low islands, on the ledges of cliffs, or in bushes or trees growing in swamps or lakes. The nests placed in trees or bushes, are composed mainly of sticks, but those by the sea are usually of seaweed and guano. Several species are of some importance as producers of guano, particularly on the coasts of South Africa and Peru, and it has been claimed that the Guanay Cormorant of the Peruvian coast is the most valuable wild bird in the world. The eggs, two to six in number, are pale blue or pale green, but this colour is largely concealed by a white, limy covering. The young, when hatched, are naked ; later they become covered with grey, brown or black down.

[W. S. Berridge.
GREAT FRIGATE-BIRD (*Fregata minor*).
The names Frigate-bird and Man-o'-War Hawk given to these birds indicate the ferocity with which they pursue other sea-birds and make them disgorge their prey.

They remain in the nest until they are fledged.

The Common Cormorant (*Phalacrocorax carbo*) inhabits the coasts, rivers and swamps of eastern North America, Europe, Africa, Asia, Australia and New Zealand. Its plumage is glossy greenish-black, with the chin and sides of the face white ; immature birds, and adults of the African race, have the breast also white or whitish ; in the breeding season adults have white patches on the flanks, and scattered white plumes on the head and neck.

The Green Cormorant or Shag (*Phalacrocorax aristotelis*) inhabits islands and rocky coasts of the eastern North Atlantic from Iceland and Norway to Morocco and of the Mediterranean from the Balearic Isles to Greece. It is generally more plentiful than the preceding species on the rocky western coasts of the British Isles, and may be distinguished by its smaller size and glossy, greenish-black plumage. In the early months of the year it bears a crest of feathers curving forwards, but this is shed about June.

Anhingidae (*Darters*). This family includes four species found respectively in Africa, Southern Asia, Australia and tropical America. They have long, slender, sharp - pointed bills ; small heads ; very long, slender

[Neville Kingston.
AMERICAN DARTER OR WATER TURKEY (*Anhinga anhinga*).
Note the kink in the neck which when suddenly straightened results in the darting forward of the dagger-like bill.

necks ; large wings ; long tails ; short legs, and large, webbed feet. In the males the plumage is mainly glossy greenish-black, but in females it is brownish. Darters frequent large rivers, lakes, and lagoons, in which they pursue and spear fish beneath the water. For this operation their necks are specially adapted, as the vertebrae are so arranged as to give the neck a permanent kink, which can be momentarily straightened by the action of the muscles and results in the rapid forward thrust of the bill, from which the birds derive their name. When swimming at the surface, they normally have the whole body submerged, only the long, slender neck and head showing above the surface, and suggesting a snake ; hence they are commonly called " Snake-birds." The American form is also known as the " Water Turkey." Darters fly strongly, and are fond of sailing round in the air. They may also often be seen perched in trees over-hanging the water. They build nests of sticks in colonies in trees near or

[Kershaw.

GREY HERON (*Ardea cinerea*).
The largest resident British bird, formerly protected as the noblest game at which falcons were flown.

in the water, and lay four eggs with white, chalky shells. The young, when hatched, are naked, and already have very long necks.

Fregatidae (*Frigate-birds*). There are five species of these large, tropical sea-birds. They have long, slender bills with a sharp hook at the end ; short necks ; very long wings ; long, forked tails ; very short legs ; small feet, and four toes all united by webs at their bases. The plumage of adults is either entirely black, or black above with white areas below ; the young have white heads. Between the edges of the lower mandible, on the chin, there is a patch of naked skin ; in the males this forms a bright red pouch, which can be inflated to a very large size, and is the bird's chief ornament in the breeding season. Frigate-birds are the most completely aerial of water-birds, never settling on the water, or on a level coast, but remaining in the air throughout the day, sailing round on motionless wings, plunging down to the surface of the sea to pick up some floating object, or pursuing

423

other sea-birds to make them disgorge their booty. At dusk they retire in companies to roost in some favourite clump of trees near the coast. In some of the Pacific Islands, they are domesticated, and are used like Pigeons for sending messages from one island to another. They breed in colonies on tropical islands, constructing large, clumsy nests of sticks, placed in trees, on bushes or on rocks. A single white egg is laid and the chick is entirely naked when hatched, but later acquires a covering of white down, which is soon replaced by feathers.

Order CICONIIFORMES (Herons, Storks, Flamingoes)

This group contains a comparatively small number of species of wading birds with long necks and very long legs, mostly of large size. It is represented in all parts of the world.

Ardeidae (*Herons and Bitterns*). This family contains about one hundred species of wading birds found almost throughout the world. Their bills are long, pointed, rounded above and compressed laterally ; their necks are long ; their bodies compressed and covered with loose feathers, which make them appear larger than their real size ; their broad wings have eleven primaries ; their tails are short ; their legs are usually very long and their toes fairly long, the claw of the middle front toe being serrated. They feed largely on fish, frogs and crustacea, which are secured by a lightning-thrust downwards with the bill whilst standing in shallow water or wading slowly about. The Night-herons (*Nycticorax*) as their name implies are largely nocturnal, and Bitterns frequent reed-beds or

[*Arthur Brook.*

GREAT WHITE HERON (*Casmerodius albus*).
This fine bird, here seen at its nest in Hungary, is now very rare in Europe, owing to persecution and the drainage of the marshes.

[*Walter E. Higham.*

BITTERN (*Botaurus stellaris*).
The remarkable booming note of this bird is again to be heard on the Norfolk Broads.

dense cover. When flying, the members of this family usually have the long neck curved in an S so that the beak alone is in advance of the breast, but the long legs are outstretched behind. Their notes are harsh croaks and hoarse squawks; whilst Bitterns also make loud booming calls. Their nests are large structures of sticks or reeds, either in trees, on bushes, cliffs or towers, or amongst the reeds in a swamp. The eggs are usually bluish or greenish, sometimes buff or white. The young, when hatched, have a scanty covering of down and remain for a long time in the nest until they are fledged. In the breeding season, many species, especially the white ones known as Egrets, bear elegant soft plumes on the head, neck, breast or back. These are known in the millinery trade as " Ospreys" or "Aigrettes," but as their collection involves killing the parent birds at the nest, and leaving the young to starve, their import into most civilized countries, except France, is prohibited.

[D. Seth-Smith.
BLACK-CROWNED NIGHT HERON (*Nycticorax nycticorax*).
A nocturnal species found almost throughout the world, but only occasionally visiting the British Isles.

The Grey Heron (*Ardea cinerea*) is found over the greater part of Europe and Asia, birds from the colder regions visiting South Africa and India in winter. It is one of the largest members of the family and the largest common bird in the British Isles. Its plumage is mainly grey, dark above and pale below, with the wing-quills and a patch on the shoulders black; the head and neck are mainly white, the former having a black crest and two long black feathers hanging from it down the back of the neck. The Heron was formerly protected in England, as being the noblest game at which Falcons were flown. Like many other members of the family, it nests in colonies, known as heronries, sometimes of very large size.

The Common Bittern (*Botaurus stellaris*) is found in reed-beds in many parts of Europe, Asia and Africa. Its plumage is chiefly buff, barred above and streaked below with black; the crown and nape are black. In the British Isles it became extinct in the middle of the 19th century, but since 1911 has re-established itself as a breeding species in Norfolk.

426

Cochleariidae (*Boat-bills*). This contains only one species, found in Central and northern South America. In most structural features it resembles the Herons, particularly the Night-herons, but the long bill is very broad and flattened and the upper mandible is deeply grooved on each side of a central keel. Boat-bills frequent mangrove swamps and are nocturnal in habits. Their plumage is mainly grey with black on the back and flanks, white on the forehead and some rufous

[*W. S. Berridge.*
HAMMER-HEAD (*Scopus umbretta*).
The enormous roofed nests of these birds are a feature of African scenery.

colour on the underparts. The head is adorned with a long drooping crest of blueblack feathers.

Balaenicipitidae. This family contains only the Shoe-bill or Whale-headed Stork (*Balaeniceps rex*), an inhabitant of the swampy districts near the upper White Nile in the southern Sudan, and adjacent parts of Uganda and the Belgian Congo. It is a very large bird, standing five feet high, with long legs, and an extraordinary bill. This is flattened and swollen, and has a ridge along its upper surface terminating in a hook; from its shape are

[*Neville Kingston.*
BOAT-BILL (*Cochlearius cochlearius*).
A nocturnal bird found in tropical America.

427

SHOE-BILL (*Balaeniceps rex*).
[*D. Seth Smith.*
This large bird, also called the Whale-headed Stork, inhabits the swamps of eastern tropical Africa.

derived the bird's various names, including the Arabic "A b u m a r k u b" (Father of a Shoe). Its plumage is brownish-grey, with blackish wings and tail, the bill being yellow with dusky mottlings. A crest of short feathers curling forward on the top of the head adds to its singular appearance. Its food consists of fish, frogs, snakes, molluscs and carrion. The nest is a scantily-lined hollow on the ground containing two to twelve chalky-white eggs.

Scopidae. The Scopidae include only the Hammer-head or Hammer-kop (*Scopus umbretta*) found throughout Africa south of the Sahara and also in Madagascar and south-west Arabia. It is a comparatively small Stork-like bird, no larger in body than a Raven, but with fairly long neck and legs. Its long, keeled, greatly-compressed bill has a small hook at the tip; the rounded wings have ten primaries; the feet have four long toes of which the middle and outer front ones are united by a small web at the base.

The plumage is almost uniformly dull brown, glossed with purple, but the tail is barred with black. A long crest on the back of the head, generally carried horizontally, accounts for its South African names. The Hammer-head frequents the neighbourhood of water and feeds on fish, reptiles, frogs, worms, molluscs and insects; in flight the neck is somewhat curved, but the legs are outstretched. Its nest is an enormous structure of sticks, roots, clay, etc., roofed over with a flat covering of sticks leaving an entrance at the side. It is usually placed in a tree, or occasionally on a rocky ledge or on the ground, and is used year after year. The three to five eggs are white.

Ciconiidae (*Storks*). There are about twenty species of Storks. They are very large, wading birds, including some of the largest birds capable of flight. They mostly have long, stout bills, either straight or slightly curved up or down; the head and neck are frequently partly naked; the wings are very large with eleven or twelve primaries; the short tail consists of twelve broad feathers; the front toes are usually short with flattened claws and are partially united by webs, whilst the hind toe is somewhat elevated. Storks occur in most parts of the world, but are absent from the greater part of North America and Australia, the Malay Archipelago and New Zealand. They feed on the ground or in marshes on fish, frogs, reptiles, insects, etc., in search of which they patrol fields, open country and swampy localities. On the wing they fly with neck and legs outstretched and sometimes rise to great heights and circle round in the air. At times they indulge in grotesque dances and make a loud clattering noise with the bill, but they are generally silent, being practically voiceless. Their nests are large structures of sticks, generally built in trees, but sometimes on cliffs or buildings. The three to six eggs are white and chalky, and the nestlings when hatched have very scanty

[*James's Press.*

ADJUTANT (*Leptoptilos dubius*).
This large Stork is a well-known scavenger in Indian towns.

[*Keystone.*

MARABOU STORKS (*Leptoptilos crumeniferus*).
Feeding in company with vultures on a dead zebra in the African bush.   The curious pouch on the front of the neck is
not a receptacle for food as is commonly supposed.

down, but in a short time get a growth of longer and denser white or grey down.

The White Stork (*Ciconia ciconia*) has the plumage entirely white except on the wings, which are mainly black.   Its bill and legs are red. It breeds in many parts of Europe, but not in the British Isles, where it is only an occasional visitor ; it nests also in North Africa and many parts of Asia.   It migrates for the winter to Africa and India.   Where it is protected, it commonly breeds in towns on the roofs of houses, chimneys and towers or on wheels or baskets erected on poles for its use, but it also builds in trees.

The Adjutant (*Leptoptilos dubius*) is a very large Stork found in India, Burmah and the Malay Peninsula.   Its whole head and neck are bare with a very few scattered, short hairs, the naked skin being yellowish-red mixed with flesh colour ; a ruff of white feathers borders the upper part of the back ; the plumage of the upper parts is slaty-black ; the wing-quills are black ; there is a silvery-grey band on each wing ; the under parts are white ; the bill is pale greenish and the legs greyish-white.   From the front of the neck hangs a bare, fleshy, reddish pouch, sometimes sixteen inches or more long.   It is connected with the nasal cavity and is not a receptacle for food as is commonly supposed.   The Adjutant is largely a scavenger, feeding on carcasses in company with Vultures, and examining rubbish heaps and garbage dumps in Indian cities, but it also frequents ditches and pools, where it captures fish, frogs, etc.   The " Marabou

[Sport & General.

WHITE STORKS (*Ciconia ciconia*).
A pair with their nest and young on a tower in a Bavarian village—a familiar sight in many parts of Germany.

feathers " of commerce are the under tail-coverts of this bird and related species.

431

Threskiornithidae (*Ibises and Spoonbills*). This family contains about thirty species of large, wading birds found in most parts of the world except New Zealand. They have long bills, which in Ibises are nearly cylindrical and strongly curved downwards, whilst in Spoonbills they are flattened, narrowed in the middle and dilated at the end into a flat " spoon " ; the fairly large wings have eleven primaries ; there are twelve tail-feathers ; the legs are usually rather stout, and the toes are generally long, the three front ones being united by webs at the base. Spoonbills feed in shallow water, swinging the bill from side to side ; some Ibises feed in the same way, but others probe soft ground for worms or pick up insects, frogs, etc., on the land. In flight, the neck and legs are carried outstretched. Most of the species are sociable and frequently associate with other species or with Herons and Egrets. The nest is sometimes among reeds or on ledges of cliffs, but more

[*D. Seth-Smith.*

SACRED IBIS (*Threskiornis aethiopica*).
Parent bird feeding its young. Note that the bills of the latter are straight, though in the adult bird they are strongly curved.

often in bushes or trees, frequently in heronries or colonies of various species ; it is a moderate or large structure of reeds or sticks. The eggs are from two to five in number, dull white, bluish or greenish, usually with reddish or brownish markings. The nestlings are covered with down, and when the nest is in a tree, remain in it until they are fledged, but when it is on the ground, they wander away from it earlier.

The Sacred Ibis (*Threskiornis aethiopica*) has the head and neck devoid of feathers, the naked skin being black ; the plumage is white, except the

[British Museum (Natural History)]

SHOE-BILL OR WHALE-HEADED STORK
(*Balæniceps rex*)

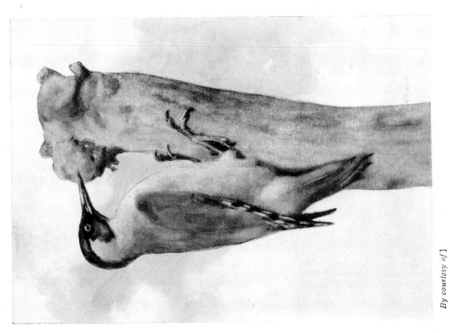

By courtesy of]

GREEN WOODPECKER (*Picus viridus*)

tips of the flight feathers, which are greenish-black, and the inner part of the wing, which is metallic purplish-black. It occurs throughout Africa, south of the Sahara, and in Madagascar, but is not now found in Egypt,

[*Arthur Brook.*

GLOSSY IBIS (*Plegadis falcinellus*).
The only kind of Ibis that breeds in Europe, sometimes visiting the British Isles.

where in dynastic times it was common. It was an object of veneration, being regarded as intimately connected with the fertility of the Nile, and many mummies of this bird are in existence. The birds were quite common in the delta till 1800, but have not been observed there since 1876.

AVES (ORDER CICONIIFORMES)

The European Spoonbill (*Platalea leucorodia*) has the plumage entirely white in winter, but in the breeding season it has a long white crest tinged yellowish-buff and some yellowish-buff feathers at the base of the neck. The legs are black, the bill black with yellow tip and the naked skin of the throat yellow. It breeds in various parts of Europe, North-Eastern Africa and Asia, and winters in tropical Africa and Asia. It frequently visits the British Isles, where it nested in various localities until the 16th and 17th centuries, being then known as the " Popeler," " Shovelard " or " Shoveler."

Phoenicopteridae (*Flamingoes*). There are six species of Flamingo. They are found in Europe, Asia, Africa and Central and South America.

By courtesy of]   [*Carl Hagenbeck's Tierpark, Stellingen.*
FLAMINGO (*Phoenicopterus antiquorum*).
These lovely birds, rosy pink with scarlet and black wings, have a unique method of feeding with the head upside down.

Flamingoes have small heads and very long, flexible necks ; the very peculiar bill is abruptly bent down in the middle and high at the base, the lower jaw is large and almost immovable whilst the upper is smaller and freely movable, and both are fringed with transverse horny ridges as in Ducks ; the large, fairly long wings have twelve primaries ; the short tails have fourteen weak feathers ; the legs are excessively long and slender, with unfeathered " thighs " ; the feet have three short front toes united by webs, whilst the hind toe is either absent or small and elevated. The plumage is pinkish-white or light scarlet with bright scarlet wing-coverts and black wing-quills.

Flamingoes are sociable birds, usually found in immense flocks wading in shallow lagoons or on the borders of salt lakes. Their method of feeding is peculiar, the head being held upside down with the bill pointing backwards immersed in the water. They fly with neck and legs outstretched, often in V-shaped formations, and like the Ducks, they moult all the wing-quills at the same time so that they are temporarily incapable of flight. The nests are mounds of mud with a slight hollow on the top, usually built in close proximity to one another in shallow water. The female lays one or two white eggs with chalky covering and sits on the nest with legs folded beneath her, not hanging down the sides or stretched out behind as was formerly believed. The nestlings, covered with white, woolly down, have short, straight bills and can run as soon as they are hatched.

[*Arthur Brook.*

EUROPEAN SPOONBILL (*Platalea leucorodia*).
Part of a Hungarian breeding colony; three hundred years ago these birds nested in England.

435

Order ANSERIFORMES (Ducks, Geese, Swans and Screamers)

This Order contains only two families, the members of which are very different in external appearance, though agreeing in various anatomical features. Each family constitutes a suborder.

Suborder **Anseres** : Family *Anatidae* (Ducks, Geese and Swans).

Suborder **Anhimae** : Family *Anhimidae* (Screamers).

Anatidae (*Ducks, Geese and Swans*). This family contains many species of large or moderate-sized aquatic birds found in all parts of the world. They usually have small heads ; long necks (very long in Swans) ; heavy bodies ; large, somewhat pointed wings ; short tails ; short stout legs set far back near the tail ; and feet in which the three front toes are united by webs, whilst the hind toe is small and elevated. The bill varies much in form, being long and wide in most Ducks, long and thin in Mergansers, and short and conical in Geese ; it is covered with a soft, sensitive membrane ending in a horny process called the " nail " ; in many species there is a series of ridges present on each side of each jaw, set transversely, and acting as strainers, whilst in Mergansers they point backwards and help to hold slippery fish. In Swans, most Geese and most of the Ducks found in the southern hemisphere, the sexes are similar in plumage. In most Ducks of the northern hemisphere, the males, or drakes, are much more brightly coloured than the females, or ducks. In these species the males take no part in incubation or the rearing of the family, but as soon as the female begins sitting, they leave her and moult into an " eclipse " plumage, which is usually very similar to that of the female. In all the members of this family, the wing-quills are moulted simultaneously so that for a short period the birds are incapable of flight. A feature of the plumage of many Ducks is a patch of brightly-coloured feathers, often with metallic sheen, on the wing, known as the " speculum."

Members of the family are found on the sea near the coast, as well as on lakes, rivers and ponds, whilst a few frequent mountain torrents. Swans and many Ducks feed mainly on aquatic plants which they obtain from the bottom in shallow water by immersing the head and neck and tilting the body so that the tail is raised vertically ; many Geese are even more completely vegetarian, leaving the water and browsing on grass or cultivated crops ; the Diving Ducks feed largely on mussels and other molluscs, for which they dive to considerable depths ; whilst the Mergansers feed principally on fish, which they pursue under water, propelled by their feet. Most of the members of the family fly swiftly, often in V's or wedge-shaped flocks, with the neck outstretched in front. During the winter they commonly associate in large flocks, and the species which breed in high latitudes migrate to spend that season in warmer climes where the water does not become frozen.

The nest is placed on the ground or in a hole, sometimes in a hole in a tree at a considerable height. It is lined with down from the body of the parent. The eggs vary in number from two to twelve or more and are smooth and hard-shelled, white, creamy or greenish in colour. The young are covered with down and take to the water soon after hatching.

The birds of this family are much sought after by sportsmen, many of them being excellent for the

By courtesy of]   *[Carl Hagenbeck's Tierpark, Stellingen.*
MUTE SWAN (*Cygnus olor*).
The male (or cob) on the left can be distinguished from the female (or pen) by the large knob above his bill.

table, and most of them from their wariness and the rapidity of their flight providing excellent sport. Several have been domesticated and are familiar inhabitants of farmyards, whilst many others are kept in semi-domestication on ornamental waters in parks.

The Mute Swan (*Cygnus olor*) breeds in a wild state from Denmark and southern Scandinavia through Central and Eastern Europe to Turkestan and Mongolia, and winters round the Mediterranean and Caspian Seas and eastward to India. It was introduced into the British Isles and kept in semi-domestication at least as early as the 12th Century and is now familiar in all parts of the world. The plumage of the adult is pure white, with the bill orange and the face and knob above the base of the bill black. The young, known as cygnets, have grey plumage and black bills.

The Whooper or Wild Swan (*Cygnus cygnus*) breeds in northern Europe and Asia and winters in southern Europe and Central Asia. It is almost as large as the Mute Swan, but the neck is straighter, the bill is black at the tip and yellow at the base, and there is no knob above it. It has a loud, trumpeting call.

Bewick's Swan (*Cygnus bewickii*), very similar to the Whooper, but smaller and with less yellow on the bill, breeds in northern Russia and Siberia and winters in the British Isles, northern Europe, central Asia, China and Japan.

The Black - necked

[Otho Webb.
BLACK SWAN (*Chenopis atrata*).
The emblem of Western Australia, where it was discovered by a Dutch expedition in 1697.

Swan (*Cygnus melancoriphus*) is a native of temperate South America and is frequently seen in captivity. It is much smaller than the Mute Swan and the plumage of its head and neck is black ; the bill is blue and the knob above it red.

The Black Swan (*Chenopis atrata*) is a native of temperate Australia and Tasmania and has been completely acclimatized in New Zealand. It is frequently kept in confinement in other parts of the world. Its plumage generally is dull black, but the wing-quills are white and the beak bright red, with no knob at the base.

The Greylag Goose (*Anser anser*) is found in many parts of Europe and Asia, breeding in the more northerly portions and migrating south for the winter. A few still breed in northern Scotland. It is the ancestor of the Domestic Goose and much resembles the familiar grey goose of farmyards, but is rather smaller.

By courtesy of]   *[Canadian National Railways.*
SNOW GEESE (*Chen hyperborea*).
These birds breed in Arctic America and probably also in Siberia, and come south in winter, occasionally to Britain.

The White-fronted Goose (*Anser albifrons*) breeds in the Arctic regions of both hemispheres and winters south to the British Isles, the Mediterranean, northern India, China, Japan, Mexico and Florida. It is smaller than the Greylag, with a white patch above the bill and black bars on the breast.

The Bean Goose (*Anser fabalis*) breeds in northern Siberia and winters south to the British Isles, the Mediterranean, Turkestan, China and Japan. It is as large as the Greylag but slimmer, with darker plumage and a longer bill.

The Pink-footed Goose (*Anser brachyrhynchus*), smaller than the Bean Goose, with a short bill, breeds in Iceland and Spitzbergen and winters in north-western Europe, principally on the east coast of Great Britain.

The Brent Goose (*Branta bernicla*) has the head, neck, breast and tail black, the upper parts brownish black, the underparts grey, the tail-coverts and a small patch on each side of the neck white. It is a small goose, largely maritime in habits, feeding principally on grass-wrack (*Zostera marina*) on mudflats at low tide. It breeds in the arctic regions of both hemispheres and winters on the temperate coasts of the North Atlantic and North Pacific.

438

The Barnacle Goose (*Branta leucopsis*), somewhat larger than the Brent, has the forehead, cheeks and chin white, the crown and neck black, the upper parts grey barred with black and white, the wing-quills and tail blackish, the breast greyish and the tail-coverts white. It breeds in Greenland and Spitzbergen and winters on the coasts of the British Isles, the North Sea and the Baltic.

By courtesy of Carl Hagenbeck's Tierpark, Stellingen.
ORINOCO GOOSE (*Neochen jubata*).
An inhabitant of the Amazon and Orinoco rivers and their tributaries.

The Canada Goose (*Branta canadensis*) is the familiar wild goose of North America, breeding in Alaska, Canada and the northern United States and migrating for the winter to the southern States. In the British Isles it is kept on lakes in many parks and in some districts may be regarded as acclimatized. Its head and neck are mainly black, but the throat and a patch on each side of the head are white. The back and wings are greyish-brown, the tail black and underparts greyish-white.

The Muscovy Duck (*Cairina moschata*) is a native of tropical South America and was domesticated by the Indians before European settlement. It is frequently kept in poultry yards in other parts of the world. It is a long, low bird with short legs and glossy, greenish-black plumage with white patches in the wings. The male is much larger than the female and has the face bare, the naked skin being mottled black and red.

The Sheldrake (*Tadorna tadorna*) is found on the coasts of Europe and of the salt lakes of eastern and central Asia, migrating southward in winter. The plumage in both sexes is mainly white, the head being greenish-black, the belly and tail black and a band round the breast and shoulders, chestnut. The bill is bright red and the legs pinkish red. It breeds in holes in sand-hills near the sea.

The Mallard or Common Wild Duck (*Anas platyrhynchos*) breeds in Europe, northern Asia and northern North America, and migrates south to North Africa, India, Central America and the West Indies. The male is pencilled grey with a brilliant green head, white collar and chestnut breast; the stern is black, with the black centre-feathers of the otherwise

[*W. S. Berridge.*
EMPEROR GOOSE (*Philacte canagica*).
This handsome bird inhabits the countries on both sides of the Behring Sea.

whitish tail curled up. The female is mottled brown. Both sexes have on the wing a metallic blue speculum with white edges, and bright orange legs. This species is the ancestor of the various breeds of domestic ducks, of which the Rouen resembles the wild bird in colouring, but is much larger and heavier. The Aylesbury is pure white and also larger than its wild ancestor. The Indian Runner is remarkable for the posterior position of its legs and consequently stands much more upright than other ducks.

The Gadwall (*Anas strepera*) breeds in Europe and Asia, from Iceland and the British Isles to Kamchatka, and in North America, and winters south to the tropics. The drake has the head greyish-brown, most of

the plumage mottled and marbled with shades of grey, the rump and tail-coverts black, a chestnut patch and a white speculum on the wing. The duck is spotted and mottled with brown and has a white speculum.

The Wigeon (*Mareca penelope*) is decidedly smaller than the Mallard. The male is pencilled grey with a chestnut head, cream-coloured forehead, white abdomen and black stern. The wings have a large white patch. The female is brown with white underparts. In summer it is found in northern Europe and Asia, migrating south

By courtesy of Carl Hagenbeck's Tierpark, Stellingen.
GREYLAG GOOSE (*Anser anser*).
The ancestor of the domestic goose.

in winter to north Africa, India and China. In the British Isles it is plentiful in winter, and some breed in northern Scotland.

The Teal (*Anas crecca*) is the smallest species of duck, no larger than a pigeon. The plumage of the male is pencilled grey with a chestnut head, green band along the side of the head and cream and black stripes on each side of the back. The female is mottled brown. Both sexes have a bright green speculum. Teal are found throughout Europe, North Africa, Asia, North and Central America, breeding in the northerly portion of their range and wintering chiefly in the south.

The Garganey (*Anas querquedula*) is chiefly a summer visitor to Europe and northern Asia, breeding from Britain to Kamchatka, and winters in tropical Africa, India and the Malay region. The plumage of the drake exhibits various shades of brown, with a broad white stripe over the eye, elongated scapular plumes black with a median white stripe, wing-coverts bluish-grey and belly white. The duck is mottled brown and both sexes have the speculum green between two white bars.

DUCKS (ANATIDAE)

The Pintail (*Anas acuta*) has almost exactly the same geographical range as the Teal. It is a slender, graceful duck with long neck and tail. The male is pencilled grey with a brown head, white neck and underparts and black patches on the shoulders. The two central tail feathers, which are very long, are black. The female is mottled greyish-brown.

The Mandarin Duck (*Dendronessa galericulata*), a native of China and Japan, is often kept in confinement or semi-captivity on ponds. The male in full plumage is one of the most brilliantly-coloured birds. He has a large copper and green crest, an orange ruff on the neck, and the innermost

[*Stanley Crook.*

SHELDRAKE (*Tadorna tadorna*).
A drake guarding chicks. In this species the male does not leave all family cares to his partner as do most male ducks.

wing-quills, which are also orange, greatly enlarged and forming a fan at each side. Above these the long shoulder-plumes are black and white. In addition, the breast is purple, a line above the eye and the belly are white and there are bright blue lines on the back and sides. The female is mottled brown with a white belly.

The Shoveler (*Spatula clypeata*) is remarkable for the great width of the tip of its long bill and the great development of the sifting-ridges at the sides. The male has the head green, the breast white and the underparts chestnut. The female is mottled brown. In both sexes the inner half of the wing is light blue and the speculum green. This species has

441

a very wide range, which includes almost the whole northern hemisphere, and in winter it reaches Ceylon, Borneo and Colombia.

The Pochard (*Nyroca ferina*) is a diving duck distributed on lakes and ponds all over the northern parts of the eastern hemisphere. The male has the head chestnut, the breast and stern black and the rest of the body pencilled silvery-grey. The female is dull grey with a brown head and breast.

The Canvasback (*Nyroca valisineria*) is similar to the Pochard, but larger and with a long black bill. It feeds largely on the wild celery (Vallisneria) and this gives its flesh an excellent flavour, which makes it in great demand for the table. It is a native of North America.

[*G. K. Yeates.*

MALLARD OR COMMON WILD DUCK (*Anas platyrhynchos*) ON THE DECOY POND.

The Tufted Duck (*Nyroca fuligula*) is found on lakes and ponds throughout Europe and northern Asia, and in winter reaches Abyssinia, India and the Malay Archipelago. The male is black, with white flanks and belly and a white bar in the wing, and has a tuft of elongated black feathers on the back of the head. The female has a shorter tuft and is blackish-brown with brown flanks, white belly and white wing bar. In recent years this species has increased remarkably in the British Isles, where it now breeds in almost all counties.

The Scaup Duck (*Nyroca marila*) is a northern species, breeding in high latitudes in both hemispheres and occasionally as far south as Scotland. The drake has the head, neck and breast black, the back white with fine wavy black cross-lines, the belly and a patch in the

442

wing white, and the stern blackish-brown. The duck is brownish, nearly black on the head and neck, with a conspicuous white patch round the base of the bill. In winter the Scaup is chiefly a maritime species and occurs on the coasts of western Europe, the Mediterranean, Black Sea and Persian Gulf, the coasts of China and Japan and both coasts of the United States.

By courtesy of]   *[Carl Hagenbeck's Tierpark, Stellingen.*
CAROLINA DUCKS (*Aix sponsa*).
These handsome birds, often kept on ornamental waters, are known in their native land, North America, as Wood Ducks or Summer Ducks.

The Goldeneye (*Bucephala clangula*) is found throughout the northern hemisphere. The male has a dark-green head with an oval white patch before the yellow eye ; the back and wings are black, with white shoulder-streaks and wing-patch, and the underparts are white. The female is smaller with a dark brown head, white neck and underparts and dark grey upper parts.

The Long-tailed Duck or Old Squaw (*Clangula hyemalis*) has a circumpolar range in summer, and in winter moves south to the ice-free waters of northern Europe, Asia and North America, including the seas round Scotland and north-eastern England. The most striking feature of the species is the great elongation of the two central tail-feathers of the drake, whose plumage in winter is mainly black and white, but in summer largely brown.

[W. S. Berridge.
MANDARIN DUCKS (*Dendronessa galericulata*).
The drake of this species is one of the most gorgeous of birds ; the fans on his wings make him unique.

The Black Scoter (*Oidemia nigra*) breeds in the Arctic regions in the vicinity of freshwater lakes and swamps, and in winter is found on the coasts of the temperate parts of the northern hemisphere. It feeds almost solely on mussels, which it obtains by diving. The male is entirely black, the female greyish-brown with whitish cheeks and belly.

The Velvet or White-winged Scoter (*Melanitta fusca*) has much the

443

same range as the Black Scoter, both in summer and winter, but on British coasts is much less numerous. It is a somewhat larger bird, with a conspicuous white patch in the wing.

The Eider (*Somateria mollissima*) is a large marine duck found on Arctic and northern coasts on both sides of the North Atlantic. The male has the upper parts mainly white, the top of the head, wing-quills, underparts and stern black, the breast pale buff and a band round the back of the head green. The female is entirely barred with brown. The nest is always close to the sea, and, as in other ducks, the female plucks down from her breast to line it and cover the eggs. The down in this species is very fine and elastic and is collected from the nest in Scandinavia and Iceland, where the birds are specially protected and breed in colonies.

The Steamer-duck or Loggerhead (*Tachyeres brachyptera*) is the largest of the diving ducks, the male having a very heavy body, as large as that of a goose. In colour it is slate-grey with a white belly and wing-bar and an orange-yellow bill and feet. The smaller female is darker in colour. The wings are very small and the birds can fly only when quite young, soon becoming too heavy. The adults escape from danger by paddling along the surface of the water, flapping their wings. The Steamer-duck inhabits the Straits of Magellan, the coasts of Chile and Patagonia and the Falkland Isles.

[J. D. Rattar.
EIDER DUCK (*Somateria mollissima*).

The Goosander (*Mergus merganser*) is the largest of the saw-billed ducks, or Mergansers, which feed on fish. The male is mainly white, tinged with salmon-colour, with a green head, black on the back and wings and a grey tail. He has a short crest. The female has a chestnut head with a long straggling crest, grey upper parts and white underparts. Both sexes have long, slender red bills. This species is found all round the northern hemisphere, breeding in northern localities and in winter reaching North Africa, India, China, Mexico and Bermuda. In summer it frequents lakes and mountain torrents, but in winter is found on estuaries as well as on inland waters.

The Red-breasted Merganser (*Mergus serrator*) is much more maritime in winter than the Goosander, being chiefly found on sea-coasts, but it breeds on freshwater lakes as well as inlets of the sea. Its breeding range extends from Ireland and Scotland through northern Europe, Siberia and North America, and it winters south to the Mediterranean, the coast of China, California and Florida. The drake has a crested green head,

444

white neck, chestnut upper breast with black streaks, and large white patches in the wings. The duck much resembles the female Goosander but is smaller.

The Smew (*Mergellus albellus*) breeds in northern Europe and Siberia and winters on the coasts and lakes of Europe, including the British Isles, and Asia, south to the Mediterranean, Persia, northern India, southern China and Japan. The drake is largely white, with black patches on the head, back, wings and tail and with a long, white crest. The duck is considerably smaller, with a reddish-brown head without a crest.

Anhimidae (*Screamers*). This family contains three species of large terrestrial birds found in Central and South America. They have small heads and long necks; their bills are short, covered with soft skin and terminating in a blunt hook; their wings are broad and rounded, with eleven primaries, and each has two sharp spurs near the angle, of which the foremost is the bigger; the legs are stout and rather long, and the long toes, all at the same level, have strong claws, the front ones being connected at the base by small webs. The plumage, which is similar in the two sexes, is mainly black or grey, lighter on the head. One species has a long, slender horn on the forehead, whilst the other two are crested.

Screamers are remarkable for the great development of air-sacs beneath the skin. They inhabit swampy localities, wading in shallow water and swimming with buoyancy. At times they rise high into the air and circle round uttering their very loud calls. These are also made when the birds are on the ground and can be heard for a distance of two miles. The food consists of vegetable matter. The nest is a great pile of reeds and rushes in a wet situation, and contains four to six buffish-white eggs. The young are covered with yellowish-brown down and the spurs on the wings develop very early. They are frequently reared by the natives in poultry yards, where they act as defenders of the fowls, attacking invaders by the use of their sharp spurs.

By courtesy of]   *[Carl Hagenbeck's Tierpark, Stellingen.*
HORNED SCREAMER (*Anhima cornuta*).
An inhabitant of tropical South America, allied to the geese and ducks in structure, though so different in appearance.

Order FALCONIFORMES (Birds of Prey)

Members of this very large Order occur in all lands, except the Antarctic, but though some species frequent sea-coasts, none is marine. The group is characterized by the strong, hooked bill with sharp cutting-edges and

445

with a " cere " or patch of fleshy skin at the base of the upper mandible. All the species are carnivorous, and have great powers of flight ; and the female is larger and more powerful than the male. The feet in all cases have four toes, which usually have sharp curved claws. The eggs are either pure white or white with red blotches, and the clutch is usually small, rarely more than five. The young remain in the nest for a long period and are cared for by the parents.

This Order includes two Suborders, namely, *Falcones* and *Cathartae.*

Suborder FALCONES
Family Sagittariidae

Secretary-bird (*Sagittarius serpentarius*). This curious bird is the only species of the only genus in the family. It comes from southern and tropical Africa, and stands about four feet high. Its short, strong beak is greatly arched, its neck is long, its wings are large and broad with eleven primaries, its tail has twelve feathers of which the central pair are long and drooping, its long legs are feathered down to the " knee-joint,"

[*Sport & General.*
SECRETARY-BIRD (*Sagittarius serpentarius*).
Protected in most parts of Africa as a destroyer of snakes.

and its feet have four short toes with blunt claws. The plumage is mainly bluish-grey, with the primaries, lower back and a band at the end of the tail, black. On the back of the head there is a loose crest of ten black and grey feathers in pairs and from these it derives its name, as they are supposed to resemble quill-pens behind the ears of a clerk or secretary. The cere, the naked sides of the face and the legs are yellow.

The Secretary-bird stalks about on the plains feeding on small mammals, birds, lizards, tortoises, insects and snakes. It has a special partiality for

[Arthur Brook.

MERLIN (*Falco columbarius*).
The smallest British falcon, nesting on the ground among heather.

[Stanley Crook.

PEREGRINE FALCON (*Falco peregrinus*).
Generally reputed the swiftest and most fearless of birds.

the latter, readily attacking even the most venomous species, kicking forwards with its long legs and shielding its body with outspread wings. It builds a huge nest of sticks and mud in a tree or bush and lays two to three eggs, white with rusty markings. The young are covered with white down and remain in the nest for many weeks.

Family Falconidae (*Falcons, Kestrels and Carrion-hawks*)

The Falconidae include the long-winged hawks of the falconer and the forms allied to them in structure. They are found in all parts of the world, and range in size from the Gyrfalcon of the Arctic regions, two feet in length, to the Finch-hawk of the Malay Peninsula, no larger than a sparrow. The Falcons capture their prey by " stooping " upon it at great speed from the air and striking with their talons ; Kestrels hover in one spot with

448

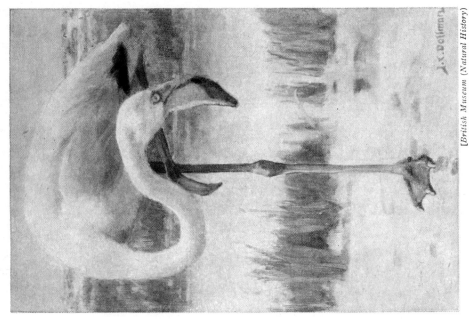

[British Museum (Natural History)]

FLAMINGO (*Phoenicopterus roseus*)

By courtesy of]

GOLDEN EAGLE (*Aquila chrysaëtus*)

[Waller E. Higham.

KESTREL (*Falco tinnunculus*).
Often called the " Wind-hover " from its habit of hanging in the air with rapidly beating wings while it scans the ground for mice.

By courtesy of Carl Hagenbeck's Tierpark, Stellingen.
HARPY EAGLE (*Harpia harpyja*).
An inhabitant of the jungles of tropical America, feeding on monkeys and other mammals.

swiftly-beating wings whilst they scan the ground below, whereas the Carrion-hawks walk about on the ground in search of frogs and reptiles, as well as joining Vultures in feeding on carrion.

Peregrine (*Falco peregrinus*). This bird occurs in almost all parts of the world except New Zealand and some of the Pacific Islands. In both sexes the crown, nape and cheeks are blackish, the upper parts slate-grey and the underparts buffy-white or rufous barred with black. The female is called the Falcon by falconers and the male, the Tiercel. For its size the Peregrine is the most powerful and courageous of all the birds-of-prey, feeding on ducks, waders, pigeons, grouse, partridges, rooks and other birds, as well as rabbits. It builds no nest, but lays its two to four eggs in a hollow on the ledge of a cliff or in the old nest of a raven, crow, heron, etc.

Hobby (*Falco subbuteo*). This breeds in England and throughout the greater part of Europe, Asia and north Africa, wintering in tropical and southern Africa and tropical Asia. In colouring it is much like a diminutive peregrine, but its wings are proportionately longer and it feeds mainly on large insects captured in the air. It also preys on small birds, including swallows, and even swifts, caught on the wing.

Merlin (*Falco columbarius*). This breeds in northern Europe, Asia and North America, the majority migrating south to winter in southern Europe, North Africa, India, and Central and northern South America. It is the smallest member of the family found in Europe and feeds largely on larks, pipits, small waders, etc. Its upper parts are slaty-blue, the tail has broad bars of black and a white tip. The underparts are buff streaked with blackish. Its four to six eggs are laid in a hollow on the ground, on the ledge of a cliff or in the old nest of some other bird.

Kestrel (*Falco tinnunculus*). This is one of the commonest birds-of-prey in Europe, northern and tropical Africa and the greater part of Asia. The male has the head, neck, lower back and tail bluish-grey, the latter with a broad subterminal band of black and a white tip; the back is chestnut with small black spots and the underparts buff, streaked and spotted with black. The female is reddish-brown above barred with black. It feeds almost entirely on mice, lizards and large insects, occasionally taking bats or small birds. Its four to six eggs are laid either in the old nest of a crow, magpie, pigeon, etc., or in a cavity of a cliff, building or hollow tree.

[*Arthur Brook.*

GOLDEN EAGLE (*Aquila chrysaëtos*).
The largest surviving British bird of prey, still to be seen in most parts of the Highlands of Scotland.

[D. Seth-Smith.
GREENLAND FALCON
(*Falco rusticolus candicans*).
This bird is now regarded as a pale race of the Gyr-falcon.

Family Accipitridae
(*Eagles, Buzzards, Kites, Harriers, Vultures and Osprey*)

This family contains a very large number of species and is represented in all parts of the world. It includes the species known to falconers as broad-winged hawks, the wings being less pointed than in Falcons and much wider. The flight is not so rapid, the birds of this family commonly sailing round in the air scanning the ground for prey or gliding amongst trees and bushes and coming upon it un-

awares. Most of the species will feed upon dead animals as well as upon game they capture alive ; Vultures feed almost exclusively on carrion.

Golden Eagle (*Aquila chrysaëtos*). This bird is distributed over Europe, north-west Africa, northern and central Asia and North America, chiefly inhabiting mountainous regions, but also found in forests. The adult bird is very dark brown with the back of the head and nape golden-tawny and the tail mottled with grey ; immature birds have the bases of the feathers white and show a

[Reginald Gaze.
GOSHAWK (*Accipiter gentilis*).
A male bird trained for falconry with the jesses attached to its legs.

452

[Arthur Brook.

BUZZARD (*Buteo buteo*).
The shrill mewing call of this bird is a familiar sound in most hilly or afforested parts of Europe, including northern and western Britain.

453

[James's Press.

LAMMERGEIER (*Gypaëtus barbatus*).
The largest bird of prey of the eastern hemisphere, inhabiting mountain ranges in many parts of the old world.

white band across the base of the tail. The legs are feathered down to the feet. It feeds on hares, rabbits, marmots, fawns, l a m b s, grouse, waterfowl a n d other large birds, and some of these items have led to its being extermin-ated in regions where sheep-farmers or game-preservers have waged war upon it. In the British Isles it is now confined to the Highlands of Scotland, but was formerly found also in southern Scotland, northern England, Wales and Ireland. The nest is a large structure of sticks built in a tree or on the ledge of a cliff, and two to three eggs are laid.

Buzzard (*Buteo buteo*). The Buzzard is found throughout Europe and northern Asia, chiefly in forests or in hilly and mountainous country. In the British Isles it now breeds only in Scotland, Wales and western England, but occurs elsewhere at other seasons. Its plumage is entirely brown, but there is great individual variation in its shade and in the amount of mottling with lighter tints. It feeds on small mammals, reptiles, frogs and large insects, occasionally taking small birds. It builds a nest of sticks either in a tree or on the ledge of a cliff and lays three or four eggs.

Hen Harrier (*Circus cyaneus*). This Harrier occurs throughout most of Europe, northern Africa, Asia and North America, breeding in the northern parts of its range and wintering further south. The male has the upper parts and the breast bluish-grey, the rump and the underparts white ; the much larger female is dark brown above with the rump white and the tail with dark bars, beneath buffish-brown with darker stripes. Like other Harriers, this species frequents open country, moors, downs, fields and marshes, systematically quartering the ground in search of small mammals, birds and their eggs and young, reptiles and frogs. The nest is placed on the ground among heather or reeds or in corn-fields and is often a bulky mass of roots and plant-stems. The four to six eggs are bluish-white, usually without markings.

Montagu's Harrier (*Circus pygargus*) is a smaller, more slender bird than the Hen Harrier, with proportionately longer wings, which breeds in England

and in the warmer parts of Europe and Central Asia, wintering throughout
Africa and in tropical Asia.

The Marsh Harrier (*Circus aeruginosus*), as its name implies, frequents
swamps and lakes, placing its nest among the reeds, and feeding largely on
young waterfowl as well as on frogs and reptiles. In such localities it is
found throughout Europe, North Africa and western Asia in summer

[*Capt. W. F. Knight.*

OSPREY (*Pandion haliaëtus*).
The male bird is here seen carrying a large fish to the nest.

wintering in the tropics. In the British Isles it was formerly widespread
but is now restricted to the Norfolk Broads. Its plumage varies much
according to sex and age, but is predominantly dark brown, with a yellowish
head, and it is a stouter bird than the Hen and Montagu's Harriers, with
broader wings.

Kite (*Milvus milvus*). This bird occurs throughout Europe, also in
north-western Africa, the Canary Isles and the Cape Verde Islands. In
the British Isles it was formerly abundant but at the present time is only

455

By courtesy of] [Carl Hagenbeck's Tier-park, Stellingen.
KING CONDOR (*Sarcorhamphus papa*).
The plumage of this South American vulture is creamy white and black, the bare skin of its head and neck red, orange, yellow and blue.

very occasionally met with except in Wales, where a few pairs still breed. The sexes are almost alike, but the male is slightly smaller and more brightly coloured than the female. The head and neck are white, striped with black, the back and tail rufous, the primaries blackish and the underparts rusty, striped with dark brown on the breast. The tail is very deeply forked. Kites feed on small mammals, young birds, reptiles, frogs and insects as well as on carrion; in fact, anything that they can find or surprise on the ground. In former times they were valuable scavengers. The nest of sticks is usually placed in a tree and the eggs are commonly three.

Sparrowhawk (*Accipiter nisus*). The Common Sparrowhawk is found throughout Europe, and in northern Africa and most of Asia. It is common in the British Isles. The very small male has the upper parts slaty-blue and the underparts buff, barred with reddish-brown; the much larger female is greyish-brown above and greyish-white barred with brown below. The food consists principally of other birds, which

[Eric Hosking.
CHILEAN EAGLE (*Geranoaetus melanoleucus*).
This striking bird with grey plumage and black breast is wide-spread in South America.

are snapped up as it glides with rapid but stealthy flight along hedges or the skirts of woods. The nest of sticks is built in a tree, but frequently the old nest of a Crow or other bird is adapted and added to ; four to six eggs are laid.

Griffon Vulture (*Gyps fulvus*). This bird is found in most parts of Africa and Asia and in eastern and southern Europe. It is one of the largest members of the family, being about four feet long and having a wing-span of nine feet, whilst it weighs from eighteen to twenty pounds. Its plumage is brown, becoming almost black on the wings and tail ; the head and neck are devoid of feathers, but are covered with short white down, and there is a ruff of long white filaments round the lower neck. Its food, like that of other vultures, is the carcasses of dead animals. These it discovers while circling at a great height, and as soon as one bird sights a carcass and descends to feed,

[*H. E. Pounds.*

Sparrowhawk (*Accipiter nisus*).
Still common in wooded parts of the British Isles despite the enmity of the gamekeeper.

other Vultures note its behaviour and come to investigate, so that a large number frequently assemble in a very brief period. The nests of branches and grass are built on overhung ledges of cliffs and many pairs often breed in close proximity. The single egg (occasionally two) is usually white, but is sometimes blotched with rusty brown.

Osprey (*Pandion haliaëtus*). This is one of the most widely-distributed birds, being found almost throughout the world, except in southern South America, New Zealand and some of the Pacific Islands. It no longer

457

breeds in the British Isles, though until recently it did so in Scotland, but individuals appear every year on migration. Its food consists of fish, upon which the bird plunges, often from a considerable height, and which are seized and carried away in its feet. It is frequently called the " Fish-hawk." Its claws are sharp and much curved, the soles of its feet are very rough, and the outer toe can be turned backwards. The plumage of the upper parts is brown, of the head and underparts white somewhat streaked and spotted with brown, and there is a dark line from the eye across the cheek. The nest is a very large pile of sticks with a small cavity on the top, and is placed in a tree or on a cliff or rock, either on the sea-coast or near a lake. Two or three eggs are laid.

[James's Press.
VOCIFEROUS SEA EAGLE
(Haliaëtus vocifer).
The African representative of the American Bald Eagle and the European White-tailed Eagle.

Suborder CATHARTAE
Family Cathartidae (American Vultures)

This family contains six species of large birds-of-prey found in North and South America. They have hooked but rather slender and weak bills ; the head and neck are more or less bare ; their wings are very large and their feet have slender toes and blunt claws. In their habits they differ little from the Griffon and other Vultures of the eastern hemisphere, spending the day circling high above the ground on the look-out for carrion and at night roosting in companies. They are generally silent birds, uttering low grunts or hissing sounds when alarmed or excited. They build no nest but lay from one to three eggs under logs on the ground or in caves. The young when hatched are naked, but soon become covered with thick white or buff down.

Turkey Buzzard (*Cathartes aura*). This bird is found from southern Canada to northern Patagonia, but is most abundant in the tropics and withdraws from the colder regions in winter. Its plumage is glossy black and the naked skin of its head and neck is bright red.

Condor (*Vultur gryphus*). The Condor occurs along the western side of South America from Ecuador to the Straits of Magellan, and also in Patagonia. Though perhaps most commonly found high up in the Andes, it is not

458

RÜPPELL'S VULTURE (*Gyps ruppellii*).
One of the commoner vultures of the Sudan and
adjacent parts of Africa.

infrequent down to the coast. It is the largest existing bird capable of flight, its wing-expanse frequently exceeding twelve feet, whilst the largest specimen on record measured fifteen feet. Its plumage is mainly brownish-black, with a large white patch on each wing and an oblique ruff of white down on the lower neck. The head and neck are bare, the skin on the latter being curiously wrinkled, whilst the male has a fleshy crest or comb on the forehead and a large wattle on the throat. These parts are dull red. Condors are said at times to attack young or sick animals and

they visit the guano islands off the Peruvian coast to devour the eggs of cormorants, gannets and pelicans, but their food is mainly carrion. They breed on ledges of cliffs, laying two white eggs, and the young are said to remain in the nest for nearly a year before they can fly.

Family Teratornithidae

This family contains the extinct bird *Teratornis merriami*, an almost complete skeleton of which has been obtained in the asphalt beds of Rancho La Brea, near Los Angeles, California. These are of Pleistocene age and

Photos]   [W. S. Berridge.
KOLBE'S VULTURE (*Gyps coprotheres*).
The South African representative of the European Griffon.

of the bird remains found in them more than half the species are still living, so that Teratornis was contemporary with many existing North

[*Walter E. Higham.*

MONTAGU'S HARRIER (*Circus pygargus*).
The hen bird at her nest on the ground. Note the varying sizes of the chicks, showing that incubation began when the first egg had been laid.

American birds. It was allied to the Condors, but exceeded them in size, being the largest flying bird known.

460

Order GALLIFORMES (Game-birds)

A large group of birds which has representatives in all parts of the world. Its members are either terrestrial or arboreal, and are usually of moderate or large size. They have stout, arched bills of moderate length, and feed largely on grain, berries, shoots of plants and other vegetable matter, varying their diet with insects, snails, etc. They form an important element in the food-supply of mankind, many species in the wild state providing sport (Pheasants, Partridges, Quails, Grouse, etc.) while a number have been domesticated (Fowls, Turkeys, Guinea-fowls).

This Order includes two very different Suborders, *Galli* and *Opisthocomi*.

Suborder GALLI
Family Megapodiidae (*Mound-birds*)

This family contains about twenty species of large or moderate-sized terrestrial game-birds found in Australia and the islands of the Malay Archipelago, the range of the family extending east to Samoa, north to the Philippines and westward to the Nicobar Islands. They have short, stout arched bills ; short, broad wings with ten primaries ; rather long tails and very stout legs and large feet, with the four toes all at the same level. The sexes are alike in all the species, but the colouring of the plumage varies greatly, and many have the head and neck more or less naked, the bare skin being usually brightly coloured. They are shy birds which frequent forests or bushy localities, often near the sea ; they run swiftly, and when alarmed often fly heavily up into the lower boughs of trees. Their food consists of fruits, berries, worms, snails and insects.

In their breeding habits the Mound-birds differ from all other birds, as their eggs are deposited in incubators and not in nests. These incubators consist of mounds of earth or sand, mixed with sticks and leaves, scratched up by the birds with their powerful feet from a large area. The mound is constructed largely or entirely by the male bird, which begins to scratch up material some months before the breeding season. The first season's mound is only small, but as it is added to year after year, it may ultimately attain a very large size.

In the case of the Australian Scrub-fowl mounds ten feet high and seventy feet in circumference are often met with, and a specially large one was estimated to contain two hundred and ninety-seven cubic yards of material weighing approximately three hundred tons. Each female probably lays from nine to fifteen eggs in a season, at intervals of about three days. Sometimes three or four females lay in the same mound, so that it may contain over forty eggs. The female deposits her egg in a hollow which she scratches out in the mound. The eggs are very large in proportion to the size of the bird and have very thin shells, in colour they may be white, pinkish or yellowish when fresh, but soon become stained brown. As soon as an egg has been laid, the male bird places it

461

By courtesy of]   [Carl Hagenbeck's Tierpark, Stellingen.
HELMETED CURASSOW (*Pauxi pauxi*).
An inhabitant of northern South America, also called the " Cashew-bird."

in an upright position with the smaller end downwards. The eggs are often arranged in irregular circles. Those first laid forming the lowest ring, those in the higher rings never being vertically above those at lower levels. While incubation is in progress, the birds are never far from the mound, and constantly work at it, opening it up to admit sunshine or moisture as required, or banking it up in unfavourable weather, By these means a temperature of about 95°F. is maintained in the interior of the mound. The eggs hatch after about two months and the chick gradually scratches its way to the surface ; though its body is covered with down, the quill-feathers of the wings are already large and it can fly almost immediately. Its legs also are strong, and it at once starts to scratch for food and lead an independent existence, the care of the parents being entirely devoted to the incubator.

Brush Turkey or Scrub Turkey (*Alectura lathami*). This bird inhabits forests and scrubs in Queensland and New South Wales. It is about two feet long, and its plumage is dull black ; the naked skin of its head and neck are red and large wattles on the lower neck are either yellow or purplish-white. The mound of this species is comparatively low, usually only from two to four feet high, with a circumference of about thirty-five feet. It is composed mainly of leaf-mould and is usually in the shade of trees, so that the necessary temperature is derived more from the decay of moist vegetable material than from the sun.

Mallee Fowl (*Leipoa ocellata*). The Mallee Fowl inhabits the inland districts of southern and western Australia. It is about two feet long and its plumage is mottled with rufous, brown and white, the markings on the back and wings resembling eyes ; it has a small fuscous crest. Its mound is usually formed in an open situation among low trees or bushes and consists largely of sand, with a bed of leaves and other debris in the centre, in which the eggs are placed. The overlying sand is scratched off by the birds in sunny weather and replaced at night or in dull weather, the heat being mainly derived from the sun.

MOUND-BIRDS AND CURASSOWS

Family Cracidae (*Curassows*)

This family contains about forty species of large or moderate-sized arboreal game-birds found in tropical America from southern Texas to northern Argentina. They are usually handsome birds with broad wings, rather long tails and very large feet, in which the long hind-toe is at the same level as the three front ones. Many of the species have brightly-coloured, fleshy wattles on the cheeks or throat and some have excrescences on the forehead. They frequent forests, feeding on leaves and fruit, and some species rarely descend to the ground. They build large, loosely-constructed nests of twigs, grass, moss and leaves on a horizontal branch, bush or stump, and lay from two to five white eggs with a hard granulated shell. The young climb and hop about the trees soon after they are hatched.

Family Gallinuloididae contains one of the few species of fossil birds of which a nearly complete skeleton is known. *Gallinuloides wyomingensis* from the middle Eocene beds of Wyoming shows much resemblance in structure to the Curassows.

[*Arthur Brook.*

CAPERCAILLIE (*Tetrao urogallus*).
A female on her nest in Scotland, where the species is now thoroughly re-established by introductions from the Continent after having been exterminated in the eighteenth century.

AVES (ORDER GALLIFORMES)

Family Tetraonidae (*Grouse*)

This family contains about twenty species of large or moderate-sized game-birds, terrestrial or partially arboreal in habits. They occur in the northern portions of the northern hemisphere. From members of the other families of the Order, Grouse are distinguished by having the nostrils covered by feathers and the legs partly or completely feathered. They never have spurs on the legs. In some species the feathering of the legs extends to the toes, in the remainder the toes have comb-like rows of scales on the sides which are moulted annually. Sometimes the sexes are alike, more usually the males are larger than the females and more brightly coloured. These species are polygamous and the males strut about, dance or fight in the mating season, frequently making booming or drumming sounds. Several of the American species have air-sacs at the sides of the neck, which can be inflated and give resonance to the booming calls. The nest is a hollow on the ground, usually sheltered by shrubs or low vegetation, and numerous eggs are laid. The young are hatched thickly covered with down, usually of a pronounced pattern, and leave the nest soon after birth. In the autumn, Grouse unite in small flocks. Their flight is rapid and accompanied by a startling whirr, caused by the quick strokes of their concave, stiff-feathered wings. When they have attained speed, periods of flapping are alternated with gliding, when the curved wings are held rigid.

Capercaillie (*Tetrao urogallus*). This bird inhabits the coniferous forests of northern Europe and western Siberia and of the Pyrenees, Alps, Carpathians, Balkans and Urals. It became extinct in the British Isles about 1770, but was reintroduced in Perthshire in 1838 and is now fairly common in central Scotland. It is the largest member of the family, the cock, which is considerably larger than the hen, approaching the turkey in size. His plumage is greyish or brownish black, darker below and deep glossy green on the breast. The hen is chiefly brown, mottled with buff and white. Capercaillies spend much of their time in the trees, feeding on the tender shoots of pines and larches, as well as on berries in the autumn. The six to twelve eggs are pale reddish-yellow with brown spots and blotches.

Black Grouse (*Lyrurus tetrix*). This grouse occurs in mountainous and hilly districts throughout most of Europe and Siberia, including the western and northern parts of Britain, though it is not found in Ireland. The male, known as the Black-cock, is bluish-black with white patches in the wings and beneath the tail. The tail-feathers curve outwards at the end on each side. The female, or Grey-hen, is brownish above, barred with chestnut and greyish on the breast, with some white in the wings. This species frequents woodlands as well as open country, usually in the vicinity of water, feeding on berries, seeds, buds and shoots of various plants. The six to ten eggs are yellowish-white spotted with orange-brown.

464

GROUSE (TETRAONIDAE)

Red Grouse (*Lagopus scoticus*). This is the only species peculiar to the British Isles, where it occurs on the moorlands of Scotland, northern England, Wales and Ireland. Its food consists mainly of the shoots of heather and other moorland plants, but the young chicks also eat numerous insects. The colour of the plumage varies considerably in different individuals, the cock being mainly brownish-red barred and mottled with black, whilst the hen is paler reddish-brown or yellowish-brown marked with brownish-black. The eight to ten, or even fifteen, eggs are buffish-white mottled with red or brown.

Ptarmigan (*Lagopus mutus*). This inhabits the Arctic regions of Europe, Asia and America and the summits of the principal mountain ranges of

[*Charles Reid.*

PARTRIDGES (*Perdix perdix*).
The familiar game-bird of the cultivated districts of the British Isles.

Europe and northern Asia above the level of trees. In summer the plumage is mainly brownish-grey, but the wings are white. In winter the plumage is entirely white. The eggs resemble those of the Red Grouse, but are smaller and paler.

Family Perdicidae (*Partridges and Quails*)

This family contains many species of terrestrial game-birds of small or moderate size and is represented in all parts of the world but southern South America and the Pacific Islands. Members of this family are usually plainly-coloured, shades of brown and grey predominating in the plumage, sometimes diversified with black, white or rufous. The sexes are usually similar and the males are monogamous. Spurs on the legs are only found in a few of the species and special ornaments are rare, though many of the American species have crests. Most of the species roost on the ground and only exceptionally fly up into trees. The nest is a hollow, and the numerous eggs are white, yellowish or olive, either plain or spotted with rufous or brown. The downy chicks can run soon after hatching.

Common Partridge (*Perdix perdix*). This is widely distributed in Europe and western Asia, frequenting open country in the vicinity of bushes or thickets, and fields surrounded by hedges. It feeds on shoots, leaves and seeds of various plants, in summer also taking insects. The brown upper plumage varies considerably in shade in different individuals, and the chestnut horseshoe-shaped mark on the grey breast is much more distinct in some individuals than in others.

Red-legged or French Partridge (*Alectoris rufa*). This bird is a native of south-western Europe and the Canary Islands. It was introduced into England about 1770 and is now well established in most of the eastern and southern counties. It is slightly larger than the Common Partridge, has white cheeks and throat bordered by a black band, chestnut, white and black stripes on the flanks, and red legs.

[*M. H. Crawford*

QUAIL (*Coturnix coturnix*).
This little migratory game-bird has become very scarce in Britain.

Quail (*Coturnix coturnix*). This bird ranges throughout Europe, Asia and Africa, and in the northern parts of its range is chiefly only a summer visitor. Very large numbers cross the Mediterranean in autumn and spring, and at the former season immense numbers are captured in nets all along the north coast of Africa when they arrive exhausted after their passage. From Egypt alone over a million were annually exported prior to 1914, and, in addition, great numbers were consumed locally. In spring very many are shot or captured in the southern countries of Europe. It is not surprising that in recent years the species has greatly decreased in numbers and comparatively few now visit the British Isles. The Quail resembles a very small Partridge with light streaks on the upper parts. Its curious three-syllabled call-note resembles the words " Wet-my-lips."

Francolins (*Francolinus*). The plumage of these birds is in the main black, marked with white, buff-yellow and chestnut. There are some thirty-five species, thirty found in Africa and five in Asia.

GREY PEACOCK-PHEASANT
(*Polyplectron bicalcaratum*).
An inhabitant of the jungles of the Malay Peninsula and Sumatra.

Family Phasianidae

(*Fowls, Pheasants, Peacocks, etc.*)

The Pheasant family contains numerous species of large or moderate-sized terrestrial or semi-arboreal game-birds. Their head-quarters are the jungles and mountain-forests of south-eastern Asia, but some members of the family occur in almost all parts of Asia and reach south-eastern Europe. In the majority the sexes are different, the hens being often comparatively dull-coloured whilst the cocks have most brilliant plumage, some of them being amongst the most magnificently-coloured birds. In very many species the tail is very long, the feathers being arched ; fleshy combs and wattles are often present on the head ; the legs are long and are frequently furnished with one or more spurs, and the feet are large and strong, having four toes, of which the posterior one is at a higher level than the three in front. The males are commonly polygamous and crow in rivalry ; the females make various clucking calls. The nest is always a mere hollow on the ground and numerous eggs are generally layed. The chicks are covered with down and run shortly after hatching.

Red Jungle-fowl (*Gallus gallus*). The ancestor of the domestic breeds, is a native of India, the Indo-Chinese countries and the Malay Peninsula and Archipelago east to the Philippine Islands and Timor. It closely resembles the Black-breasted Game breed of poultry fanciers and inhabits forests, jungles, and bamboo-thickets, coming out into clearings to feed. The cock crows like a Bantam. The hen lays from eight to ten creamy-white eggs.

The Jungle-fowl was probably first domesticated in Burma and was introduced into China about 1400 B.C. It is not mentioned in the Old Testament or in Homer, nor is it figured on ancient

Photos]   [*D. Seth-Smith.*
JAVAN OR GREEN JUNGLE-FOWL (*Gallus varius*).
A native of Java, Lombok and Flores, where it represents the Red Jungle-fowl from which the domestic fowl has developed.

467

Egyptian monuments, but it appears on Babylonian cylinders of the 7th to 6th centuries B.C. and on Lycian marbles of about 600 B.C. It is mentioned by Pindar and Aristophanes, the latter calling it the Persian bird, indicating that it was probably brought to Greece from Persia.

During the very long period in which poultry have been domesticated a large number of distinct breeds have been produced, differing in size, colour, the form of the comb and the shape of the tail, as well as in the feathering of the legs. The least modified are the various Game breeds, developed when cock-fighting was a universal sport, in which the very strong legs have strong, sharp spurs. In some of the breeds which are reared specially for the table the birds are very much heavier than the wild original stock. In other breeds the hens have been specially selected for their egg-laying capabilities and individuals often lay more than three hundred eggs in a year. Finally, Bantams and other " fancy " breeds are kept with no special utilitarian object.

[D. Seth-Smith.
ARGUS PHEASANT (*Argusianus argus*).
This picture gives an excellent idea of the remarkable display of the cock bird.

Common Pheasant (*Phasianus colchicus*). This ranges in its original wild state from south-eastern Europe across Central Asia to China and Japan, the birds from different regions in this large area presenting minor differences in colour. The most westerly form, which has no white on the neck, is believed to have been introduced into western Europe, including the British Isles, by the Romans. During the 19th century the Chinese form, with a white ring round the neck, was introduced into England and crossed freely with the established race, whilst smaller numbers of various other races have also been introduced. The birds now

[*Photopress.*

LADY AMHERST'S PHEASANTS (*Chrysolophus amherstiae*).
The cock bird is displaying his wonderful cape of white feathers with blue-black bars, to the hen.

found in the British Isles and also in western Europe and North America are thus the mixed descendants of various Asiatic races. The appearance and habits of the Pheasant are too well-known to need description.

Golden Pheasant (*Chrysolophus pictus*). This bird is a native of southern China and Tibet, and is frequently kept in aviaries. It is much smaller than the Common Pheasant. The cock has a crest of golden, hair-like feathers and on the back of the neck an erectile cape of truncated orange feathers with blue-black bars; the back is green and purple, the rump golden and the underparts scarlet; the arched tail is black and its central feathers are very long.

Lady Amherst's Pheasant (*Chrysolophus amherstiae*) of western China and eastern Tibet, is similar in form to the Golden Pheasant, but the cock is very differently coloured. His crest is red, his cape white with blue-black bars, his throat, chest and back dark green, his underparts white and his tail black and white.

Silver Pheasant (*Gennaeus nycthemerus*). This is also a native of south China and is frequently seen in captivity. It is a small species with an exceptionally long tail. The cock has the crest and underparts purplish-black, whilst his back and tail are white marked with black and his naked cheeks are red.

Argus Pheasant (*Argusianus argus*). This inhabits the forests of the Malay Peninsula and Sumatra. The plumage of the cock is a mixture of black, rufous and buff. The secondary feathers of the wing and the middle tail-feathers are extremely large and are decorated with many eye-like spots with reddish-yellow or white centres ringed with black. When the bird displays, these enlarged feathers are spread out to form a great fan.

469

[W. S. Berridge.

JAVAN PEACOCK (*Pavo spicifer*).
Displaying its ornamental train to best advantage.

[Neville Kingston.

PEACOCK (*Pavo cristatus*).
Seen from behind, showing how the train is supported by the stiff tail-feathers
during display.

Peacock (*Pavo cristatus*). This is a native of India and Ceylon, and has been kept in parks and gardens in Europe since classical times, and its flesh was formerly highly valued at banquets. Its appearance and h a r s h scream are too familiar to need description, but it is worth mentioning t h a t the wonderful train of the cock bird is formed by the greatly-elongated tail-coverts and when it is spread, is supported by the stiff tail-feathers which are raised behind it.

PEACOCKS AND GUINEA-FOWLS

Family Numididae (*Guinea-fowls*)

The family Numididae contains about seven species of rather large terrestrial birds found in Africa, south of the Sahara, Arabia, Madagascar and the Mascarene islands. They have the head and neck partly or completely devoid of feathers, the naked skin being usually blue, sometimes red or yellow. In some, including the Domestic Guinea-fowl, there is a bony casque on the top of the head, in others a crest of curly feathers. Some species have spurs on the legs. The plumage is usually black, more or less diversified with white and with white or blue spots on the black feathers.

Guinea-fowls are usually found in flocks in rather open country with scattered bushes and trees. They run swiftly on the ground, flying up into trees to roost at night or when disturbed. They feed on grass, seeds, roots, berries and insects. The nest is a depression on the ground, usually in the shelter of a tussock, and contains from twelve to twenty yellowish eggs freckled with rusty.

Domestic Guinea - fowl (*Numida meleagris*). This is a native of West Africa and was probably brought to Europe in the 15th century by the Portuguese. It has altered little in domestication. Some species of Guinea-fowl was known to the Greeks and Romans in classical times, but there is no evidence that it continued in domestication during the Middle Ages. The bird and its call, " come-back, come-back," are too well-known to need description.

By courtesy of]   [Carl Hagenbeck's Tierpark, Stellingen.
VULTURINE GUINEA-FOWL
(*Acryllium vulturinum*).
The most curious member of this African family.

Family Meleagridae (*Turkeys*)

The Turkey family contains only two species. Both are very large birds, natives of North and Central America. They frequent wooded country, associating in small flocks and roosting in the trees. The males

471

are polygamous and fight for the possession of the harem. The females alone incubate the eggs and care for the brood. The nest is a mere hollow on the ground at the base of a bush or tree and contains from ten to fourteen eggs, pale creamy - buff evenly speckled with greyish-brown. The downy chicks can run very soon after they are hatched.

Common Turkey (*Meleagris gallopavo*). This bird in the wild state is found from southern Canada through the eastern and southern United States to Mexico.

[*F. W. Bond.*

WILD TURKEY (*Meleagris gallopavo*).
The North American ancestor of the domestic bird, which since its introduction from Mexico in the sixteenth century has become specially associated with Christmas feasts.

It was plentiful in the early period of European settlement in America, but is now only found in the more inaccessible regions. In Mexico it had been domesticated before the Spanish conquest and was introduced into Europe almost immediately, being known in England by 1541. It has varied little in domestication and its appearance and habits are too well-known to need description.

OCELLATED TURKEY (*Meleagris ocellata*).
This second member of the Turkey family, native of Central America, has never been domesticated.

[*Keystone.*

472

Suborder OPISTHOCOMI

Family **Opisthocomidae** contains only the Hoatzin (*Opisthocomus hoazin*) of northern South America. This curious bird is somewhat smaller than a Pheasant, with a long, thin body, fairly long neck, short, rounded wings with ten primaries, and a long tail of ten stiff feathers. Its strong bill, whose upper mandible has serrated edges, is surrounded by bristles; its eyelids are furnished with lashes; its legs are short and stout and its feet large. In both sexes the plumage is olive-coloured with white markings above and dull rufous below; a long, loose crest on the head and the tip of the tail are yellowish; round the eyes the naked skin is bluish-black. From its strong musky odour it is known in Guiana as the "Stink-bird."

The Hoatzin lives in

[F. W. Bond.

HOATZIN (*Opisthocomus hoazin*).
The fame of this bird is mainly due to the fact that its chicks have functional claws on two digits of the wings—a very reptilian character.

trees on the borders of rivers or lagoons, feeding on leaves and fruits, and having an enormous "crop," larger than in any other bird. Its note is a hissing screech. It flies heavily for short distances and hops and scrambles about among the branches. Its nest is a loose platform of sticks, and the eggs, from three to five in number, are yellowish-white with reddish and lilac spots. The young are covered with scanty reddish-brown down and can see, run, climb, dive and swim as soon as they are hatched. The digits of the wing corresponding to the thumb and first finger bear hooked claws, which the nestling uses in addition to its bill and feet in climbing about the branches until it can fly.

473

Order GRUIFORMES (Bustards, Rails, Cranes, etc.)

The members of this Order are usually moderate-sized or large birds with fairly long necks and legs and with feet in which the hind toe, when present, is at a higher level than the three front ones. A considerable proportion of the species frequent swamps and reed-beds and most of the remainder are strictly terrestrial. Representatives of the Order are found in all parts of the world, but the total number of species included in it is comparatively small. They are undoubtedly the remnants of an ancient group of birds and the survivors differ much in structure.

Family **Mesoenatidae** (*Roatelos*) contains only three species, and these are peculiar to Madagascar. They have rather long, slender, somewhat curved bills; rounded wings with ten primaries; moderately short tails of twelve broad feathers; rather weak legs; and large feet with three toes in front and one behind, all at the same level, with small nearly straight claws.

Family **Pedionomidae** contains only the Plain-wanderer (*Pedionomus torquatus*), which inhabits inland districts in south-eastern Australia. It is a small, quail-like bird, seven inches long, with short bill, short, rounded wings, short tail, rather long legs, and feet with four toes, of which the hind one is short. The plumage is reddish-brown above, buff below, more or less barred with black. The female, which is rather larger and more brightly coloured than the male, has a broad white collar, spotted with black, round the neck; in the male the collar is brown and buff. Plain-wanderers run rapidly over the open grassy country which they frequent, but their flight is feeble and they do not take wing at all readily. Their nest is a mere hollow in the ground, and the four or five pear-shaped eggs are yellowish or greenish-white, spotted and blotched with olive and grey.

Family **Turnicidae** (*Button-quails* or *Hemipodes*) includes about fourteen species of small terrestrial birds found in southern Europe, Africa, Arabia, southern Asia, the Malay Archipelago, Australia and New Caledonia. They have short bills; broad, rather short wings with ten primaries; short tails of twelve feathers; long, slender legs; and feet with only three toes, which have small, curved, sharp claws. Their plumage exhibits black, brown, chestnut, buff and white tints. In some species the sexes are similar, but in the majority the female is larger and more brightly coloured than the male, whose plumage resembles that of the young. It is stated that the male incubates the eggs and cares for the chicks.

Button-quails, also known as Bustard-quails or Hemipodes, frequent grassy plains or bushy thickets, running strongly but flying with reluctance and only for short distances. Their food consists of seeds and insects. Their nests are hollows in the ground lined with dry grass and sometimes also partly domed with grass. The three to five pear-shaped eggs are buff or grey with spots of grey, purplish or brown. The young run as soon as they are hatched.

CRANES (GRUIDAE)

Family **Gruidae** (*Cranes*) includes about sixteen species of very large birds found in North America, Europe, Africa, and Asia, with one species in Australia. They have straight, somewhat-compressed bills ; long necks ; large, rounded wings with eleven primaries ; short tails of twelve feathers; very long legs ; and feet with four toes, of which the three front ones are stout and more or less connected by webs at the base, whilst the small hind one is raised and has a sharp claw. In most of the species the plumage is largely grey, but some are almost entirely white and several have patches of black, white or other colours. Several species have long ornamental plumes on the neck or back ; the Crowned Cranes (*Balearica*) have remarkable tufts of wiry feathers on the top of the head ; the majority have part of the head bare of feathers, the skin being c o v e r e d with papillae usually red in colour ; whilst a few have fleshy wattles on the throat.

Cranes inhabit open plains and morasses, feeding on seeds, plant-shoots, bulbs, etc., with the addition of worms, reptiles, frogs, small mammals and l a r g e insects. Except

[*D. Seth-Smith.*
DEMOISELLE CRANE (*Anthropoides virgo*).
This graceful bird breeds in eastern Europe and northern Asia and winters in north-east Africa and southern Asia.

when breeding, they are commonly found in flocks, and they frequently indulge in remarkable dances with their wings outspread, bowing to one another, leaping in the air and performing various other antics. They are among the largest birds capable of flight and usually run for some distance flapping their wings before rising from the ground.

475

By courtesy of]   [*Carl Hagenbeck's Tierpark, Stellingen.*

KAFFIR CRANE (*Balearica [pavonina] regulorum*).
This is the South African representative of the Crowned Cranes, remarkable for the spreading tuft of twisted bristles on the head.

Those which breed in northern latitudes migrate to the tropics for the winter, flying in flocks at great altitudes and only occasionally alighting on the journey. Their loud, trumpeting notes are uttered during flight as well as on the ground. The nest is always on the ground, sometimes merely a hollow, in other cases a large pile of vegetation in a swamp with a small hollow at the top. The eggs are two, or rarely three, creamy, buffy or bluish-white, usually with reddish-brown and purplish spots and blotches. The nestlings are clothed in tawny down and can run soon after they are hatched.

Family Aramidae (*Limpkins, Courlans, Crazy Widows or Lamenting Birds*) contains only one species, found in South America, Central

America, Florida and the West Indies. They have long, slender, compressed bills, which are very hard and usually bent slightly sideways at the tip ; their wings are short and rounded, with eleven primaries ; their tails short ; and their legs and toes long. Their plumage is glossy olive-brown, striped with white on the head and neck, more bronzy on the wings and tail. They frequent swamps and the borders of wooded streams, during the day-time perching in trees, but at evening descending to the ground or the water-side in search of mussels, snails and slugs. These t h e y carry to favourite feeding grounds, where they hold them with their feet while they break the shells with blows from their powerful bills till they can drag out the mollusc. They fly heavily with the legs dangling. Their notes are loud wails and clucking calls, the latter having earned for the n o r t h e r n form in Jamaica the name of " Clucking Hen." The nest is a rather large s t r u c t u r e, generally placed in a tussock, and the four to ten eggs, large for the size of the bird, are buff, spotted and blotched w i t h brown and grey. The young are covered with dense brown down.

[*D. Seth-Smith.*

GREAT COURLAN (*Aramus vociferus*).
Courlans feed mainly on molluscs, whose shells they break with their powerful bills.

Family **Psophiidae** (*Trumpeters*) includes three species found in tropical South America. Their bills are short, stout and somewhat curved ; their heads small ; their necks rather long ; their wings short and rounded, with ten primaries ; their tails short ; and their legs very long. The plumage is mainly black, often with metallic sheen on the feathers of the neck, and in most species there are patches of lighter colour on the wings. Trumpeters frequent moist forests, where they are often found in flocks.

477

AVES (ORDER GRUIFORMES)

They run swiftly and can swim, but rarely fly. The ranges of the various species are separated by the great rivers, different species occurring on the opposite banks of the Amazon, Rio Negro, etc., so that it would appear that they cannot cross wide stretches of water. Their name is derived from their loud, deep-toned cry, which is uttered with widely-opened bill. They lay creamy- or greyish-white eggs.

Family Rallidae (*Rails and Coots*)

This family includes a large number of species found in all parts of the world. They are small or moderate-sized birds, the great majority of which frequent reed-beds or dense vegetation in damp localities, and their bodies are very much compressed, enabling them to traverse the narrow passages between the plant-stems. The bill is stout, but varies much in length; in many species a horny shield is present on the lower part of the forehead, extending upwards from the base of the bill. The wings are generally short and rounded, and in a considerable number of the insular species, they are too small to support the bird in the air. The legs are generally fairly long and in some of the terrestrial forms they are extremely stout. The toes are long and slender and have sharp, curved claws; in the Coots the front toes have broad lobes of skin along the edges.

[L.J. Langford.

MOORHEN (*Gallinula chloropus*).
Also called Waterhen, this species is found on almost every pond in England.

[T. M. Fowler.

CORN CRAKE (*Crex crex*).
The Land Rail, as this bird is often called, frequents meadows and cornfields, constantly uttering its " craking " note.

Rails are generally skulking birds, which run swiftly to cover when disturbed, have considerable difficulty in rising from the ground or the water, and fly heavily with continuous wing-beats. Nevertheless, many species are migratory and annually traverse great distances of land and sea. Most of the species swim readily and the Coots are almost completely aquatic, obtaining much of their food by diving. Their food consists of worms, molluscs, insects, green herbage, roots and aquatic plants and seeds. They make curious harsh calls and notes, chiefly heard from the reed-beds at dusk. Their nests are usually built close to water and constructed of aquatic plants, reeds, sedges, etc. The eggs vary in number from two to ten or more and are commonly buff with reddish or black markings. The young when hatched, are covered with down, which is commonly black, and leave the nest almost at once, running and swimming readily.

Land Rail or Corn Crake (*Crex crex*). This bird has the plumage of the upper parts mainly yellowish-brown, each feather having a dark centre ; the underparts are buffish-white with broad buff and brown bars on the flanks. In summer it is widely distributed in Europe and western and central Asia, wintering in Africa and Arabia. It was formerly common in summer almost everywhere in the British Isles, but in recent years has rapidly

479

become scarce in southern and eastern England. Unlike most Rails, it is not a frequenter of swampy localities but is found in meadows and corn-fields. Its note is a constantly-repeated "crake," uttered almost continuously towards evening.

Spotted Crake (*Porzana porzana*). This is a smaller bird than the Corn Crake and is also a summer visitor to the greater part of Europe and western Asia, wintering in the countries round the Mediterranean and in northern India. It is a very shy bird, living in dense reed-beds and is consequently rarely seen. Its plumage is mainly olive-brown, with small white spots, but the flanks are barred with brown and white, the belly grey and the under tail-coverts buff.

Water Rail (*Rallus aquaticus*). This bird is found in swamps throughout Europe and Asia and is only partially migratory. In the British Isles it is probably commoner in winter than in summer, and is certainly most often seen when frosts force it to leave the shelter of the reeds in search of food. Its most conspicuous feature is its long red bill ; the plumage of the upper parts is olive-brown, streaked with black, and of the underparts grey with black and white bars on the flanks.

Waterhen or Moorhen (*Gallinula chloropus*). The Moorhen is found in suitable localities throughout Europe, North Africa, Asia, North, Central and South America. Its upper parts are chiefly dark olive-brown ; the

[Arthur Brook.

Coot (*Fulica atra*).
More aquatic than the other Rails, each toe being separately webbed.

[D. Seth-Smith.

SUN-BITTERN (*Eurypyga helias*).
This native of Brazil and Guiana is here seen displaying its wonderfully mottled plumage.

head, neck and underparts dark grey, with conspicuous white patches on each side below the tail. The adult has the tip of the bill yellow, the base and a broad plate on the forehead red; the legs are greenish-yellow with red bands at the joints. It frequents marshy pools, ponds and streams swimming well with a constant nodding motion of the head. It also dives freely, using its wings under water.

Common Coot (*Fulica atra*). This bird is found throughout Europe, North Africa, Asia and Australia. Its plumage is dark slaty-grey above and sooty-black below; the horny plate on the forehead being white. It frequents large ponds and lakes, and in winter often congregates in great flocks on the larger sheets of water.

Family **Heliornithidae** (*Finfoots*) contains only three species, one found in tropical America, one in Africa, and one in the Malay Peninsula and Sumatra. They are rather small birds with fairly stout, straight bills; small heads; thin necks; long, pointed wings with eleven primaries, and a curved spine on the angle; short legs, twisted outwards; and toes with short, sharp claws and broad, scalloped webs. They frequent swamps and rivers in jungle country, swimming and diving well and often perching on the boughs of trees overhanging the water. They feed on fish, crustacea, insects and seeds.

Family **Rhynochetidae** contains only the Kagu (*Rhynochetus jubatus*) found in New Caledonia. It is a bird about the size of a fowl with a large head and very large eyes. The bright red bill is fairly long, flattened and pointed. The wings are broad and rounded, with ten primaries, and the tail of twelve feathers fairly long and also rounded. The red legs and feet resemble those of the Sun-bitterns but are shorter and stouter. The plumage generally is slaty-grey, but when the bird spreads its wings, these are seen to be barred and spotted with white, rusty and black. On the back of the head and neck there is a crest of long, whitish-grey feathers. The Kagu inhabits forested mountain-sides or the neighbourhood of lakes, and is said to be largely nocturnal. It walks quickly in a stately fashion, often pausing and remaining motionless for some time ; it also frequently indulges in strange dances and extraordinary antics, often with the delicate crest-feathers spread round its head. It feeds on insects, worms, snails, etc. Its eggs are reddish-buff with brown and grey markings.

Family **Eurypygidae** (*Sun-bitterns*) contains only one species, found in Central America, Colombia, Guiana and Brazil. They have long, rather slender bills with blunt tips ; long necks ; broad, rounded wings with ten primaries ; long, rounded tails of twelve feathers ; fairly long slender legs ; and feet with four toes, of which the three front ones are long and have curved claws. The plumage is variegated, mottled, barred and striped with black, brown, chestnut, bay, buff, grey and white. Sun-bitterns frequent the wooded, swampy banks of large rivers, where they walk quietly about with the body horizontal and the head and neck outstretched. They feed on small fish, insects, etc. At times, they execute fantastic dances when the broad wings and tail are spread in semi-circles

[Will F. Taylor.
GREAT BUSTARD (*Otis tarda*).
Formerly an inhabitant of Salisbury Plain and East Anglia, but exterminated in England about 1838.

almost concealing the body and displaying their intricate, moth-like colour patterns. The nest of sticks and mud is placed on low branches and the eggs are reddish-buff with brown and grey markings. The nestlings are covered with mottled down, and remain for some time in the nest.

Family **Phororhachidae** includes a number of species of extinct birds found in the Miocene beds of Patagonia. *Phororhacos*, a genus of which several species have been described, had an enormously large and heavy head with a very deep bill ; the upper mandible ended in a strong hook and the lower curved upwards to meet it. The wing was well-developed, but too small to be capable of lifting the bird, and the tail was long. The legs were long and fairly stout and the hind toe was present. *Brontornis burmeisteri*, the largest known member of the family, probably stood about seven feet high. The head of this great bird was not so large as in other species and its legs were shorter but stouter.

Family **Cariamidae** (*Cariamas*) contains only two species found in Brazil, Paraguay and northern Argentina. They have short, broad, rather hooked bills ; rather long necks ; short, rounded wings with ten primaries ; long, rounded tails of twelve feathers ; long legs and four toes with sharp, curved claws. Their plumage is brownish-grey above marked with zig-zag

[*D. Seth-Smith.*
GREAT BUSTARD (*Otis tarda*).
A cock bird displaying, a performance accompanied by a booming note.

bars and whitish below with brown stripes. Tufts of feathers spring from the sides of the face in front of the eyes forming a sort of crest. They stalk about on plains or in open forest country, and towards dusk make loud screaming calls. They build nests of sticks in low trees or bushes or on the ground and lay two pale eggs, blotched with reddish-brown. The downy young leave the nest soon after hatching.

Family **Otididae** (*Bustards*) contains about thirty species of large or moderate-sized terrestrial birds peculiar to the eastern hemisphere. They have rather short, blunt, curved bills ; flattened heads ; thick necks ; broad, rounded wings ; fairly long, rounded tails ; stout legs ; and feet without a hind toe. The three front toes are short and stout with flat soles and flattish nails. Bustards inhabit plains, steppes and deserts, where they stalk about or run rapidly. Their plumage is usually mottled with tints of brown, black and buff, the males, which are larger than the females, generally having tufts of ornamental plumes on the head and neck. In several species the adult males can inflate a pouch on the fore neck with air, whilst at the same time they spread out their neck plumes, depress their wings and raise their fan-shaped tails, strutting about like Turkey-cocks and making booming noises. Bustards are omnivorous feeders. They deposit from two to five eggs in a hollow in the ground. The ground colour of the eggs is of various shades of brown or greenish and they are marked with purplish or dull red. The nestlings are covered with mottled down.

483

Order DIATRYMIFORMES

A group of extinct birds, of which several species are known from the Eocene rocks of North America. One of them, *Diatryma steini*, from the lower Eocene of Wyoming, is one of the few fossil birds found that is represented by a nearly complete skeleton. It was a gigantic terrestrial bird standing about seven feet high and, though not as tall as an Ostrich, was heavier in body. It had a massive head and neck, with a great arched, compressed bill ; its wings were very small, so that it was certainly incapable of flight ; its legs were very strong ; and its feet had three strong toes in front and a small hind toe at a higher level.

Order CHARADRIIFORMES (Plovers, Gulls, Auks, etc.)

A very large group of birds, represented in all parts of the world, whose members exhibit great differences in external appearance and habits, but are similar in anatomical characters.

There are three Suborders : *Charadrii* (Plovers, etc.), *Lari* (Gulls, etc.) and *Alcae* (Auks, etc.).

Suborder CHARADRII

Family **Jacanidae** (*Jacanas*) includes about seven species of rather small aquatic birds found in tropical and sub-tropical regions of both hemispheres. They have moderately long, straight bills with a fleshy lobe or " leaf " rising from the base ; their wings have a horny spur developed on the angle ; their legs are rather long and their toes are excessively long with extremely long claws. They frequent lakes, lagoons and sluggish rivers, running over the leaves of water-lilies and other aquatic plants with ease, since their weight is distributed by their long toes. Their nests are slight structures of water-weeds built on floating vegetation and their eggs, usually four in number, are deep brown, with black scrawl-like markings all over them, and extremely glossy.

Family **Haematopodidae** (*Oystercatchers*) includes about ten species of large wading birds distributed over the sea-coasts of the world. They have very long, hard, compressed bills, which are much deeper than they are broad at the end, with the tip rounded or truncate in profile (not pointed). Their legs are fairly long and very stout, the hind toe is absent, and the three short, stout front toes are partially connected by webs at the base. The plumage is either black and white, or entirely black, or sooty brown, and the bill and legs usually red, sometimes orange or yellow. Oystercatchers feed on mussels, limpets and other molluscs, which they detach from the rocks and split open with their powerful chisel-shaped bills, or on cockles, clams, etc., on sandy beaches, as well as on shrimps and sand-worms. Their nests are mere hollows on sand-hills or rocks, and they lay from two to four, usually three, eggs, yellowish with black and grey spots and blotches. The young are covered with mottled down, and can run soon after hatching.

484

[W. Bickerton.

PIED OYSTERCATCHER (*Haematopus ostralegus*).
Offen appropriately called the Sea-Pie, from its black and white plumage.

[B. W. Cooper.

LAPWING (*Vanellus vanellus*).
Also known as Green Plover or Peewit, from its note.

AVES (ORDER CHARADRIIFORMES)

Pied Oystercatcher (*Haematopus ostralegus*). This is found on sea-coasts in most parts of the world, but is absent from those of tropical Africa, much of tropical Asia, and the island groups of the tropical Pacific. In many parts of its range it is strictly confined to the sea-coast at all seasons, but in Scotland, many parts of Europe, and Siberia, it is found on the shores of freshwater lakes and rivers, and even in wet fields and grass-land at a distance from any considerable watercourse. The head, neck, upper breast, upper back, shoulders, wing-quills and tail are black, the rest of the plumage white, the bill orange-vermilion and the legs pinkish-red.

Family Charadriidae (*Plovers and Turnstones*)

This family includes seventy or more wading-birds, distributed throughout the world. They have comparatively short bills, hard at the tip but softer at the base; fairly long legs; three toes in front, occasionally united by webs at the base, and the hind toe small or sometimes absent. They frequent sea-coasts, damp meadows, moors or open plains, and feed largely on snails, slugs, crustacea and insects. They run swiftly and their flight is usually rapid. Their nests are often little more than hollows slightly lined with grass, and they usually lay four pear-shaped greenish or buff eggs with darker markings. The downy young can run almost as soon as it leaves the egg.

Lapwing, Green Plover or Peewit (*Vanellus vanellus*). This is a very plentiful species in the British Isles and is found in summer right across Europe and northern Asia, many moving south to the Mediterranean countries, Persia and northern India for the winter. Its back and wings are bronzy green; the face, breast, wing-quills and tip of the tail, black; the sides of the head, underparts and most of the tail white, with the tail-coverts rufous. It has a long, slender greenish-black crest of curved feathers. The wings are extremely rounded at the tips and the flight is curiously flopping, the birds often tumbling in the air. The name Peewit is derived from the constantly-uttered cry.

Dotterel (*Eudromias morinellus*). This bird breeds on the tundras of northern Europe and Asia and in elevated regions further south, including the highest ranges of Scotland and northern England, wintering in the Mediterranean countries, Arabia and Persia. The plumage exhibits various shades of grey, brown and reddish, the most striking feature being a broad white band extending over each eye and round the nape.

Kentish Plover (*Charadrius alexandrinus*). This is one of the smallest members of the family, with sandy-brown upper plumage, rufous crown, white forehead, neck and underparts, and a black patch on each side of the breast. It is found on sea-coasts, sand-plains and the shores of salt-lakes in almost all the warmer parts of the world, but in the British Isles is only a summer visitor to the coasts of Kent.

486

Ringed Plover (*Charadrius hiaticula*). This Plover is a more northern bird than the preceding, breeding on sea-shores in the Arctic and northern portions of both hemispheres. It is common on the coasts of the British Isles. It is brown above, with white forehead, neck and underparts, some black on the head and a broad black band across the breast. Its legs are orange-yellow.

Golden Plover (*Pluvialis apricaria*). This bird breeds on the tundras and northern moorlands of Europe and western Siberia, including the British Isles. In summer the upper parts in both sexes are blackish-brown, profusely spotted with yellow, whilst the throat, breast and underparts

[*Arthur Brook.*

GOLDEN PLOVER (*Pluvialis apricaria*).
Breeds on the moorlands of Scotland, Ireland, Wales and northern and western England.

are black. In winter the underparts are white and the upper parts yellower. At that season it is found on sea-coasts of the Mediterranean countries and western Europe, including the British Isles, as well as in fields and pastures inland, usually in considerable flocks.

Grey or Black-bellied Plover (*Squatarola squatarola*). Like the Golden Plover, this has the underparts black in summer and white in winter, but the axillary feathers of the wing are always black. The upper parts are mottled and barred with brownish-black and white. It is a larger bird than the Golden Plover, and in the breeding season is confined to the tundras and barren grounds of Siberia and North America, but in winter is found on sea-coasts almost throughout the world.

Turnstone (*Arenaria interpres*). This is another species which may be found on almost all the coasts of the world in winter, and breeds round the North Pole. Its breeding range includes Iceland and Scandinavia, North Russia, Siberia and arctic North America. In summer the head, neck, breast and shoulders are mottled with black and white, the mantle is chestnut and black, and the rump and underparts white, in winter the colours of the plumage are duller. The legs are orange-red. The Turnstone delights in rocky coasts, though it is also found on muddy and sandy beaches at times. With its bill it turns over patches of seaweed, stranded objects and small stones in order to feast on the sand-hoppers, worms, etc. thus revealed.

Family Scolopacidae (*Snipe, Woodcock and Sandpipers*)

This family includes eighty or more species of wading-birds, varying greatly in size. The bill is usually long and rather slender. In the Snipe and Woodcocks it is straight and smooth with a soft, sensitive tip ; in the Sandpipers either straight or curved, and with the groove in which the nostrils are situated continued almost to the tip. The eyes are usually large and often situated relatively high on the sides of the head ; this being most marked in Woodcocks in which the ear is actually in front of the eye. The legs are usually long, the three front toes are sometimes united by webs at the base and the hind toe is either small or absent.

The members of this family frequent sea-coasts, the banks of rivers and lakes or swampy localities. They feed largely on worms, crustacea and molluscs obtained by probing wet ground with their bills. They run swiftly and commonly associate in flocks. Though many of the species are very widely distributed over the world during the greater part of the year, a large proportion breed in the Arctic regions or in high northern latitudes. Their nests are usually placed in tussocks in swampy localities and their eggs are generally four in number, pear-shaped, buffish or greenish with dark markings. The young are covered with down, and can run very soon after hatching.

Common Snipe (*Capella gallinago*). This breeds in suitable localities

[Stanley Crook.

COMMON SNIPE (*Capella gallinago*).
With its extremely long, sensitive bill the Snipe probes swampy ground for its food.

[Arthur Brook.

WOODCOCK (*Scolopax rusticola*).
Its wonderfully mottled plumage makes the Woodcock almost invisible in its woodland haunts.

throughout the temperate and sub-Arctic regions of the northern hemisphere, many migrating south to the tropics in winter. Its plumage above is mottled and barred with black, brown, rufous and buff, the breast buff streaked with brown and the underparts white. During the breeding season both sexes produce a remarkable " drumming " or " bleating " sound while on the wing. This is due to the rapid vibration of the outer tail-feathers, which are spread out from the rest and held rigid during the bird's headlong descent from a considerable height.

Jack Snipe (*Lymnocryptes minima*). This is similar in coloration to the Common Snipe, but considerably smaller. It breeds in Scandinavia, north Russia and Siberia, and in winter is found in the British Isles, southern Europe, northern Africa, Mesopotamia, Persia and India. It frequents swampy localities like its congener, but is less sociable, and when flushed usually rises silently and only flies a short distance before pitching again.

CURLEW (*Numenius arquatus*). [*B. W. Cooper.*
The wild calls of this wary bird are characteristic of the wilder parts of the British Isles.

Woodcock (*Scolopax rusticola*). This breeds throughout most of Europe and northern Asia, large numbers migrating southwards for the winter. The plumage of the upper parts is rufous-brown, barred and freckled with grey and black, the underparts being lighter. During the daytime the birds rest among grass or under bushes in wooded country, and at dusk fly to swampy localities to feed. In the breeding season the birds indulge in curious nuptial flights at dusk, flying with slow, steady wing-beats over an oval or triangular course, and following precisely the same course night after night. During this flight, sometimes called " roding," the bird makes most curious chuckling and squeaking sounds. The Woodcock is also unique among birds in having the ear-opening in front of the eye. This is, perhaps, an adaptation to enable it better to hear the movements underground of worms, on which it feeds by thrusting its very long bill into soft ground.

Curlew (*Numenius arquatus*). In Scotland this is called the Whaup. It is the largest European member of this family, and has a long curved bill. Its upper plumage is pale brown marked with darker streaks, its rump white and its undersurface whitish with dark streaks on the neck and breast. It breeds on moors and in upland pastures in most parts of the British Isles where such habitats occur, and throughout the greater part of northern Europe and western Siberia. In winter, it chiefly frequents sea-coasts, especially muddy estuaries, congregating in large flocks, and at this season its range extends to the Mediterranean and the coasts of Africa. It is a very wary bird, and when alarmed utters the loud call-note " cour-lie," which has given it its name in many languages.

Whimbrel (*Numenius phaeopus*). This resembles the Curlew in colouring except that the crown of its head is dark brown with a pale median stripe. It is also much smaller. It has a more northerly breeding range than its larger relative, nesting in Iceland, Scandinavia and northern Russia, also in the Faeroe Isles, and, in small numbers, in the

[*D. Seth-Smith.*
WHIMBREL (*Numenius phaeopus*).
As a breeding species in the British Isles almost confined to the Shetlands.

Shetlands and Orkneys and north-western Highlands. In the British Isles it is chiefly known as a spring and autumn passage-migrant on the coasts.

Bar-tailed Godwit (*Limosa lapponica*). This breeds in northern Scandinavia, Russia, Siberia and Alaska and winters south to Africa, India and Australia. Large numbers appear on the coasts of the British Isles on migration and many spend the winter feeding on mud-flats in estuaries and bays. In winter plumage the upper parts are greyish-brown, the tail-coverts white with dark bars and the underparts mainly white. The very long, almost straight, bill is pinkish-brown at the base and darker at the tip. In breeding plumage the head, neck and breast are chestnut-red.

Black-tailed Godwit (*Limosa limosa*). In winter this bird is ashy-brown above and greyish below, with a white bar in the wing, a conspicuous

491

white rump, and the tail-feathers with broad black tips. In summer, the head, neck and breast are reddish-fawn in colour. This species breeds from Belgium and Holland across Europe and Asia to Mongolia and winters in the tropics. It formerly nested in some of the eastern counties of England, but now only occurs in the British Isles on migration.

Knot (*Calidris canutus*). This bird has a much shorter bill and legs than the members of the family described above. In winter its plumage is ashy-grey above with white tail-coverts and underparts, but in breeding plumage the head, neck and breast are chestnut and the mantle blackish marked with chestnut and white. In winter it is found on sea-coasts throughout the world, ranging south to Australia, Africa and Patagonia, though many remain on the coasts of the British Isles. Its breeding-grounds are entirely within the Arctic circle in both hemispheres.

[*Capt. H. M. Salmon.*

DUNLIN (*Erolia alpina*).
The commonest wader on British coasts in winter, some remaining to breed on moorlands.

Purple Sandpiper (*Erolia maritima*). This breeds from the Arctic coasts of America, Europe and Siberia south to Iceland, the Faeroe Isles and Scandinavia, moving southward in winter, when it is widely distributed on rocky portions of the coasts of the British Isles. The upper parts are blackish or brownish-grey, somewhat purplish in winter, the throat and breast greyish-brown and the underparts whitish with brown streaks on the flanks. The relatively short legs are ochre-yellow.

Dunlin (*Erolia alpina*). This is in winter the most abundant of the small wading birds often called indiscriminately Stints, Sandpipers or Sandlarks, which occur in flocks, often of large size, on the sandy or muddy parts of the coastline, and feed on the marine worms, crustacea and molluscs exposed at low tide. At that season it is grey above and white below, but in the breeding plumage, which it acquires in spring, its upper parts are variegated with chestnut and black, and it has a large black patch on the

492

GREENSHANK (*Tringa nebularia*).
This fine wader breeds in small numbers on the moors of northern Scotland.

Photos]   [*Arthur Brook*.
COMMON SANDPIPER (*Actitis hypoleucos*).
Also known as " Summer Snipe," this lively bird frequents streams and lake-sides in the northern and
western parts of the British Isles in summer.

493

[D. Seth-Smith.

REEVE (*Philomachus pugnax*).
Much smaller than her mate, and lacking the ruff which gives him his name, the plumage of the Reeve is beautifully shaded.

lower part of the breast. It breeds on the moorlands and tundras of northern Europe, Asia and America and is a c o m m o n nesting species in Scotland, occurring also in small numbers in the breeding season in northern and western England, Wales and Ireland.

Common Sandpiper (*Actitis hypoleucos*). This frequents the banks of rivers and lakes with gravelly or rocky shores. It breeds wherever such habitats occur in temperate Europe and Asia from the Arctic circle south to the Pyrenees, Carpathians and Himalayas, and is plentiful in summer in most of the hilly regions of the British Isles. Its plumage is bronzy-brown above, greyish on the breast and pure white below. In winter it is found throughout Africa, tropical Asia and Australia.

Green Sandpiper (*Tringa ocrophus*). This has the upper parts greenish-brown, the neck and breast dull white thickly streaked with brown, and the belly and tail-coverts white. In flight it appears nearly black with conspicuously white tail and underparts. It winters in the British Isles, southern Europe, tropical Africa and southern Asia and breeds in northern Europe and Siberia. It frequents streams, ponds and swamps and usually lays its eggs in the deserted nest of some other bird in a tree, sometimes as much as thirty-five feet from the ground.

Redshank (*Tringa totanus*). This is a larger bird than the Common Sandpiper, and breeds in wet meadows, marshes and boggy moors. Its upper plumage is brown in summer, greyish in winter, the tail and underparts are white, more or less barred and streaked with brown, whilst the rump and secondary quills are white. These white areas are concealed when the bird is on the ground, but are very conspicuous in flight, forming a broad band of white round the back of the wings and across the tail. Its long, slender legs are bright orange-red. During summer it is found in suitable localities throughout the greater part of temperate Europe and Asia, and in the British Isles has increased greatly as a breeding species in recent years.

Greenshank (*Tringa nebularia*). This is somewhat larger than the Redshank, greyer in plumage, with a larger area of white on the lower back and none in the wings. Its legs are olive-green and its long bill is slightly up-turned. It is a summer visitor to the northern parts of Europe and Siberia, a limited number breeding in the western Highlands of Scotland. In winter it frequents sea-coasts, chiefly in the tropics, though some are found at this season in Ireland.

Ruff (*Philomachus pugnax*). This bird whose female is known as the *Reeve*, is in many respects the most remarkable member of this family. The Reeve, rather smaller than a Redshank, has most of the plumage brown, each feather having a pale margin, so that the general effect resembles that familiar in the hen Pheasant. The bill is shorter than in most Sandpipers and the fairly long legs are yellowish. For the greater part of the year the plumage of the Ruff is similar, but he is about a third larger in size. In spring, however, he undergoes a remarkable change. The feathers of his face fall off and fleshy caruncles develop there, tufts of curled feathers sprout on the sides of the head, and a great ruff of strong feathers develops on the front and sides of the neck. These changes take place in a surprisingly short time, and a very remarkable feature is the enormous variety of colouring displayed by these adornments. The feathers of the ruff and of the ear-tufts vary independently and either may be black or chestnut or brown or cream-coloured or white more or less barred with darker colours, so that it is very difficult to find two Ruffs alike in the breeding season

On arrival at the breeding - grounds each Ruff occupies a small area on which he spends most of his time, a number of birds adopting terri-tories in close prox-imity. When a Reeve appears in the neigh-bourhood, each Ruff displays his ornamen-tal plumes to the best advantage, posturing, racing and flying about, or indulging in sparring matches with a neighbour. The Reeve uncon-cernedly selects a mate, and it is only rarely that another

[*Arthur Brook.*

STONE CURLEW (*Burhinus oedicnemus*).
Known also as " Thick-knee " and " Norfolk Plover." This species breeds in open country in southern and eastern England.

[*H. N. Southern.*
AVOCET (*Recurvirostra avosetta*).
Until about one hundred years ago this handsome bird nested
in England in marshy districts from the Humber to the Channel.

Ruff attempts to interfere by an actual attack on the selected candidate.

The species breeds throughout a great part of northern and central Europe and Siberia, and formerly did so in the marshy districts of England. It now only occurs in the British Isles on migration in autumn and spring, on its way to and from its winter quarters in Africa.

F a m i l·y Recurvirostridae (*Avocets and Stilts*) contains about seven species of wading birds with very long, slender bills, either straight or (in the case of the Avocets) curved upwards at the tip ; their necks are long and their legs very long and slim ; the three front toes are more or less united by webs at the base and the hind toe is rudimentary or absent. Their plumage is black and white, in one species entirely black, sometimes with patches of chestnut. Members of the family occur in almost all parts of the world, frequenting lagoons, lakes and swamps. Here they wade about seeking for their food, which consists of aquatic insects, crustacea and molluscs picked up from the surface or from near the bottom. To obtain the latter, the head and neck are submerged. When they wish to cross a channel where the water is too deep for wading, they swim readily. They generally breed in colonies near the water's edge, constructing slight nests of grass or weeds, and laying from three to five, usually four, pear-shaped eggs, buff with black or grey spots and markings. The young are covered with yellowish down with dark markings and run or swim within a few hours of hatching.

Family Presbyornithidae contains a fossil bird, *Presbyornis*, from the middle Eocene. It seems to have resembled an Avocet, but was probably more aquatic and swam more readily.

Family Phalaropodidae (*Phalaropes*) contains three species of small maritime birds, which, except during the breeding season, are found in flocks on the sea, frequently far from land. They have straight, slender bills, rather long necks, very much compressed legs and long toes with lobed, fringing webs. They breed in the Arctic regions and northern

496

latitudes of both hemispheres, often at a distance from the coast, but usually in the neighbourhood of lakes or swamps. In these localities they obtain their food by spinning rapidly round in shallow water, stirring up the mud or weeds and picking out aquatic insects, crustacea and molluscs brought to the surface. The female Phalarope is larger and more brightly coloured than her mate, and she does the wooing and takes the lead in selecting the nesting site. When she has laid the eggs, her part is finished and the male incubates them and raises the brood. The nest is a slight hollow in the ground, lined with a little grass or moss, and the three or four pear-shaped eggs are grey or buff blotched with chocolate or brown. The chicks can run as soon as they are hatched, and are covered with buff-coloured down striped and mottled with black.

Northern or Red-necked Phalarope (*Lobipes lobatus*). This bird breeds in the Arctic and northern regions of both hemispheres, including certain localities in the Shetlands, Orkneys, Hebrides and western Ireland. In summer the female has the head, hind-neck, breast and shoulders grey, the back and wings darker grey, mottled with rufous and with a white bar on the wing, the sides and front of the neck being chestnut and the chin and underparts white. The smaller male has much duller and less well-defined colours on the head and neck. In winter both sexes are much paler, the head, neck and under-parts being mainly white, except for a dark streak through the eye.

Family **Dromadidae** contains only the Crab-plover (*Dromas ardeola*), found on the African and Asiatic coasts of the Indian Ocean from Natal to the Andaman and Nicobar Islands. It is a white bird about sixteen inches long, with black back and wings and a grey tail. The bill is straight, hard and compressed and the legs long. It haunts sand-banks and feeds on small crustaceans, and differs most remarkably from all other waders in laying a single large white egg in a deep burrow in the sand. The nestling is covered with grey down and remains in the burrow for a considerable time after it is hatched.

Family **Burhinidae** (*Stone-curlews* or *Thick-knees*) contains

[*D. Seth-Smith.*
BLACK-WINGED STILT (*Himantopus himantopus*).
The excessively long legs from which this wader takes its name are rosy pink in colour.

about nine species of large terrestrial birds. They have stout bills, big heads, very large eyes, long necks and wings, very long legs and feet with only three toes. Their plumage is mainly brown and buff with markings of black and patches of white. They are found in tropical America and Haiti, and almost throughout the eastern hemisphere, being most numerous in Africa. They chiefly frequent open downs, steppes and plains and are crepuscular in habits. Their food consists mainly of snails, slugs, worms and insects, and they utter wailing cries during the night. They lay on the bare ground two stone-coloured eggs, blotched or scrawled with black, small in proportion to their size.

European Stone-Curlew or Norfolk Plover (*Burhinus oedicnemus*). This bird breeds in India, western Asia, northern Africa, the Canary Isles and southern and central Europe, west to eastern England, where it frequents chalk downs and open heaths from East Yorkshire to Wiltshire and Dorset, being most plentiful in East Anglia. In winter the birds from the northern part of the breeding range move southward and at that season some are found in Devon and Cornwall.

[W. S. Berridge.

Two-banded Courser (*Rhinoptilus africanus*).
Widely spread in the drier parts of eastern and southern Africa.

Family **Glareolidae** (*Pratincoles* and *Coursers*) includes a number of terrestrial birds found in Africa, south-eastern Europe, western and central Asia, India, the Malay Archipelago and Australia. They have comparatively short bills, rather long wings, square or forked tails and long, slender legs. Their plumage is commonly sandy or rufous, harmonizing in tint with the soils of the arid regions which they mostly frequent, but the majority have black and white markings, specially on their wings, which are conspicuous in flight. They run swiftly on the ground and feed mainly on insects, especially grasshoppers and locusts. The Pratincoles hawk for these on the wing and have a Swallow-like flight. They lay on the bare ground from two to four eggs, buff or grey with markings of various colours, and the downy young can run within a few hours of hatching.

Family **Thinocoridae** (*Seed-Snipe*) contains four or five species of small, terrestrial birds peculiar to South America. They are found from the Andes of Ecuador and Peru and the high plateaus of Bolivia to the plains of Patagonia and the coasts of the Straits of Magellan and the Falkland Islands. They are plump birds with short, strong, curved bills superficially resembling Partridges when squatting on the ground, but their legs and feet are slender and their wings long and pointed, and when flushed, they rise suddenly and fly with rapid, twisting flight like Snipe, uttering similar sharp alarm-notes. They feed entirely on vegetable matter—seeds, buds and leaves, and can run swiftly on the ground, whilst their mottled plumage harmonizes well with the bare, rocky country which they often frequent. Their nest is a slight depression in the ground, and they lay four pear-shaped eggs, buff thickly speckled with chocolate and purplish. The nestling is covered with light and dark brown down.

Family **Chionididae** (*Sheath-bills*) contains only two species of shore-birds found in the sub-antarctic islands of the Indian Ocean and South Atlantic and on the coasts of the Straits of Magellan. Their plumage is entirely white ; their bills short, curved, with a wide gape and a separate horny sheath covering the base of the upper mandible ; their wings are long and have a blunt black spur on the angle ; their tails, slightly forked ; their legs short and their toes not united by webs. They are frequently met with at a considerable distance from land, flying strongly or sailing with outspread wings, but are generally found on rocky coasts, feeding on mussels, crustaceans, sea-weed and the eggs of other birds. The species which occurs in the Falkland Islands is there known as the " Kelp Pigeon," and superficially Sheath-bills have a considerable resemblance to Pigeons. They build nests of dry plant-stems in hollows among rocks or the burrows of Petrels, and lay two or three eggs, buff, thickly blotched with purple or red. The young are covered with grey down.

Suborder LARI

Family **Stercorariidae** (*Skuas*) contains four species of dark-plumaged, long-winged sea-birds breeding in high latitudes in the northern and southern hemispheres, but occurring in temperate and tropical seas during winter. They have stout, hooked beaks, with the basal portion of the upper mandible covered by a separate horny plate. When on land during the breeding season, they feed on small mammals and large insects as well as on the eggs and young of other birds. They also feed on carrion and at sea on any floating animal matter or refuse that they can pick up from the surface. In addition, they attack Shearwaters, Gulls and Terns and force them to give up any food they may have secured. If the victim is pursued on the wing and drops a fish, the Skua swiftly plunges down and seizes it, in many cases before it reaches the water.

Skuas nest on the ground, laying from two to four eggs in a hollow slightly lined with grass or weeds. The eggs are generally olive-brown with large spots of dark brown or purplish. The young, when hatched, are covered with down, dark brown above, lighter below, and are dependent on their parents for food until they are fledged.

Great Skua (*Catharacta skua*). This is called Bonxie in the Shetlands, and in the northern hemisphere is known to breed only on Iceland, the Faeroes, Shetlands and Orkneys, but in the southern hemisphere it is represented by various races breeding in southern South America, islands in the southern oceans and the Antarctic continent. It is a heavily-built bird, whose plumage is mottled with various shades of brown, with conspicuous white patches in the wings. Outside the breeding season it is widely distributed in the North Atlantic as well as in the southern oceans.

[*T. M. Fowler.*
ARCTIC SKUA (*Stercorarius parasiticus*).
Remarkable for the variability of its plumage, some birds being white underneath, others dark above and below.

Arctic Skua or Parasitic Jaeger (*Stercorarius parasiticus*). This is a smaller and slimmer bird with the two central tail-feathers elongated and pointed. In colouring it is very variable ; the top of the head, back, wings and tail are always ashy-brown, but in dark individuals the underparts are almost the same colour, while the lightest birds have the sides of the head and neck straw-yellow and the chin and breast white. This species breeds in Alaska, Canada, Greenland, Iceland, northern Europe and Siberia, the breeding range including the Shetlands, Orkneys, Hebrides and a few localities in the north of Scotland. In winter it ranges over the oceans south to Argentina, South Africa, Australia and New Zealand.

Family Laridae (*Gulls and Terns*)

This family includes about ninety species of aquatic birds found on sea-coasts in all parts of the world, and frequently also on lakes, swamps and rivers at a distance from the sea. The majority have the plumage in the adult, grey above and white below ; in the young, mottled with brown. They have long wings, short necks, and short legs, with webs uniting the three front toes and the hind toe small or absent. The bill is usually nearly straight and rather slender, but is stout and somewhat hooked in a few of the larger species of Gulls. Terns feed on small fish, which they obtain by diving from the air, or on large insects. They very rarely settle on water. Gulls, on the other hand, constantly rest on the water and in feeding are largely scavengers, picking up carrion, stranded fish, crabs, molluscs and worms on beaches, as well as garbage and refuse from ships in harbours.

[*Gibson & Sons.*

GREAT BLACK-BACKED GULL (*Larus marinus*).
The largest member of its family, breeding on the western coasts of Britain from the Scillies to the Shetlands.

Gulls usually build fairly compact nests of seaweed, grass, weeds or sticks on ledges of cliffs, low islands, sandbanks or beaches, on tussocks in lakes or swamps and occasionally in bushes or trees. Some Terns build nests of seaweed in trees or bushes, but the majority deposit their eggs in a hollow in the sand or shingle. The eggs are from one to five in number, white, yellowish, brown or greenish in ground colour, generally spotted or blotched with black, brown, reddish, purplish or grey. The young, when hatched, are covered with mottled down, and though they may leave the nest at an early age, are dependent on their parents for food until they can fly. Gulls and Terns are sociable in habits, generally breeding in colonies and associating in flocks on the sea. Their calls

[*Arthur Brook.*

HERRING GULL (*Larus argentatus*).
The commonest of the larger gulls on British coasts.

501

[H. E. Pounds

KITTIWAKE (*Rissa tridactyla*).
The most maritime of the gulls, not often coming to land except to the cliffs where it breeds.

are usually harsh screams and most species are noisy, especially when breeding.

Herring Gull (*Larus argentatus*). This bird, about two feet in length, is the most widespread and commonest Gull of the northern hemisphere, breeding on the coasts of Europe, northern Asia and northern North America. It has a yellow bill, pink feet and black and white tips to the wings.

Lesser Black-backed Gull (*Larus fuscus*). This is the same size as the Herring Gull, from which it differs in having the mantle dark grey or black and the feet yellow. It breeds on sea-coasts, islands in lakes or moors in northern and western Europe, including the British Isles, and winters on the coasts of Spain and Portugal and in Africa.

Great Black-backed Gull (*Larus marinus*). This is the largest member of the family, about two feet six inches in length, and has a black mantle and pale pink feet. It breeds on both sides of the North Atlantic and is common on the coasts of the British Isles at all seasons.

Mew or Common Gull (*Larus canus*). This in plumage resembles the Herring Gull, but has more white on the wing-tips and is decidedly smaller, about eighteen inches in length. Its bill and feet are greenish yellow. It breeds chiefly on inland lakes, in the British Isles, Scandinavia, Russia, northern Asia, Alaska and western Canada, but frequents sea-coasts in winter.

Black-headed Gull (*Larus ridibundus*). This Gull, about one foot long, is a common and widespread species in the eastern hemisphere. It breeds on swamps and reedy lakes in Europe and northern Asia, and in winter is found on the coasts of Europe, northern Africa and most of Asia. Its bill and feet are red, and in summer the head is dark brown, appearing black at a distance.

Kittiwake (*Rissa tridactyla*). This is the most completely marine of the Gulls, ranging all over the temperate North Atlantic and North Pacific Oceans, and Arctic Seas. It breeds on the ledges of cliffs, often in very large colonies, on the coasts of the Bering Sea, the Gulf of St. Lawrence, Labrador, arctic Canada, Greenland, arctic Europe, the British Isles and northern France. It is a small species, about a foot long, with completely black tips to the wings, yellow bill, black feet and a slightly forked tail.

Common Tern (*Sterna hirundo*). This is found in summer on the coasts of eastern North America, Europe and northern Asia, migrating to tropical coasts for the winter. It is about fourteen inches long, but nearly half this length is that of the deeply-forked tail. Its bill and feet are red, the former with a dusky tip, and the top of the head is black in summer.

Arctic Tern (*Sterna paradisaea*). This closely resembles the Common Tern, but the bill is completely red, the legs are shorter and the streamers in the tail even longer. Its breeding range is more northerly than that of its ally, but overlaps it and in many places in the British Isles they breed together. The Arctic Tern performs the most extensive migration of any bird, as it breeds to within 8° of the North Pole and in the northern winter is found on the coasts of the Antarctic Continent.

Roseate Tern (*Sterna dougalli*). This bird breeds in many localities in the tropical Atlantic, Indian and western Pacific Oceans, and in the temperate

[*B. W. Cooper.*

BLACK-HEADED GULL (*Larus ridibundus*).
Unlike most other gulls this small species nests in swamps and on the margins of lakes, often far inland.

north Atlantic on the coasts of the eastern United States and the British Isles. It is smaller than the two preceding species, with very long tail-streamers, whitish plumage often suffused with rosy on the breast, and bill mainly black.

Little Tern (*Sterna albifrons*). This is the smallest member of the family, has the forehead white at all seasons, the bill yellow with a black tip, and the feet orange-yellow. It breeds in small colonies on sandy beaches on sea-coasts and rivers in almost all the warmer parts of the world and as far north as Massachusetts, the Baltic and the British Isles.

Sandwich Tern (*Thalasseus sandvicensis*). This is a large species with

the black feathers on the head elongated to form a loose crest, the bill black with a yellow tip and the feet black. It breeds on the coasts of the United States and Mexico, the West Indies, and southern and western Europe, including the British Isles, and winters south to Patagonia, the Cape of Good Hope and India.

[*Otho Webb.*
WHITE-CAPPED NODDY (*Anous minutus*).
The tropical terns, called Noddies, build nests of seaweed on the branches of trees.

Black Tern (*Chlidonias nigra*). Unlike the species mentioned hitherto, this frequents fresh-water lakes and marshes and feeds largely on insects. In breeding plumage the head and neck are black, the mantle and tail slate-grey, the breast and abdomen dark grey and the under tail-coverts white. In winter the breast and abdomen are white and the head white mottled with grey. Its tail is only slightly forked. It usually makes a floating nest among swamp vegetation and breeds in Canada, the United States and Europe south of the Baltic. It formerly nested in several parts of England, but now only occurs on migration. It winters in South America, tropical Africa and north-west India.

Family **Rynchopidae** (*Skimmers or Scissor-bills*) contains three species of long-winged sea-birds, resembling large Terns, with black or dark brown upper parts and white foreheads and underparts. Their legs are short, their feet small and webbed and their tails moderately forked. Their bills

[L. J. Langford.

PUFFIN (*Fratercula arctica*).
This quaint bird with its enormous brightly-coloured bill is known also as Sea Parrot, Coulterneb and Tammy-Norie.

[J. Kershaw.

COMMON TERN (*Sterna hirundo*).
These graceful birds breed in colonies on many parts of the coasts of the British Isles.

505

[*Gibson & Sons.*

RAZORBILLS (*Alca torda*) AND A PUFFIN (*Fratercula arctica*).
The Razorbill is the nearest living relative of the extinct Great Auk or Garefowl.

are quite unlike those of any other birds. The lower mandible is much
longer than the upper one, and both its edges are compressed to a knife-
like thinness ; the end of the upper mandible is grooved beneath to receive
the very sharp lower mandible when the bill is closed. When seeking food,
Skimmers fly rapidly just over the water with the bill open and the long
lower mandible cutting the surface. By this method they capture small
fish and other animals and aquatic weeds. Their fishing is mostly done
at dusk or dawn or on moonlight nights, and they commonly spend the
hours of daylight resting on sandbanks. They breed in colonies, laying
their eggs in mere hollows in the sand. The large eggs, from three to five
in number, are whitish or buffy with spots or blotches of brown, chocolate
or purple. The young are covered with sandy-coloured down, and have
fairly normal bills with which they can pick up objects from the ground,
but as soon as they can fly, the lower mandible rapidly elongates. Skimmers
are found on the coasts, large rivers and lakes of the warmer parts of
America, Africa and India.

Suborder ALCAE
Family Alcidae (*Auks, Guillemots, Razorbills and Puffins*)
This family includes twenty-two species of marine birds confined to
the oceans and seas of the northern hemisphere. They are small or moderate-
sized birds with short necks, small, narrow wings with eleven primaries
and very short tails of from twelve to eighteen feathers. Their legs are
short and are placed very far back near the tail, and they have only three
toes, which are connected by webs. Except during the breeding season,

they spend all their time at sea, usually in flocks, obtaining their food, which consists mainly of fish and crustacea, by diving from the surface and pursuing their prey under water by the use of their wings. Their flight is direct and rapid, their small wings being flapped very rapidly, but they do not fly very far. They congregate for breeding on islands and cliffs, their breeding colonies often containing many thousands of birds, frequently of several species intermingled. They either make no nest, or merely collect some grass and feathers, and deposit one, two or three eggs on ledges of cliffs or in caves, crevices among rocks or holes. Their oval or pear-shaped eggs are very large in proportion to the size of the bird and are either white or variously marked. The young, when hatched, are covered with dark-coloured down, and are dependent on their parents for food till they are fledged. At sea Auks are usually silent, but in their breeding colonies they utter curious growling, moaning and yelping notes. On land they commonly stand upright owing to the posterior position of their feet. Some species stand on the feet only, others rest on the feet and legs.

Great Auk (*Pinguinus impennis*). This was much the largest member of

[*J. E. Ruxton.*

GUILLEMOTS (*Uria aalge*).
One of the birds shown has a white ring round the eye and line behind it. Such birds were formerly thought to constitute a separate species called the Ringed Guillemot.

507

the family, about thirty-three inches long, but its wings were so small that it was quite incapable of flight. Its plumage was black above and white below, with a large white patch on the face. Its bill was long and deep but narrow. It formerly bred on islets near Newfoundland and Iceland and occurred occasionally on the coasts of the British Isles. The two last survivors were captured alive near Iceland in 1844. About eighty specimens exist in museums and nearly as many of its large pear-shaped eggs, which are white or buff with spots and scrawls of black or brown.

Razorbill (*Alca torda*). This obtains its name from its deep and very narrow bill, which is black, crossed by a white band. Its plumage is black above and white below, but in summer the throat and neck are also black and there is a white line from the bill to the eye. It breeds in crevices

[W. J. Clarke.

LITTLE AUK (*Alle alle*).
Also known as Dovekie and Rotge. This little bird breeds in immense numbers in the Arctic regions.

and on ledges of cliffs in the Bay of Fundy, the Gulf of St. Lawrence, southern Greenland, Iceland, Scandinavia, the British Isles and Brittany, and in winter is more often seen near the coasts than other members of the family.

Common Guillemot (*Uria aalge*). This bird has the upper parts sooty brown and the underparts white. Its bill is long, straight and pointed. It inhabits the North Pacific and North Atlantic Oceans, breeding on the coasts from Alaska, Greenland and Bear Island south to California, Nova Scotia, the British Isles and Portugal. Its single, pear-shaped egg, laid on ledges of cliffs, varies remarkably in colour, no two being quite alike. They may be white, buff, pale-blue or green, mottled, blotched, streaked and scrawled with black, brown, purple or red markings.

Black Guillemot (*Cepphus grylle*). This breeds on both sides of the North Atlantic and adjacent parts of the Arctic Sea, south in America to Maine and in Europe to Scotland, the Isle of Man and Ireland. It lays two eggs in crevices among rocks. In summer it is entirely black, except for a large white patch on the wings, in winter the body plumage is white, mottled with black on the upper parts. The bill, which is narrow and pointed like that of the Guillemot, is black externally but vermilion inside, and the feet are vermilion.

Common Puffin or Sea Parrot (*Fratercula arctica*). The Puffin, about twelve inches long, has the upper parts black and the underparts white, with greyish-white cheeks. Its feet are vermilion, and it has a very large triangular bill, greyish-blue at the base, vermilion at the tip, crossed with

[*Arthur Brook.*

BLACK GUILLEMOT (*Cepphus grylle*).
Unlike the larger Common Guillemot, this species nests in holes or crevices and lays two eggs.

lines of yellow. In autumn the horny sheath of the bill is shed in several pieces so that during the winter it is smaller and is not so brightly coloured. The bird inhabits the North Atlantic and adjacent parts of the Arctic Seas, breeding from arctic coasts south to Maine, the British Isles and Brittany. It lays a single white egg with faint brownish or lilac markings in a hole on an island or sea-cliff.

Order COLUMBIFORMES (*Sandgrouse and Pigeons*).

This Order contains a very large number of species and is represented in all parts of the world. The Pigeons and Sandgrouse, though agreeing in a number of internal characters, have few obvious characteristics in common. The birds of both groups, however, have eleven primaries in the wing and generally have the legs, and sometimes the toes, partly covered with feathers. They feed almost entirely on seeds, berries and fruits, and are much more dependent on the presence of water for drinking purposes than are most other birds. In arid regions they make long flights daily to rivers or pools and, unlike other birds, immerse their bills and take continuous draughts, instead of sips.

The three Families contained in the Order are included in two very distinct Suborders :

Suborder **Pterocletes** : Family *Pteroclidae* (Sandgrouse).

Suborder **Columbae** : Families *Columbidae* (Pigeons and Doves) and *Raphidae* (Dodos and Solitaire).

Family **Pteroclidae** (*Sandgrouse*) contains about sixteen species inhabiting desert, steppes or arid plains in Africa, southern Europe, western and central Asia and India. They have short, fairly stout, arched bills ; long, pointed wings ; wedge-shaped tails and very short legs. The hind toe is either rudimentary or entirely absent. Their plumage harmonizes with the bare ground on which they live, being various shades of buff or brown, with grey, black, orange and white markings. They associate in flocks and fly swiftly, also running on the ground. The nest is a hollow in the ground and they lay three eggs, whitish, buff or greenish in ground colour with brown, reddish and violet markings.

Pallas's Sandgrouse (*Syrrhaptes paradoxus*) is normally an inhabitant of a large area extending from south-east Russia to Mongolia, breeding in great numbers in western central Asia. From these regions it occasionally migrates into China or into Europe, sometimes in vast numbers. These irruptions have occurred at irregular intervals in the past and their cause is unknown. The birds reached as far west as the British Isles in 1859, 1863, 1872, 1876, 1888, 1890, 1891, 1899, 1904, 1906, 1908 and 1909. The largest invasions were in May, 1863 and 1888, when the birds arrived all along the east coast and spread to all parts of the country. In the years 1888 and 1889, a few actually bred in England and Scotland, though it is not known that they succeeded in rearing any young.

Family Columbidae (*Pigeons and Doves*)

This family contains more than five hundred species, which range in size from the Pigmy Doves of South America, only about six inches long, to the Gouras of New Guinea, nearly as large as hen Turkeys. Pigeons are found in all parts of the world, but their headquarters are the islands of the Malay Archipelago and the South Pacific, where more than half

510

[*Capt. H. M. Salmon.*

TURTLE DOVE (*Streptopelia turtur*).
Like most pigeons this species makes a very frail nest of sticks.

the species are found. Though the smaller members of the family are commonly called Doves, and the larger ones Pigeons, these names are more or less interchangeable, the largest British species being called both Wood Pigeon and Ring Dove, and the term " Pigeons " must be understood as including all the members of the family. Pigeons have very characteristic bills, the basal portion, in which the nostrils are situated, being covered with soft skin and the terminal portion being hard, arched and somewhat enlarged. Their heads are small and their tails usually rather long and rounded or wedge-shaped, consisting of from twelve to twenty feathers. Their feet have three toes in front and one behind.

Pigeons are monogamous and probably pair for life, but most species associate in flocks. The majority build frail platforms of sticks, but some lay their eggs on the bare ground or in holes in trees or caves. The eggs are invariably white and almost always two in number. The young, when hatched, are naked, except for scattered hair-like bits of down. They are fed on " pigeon's milk," which is the partly-digested food regurgitated from the crops of their parents. The voice of all Pigeons is a " coo," though the notes of different species vary greatly.

Rock Dove (*Columba livia*). This bird has the plumage generally greyish blue, lighter below, the lower back white or pale grey, two bars across the wing and the end of the tail black. The bill and feet are reddish and the feathers of the neck and upper breast shot with metallic purple and green. It inhabits cliffs on the coast or in mountainous districts in many parts of Europe, north and west Africa, western and central Asia

511

and India. It is the undoubted ancestor of the Domestic Pigeon, which has been bred in captivity from remote antiquity, and under domestication has varied enormously in colour, size and even in structure, at least a hundred and fifty different races having been evolved. Though these breed true, the characteristics of the wild bird soon reappear when the various races are crossed promiscuously, and all the races retain the antipathy of their wild ancestor to perching in trees. The most distinct races of the Domestic Pigeon are : " Pouters," which have long bodies and legs and a very large gullet, which they inflate with air ; " Carriers," which have a long, pointed bill and much carunculated bare skin round the eyes ; " Fantails," which may have as many as forty-two tail-feathers, whilst the wild bird has only twelve ; " Jacobins," which have the feathers of the neck turned forward to form a hood, and long wings and tail ; and " Tumblers," with very short bills and the curious habit of turning back somersaults during flight and even on the ground. " Homers " must also be mentioned, for though in colour and form they have not diverged greatly from the wild stock, constant training and selection has developed in them a wonderful capacity to find their way back to their lofts from great distances, and they are valuable, especially in warfare, for carrying messages, as well as providing a sport which has devotees in many countries.

Wood Pigeon or Ring Dove (*Columba palumbus*). This is a larger bird than the Rock Dove, with patches of white on the wings and the sides of the neck, and the breast vinous-red. It is found throughout Europe, and in western and central Asia and northern Africa. From northern Europe

[*Charles Reid.*

WOOD PIGEONS OR RING DOVES (*Columba palumbus*).
An abundant species in the British Isles, doing much damage to green crops.

MACAWS (*Ara*)

These are the largest and among the most gaudily coloured of all the parrot tribe. They are restricted to the forest regions of Central and South America. Their large and enormously strong beaks enable them easily to break the stones of fruit and hard-shelled nuts.

large numbers migrate southward for the winter, and though it is common at all seasons in the British Isles, its numbers are much greater during the winter. It feeds on grain, acorns, berries, etc., and on clover and turnip leaves, and the large flocks do much injury to crops.

Stock Dove (*Columba oenas*). This is a smaller bird than the Wood Pigeon, with which it frequently associates, and its

[*W. S. Berridge.*
CRESTED PIGEON (*Ocyphaps lophotes*).
One of the Australian pigeons known as Bronzewings from the patch of metallic feathers on the wing forming a speculum like that of a duck.

plumage is entirely grey-blue, except for the brownish-black wing-quills and a blackish bar near the end of the tail. It breeds in holes in old trees or cliffs or in the ground, and inhabits Europe, North Africa and western Asia. In the British Isles it has become much commoner in recent years, and though formerly confined to England, now breeds in many parts of Scotland and Ireland.

Turtle Dove (*Streptopelia turtur*). This is a summer visitor to Europe south of the Baltic, and breeds also in North Africa and western Asia, wintering in Africa. In the British Isles it is common in summer in the south and east of England and appears to be gradually extending its range to the north and west. It is the smallest European member of the family, and its plumage is predominantly cinnamon-brown with the head, nape and rump grey, and the belly and broad tips to the tail-feathers white.

Family Raphidae (*Dodos and Solitaires*)

This family contains three species of large flightless birds, formerly found in the Mascarene Islands.

Dodo (*Raphus cucullatus*). The Dodo of Mauritius was a clumsy bird as large as a Turkey, with a huge blackish bill terminating in a hook, and short yellow legs, the upper parts of which were feathered. The plumage was dark grey, with the breast and a tuft of curly feathers representing the tail whitish, the short, functionless wings being yellowish white. The Dodo was discovered by the Dutch in 1598, and several living specimens were brought to Europe, but by 1681 it had become extinct, probably due to the introduction of pigs and other animals into Mauritius. It is said to have laid a single large white egg on a mass of grass.

Solitaire or White Dodo (*Raphus solitarius*). The Solitaire of Réunion was apparently similar in form, but had white plumage varied with yellow. It is mentioned by several travellers who visited the island in the 17th century.

Solitaire (*Pezophaps solitarius*). The Solitaire of Rodriguez was a much more slender and graceful bird than the Dodo. It was larger than a Swan; with an elongated, slightly-hooked beak; a long, straight neck; and more slender, longer legs. The males were larger than the females and were brownish-grey in colour, whereas the latter were of various shades of brown. The males had a spherical mass of bone developed on their rudimentary wings, which they used when fighting, whirling themselves round and making a whirring noise with their pinions. The Solitaire laid a single large egg on a heap of palm-leaves a foot or more high. It became extinct in the 18th century.

[*A. M. Willford.*

CUCKOO (*Cuculus canorus*).
Two young birds, the lower one fledged, the upper about to be fed by its foster-parent, a Meadow Pipit (*Anthus pratensis*), perched on its back.

514

Order CUCULIFORMES (Cuckoos and Plantain-eaters)

This Order comprises a large number of small or moderate-sized birds found in all parts of the world. They vary greatly in external appearance, colouring and habits, but have many structural features in common, including a number which they share with the Parrots. The Order contains two Suborders, each containing a single Family.

Family **Musophagidae** (*Plantain-eaters* or *Touracos*) contains about twenty-five species, found in Africa south of the Sahara. They are arboreal, fruit-eating birds of moderate or rather large size, with very small heads, long necks, short round wings with ten primaries and long, broad tails of ten feathers. Their bills are usually stout and broad, with the upper mandible

[*James's Press.*

MACAW (*Ara sp.*).
The Macaws of tropical America, with their enormous beaks, are the giants of the parrot family.

arched and its edges serrated. Their legs are stout and their toes have strong claws. The outer toe can be turned either forwards or backwards. The plumage is generally metallic-blue or green or greyish-brown, with patches of crimson or yellow. A remarkable feature of the red colouring, which is a compound of copper called turacin, is that it is so soluble that it is washed out of the feathers by rain, or when the bird bathes, but is soon renewed. All the species have erectile crests, and the sexes are similar. They build flat nests of sticks in trees and lay three bluish- or greenish-white eggs.

Family Cuculidae (*Cuckoos*)

The Cuckoo family includes a large number of species found in all parts of the world, though only a few occur in the temperate parts of the northern hemisphere and in New Zealand. The bill varies much in size and shape, but is always compressed and somewhat curved at the tip and has no bristles

515

[W. S. Berridge.

WHITE-CRESTED TOURACO (*Turacus corythaix*).
This brilliantly plumaged bird is known in South Africa as the Knysna Lourie.

at the base. The wing contains ten primaries and the long, rounded or wedge-shaped tail has ten (or eight) feathers. The feet have two toes directed forward and two backward.

The American species of the family build nests of very rude construction, but almost all the Cuckoos found in the eastern hemisphere are parasitic, laying their eggs in the nests of other birds and leaving them to be hatched and the young reared by the foster-parents. The young Cuckoos either throw the other eggs or young out of the nest soon after they are hatched or, by their rapid growth, crowd out or suffocate the young of the other species.

Common Cuckoo (*Cuculus canorus*). This has the head and upper parts greyish-brown and the underparts white, with dusky bars. It is a summer visitor to Europe and northern Asia, wintering in Africa, tropical Asia and the Malay Archipelago. Its striking disyllabic note, from which it derives its name, is first heard in the British Isles about the middle of April, or occasionally somewhat earlier. It is constantly uttered by the cock-bird when perched and when flying in the daytime and sometimes after dark, but about June he " changes his tune " and stutters or becomes hoarse. The female makes a gurgling or bubbling call. Each hen lays from twelve to twenty eggs in a season, normally on alternate days. These she lays or places in the nests of some one other species of bird, unless she is unable to find a nest of this species at the appropriate stage, when she will place the egg in any other nest she can find. Only one egg is placed in each nest and usually one of the eggs of the victim is removed and eaten.

If two Cuckoo's eggs are found in the same nest, they have been laid by different birds. The species most commonly parasitized by the Cuckoo in England are the Meadow Pipit, Pied Wagtail, Hedge Sparrow, Sedge Warbler and Reed Warbler. The eggs are very small in proportion to the size of the Cuckoo and vary much in colouring, frequently, but not always, resembling those of the species parasitized. When two or three days old, the young Cuckoo, still blind and naked, begins to throw out the other occupants of the nest, eggs or young birds being carried to the edge of the nest in a cavity of the back and then suddenly ejected. Thenceforth the foster-parents devote themselves entirely to feeding the young Cuckoo, which has an insatiable appetite and grows rapidly. The Common Cuckoo, like many other members of the family, feeds largely on hairy caterpillars, which are eaten by few other birds. About August the adults depart for Africa, but the young do not follow till September or October.

Order PSITTACIFORMES (Parrots, Macaws, Cockatoos and Lories)

The Order Psittaciformes contains a very large number of species, almost all of them arboreal, found throughout the world except in the temperate regions of the northern hemisphere. A single species was, until recently, widely distributed in the central and southern United States, but is now restricted to a limited area in Florida. The most characteristic feature of the birds of this Order is the bill, which is short and stout, with both mandibles strongly arched. The upper mandible differs from that of all other birds in being hinged to the skull so that it is movable, and it ends in a hooked point. The lower mandible is truncated and nearly square at the tip.

[W. S. Berridge.

COCKATEEL (*Leptolophus hollandicus*).
This little Australian parrot, resembling a diminutive cockatoo, is a favourite cage bird.

[James's Press.]
GREEN-NECKED AMAZON PARROT (*Chrysotis sp.*).
The South American parrots called Amazons, of which there are numer-
ous species, include some of the best talkers.

The wings have ten primaries and the tail twelve (or fourteen) feathers. The legs are generally short and covered with rough scales, and the feet have two toes in front and two behind. Parrots and their allies use their feet like hands to hold their food, a habit found in few other birds. When climbing about the branches of trees, they use the beak in addition to the feet. In length members of the Order vary from three inches in the Pigmy Parrot of New Guinea to thirty inches in the Palm Cockatoo of the same country. Many of the species are commonly kept in captivity and a considerable number of them learn to talk and to whistle tunes. They frequently live to a great age in confinement. All lay white eggs, usually in holes in trees.

The Order contains two families : *Psittacidae* (Parrots, Macaws and Cockatoos), and *Loriidae* (Lories, Fig-parrots and Nestors).

Family Psittacidae (*Parrots, Macaws and Cockatoos*)

This family contains the majority of the members of the Order and is represented in America, Africa, Asia and Australasia. The birds of this family have the inner side of the hook of the upper mandible file-like, there being a series of parallel transverse grooves on each side. Their tongues are smooth and short, usually thick and fleshy.

Grey Parrot (*Psittacus erithacus*). A native of tropical Africa, this is one of the most familiar cage-birds and probably the most accomplished talker, though individuals vary. It is a large species with the plumage mainly ashy-grey, the primaries black, and the short tail, red.

Blue-and-yellow Macaw (*Ara ararauna*). Like its allies, this bird

518

has an enormously powerful beak and the naked, flesh-coloured face is crossed by lines of feathers. This and the other Macaws have also extremely long tails. It is a native of tropical South America.

Sulphur-crested Cockatoo (*Cacatua galerita*). This Cockatoo inhabits northern and eastern Australia and Tasmania, where it is generally found in flocks. It is white, with an erectile crest of long yellow feathers, and there is yellow on the cheeks and beneath the wings. Much of its food is obtained on the ground, where it picks up seeds or digs up roots and tubers.

Cockateel (*Leptolophus hollandicus*). This bird wanders in large flocks over the interior districts of Australia, feeding on seeds of grasses, etc. Its plumage is dark grey, with yellow forehead, yellow and orange cheeks and a white patch in the wings, and it has an elegant crest.

Budgerigar (*Melopsittacus undulatus*). This has much the same distribution and habits as the Cockatiel, and is even more familiar as a cage-bird. The plumage of the wild birds is mainly green, varied with yellow, with the central tail-feathers and a patch on the cheeks, blue. In recent years cage-birds have been produced with various colours unknown in the wild state and a number of colour varieties which breed true have been established. These new colours include sage-green, blue, yellow and white.

[*W. S. Berridge.*

KEA (*Nestor notabilis*).
A large New Zealand parrot inhabiting the mountains of the South Island, which is alleged to attack sheep.

AVES (ORDER PSITTACIFORMES)

Family Loriidae (*Brush-tongued Parrots, Lories, Fig-parrots and Nestors*)
This family contains numerous species found in Australia, New Zealand and New Guinea and the neighbouring islands. These birds have the inner edges of the upper mandible smooth, and the tongue fringed or brush-like at the tip. Most of the species feed largely on honey, which they extract from the flowers with their brush-tongues, as well as on soft fruits.

Kea (*Nestor notabilis*). This bird is an inhabitant of the mountainous districts of the South Island of New Zealand. It is the largest member of the family, measuring twenty-two inches in length. Its plumage is chiefly brownish-green, with a reddish-rump, some blue on the wings, and the tail green, with a black bar near the tip. The upper mandible of the bill is exceptionally long and much less arched than in most parrots, and its food consists not only of honey and berries, but also of insects extracted from beneath bark, etc., and of carrion. It has earned much notoriety from having acquired the habit of attacking sheep. It is stated that it perches on their backs and digs its long bill into the flesh till it reaches the fat over the kidneys, but accounts are conflicting and it is probable that the amount of injury caused by Keas has been greatly exaggerated.

By courtesy of the]   *[Commonwealth of Australia.*
PINK COCKATOO (*Cacatua leadbeateri*).
This lovely species with pink plumage and red and yellow crest inhabits the interior districts of Australia, where it is called the Major Mitchell, after the explorer who discovered it.

520

TAWNY OWL (*Strix aluco*).
The mottled plumage of this owl makes it inconspicuous in the daytime.

[*Arthur Brook.*

Order STRIGIFORMES (Owls)

This Order includes a large number of species and is represented in all parts of the world. They are all chiefly nocturnal in their habits, rarely being seen on the wing during the daytime, and they are entirely carnivorous, feeding on small mammals and insects, as well as on bats, birds, reptiles, fish, worms and snails. They have large heads with short, curved, hooked bills; and very large eyes, both turned forward and surrounded by " discs " of feathers supported by " ruffs " of stiff, short, recurved feathers, originating from folds of skin on the cheeks. Owls have little power of moving the eye-ball, hence the whole head is constantly turned to watch passing objects, etc., and the neck can be twisted through 180 degrees. When closed, the eye is covered by the upper eye-lid, instead of the lower as in other birds. The wings are long and rounded, containing eleven primaries, and the tail, usually rather short, contains twelve feathers. The plumage is exceptionally soft and the flight absolutely noiseless. The legs are comparatively short and generally feathered; the toes have sharp, curved claws used for seizing the prey; they are padded beneath and frequently feathered above, and the outer toe can be turned backwards or forwards at will. When perched on a bough an Owl commonly sits with two toes each way, but on the ground with three in front and one behind. Almost all Owls lay oval, pure white eggs. The Order contains two families : *Strigidae* (Brown Owls) and *Tytonidae* (Barn Owls).

521

AVES (ORDER STRIGIFORMES)

Family **Strigidae** (*Brown Owls*) contains most of the species of Owls. The majority have the plumage brown, mottled with black, grey, yellow and white, and frequently also barred. Many have a tuft of feathers on each side of the head above the ears. The members of this family range in size from diminutive insectivorous Owls only five inches long to the great *Hawk Owls*, and *Eagle Owls*, thirty inches long, which prey on hares, fawns, grouse, etc.

Tawny or Wood Owl (*Strix aluco*). This Owl is found in forests and wooded regions throughout Europe, western Asia and north-west Africa. In the British Isles it is the commonest owl, and its long-drawn, quavering hoot may be heard at night even in towns. Its plumage is mottled and streaked with brown, some individuals having grey as the predominating colour, others rufous. Grey and rufous phases exist in many other species of Owls. The Tawny Owl, also called the Brown Owl or Wood Owl, lays three or four eggs in a hollow tree or the deserted nest of some other bird.

Short-eared Owl (*Asio flammeus*). This is a somewhat larger bird than the Tawny Owl and the general tint of its plumage is buffish-brown. Its very short ear-tufts are only raised when the bird is excited and are not normally visible. It frequents open country such as moors, grassy hill-sides, dunes and fens, nesting and settling on the ground and has an enormous geographical range, including North and South America, Europe, North Africa and northern and central Asia. In the British Isles it is uncommon in summer, but many individuals from further north arrive in

[*D. Seth-Smith.*
GREAT HORNED OWL (*Bubo virginianus*).
This most powerful of American owls has been known to strike down geese and turkeys many times its own weight.

[Stanley Crook.

BARN OWLS (*Tyto alba*).
The White Owl or Screech-Owl is probably the most widespread species of bird in the world, being absent only from Norway, northern North America and New Zealand.

autumn to spend the winter. On the occasion of plagues of voles numbers have remained to breed in the areas affected as long as the plague lasted.

Long-eared Owl (*Asio otus*). This is a smaller and slimmer bird than either of the preceding and has very long ear-tufts. It frequents woods, especially small plantations of coniferous trees, and usually lays its eggs in the old nests of other birds, sometimes on the ground among heather. Owing to its nocturnal habits and the fact that it is much more silent than

[Walter E. Higham.

SHORT-EARED OWL (*Asio flammeus*).
This owl, which feeds principally on voles, is almost completely terrestrial.

523

most other owls, it is comparatively rarely seen, but occurs in North America, Europe, including the British Isles, and northern Asia.

Little Owl (*Athene noctua*). This was the bird of Minerva and the symbol of Athens. It is an abundant resident in the countries round the Mediterranean and is found north to Holland and the Baltic countries. To the British Isles it was formerly only an occasional visitor, but about 1890 was acclimatized in several parts of England and is now a common resident in England and Wales, north to Lancashire and Yorkshire. It is much smaller than the other owls here described and much less completely

[*J. Kershaw.*

LONG-EARED OWL (*Asio otus*).
This owl generally rears its young in the old nest of a crow, pigeon, or hawk.

nocturnal, often flying about in the daytime, and frequently perching on stumps or on the ground in the open.

Family **Tytonidae** (*Barn Owls*) contains only a few species of moderate or large size, but one or more occurs in all parts of the world except New Zealand. The bill is longer and less curved than in the Brown Owls, the facial discs are more or less triangular, the claw of the middle front toe has a serrated margin, and the plumage is buff or greyish above, whitish below.

524

White-, Barn-, or Screech-owl (*Tyto alba*). This Owl occurs almost throughout the world. It is golden-buff above, marked with brown, grey and white ; white below, with black spots. When hunting at night, it makes a weird screech ; and when perched during the day, a snoring sound. It lays its eggs in hollow trees, towers, belfries, pigeon-cotes, etc.

Order CAPRIMULGIFORMES (Nightjars, Frogmouths, Potoos and Oil-bird)

This is a considerable group of moderate-sized or fairly large birds, represented in all parts of the world except New Zealand and most of the Pacific Islands. They are nocturnal or crepuscular in habits. They have wide bills surrounded by bristles, and soft plumage mottled and pencilled with various shades of brown and rufous, usually with spots or patches of white.

Steatornithidae. This family contains only the Oil-bird or Guacharo (*Steatornis caripensis*), which inhabits northern South America from Trinidad and Guiana to Peru. It has a stout, hooked bill, with stiff bristles at the base, large wings, and small legs and feet, the former covered with smooth, flesh-coloured skin. It spends the daytime in caves on the coast or in the mountains, and at night emerges to seek its food, which consists of oily nuts and fruit, for which it often has to travel long distances. Many birds inhabit the same cave, and when disturbed they make loud croaking or rasping cries. Their nests are flat, circular masses of clay, placed on ledges of their cave, and they lay from two to four white eggs. The young birds are excessively fat and are collected for the table, or for the extraction of the oil they contain.

Podargidae (*Frogmouths*). These are nocturnal birds of owl-like appearance found in tropical Asia, the Malay Archipelago, and Australia. They have very wide, curved, hooked bills, rather short wings, long tails, and short, stout legs ; the outer front toe is partially reversible. They build flat, stick nests on the boughs of trees and lay from one to three, usually two, white eggs.

Nyctibiidae (*Potoos*). This family includes a few fair-sized birds inhabiting tropical America, one extending to Mexico and Jamaica. They have very wide bills, without any bristles round the base ; their legs are extremely short and the middle toe is flat beneath and without serrations. In other respects they resemble Nightjars.

Aegothelidae (*Owlet-Nightjars*). This family includes a few small nocturnal birds found in Australia, Tasmania, New Caledonia, New Guinea and the Molucca Islands. In their structure they agree closely with Nightjars and Frogmouths, but in appearance they have greater resemblance to small owls. During the daytime they hide in holes in trees, making a hissing noise when alarmed. Their nests are placed in holes in trees or hollow boughs and their two to five eggs are pure white.

525

Family Caprimulgidae (*Nightjars or Goatsuckers*)

This family includes a large number of species found in all parts of the world but New Zealand and the Pacific Islands. They have flat heads and very large eyes, long wings with ten primaries, tails of ten feathers,

TAWNY FROGMOUTH (*Podargus strigoides*).
Showing the attitude of the bird when alarmed. In this position it looks exactly like a broken branch.

short legs and feet with three toes before and one behind, the long, middle front toe having a comb-like structure below. They feed on crepuscular or nocturnal insects which they catch on the wing at dusk or during the night. They make absolutely no nest, but lay two spotted eggs on the ground.

European Nightjar (*Caprimulgus europaeus*). This is a summer visitor to Europe and western Asia, wintering in Africa south to the Cape. In both sexes the plumage is mottled with shades of brown and grey, but the male has white spots on the wings and tail-feathers, which are conspicuous in flight in the daytime. The eggs are creamy-white marbled with grey and black. When perching on trees, the Nightjar almost always sits lengthwise on a branch instead of across it. The loud, vibrating "churr" or reeling call is uttered by the male when perched.

Photos]   [*Otho Webb.*
TAWNY FROGMOUTH (*Podargus strigoides*).
The bird in its normal attitude on its flimsy nest of sticks in the Australian bush.

Order MICROPODIFORMES (Humming-birds and Swifts)

A very large group of small or very small birds of which representatives occur throughout the world except in New Zealand and some of the Pacific Islands. They are, perhaps, the most aerial of all birds, having exceptionally elongated wings, and being capable of extremely rapid flight. Their legs and feet are very small and are adapted only for perching, the birds being incapable of running or hopping on the ground. They lay from one to four white eggs.

Family Micropodidae
(Swifts)

This family includes a large number of species and is represented in almost all parts of the world except New Zealand. Swifts have short, flat, triangular bills, very wide at the gape ; very long wings with ten primaries, of which the first is the longest ; tails of ten feathers, which are often rigid and pointed ; short legs, often feathered ; and feet in which either all the toes are pointed forward (True Swifts), or three forward and one inwards. The plumage is hard and mainly dark brown or blue-black, usually with some white patches.

[*L. J. Langford.*
NIGHTJAR (*Caprimulgus europaeus*).
The Fern-Owl or Goatsucker, owing to the protective coloration of its plumage, is extremely difficult to discover in the daytime.

Swifts are insectivorous and obtain all their food on the wing. They are apparently incapable of perching on trees, but when they settle, which they rarely do in the daytime, they cling to the face of a cliff or the bark

527

of a tree-trunk, roosting at night inside chimneys, hollow trees or caves. In most species, the nest is largely composed of a glutinous substance secreted by the salivary glands, in which are embedded twigs, leaves, etc.

Edible-nest Swift (*Collocalia esculenta*). This makes a nest entirely or almost entirely of this glutinous substance, and its nests are valued by Chinese and Japanese epicures. They are attached in colonies to the walls and roofs of dark caves in some of the islands of the Indian Ocean, and these caves form valuable properties in which all the accessible nests are annually collected for sale.

Common Swift (*Micropus apus*). This is a summer visitor to Europe and northern Asia, wintering in Africa as far south as the Cape. Its plumage is entirely dusky except for the whitish chin and throat. Its note is a loud, harsh scream, constantly uttered as it circles round buildings or cliffs at great speed, usually in flocks. Its nest is placed in a hole or crevice in a cliff, a building, or a hollow tree ; there are two to four white eggs.

Macropterygidae (*Crested Swifts*). This family contains about half a dozen species found in tropical Asia and the Malay Archipelago east to the Solomon Islands. They have short, flat, broad bills ; very long wings ; long, forked tails ; very short legs ; and feet with three toes in front and one behind. Their plumage is soft and they have a patch of downy or silky

[Oliver G. Pike.
SWIFT (*Micropus apus*).
This bird usually spends the whole day on the wing, but is here seen in the attitude which it adopts when roosting.

feathers on the flanks and a crest on the head. They feed entirely on insects captured on the wing, spending much time in the air, but also perching in trees. Their very small saucer-shaped nests are composed of bits of bark, etc., cemented together by saliva, and glued to the upper side of a branch. The nest is just large enough to contain the single egg, and is quite concealed by the sitting bird.

528

HUMMING-BIRDS (TROCHILIDAE)

Family Trochilidae (*Humming-birds*)

The family Trochilidae contains a very large number of small or minute birds that are found in America, chiefly in Central and tropical South America. They have long slender bills, longer in proportion to their size than in any other birds, and very long tongues in the form of a double tube, capable of protrusion beyond the tip of the bill. Their long wings contain ten primaries of which the first is almost always the longest. Their tails are of ten feathers. Their small feet have three toes in front and one behind. Almost all the species have brilliant, metallic colours in their plumage, the apparent hue of which depends on the angle from which it is viewed, and as they move swiftly about they flash like jewels. The males are commonly much more brilliant than the females and the various species possess crests, ear-tufts, neck-frills, and many other types of ornament.

PREVOST'S HUMMING-BIRD (*Lampornis prevosti*).
A Venezuelan representative of the family, which contains the smallest of all birds, and is confined to America.
[*W. S. Berridge.*

The food of Humming-birds consists of minute insects, supplemented by nectar, and most of the species obtain it by hovering in front of flowers like Hawk-moths, thrusting their bills into the blossoms, and sucking up insects and nectar through their tubular tongues. Their wings vibrate so rapidly that they appear as a faint, blurred outline on each side of the small body. Often the bird remains for a few seconds before a blossom, then darts away at a speed which renders it almost invisible, and reappears in front of another flower. The vibration of the wings is in many species accompanied by a loud humming sound from which the name Humming- bird is derived. Some species feed principally on insects found in the crevices of bark or on leaves, hovering before the tree-trunks or amongst the foliage.

The males are very pugnacious, darting furiously at one another, and circling round uttering shrill notes. They also attack much larger birds, if these come near their nests, which are rather deep, cup-shaped structures of plant down, moss, or other soft materials, felted into a very light and spongy mass, sometimes no larger than a walnut-shell, attached to twigs or leaves, often in a fork.

Order COLIIFORMES (Colies or Mouse-birds)

This Order contains only the family *Coliidae* (Colies or Mouse-birds), consisting of about nine species found in Africa. They are small birds with short, dense feathering and stout, finch-like bills. Their wings are weak and rounded and contain ten primaries and their very long tails contain ten feathers, of which the outer pair are short. They have long legs, and feet in which all four toes are normally turned forward, though the outer two are capable of being bent back. They are dull brown or grey in colour, with buff underparts and a crest on the head.

Mouse-birds are usually found in small parties in wooded country, creeping about the trees with the lower-leg applied to the branch. The birds feed almost entirely on fruit. Their cup-shaped nests of twigs, roots and grass are built near the ground in bushes or low trees, and they lay three or four dull white eggs, sometimes streaked with orange or brown.

Order TROGONIFORMES

This Order contains only the family *Trogonidae* (Trogons), comprising about fifty species found in the tropical forests of America, Africa and Asia. They are moderate-sized birds of somewhat heavy aspect, with short necks. They have short, strong, wide bills, hooked at the tip and surrounded by bristles ; their rather short wings contain ten primaries and their long tails contain twelve feathers. Their legs are short and feathered and the short, weak feet have two toes turned forward and two back ; in Trogons, however, it is the first and second toes that are behind, instead of the first and fourth as in all other birds which have two toes turned backwards. The plumage is in most species remarkable for its brilliance ; the large, soft feathers are very loosely attached to the thin skin and readily fall out.

Trogons inhabit dense, shady forests, creeping about the trees or sitting quietly on a bough, occasionally darting out into the open to seize an insect or a berry, almost all their food, including fruits, being obtained on the wing. They lay from two to four white, bluish-green or buff eggs in a cavity excavated by them in a rotten stump or bough or an ants' nest.

Quezal (*Pharomacrus mocinno*). This most beautiful and remarkable species is found in the mountains of Central America. The male has the upper parts brilliant golden-green, the wing quills black, the tail black and white, the throat green and the underparts vivid scarlet. It has a rounded crest of hair-like feathers ; long, pointed scapulars hanging over the wings and long, flowing plumes springing from the rump hanging over the tail. Though the bird is only the size of a dove, these last feathers measure from three feet to three feet six inches in length.

530

Order CORACIIFORMES (Kingfishers, Todies, Motmots, Bee-eaters, Rollers, Hoopoes and Hornbills)

This is a comparatively small group of birds, chiefly found in the tropics, exhibiting much diversity of form but agreeing in certain features of their internal anatomy. Their feet normally have three toes in front and one behind, though occasionally one toe is absent and some can voluntarily turn one of the front toes backwards. In many cases, also, the front toes are more or less united at the base. They are nearly all birds with brilliant plumage and lay white eggs in holes.

Family Alcedinidae
(*Kingfishers*)

This family includes a large number of small or moderate-sized birds distributed in almost all parts of the world, but chiefly found in the tropics and especially abundant in New Guinea and the eastern part of the Malay Archipelago. They have long, stout straight bills and large heads, frequently crested ; their wings are short and rounded, with eleven primaries of which the

By courtesy of]   *[The Commonwealth of Australia.*
LAUGHING JACKASS (*Dacelo gigas*).
The largest member of the Kingfisher family, a native of Australia, where it is called Kookaburra, and generally protected owing to its fondness for snakes.

first is small ; their tails are usually short, and their legs and feet small and weak. Their plumage is usually brilliant, but the species vary greatly in colour. They lay round, glossy, thin-shelled, white eggs in holes or burrows.

European Kingfisher (*Alcedo atthis*). This is the only representative of the family in western Europe, and is found also in North Africa and throughout Asia. Its plumage is dazzling cobalt-blue or emerald - green above, the apparent colour depending on the angle from which it is viewed, below it is orange and its feet are red. It feeds almost exclusively on small fish, for which it plunges into the water from an overhanging bough. Its nest is a bed of fishbones at the end of a burrow in a river bank.

Laughing Jackass or Kookaburra (*Dacelo gigas*). This Australian bird is the largest member of the family, about eighteen inches 'long, with a

KINGFISHER (*Alcedo atthis*).
This bird is carrying a stickleback to feed his sitting mate, holding it head foremost so that she can swallow it head first.
[*A. M. Willford.*]

powerful, s l i g h t l y - hooked bill. Its plumage is chiefly various shades of brown, with a patch of blue in the wings, and the male has also blue on the rump. It is found in open forest country and feeds on large insects, rats and mice, lizards, snakes, small birds and eggs. Its eggs are laid in a hole in a tree or a burrow excavated in the nest of a white ant. It has a very remarkable, loud, laughing call, which is uttered v e r y f r e q u e n t l y, especially at daybreak and at dusk. When one bird starts, others join in, filling the air with their boisterous mirth.

Family **T o d i d a e** (*Todies*) contains only four kinds of diminutive West Indian birds, one each in Cuba, Haiti, Porto Rico and Jamaica. They have rather long, straight, flattened, reddish bills, short wings, short, square tails and long legs, and their plumage is green above, bright red on the throat, and yellowish or pinkish-white below. They frequent wooded ravines, and feed on insects which they capture on the wing. Their three or four round white eggs are laid in a lengthy burrow, usually in sand.

Family **Momotidae** (*Motmots*) includes a small number of species mostly

532

found in Central America, a few forms extending to southern Mexico, the West Indies and tropical South America. They have rather stout, somewhat curved bills with serrated edges and a few bristles at the base ; rather short, rounded wings with ten primaries ; long, graduated tails and short legs. The sexes are similar and have green, blue, cinnamon and black plumage. In most of the species the central pair of tail feathers are elongated and have spatulate or racquet tips, the shafts being bare for a considerable distance but with barbs for a short distance at the tip. This effect is produced by the bird itself nibbling away the barbs for a space below the tips.

Motmots frequent shady forests and spend much of their time perched in the trees, darting out at intervals to secure flying insects. They also eat fruits and small reptiles. They lay three or four round, creamy-white eggs in holes in trees or banks.

Family **Meropidae** (*Bee-eaters*) includes a number of birds of moderate or small size chiefly found in Africa and in tropical Asia ; one visits Australia in the southern summer, and one visits southern Europe and temperate western Asia in the summer, not infrequently wandering north to the British Isles and other parts of northern Europe. The bill is long and slightly curved, the wing contains eleven primaries of which the first is very short, the tail consists of twelve feathers, the legs and toes are very short. The plumage in both sexes is brilliant, commonly exhibiting shades of blue, green or copper colour.

Bee-eaters are graceful, lively birds which hawk, generally in flocks like Swallows, for flying insects. They are sometimes very destructive to bees if they establish themselves in the neighbourhood of hives, though these are by no means, as their name suggests, their only or principal food. They excavate long burrows in banks, or sometimes in level ground, and lay from four to six round, glossy white eggs. They commonly breed in colonies.

Family **Coraciidae** (*Rollers*) contains about twenty species of moderate-sized arboreal birds found in Africa and tropical Asia, one species visiting Europe and northern Asia in summer and one visiting Australia in the southern summer. They have strong, rather wide, curved hooked bills ; long, rounded wings with ten primaries ; tails of twelve feathers and short legs. Their plumage is generally either blue of various shades or green, often varied with reddish. They are active, noisy birds, frequently uttering harsh, chattering notes, and capture their insect food on the wing or on the ground, also feeding on worms, frogs and small reptiles. They lay four or five glossy white eggs in a hole in a tree or bank. Their name is derived from their remarkable habit of tumbling and rolling over in the air during flight.

Family **Leptosomatidae** (*Ground-rollers*) contains only six species found in Madagascar, one of them also in the Comoro Islands. They have rather stout, slightly hooked bills and fairly long tails of twelve feathers. They frequent the forests, but most of them are mainly terrestrial, seeking at dusk large insects, lizards, etc. Their eggs are white.

Family **Upupidae** (*True Hoopoes*) contains the Common Hoopoe (*Upupa epops*) whose names are all derived from its soft, reiterated call-note " hoop, hoo." It is found in Europe, Asia and Africa, but is only a summer visitor to Europe and temperate Asia. In England a few occur regularly in spring and some also in autumn, and they have not infrequently bred in the southern counties, but their striking appearance commonly leads to their being shot.

The Hoopoe has a long, slender, slightly curved bill, broad wings with ten primaries ; a square tail of ten feathers ; short legs and rather long toes. The head, shoulders and underparts are cinnamon-coloured, the head bearing a crest of long feathers tipped with black, which is fan-shaped when fully spread; the lower back and the wings are barred with black, white and buff, and the tail is black with a broad white band. The food is mostly obtained on the ground, consisting of worms and insects, and the nest is placed in holes and is evil-smelling from the use of excrement for the lining. From four to seven dull greenish-blue eggs are laid.

Family **Phoeniculidae** (*Wood-hoopoes*) includes ten species found in Africa. They have long, curved bills ; broad wings with ten primaries ; and long, wedge-shaped tails. Their plumage is metallic purple, blue or greenish, with a white patch in the wings and some white in the tail. They are mainly arboreal and feed on insects, for which they probe the crevices of the bark or search on

[*Arthur Brook.*

HOOPOE (*Upupa epops*).
This striking bird frequently visits and occasionally nests in the British Isles.

534

[Keystone.
RHINOCEROS HORNBILL (*Buceros rhinoceros*).
The male is seen outside the nest and the bill of the immured female is protruding
from the narrow opening.

the ground. They make loud, harsh, chattering notes and breed in holes in trees, laying white eggs.

Family **Bucerotidae** (*Hornbills*) comprises about sixty species of moderate - sized or large birds found in Africa, tropical Asia and the Malay Archipelago east to the Solomon Islands. They have extremely large bills, unique in having a casque or helmet, which varies much in shape and size according to the species, developed on the upper mandible; their powerful wings have eleven primaries; their tails are long and contain ten feathers; whilst the legs are rough and scaly and the toes have flat soles. They have prominent eyelashes, a rare feature among birds.

Hornbills feed on fruits, berries, insects and reptiles; most of the species are mainly arboreal, but two species are largely terrestrial (Ground Hornbills); some forms when flying make a noise resembling the puffing of a steam engine when starting a train, which can be heard a mile away. They breed in holes in trees, the hen bird being immured in the hole throughout the period of incubation by her mate, who builds a wall of mud across the entrance, leaving only a slit through which he feeds her. The eggs are white when laid.

Order PICIFORMES (Jacamars, Puff-birds, Barbets, Honey-guides, Toucans, Woodpeckers, Piculets, Wrynecks)

A considerable group of birds, almost all of which are arboreal. They differ greatly in external appearance, but agree in certain features of their internal anatomy and in the structure of their feet, which have two toes directed forwards, and two backwards. They all lay white eggs.

CUVIER'S TOUCAN (*Rhamphastos cuvieri*).
[*D. Seth-Smith.*
The large bills of these tropical American birds are extremely light, and enable them to gather fruits which would otherwise be out of reach.

Family **Galbulidae** (*Jacamars*) includes a number of rather small birds found in tropical America. They have long, straight, compressed, pointed bills; rounded wings with ten primaries, of which the first is very small; tails of twelve feathers, of which the outer pair are very small or sometimes absent; and slender, weak legs and feet. Their plumage is generally brilliant, metallic, coppery or golden-green or blue above, sometimes chestnut or blackish, commonly also more or less rufous below. They frequent lofty forest trees, often on the edge of a clearing, and fly out from their perch to catch insects on the wing. They breed in holes and lay white eggs.

Family **Bucconidae** (*Puff-birds*) contains a number of small or moderate-sized birds found in tropical America. They have broad, stout beaks, with somewhat hooked tips; rounded wings with ten primaries; tails of twelve feathers and fairly strong legs. Their plumage is black, brown or rufous, varied with white markings, and their bills are often red or yellow. They commonly sit quietly on the boughs of trees with the feathers of the head more or less puffed out (hence their name), occasionally

536

flying out to capture some passing insect. They lay white eggs in holes.

Family **Capitonidae** (*Barbets*) includes a considerable number of heavy, ungainly birds inhabiting the forests of tropical America, Africa and Asia. They have large, stout bills, swollen at the base and beset with bristles ; moderate wings with ten primaries ; and strong feet with long claws. Their plumage commonly exhibits vivid contrasts of scarlet, blue, purple or yellow on a green ground, but some are plainly coloured. They are arboreal birds, and generally sit on the boughs of the trees for long periods without moving, at intervals uttering loud, ringing metallic notes or whistles. They feed largely on fruits, berries, buds, flowers and leaves, also on insects. They excavate holes in soft or decaying wood and lay from two to five white eggs.

The Coppersmith (*Xantholaema haematocephala*) obtains its name from its remarkably loud, metallic note, which sounds like " took-took-took." It is uttered while the bird is perched in a tree, and at each call it nods its head, first to one side, then to the other. It is common throughout India and its range extends to Ceylon, Burma, the Malay Peninsula, Sumatra and the Philippines. It is green above, and whitish below, striped with green, with the forehead and a band on the breast crimson, and patches of black, yellow and blue on the head.

Family **Indicatoridae** (*Honey-guides*) includes about ten species of small birds mostly found in Africa south of the Sahara, but with one representative in the Himalayas and one in the mountains of Malaya and Borneo. They have short, stout, pointed bills and short legs, and their plumage is mainly dull brown in colour, often tinged with yellow or marked with white or black. They lay two white eggs in the deserted nests of other birds.

Their name is derived from their remarkable habit of attracting the attention of a man by fluttering and calling in the bushes near him and then leading him to a tree in which there is a bees' nest. If he cuts out the comb to extract the honey, they feed on the grubs disclosed. They are said also to lead the ratel to bees' nests, and sometimes to lead a man to a leopard, cat, dog or snake.

Family **Rhamphastidae** (*Toucans*) includes numerous species found in the forests of tropical South and Central America recognizable at once by their enormous bills. Though both mandibles are greatly enlarged, the external walls are extremely thin and internally they are largely hollow, with a network of bony columns to give rigidity. These great bills and a ring of bare skin round the eye are often brightly coloured, sometimes in harmony with and sometimes contrasting with the bright colours of the plumage. Toucans have somewhat weak wings with ten primaries ; fairly long tails of ten feathers, often carried bent forward over the back ; stout legs ; toes with papillae below and sharp, curved claws. They live almost entirely in the tree-tops. They feed principally on fruits and seeds, but also on insects and perhaps also on birds' eggs, small birds, reptiles,

537

[T. M. Fowler.

LESSER SPOTTED WOODPECKER (*Dryobates minor*).
This little bird, also called the Barred Woodpecker, feeds chiefly on the higher boughs of large trees.

.etc. Small fruits, etc., picked with the tips of the long bill are thrown back to the throat and swallowed with a sudden upward jerk of the head. They lay two white eggs in hollow limbs of tall trees.

Family Picidae
(*Woodpeckers, Piculets and Wrynecks*)

This family includes a large number of species. They are to be found in all parts of the world except the island of Madagascar, the eastern portion of the Malay Archipelago, New Guinea, Australia, New Zealand and the Pacific Islands. The majority of the species climb about the trunks and large boughs of trees and have short legs with strong feet and claws, and tails of twelve feathers, generally with stiff, spiny shafts, which help to support the bird. They have large heads, very muscular necks and strong, wedge-shaped bills ; they obtain their food, which consists mainly of wood-boring insects, by chiselling out their burrows in the wood, using their bills as picks. They have exceptionally long tongues, which can be protruded far beyond the bill, and are often barbed at the tip, and are kept moist with a sticky secretion from large salivary glands. With their tongues they drag insects from crevices or tunnels. With their powerful bills they also excavate cylindrical holes in trees for breeding, laying their white eggs on a few chips of wood at the bottom of the cavity.

Green Woodpecker (*Picus viridis*). This bird has the upper plumage mainly green, shading into yellow on the rump, paler on the underparts ;

the crown and nape are crimson and a moustache-like band on the cheek is crimson in the male, black in the female. It has a loud, laughing call, and supplements the food it obtains from the trees by procuring ants on the ground. It occurs in wooded districts throughout most of Europe, Asia Minor and Persia, but in Britain is scarce and local north of Yorkshire and to Ireland is a very rare straggler.

Flicker or Golden-winged Woodpecker (*Colaptes auratus*). The Flicker occurs in summer throughout the United States and Canada north to the limit of trees, but the Canadian birds migrate south for the winter.

It is more addicted to ants than the Green Woodpecker, and spends much of its time on the ground in search of them. Its crown is grey, the nape bright scarlet, the back brownish-grey barred with black, the rump white, the wings and tail black and yellow, the underparts vinaceous and white with a broad crescent across the breast and black spots on the belly. The male has black moustache stripes, which are absent in the female.

Great Spotted Woodpecker (*Dryobates major*). This Woodpecker is mainly black above with patches and bars of white, white below with a crimson patch on the vent. The male also has the nape crimson. It is found in wooded parts of Europe, north Africa and northern Asia from Britain to Japan, but is only an occasional visitor to Ireland.

Lesser Spotted or Barred Woodpecker (*Dryobates minor*). Like its larger relative this bird ranges across Europe and Asia from Britain to Japan, but in

[*Arthur Brook.*

GREEN WOODPECKER (*Picus viridis*).
The largest of the British Woodpeckers, whose loud, laughing call has earned it the name of Yaffle.

539

Britain is confined to England and Wales. The upper parts are barred with black and white and the underparts buffy-white. Young birds and the adult male have the crown red, but in the female it is whitish.

Wryneck or Cuckoo's-mate (*Iynx torquilla*). This bird differs from the typical Woodpeckers in its softer plumage and its tail, which is only slightly rounded and composed of ordinary feathers without stiffened, pointed shafts. Its plumage is delicately pencilled and mottled with grey, brown, buff and black, and the sexes are similar. It is found in summer throughout most of Europe, north Africa and northern Asia, but in the British Isles only in England. In winter it is found in tropical Africa and India, but a few remain in countries round the Mediterranean. It feeds largely on ants obtained on the ground as well as on insects found in crevices of the bark of trees, but its weak bill is not used for excavating holes in wood, and it nests in natural hollows.

Order PASSERIFORMES (Perching-birds)

Between five thousand and six thousand birds, or about half the known species, are included in this Order. Its members are found in all lands, except Antarctica, but none of them is marine. Amongst them are included such familiar forms as the Crows, Finches, Larks, Tits, Warblers, Thrushes, Flycatchers and Swallows. They are mostly comparatively small, the largest being the Ravens and Lyre-birds.

Apart from certain features of the skeleton and muscular system, the chief external character distinctive of the Order is the form of the foot. This has three toes turned forward, and one behind, which is always inserted at the same level as the others. The toes can be bent downwards to obtain a firm grasp of a twig, or even of a wire, but none of them can be bent sideways. The hind toe is usually at least as long as the longest (middle) front toe.

Perching-birds construct more or less elaborate nests, and their young, when hatched, are naked and helpless, being completely dependent on their parents for days, or even weeks. Though it is impossible to frame any satisfactory definition to distinguish song from the other vocal utterances of birds, all the species pre-eminent as song-birds are members of this Order, including as it does the Nightingales, Thrushes, Warblers, Mocking-birds, Bulbuls, Finches and Lyre-birds. The form of the vocal organ (syrinx) and the number and arrangement of the muscles attached to it present four distinct types among the perching-birds, and thus permit of their division into four suborders. These are of very unequal extent, two of them containing only a few species each, whereas the other two each contain very large numbers. The so-called families into which these suborders are commonly divided are mostly groups of genera which appear to be more or less closely allied, but cannot be strictly defined, as so many forms are more or less intermediate. The form of the bill, nostrils, tongue,

540

legs and feet, and the numbers of primaries and tail-feathers are the characters chiefly considered when dividing the suborders into families, but various authorities differ greatly in their views on the question. The classification here adopted is :—

Suborder Eurylaemi
Family *Eurylaemidae* (Broad-bills).

Suborder Tyranni
Families *Dendrocolaptidae* (Wood-hewers), *Furnariidae* (Oven-birds), *Formicariidae* (Antthrushes), *Conopophagidae* (Ant-pipits), *Rhinocryptidae* (Tapacolas), *Cotingidae* (Chatterers), *Pipridae* (Manakins), *Tyrannidae* (Tyrant Flycatchers), *Oxyruncidae* (Sharp-bill), *Phytotomidae* (Plant-cutters), *Pittidae* (Pittas), *Xenicidae* (New Zealand Wrens) and *Philepittidae* (Wattled Ant-thrushes).

Suborder Menurae
Families *Menuridae* (Lyre-birds) and *Atrichornithidae* (Scrub-birds).

Suborder Oscines
Families *Hirundinidae* (Swallows), *Campophagidae* (Cuckoo-shrikes),

[*Arthur Brook.*
GREAT SPOTTED WOODPECKER (*Dryobates major*).
This is the only kind of Woodpecker which nests in Scotland, whilst in Ireland the family is not represented.

Pycnonotidae (Bulbuls), *Timeliidae* (Babblers), *Prunellidae* (Accentors), *Troglodytidae* (Wrens), *Cinclidae* (Dippers), *Paramythiidae*, *Zeledoniidae* (Wren-thrush), *Turnagridae* (New Zealand Thrushes), *Mimidae* (Mockingbirds), *Turdidae* (Thrushes), *Sylviidae* (Warblers), *Muscicapidae* (Flycatchers), *Vireonidae* (Greenlets), *Bombycillidae* (Waxwings), *Ptilogonatidae* (Silky Flycatchers), *Dulidae* (Palm-chats), *Artamidae* (Wood-swallows), *Vangidae* (Madagascar-shrikes), *Grallinidae* (Magpie-larks), *Prionopidae*

(Wood-shrikes), *Aerocharidae* (Helmet-bird), *Cyclarhidae* (Pepper-shrikes), *Vireolaniidae* (Shrike-vireos), *Streperidae* (Crow-shrikes), *Laniidae* (Shrikes), *Regulidae* (Kinglets), *Chamaeidae* (Wren-tit), *Paridae* (Tits), *Hyposittidae* (Coral-billed Nuthatch), *Sittidae* (Nuthatches), *Certhiidae* (Creepers), *Zosteropidae* (White-eyes), *Dicaeidae* (Flower-peckers), *Promeropidae* (Long-tailed Sun-bird), *Nectariniidae* (Sun-birds), *Meliphagidae* (Honey-eaters), *Mniotiltidae* (Wood Warblers), *Drepanididae* (Hawaiian Honey-suckers), *Enicuridae* (Fork-tails), *Motacillidae* (Wagtails), *Alaudidae* (Larks), *Fringillidae* (Finches), *Catamblyrhynchidae* (Plush-capped Finch), *Coerebidae* (Quit-quits), *Procniatidae*, *Thraupidae* (Tanagers), *Ploceidae* (Weaver-birds), *Icteridae* (Troupials), *Oriolidae* (Orioles), *Buphagidae* (Ox-peckers or Rhinoceros Birds), *Graculidae* (Glossy Starlings), *Sturnidae* (Starlings), *Dicruridae* (Drongos), *Ptilonorhynchidae* (Bower-birds), *Paradiseidae* (Birds of Paradise), *Creadiontidae* (Saddlebacks), *Callaeadidae* (Wattled Crows), and *Corvidae* (Crows).

Eurylaemidae *(Broad-bills)*. This family includes a small number of birds found in tropical Asia, chiefly in the Malayan region, but with one or two representatives in tropical Africa. The beak is very broad, sometimes also short and sometimes hooked at the tip ; the outer and middle toes are more or less united at the base and the small hind-toe is incapable of independent movement. Nearly all have beautiful plumage, the most remarkable being rich green. The Broad-bills inhabit forests, thickets and gardens, flying little but sitting on the branches and snapping up flying insects, some also feeding on berries and fruit.

Dendrocolaptidae *(Wood-hewers)*. The numerous species in this family are found in Central and South America, chiefly in the tropical forests. They have long, slender, straight or curved bills ; fairly long, graduated tails whose feathers have stiffened points ; and feet in which the three front toes are partially united at the base, the outer toe being as long as the middle one. In plumage, which is always some shade of brown, and in the form of the bill and tail, the Wood-hewers resemble Creepers, but in their habits they more closely resemble Woodpeckers, tapping and hammering on tree-trunks and chipping away decayed wood in search of boring insects.

Furnariidae *(Oven-birds)*. This family includes a very large number of species found in South and Central America, specially abundant in southern Brazil, Uruguay and Argentina. They vary greatly in size, form and colour, though they never have brilliant colours. Many are terrestrial but some resemble Creepers or Tits in their habits.

The Red Oven-bird or Hornero *(Furnarius rufus)* has the upper parts rufous-brown, brightest on the tail, and the underparts nearly white. It is a common and favourite bird in Paraguay, Uruguay and Argentina, inhabiting open country, gardens and the vicinity of houses, where it runs actively about on the ground. It builds a very large and remarkable nest of mud on a bare bough, post or roof of a building. Externally the structure is globular, a foot or more in diameter, and very massive, sometimes weighing eight or nine pounds ; a central partition divides it into a vestibule and an inner nest-chamber which communicate by a comparatively small hole at the end of the vestibule remote from the external entrance. In the inner chamber a nest of soft grass is built and four or five white eggs are laid.

Formicariidae (*Ant-thrushes*). In this family are a very large number of species found in South America and Central America north to Costa Rica, most numerous in the Amazonian and Guiana forests. In size they range from that of a Wren to that of a Jay, and their form also varies greatly. They are nearly all birds of plain plumage, none having any brilliant colours, and most of the species are chiefly terrestrial. They feed largely on ants and other insects. Some of them are fine songsters.

Conopophagidae (*Ant-pipits*). This family includes a few small birds found in tropical South America. They have large heads ; short, rounded wings ; and short tails. They are mainly brown in colour.

Rhinocryptidae (*Tapacolas*). The Tapacolas include a number of small terrestrial wren-like birds found in South America, chiefly on or near the Andes, one occurring as far north as the mountains of Costa Rica. They are drab in colour and have rather short, stout bills ; short, rounded wings with ten primaries ; short tails usually carried erect or bent forward over the back ; and large, strong feet. They hop or run actively on the ground, but their powers of flight are very limited. Their notes are varied and remarkable but harsh and loud.

Cotingidae (*Chatterers*). This family includes a very large number of small or moderate-sized birds found in tropical America, with two representatives in Jamaica. They differ greatly in size, form and coloration. Most species are said to feed largely on fruits.

Umbrella-bird (*Cephalopterus ornatus*). This bird of northern South America obtains its name from its huge crest of bare-shafted feathers with loosely-webbed tips ; this crest is attached to a contractile skin, and when erected and expanded forms a dome-shaped or umbrella-like ornament. The male has also an elongated, pendent, feathered wattle hanging from the fore-neck. Both sexes are entirely black, and are nearly as large as Crows.

Common Bell-bird (*Procnias nivea*). This is an entirely white bird the size of a Jay, and is found in Guiana. The male has a spiral tube on the forehead ; this tube is jet-black dotted all over with small white feathers ; ordinarily it is pendent, but when the bird is excited, it can be inflated with air and then forms an erect spire about three inches long. The bird derives its name from its deep, bell-like note which is uttered at intervals of several minutes.

Cock of the Rock (*Rupicola crocea*). The Cock of the Rock inhabits Guiana and Brazil, and is remarkable for its flattened, disc-like crest and

543

plumage of a bright orange colour. It has brown and white wings, and a partly-blackish tail.

Pipridae (*Manakins*). This family includes a large number of small birds found in tropical America. They have rather short, broad bills ; wings with ten primaries, of which the first is short ; very short tails, except in some species where the central pair of feathers is elongated ; and moderately long legs. In most species the sexes differ in colour, the males being largely black with patches of bright blue, crimson, orange, yellow or white, whilst the females are greenish.

Tyrannidae (*Tyrant Flycatchers*). The Tyrannidae include a very large number of small or moderate-sized birds distributed throughout North and South America, specially numerous in the tropics. They have somewhat hooked bills and wings with ten primaries. Many of them closely resemble the Flycatchers of the Old World, but there is great diversity of size, form and colouring among them. The majority feed almost exclusively on insects, but some of the larger forms also kill small mammals, reptiles, frogs, etc.

King-bird (*Tyrannus tyrannus*). This bird is eight and a half inches long, slaty-grey above, becoming black on the head and tail, which is tipped with white ; the underparts are white ; concealed orange-red feathers on the crown form a crest when elevated. In summer it is found throughout temperate North America, wintering in the tropics. The nest is cup-shaped and is generally built near the end of a bough ; the three to five eggs are white, spotted with brown.

Oxyruncidae. This family contains only the Sharp-bill (*Oxyruncus cristatus*), which ranges from south-eastern Brazil to Costa Rica. It is a small bird with a straight, wedge-shaped, sharp-pointed bill ; a rather short tail and strong legs. The sexes are alike in colour ; olive-green above, yellowish-white below with bars and triangular spots of black. The top of the head is spotted with black, and there is a band of elongated, orange-red feathers which form a crest when elevated.

Phytotomidae (*Plant-cutters*). The Plant-cutters include only a few small birds found in South America. They have stout, finch-like bills with serrated edges ; short wings with ten primaries ; and twelve tail-feathers. The males are brownish-grey above, with blackish wings and tail and reddish breasts ; the females are greyish above and buffy below with dark streaks. They inhabit arid regions covered with bushes, and feed on buds, leaves, berries and seeds. The nest is slight and shallow, placed in a bush, and the eggs are bluish-green with brown flecks.

Pittidae (*Pittas or Ant-thrushes*). The Pittas include about fifty species, mostly inhabiting the jungles of tropical Asia and the Malay Archipelago ; a few occur in China, two reach Australia, whilst one is found in West Africa. They are small or moderate-sized birds with stout, strong bills ; short, rounded wings ; very short tails and long legs. They are almost

544

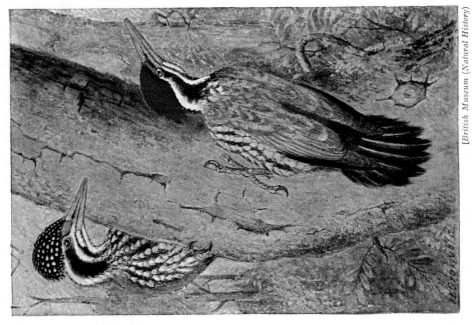

[British Museum (Natural History)

TICKELL'S GOLDEN-BACKED WOODPECKER (*Chrysocolaptes guttacristatus*)

By courtesy of]

RUFOUS-NECKED HORNBILL (*Aceros nepalensis*)

entirely terrestrial in habits. Few birds have such brightly-contrasted coloration—deep velvety black, pure white and intensely vivid scarlet, turquoise-blue and beryl-green are found in a great many—and these colours are almost always distributed in large patches standing out distinctly without any blending. The rounded nest of grass, moss and roots, with entrance at the side, is built on or close to the ground, and the eggs are usually creamy-white with brown, reddish, grey or purplish-black spots or scrawls.

Xenicidae (*New Zealand Wrens*). There are only four species and these are confined to the wooded mountain regions of New Zealand. They are very small birds with rather long, slender bills ; short wings ; extremely short tails ; rather long legs and proportion-ately very large feet. In all of them the up-per plumage is mainly green in the males and brownish in the females. They are insectivorous and obtain their food by climbing up the trunks of trees or over rocks, never flying very far. Their nests are domed and they lay white eggs.

Philepittidae (*Wattled Ant-thrushes*). This family contains only two species, found in Madagascar. They are small birds with slender, curved bills ;

[*James's Press.*

KISKADEE (*Pitangus sulphuratus*).
A large member of the American family of Tyrant Flycatchers, whose name is derived from its call. In Spanish America this is interpreted as Buen-te-veo (I see you well) and in Brazil as Bemtevi, with the same meaning.

short, rounded wings ; short tails and stout feet. The sexes are differently coloured, and the males have an area of naked skin round each eye, surmounted by a green caruncle, or wattle.

Menuridae (*Lyre-birds*). This family contains only two species, both found in south-eastern Australia. They are comparatively large birds, with short, rounded wings containing eleven primaries ; long tails of sixteen feathers ; long legs ; and very strong, large feet. They frequent gorges and damp hill-sides in forest country, scratching up fallen leaves and debris with their long feet to secure the insects, centipedes, crustaceans and snails on which they feed. The nest is a large domed structure, built on a log, in the top of a tree-fern or on a ledge of rock. A single purple,

[*Michael Sharland.*
SUPERB LYRE-BIRD (*Menura novaehollandiae*).
The female is without the extraordinary tail which, in the male bird, resembles the classical lyre.

blotched egg is laid and the breeding season is the middle of winter. The cock bird clears small circular areas in the scrub, and scratches up in the clearing a low mound of earth on which, either alone or before an audience of one or more hens, he sings, dances, and spreads his remarkable tail. Lyre-birds are, perhaps, the most gifted vocalists of all birds ; their notes are loud, clear and melodious and as mimics they are unrivalled. They incorporate in their songs not only the notes, songs and calls of other birds like the Mocking-birds, but almost every other sound, except the human voice, which they hear in their surroundings, such as the buzz of a circular saw, the whistle of a railway train, the howling of dingoes or the hammering of nails. The hen bird, though not so powerful a songster as the cock, is also an accomplished mimic.

Superb Lyre-bird (*Menura novaehollandiae*). This bird is found in the coastal forests from Victoria to southern Queensland. Both sexes are slaty-brown in colour. In the female, the tail-feathers are normal in structure, though very broad. In the male the central pair are very narrow, near their base they cross each other, and then diverge, bending round forwards near their tips ; the next six feathers on each side are furnished on each side with hair-like barbs without barbules, about a quarter of an inch apart; whilst the outer pair have very broad inner webs of a chestnut

546

colour, marked with triangular, light-coloured transparent patches, and are bent first outwards, then inwards and then sharply outwards at the tip.

Albert Lyre-bird (*Menura alberti*). This Lyre-bird inhabits sub-tropical jungles in south Queensland and northern New South Wales. The plumage in both sexes is much more rufous than in the other species and the outer

[*Michael Sharland.*

SUPERB LYRE-BIRD (*Menura novaehollandiae*).
The male bird is here seen displaying on his dancing mound.

547

tail-feathers of the male are shorter than the inner ones, uniform chestnut in colour and not curved.

Atrichornithidae *(Scrub-birds)*. This family contains only two species, one formerly found in thickets in south-western Australia, now probably extinct, the other in sub-tropical jungles of northern New South Wales and south Queensland. They have rather large bills ; extremely short wings with eleven primaries, the first of which is very small ; fairly long, rounded tails of twelve feathers ; and strong legs and feet. Their plumage is chiefly brown, and they live almost entirely on the ground among dense cover, being only capable of flying a few yards. Their notes are loud and they are clever mimics of the songs of other birds. The nest is dome-shaped, placed on the ground among dense vegetation, and the two eggs are pinkish-white with reddish-brown and purplish markings, chiefly at the larger end.

Hirundinidae *(Swallows)*. The Swallows include numerous small birds with flattened, triangular bills, very wide at the base. They have very long, pointed wings with only nine visible primaries. The tails are of twelve feathers, more or less forked, sometimes with the outer feathers greatly elongated. The legs are very short and the feet, in which the three front toes are more or less united at the base, are weak. Swallows are found in all parts of the world except New Zealand, but those species which breed in the higher latitudes of both hemispheres migrate to the tropics or beyond in winter. They are entirely insectivorous, mainly capturing flying insects on the wing, and in pursuit of their prey they spend a great part of the daylight hours hawking about in the air. Their eggs are white, sometimes without markings, sometimes with spots, and they usually breed in colonies.

Swallow *(Hirundo rustica)*. This is a summer visitor to Europe, northern Asia and North America, wintering in Africa south to Cape Colony, in tropical Asia and in tropical America. It is steel-blue above, with white spots on the tail-feathers, the outer pair of which are very long ; its forehead, throat and upper breast are chestnut ; the underparts varying in different races from white to chestnut, but usually buffy-white. Its nest is a saucer-shaped structure of mud, lined with feathers, usually placed on a beam or projection in a shed, barn or chimney, and its white eggs are spotted with reddish or ashy colour.

House Martin *(Chelidon urbica)*. The House Martin has the upper parts, except the rump, blue-black ; the rump and underparts being pure white. Its tail is forked, but the outer feathers are not specially elongated, and its legs and toes are covered with feathers. It is a summer visitor to Europe, north-west Africa and northern Asia, wintering in tropical Africa and Asia. Its mud nest is built on the vertical wall of a building under the eaves, or on a cliff below a projection, and is roofed over, with a small entrance near the top. Its eggs are pure white.

Sand Martin or Bank Swallow *(Riparia riparia)*. This Martin lays its white eggs in a nest of feathers at the end of a burrow which it excavates in the vertical face of a sand-pit, cutting or sandy river bank. It is uniform mouse-brown above and white below, with a brown band across the chest, and its tail is only slightly forked. It is found in summer throughout Europe, northern Asia and North America, wintering in the tropics.

Campophagidae (*Cuckoo-shrikes*). This family includes numerous species found in Africa, tropical Asia, the Malay Archipelago and Australia. They have fairly strong, hooked bills, rather wide at the base; and rather long, pointed wings. The plumage is soft, but the shafts of the feathers on the rump are stiff and feel spiny when the bird is handled. Their nests are usually slight cups of sticks, very small in comparison with the birds, built near the end of a branch.

Pycnonotidae (*Bulbuls*). The Bulbuls include numerous thrush-like species which are found throughout Africa and tropical Asia, extending north to Cyprus, Palestine, China and Japan, and east to the Moluccas. They have fairly long, somewhat

[*W. S. Berridge.*

SAND MARTIN (*Riparia riparia*).
The smallest British member of the Swallow family at the entrance to its nesting burrow excavated in a sand cliff.

stout, curved bills; rather short, rounded wings; and long, fluffy plumage on the rump. The majority are greenish or yellowish-brown above, often with bright yellow, orange or red on the underparts. They are mainly gregarious, arboreal birds of weak flight, frequenting gardens, orchards and thickets, and feeding on fruits and berries. Their notes are usually cheerful, mellow whistles, and it is probable that "the Bulbul" of Persian poetry was

549

really a species of Nightingale and not a member of this family.

Timeliidae (*Babblers*). The Babblers include a large number of small or moderate-sized birds, mostly with dull-coloured, soft plumage ; short, rounded wings ; and fairly large, stout legs and feet. They are most numerous in tropical Asia, but occur also in Africa and Australia, and the majority are chiefly found on the ground in forests or thickets. It is very doubtful to what extent the various birds commonly associated in the family are really related, and it has been said that any Old World Passerine birds which cannot readily be placed in other families are relegated to the Timeliidae. The more typical Babblers commonly associate in small parties and thus are frequently known as " Seven Sisters " or " Apostle-birds."

Prunellidae (*Accentors*). The Accentors include about a dozen small birds found in Europe and Asia, with rather slender but hard bills, widened at the base, rounded wings, short legs and fairly strong feet. Most of them are found in mountainous districts, where they hop about on the ground or over rocks in search of spiders, small insects and seeds. They build open, cup-shaped nests and lay blue eggs.

Hedge Sparrow (*Prunella modularis*). This Accentor is found throughout Europe and is partially migratory, some visiting North Africa, Asia Minor and Syria in winter. It is a dull-brown bird, with greyish head, frequenting shrubberies and hedgerows.

Troglodytidae (*Wrens*). This family includes numerous small birds with fairly long, slender, compressed bills ; short, rounded wings ; and comparatively long legs. In the Wrens the sexes are alike and their plumage is always some shade of brown, usually more or less barred, generally lighter below.

Common Wren (*Troglodytes troglodytes*). This bird is found throughout Europe, northern Asia and north-west Africa, inhabiting almost every type of country from lowland gardens and hedges to rocky mountain-sides. Its very short tail is usually carried erect. It has an astonishingly loud song for so small a bird. Its nest of moss, dead grass, leaves, etc., lined with feathers, is placed in a variety of situations, usually

[*Ralph Chislett.*
COMMON WREN (*Troglodytes troglodytes*).

[*T. M. Fowler.*

HEDGE SPARROW (*Prunella modularis*).
This familiar little bird with sparrow-like plumage is the British representative of the family of Accentors.

near the ground. The male builds a number of nests without lining them, and the female lines the one she selects, and lays from five to six or more eggs, white spotted with brownish red.

Cinclidae (*Dippers* or *Water Ouzels*). The Dippers include a small number of moderate-sized birds with slender bills, plump bodies, short wings and tails and rather long legs. They inhabit rivers and torrents in mountainous regions of Europe, northern Asia and western America from Alaska to Argentina. Their nests are bulky, domed structures of moss, with the opening at the side, usually built on rocks near waterfalls, and their eggs (five or six) are pure white. Though they show no special structural peculiarities to adapt them to an aquatic life, the Dippers swim and dive readily, and their food consists mainly of the larvae of aquatic insects obtained from the bottom of pools in rivers.

Common Dipper (*Cinclus cinclus*). This bird is found in most suitable localities in Europe, northern Asia and north-west Africa. In the British Isles it is common in Ireland, Scotland, Wales and northern and western England. Its plumage is mainly sooty brown, the throat and upper breast being pure white.

Paramythiidae. This family contains only one known species, *Paramythia montium*, found in the Astrolabe Mountains in south-eastern New Guinea. It is a dull-blue bird, with creamy head, black crest and fore-neck, olive-green rump, yellow vent and brownish wings.

Zeledoniidae. This family includes only the Wren-thrush (*Zeledonia coronata*), found near the summits of high volcanoes in Costa Rica and

Panama. It is a very small bird, with a short bill with bristles at its base ; a short, rounded wing with the first primary minute ; a very short tail of only ten feathers ; and very long, slender legs. The sexes are alike, the upper parts being olive-green and the underparts slate-grey, with an orange-rufous patch on the crown.

Turnagridae (*New Zealand Thrushes*). In this family are only two species, found respectively in the north and south islands of New Zealand, the former now probably extinct and the latter very scarce. They have

stout, arched, compressed bills with bristles at the base ; rounded wings and tails of t w e l v e f e a t h e r s. Their plumage is olive-brown above with bright rufous on the tail ; paler below. The nest of sticks and moss is placed in a bush or tree, and contains two eggs, white with brown spots.

Mimidae (*Mocking-birds, Thrashers*, etc.). This family includes numerous moderate - s i z e d birds found in North and South America, the West Indies and the G a l a p a g o s Is-lands, most numerous in Mexico. They have

[*Arthur Brook.*

DIPPER (*Cinclus cinclus*).
The bird is here seen outside its large domed nest, built on the rocks by a stream.

slender, rather long, usually somewhat curved, bills ; rounded wings and rather long, rounded tails.

Common Mocking-bird (*Mimus polyglottus*). This bird is found in the southern United States, Mexico and the West Indies, ranging north in small numbers to New York and New England. It is grey above and dull-white below, the wings and tail being blackish, the former with white bands and the latter with white margins. It is one of the finest song-birds, and, like the Nightingale, pours forth its song by night as well as in the daytime. Some individuals add to their own song imitations of the songs of many other birds, which are perfectly reproduced. The cup-shaped nest is a rather bulky structure placed in a bush or small tree, and the four to six eggs are bluish with reddish-brown spots.

Brown Thrasher (*Toxostoma rufum*). This bird of the eastern United States has the whole of the upper parts rufous and the underparts white, heavily streaked with black or brownish. It frequents thickets and undergrowth, but ascends trees to sing its melodious song, which is lacking in variety. The nest of this bird is built near or on the ground, and the three to six eggs are greyish white, thickly speckled with reddish-brown.

Turdidae (*Thrushes, Chats,* etc.). The family Turdidae includes a large number of small or moderate-sized birds found in all parts of the world except some of the Pacific islands. They have slender or small bills. Their plumage varies greatly, but the young of all species in their first plumage are spotted and different from the adults. The family contains many of the most noted song-birds.

[G. S. C. Ingram.
SONG THRUSH (*Turdus philomelus*).

Song Thrush (*Turdus philomelus*). The Song Thrush is brown above and buffy-white below, with dark-brown spots on the breast. It is found throughout Europe and western Asia, many moving south in winter to the countries round the Mediterranean. Its nest is a deep cup of grass, roots, etc., with a smooth inner lining of mud, usually built in a shrub or hedge, and its four to five eggs are greenish-blue with scattered black spots. It feeds on snails, earthworms, insects and berries. In the British Isles its loud and pleasing song may be heard in almost every month of the year, its distinctive feature being the repetition of each phrase two or three times.

" Lest you should think he never could recapture
The first, fine, careless rapture."

Redwing (*Turdus musicus*). This is somewhat smaller than the Song Thrush, from which it may be distinguished by the conspicuous white line over each eye and the orange-red colour of the flanks and underwing-coverts. It breeds in Scandinavia, north Russia and Siberia and winters in the temperate parts of Europe and Asia, including the British Isles, where it is common at that season.

Missel Thrush (*Turdus viscivorus*). This Thrush is decidedly larger than the Song Thrush, its upper plumage is greyer, and the spots on its breast larger. Its loud, wild song lacks the variety of its smaller relative, the few phrases being constantly repeated. Its nest is lined with dry grass and its eggs vary from tawny to greenish-blue in ground colour, with blotches and spots of brown and lilac. It is found throughout Europe, western and central Asia and north-west Africa, in the southern parts of its range being confined to the mountains in summer.

[*Tom Robinson.*

MISSEL THRUSH (*Turdus viscivorus*).
The largest of the British Thrushes, whose loud song is most heard in boisterous weather in early spring, hence its alternative name of Stormcock.

Fieldfare (*Turdus pilaris*). This is nearly as large as the Missel Thrush and is a much more handsome bird when seen at close quarters. Its head and rump are grey, its mantle chestnut-brown, its wings and tail dark brown, its breast golden-brown streaked with black and its belly white. It breeds in northern and central Europe and western Siberia and migrates southward for the winter, many visiting the British Isles. It is a social bird at all seasons, breeding in colonies, and moving about in flocks in winter, often in company with Redwings.

Blackbird (*Turdus merula*). The Blackbird is found throughout Europe, northern Asia and

[*L. J. Langford.*

BLACKBIRD (*Turdus merula*).
" The ouzel cock so black of hue with orange-tawny bill."

North Africa. The male is entirely black, with an orange-yellow bill; the female is dusky brown, with a brown bill; and the young are dark brown and spotted. Its song is a mellow fluting. The nest is strengthened with mud but lined with grass, and the eggs are bluish-green, with reddish-brown freckles or spots.

Ring Ouzel (*Turdus torquatus*). This is a summer visitor to the mountainous and upland districts of Europe, including the British Isles, wintering in the Mediterranean region. The male has the whole plumage, except a broad white gorget, brownish black, the feathers, however, have pale margins, giving the bird a somewhat grey appearance. The female is similar but duller and browner in colouring and her gorget is smaller and duller white. The Ring Ouzel's nest and eggs are similar to those of

555

the Blackbird, but are usually placed in heather or juniper bushes or among stones on rough banks in moorland country.

American Robin (*Turdus migratorius*). This bird has the top and sides of the head black, the throat white with black streaks, the upper parts grey, the underparts rufous, and the bill yellow. In summer it is found throughout Canada and the eastern United States, wintering in the central and southern States. Its song and its nest closely resemble those of the Blackbird, but its greenish-blue eggs are generally unspotted.

[*Stanley Crook.*

RING OUZEL (*Turdus torquatus*).
A shy relative of the Blackbird, which breeds in moorland districts of the British Isles.

Nightingale (*Luscinia megarhyncha*). The Nightingale has the upper parts rufous-brown, brightest at the base of the tail, the underparts dull-white, brownish on the breast. It inhabits woods and thickets and its nest of dead leaves lined with grasses is built on or close to the ground. It lays from four to five greenish or olive-brown eggs. In summer it is found in central and southern Europe, north-west Africa and parts of western Asia east to Turkestan, wintering in tropical Africa. In the British Isles it is confined to southern and eastern England and the midland counties. Its very powerful and wonderfully varied song is poured forth almost continuously day and night for a few weeks in the spring, rarely being heard after the middle of June.

556

[Tom Robinson.

STONECHAT (*Saxicola torquata*).
The male, here seen at the nest, is a handsome little bird with its black head, white collar, and reddish breast.

[Stanley Crook.

WHEATEAR (*Oenanthe oenanthe*).
One of the earliest of the summer migrants to return to the British Isles in spring, arriving towards the end of March.

Robin Redbreast (*Erithacus rubecula*). The Robin is uniform olive-brown above, the face, throat and breast reddish-orange with a border of bluish-grey, and the rest of the underparts white. It is found throughout Europe and western Asia, those from the north wintering in the Mediterranean countries and Persia. In the British Isles it is found throughout the year, and its boldness and tameness make it one of the most familiar and favourite birds. Its nest is built in a hole in a bank, stump or wall, generally near the ground, and its five, six or more eggs are white with fine freckles of sandy-red.

[*Oliver G. Pike.*

WHINCHAT (*Saxicola rubetra*).
The conspicuous white eyebrow distinguishes this species from its more familiar relative the Stonechat.

Redstart (*Phoenicurus phoenicurus*). This bird is a summer visitor to Europe and western Asia, but winters in tropical Africa. As a breeding species it is widely distributed in the British Isles, frequenting woods, parks and gardens where there are old trees, its nest being usually built in a hollow tree or a hole in a wall. The eggs are light blue and usually six in number. In south-eastern England, where it was formerly common, it has become unaccountably scarce in recent years, and in Cornwall, western Wales and most parts of Ireland it is almost unknown. The male has a white forehead, black chin, throat and cheeks, grey crown, nape and upper back, brown wings and chestnut breast, rump and tail. The female is a grey-brown bird with a chestnut tail. Both sexes have a habit of shivering their brightly-coloured tails, and the male has a brief but pleasant song.

Stonechat (*Saxicola torquata*). This bird is found throughout the greater part of Europe, Asia and Africa. In the British Isles it is generally distributed in summer, chiefly frequenting gorse-covered commons and wastes. Many remain for the winter but others migrate southwards. The male has the whole head black, a white collar on the sides of the neck and a conspicuous white patch in the wing, the breast bright rufous, the rest of

[*Reginald Gaze.*

NIGHTINGALE (*Luscinia megarhyncha*).
This far-famed songster sings much in the daytime, not only at night as supposed by many, including Shakespeare.

[*M. H. Crawford.*

ROBIN REDBREAST (*Erithacus rubecula*).
The most persistent of British songbirds, singing in every month of the year.

559

the plumage dark brown, spotted with black on the back. The female lacks the black head and is altogether duller in colouring. The nest is built near the ground, generally under a thick bush, and the five or six eggs are bluish-green with reddish-brown spots.

Whinchat (*Saxicola rubetra*). This bird has the upper parts mottled with dark brown and buff, a conspicuous white stripe over each eye and a white patch on each side of the base of the tail, and the underparts buff, with a rufous tinge on the breast. The female is similar to the male but duller. It is a summer visitor to Europe and western Asia, including the

[*Stanley Crook.*

BLACKCAP (*Sylvia atricapilla*).
The finest songster among the British Warblers.

British Isles, wintering in northern tropical Africa. It frequents heaths, commons and pastures, placing its nest on or close to the ground among dense herbage. The eggs, usually six in number, are greenish-blue, sometimes with rust-coloured spots.

Common Wheatear (*Oenanthe oenanthe*). The Wheatear is a small long-legged bird which frequents mountain-pastures, downs and grassy dunes, and in the summer is found in Europe, north Africa, northern and central Asia and Alaska, wintering in tropical Africa and India. It is brownish or greyish above and buffy-white below, with the rump and base of the tail pure white and the wings and tip of the tail black. Its nest is placed in a

[*M. H. Crawford.*

LESSER WHITETHROAT (*Sylvia curruca*).
Distinguished from its larger relative by its greyer upper parts, blacker cheeks and quite different song.

[*T. M. Fowler.*

CHIFFCHAFF (*Phylloscopus collybita*).
The earliest of the Warblers to return in spring, its well-known notes, from which it takes its name, are eagerly awaited in England.

hole in the ground or a cavity among stones, and its five to seven eggs are pale blue.

Sylviidae (*Warblers*). The Warblers include a large number of small birds distributed throughout the eastern hemisphere, the majority of those found in Europe and northern Asia migrating to warmer regions for the winter. They mostly have rather weak, slender bills and comparatively short wings and the greater number are comparatively sombrely coloured, brown, grey or greenish being the predominant tints. Most species feed principally on small insects, but some are fond of berries.

Blackcap (*Sylvia atricapilla*). The Blackcap is greyish-brown above

[*Reginald Gaze.*

WILLOW WARBLER (*Phylloscopus trochilus*).
This sweet songster is here seen bringing a spider as food for its nestlings.

and greyish-white below. The top of the head is black in the male, reddish-brown in the female. It is a summer visitor to most of Europe and western Asia. In the British Isles it is common in summer in England, but is only found in a few localities in Ireland and southern Scotland. In the countries round the Mediterranean it is found throughout the year. It is a very fine songster, pouring out its rich, melodious notes, which are loud for the size of the bird, from the shelter of a thicket or a leafy tree.

Garden Warbler (*Sylvia borin*). This bird is olive-brown above and buffish-white below. It is a summer visitor to most of Europe and western Asia, wintering in tropical and southern Africa. In the British Isles it is more widely distributed than the Blackcap, its range extending to southern Scotland and some districts of Ireland. In spite of its trivial name, it

562

SUPERB BLUE WREN.
(*Malurus cyaneus*).
The male of this striking little Warbler has the plumage of the head, back and tail of various shades of blue.

[*R. T. Littlejohns.*

inhabits woods and thickets more often than gardens, and though it has not such a variety of notes as the Blackcap, its song is much more continuous.

Whitethroat (*Sylvia communis*). This little bird has the head grey, the upper parts brown, rufous on the wings, the underparts greyish-white, with a pink tinge on the breast and the throat pure w h i t e. In summer it is widely distributed in Europe including the British Isles, and western Asia, wintering in Africa. It frequents hedges and bushy localities, and has a loud, babbling song often uttered as it rises vertically into the air.

Lesser Whitethroat (*Sylvia curruca*). This has the head grey with the sides of the face nearly black, the upper parts brownish grey and the underparts white. In summer it inhabits temperate Europe and northern

By courtesy of] [*the Commonwealth of Australia.*
SUPERB BLUE WREN (*Malurus cyaneus*).
The female has only blue in the tail. The species is common in Tasmania and south-eastern Australia.

563

Whitethroat (*Sylvia communis*).
[*T. M. Fowler.*]
One of the commonest British Warblers often called the Nettle Creeper from its liking for the tangled weeds along the hedgerows.

Photos]

Sedge Warbler (*Acrocephalus schoenobaenus*).
Like the Nightingale this bird often sings at night, but its harsh, babbling chatter is very distinct.

and central Asia and in winter is found in tropical Africa. In the British Isles it breeds commonly in England, but is almost unknown in Scotland and Ireland. It frequents hedgerows and copses and has a low babbling song only audible at a short distance with a loud rattling refrain uttered at intervals.

Dartford Warbler (*Sylvia undata*). This bird is a resident in the south of England, south-western Europe and north-west Africa, frequenting furzy commons and bushy heaths. Its upper parts are dark slaty grey, its breast reddish-brown and its long tail has white margins and tips. The eggs, four or five in number, are greenish-white, with brown markings.

Chiffchaff (*Phylloscopus collybita*). The Chiffchaff is found in summer throughout Europe and northern Asia, wintering in south-western and southern Europe, Africa and tropical Asia. It is a very small bird, brownish above and whitish below, more or less tinged with yellow. It is one of the earliest of the summer visitors to arrive in the British Isles, a few even spending the winter in southern England. It is readily recognized by the notes from which it obtains its name, chiff-chaff-chiff, etc., constantly repeated.

Willow Warbler or Willow Wren (*Phylloscopus trochilus*). This Warbler closely resembles the Chiffchaff, but is rather larger and yellower. In summer it is found throughout Europe and northern Asia, retreating further south than the Chiffchaff in winter. It has a sweet warbling song, the first few notes in an ascending scale and then descending till they fade away.

Wood Warbler or Wood Wren (*Phylloscopus sibilatrix*). This bird is somewhat larger than the Willow Wren with the upper parts yellowish-green, the breast sulphur-yellow and the belly white. It is a summer visitor to Europe which winters in tropical Africa. In the British Isles it is widely distributed, chiefly frequenting woods in which there is not much undergrowth. It has a characteristic shivering song, during the utterance of which it rapidly vibrates its wings, and also produces a loud, plaintive two-syllabled call, constantly repeated.

Grasshopper Warbler (*Locustella naevia*). This is a little brownish bird, more or less streaked, remarkable for its song, which is a continuous trill resembling the sound made by an angler's reel when the line is running off it. This species frequents thickets, especially in swampy localities, and in summer is found throughout Europe and western Asia, wintering in Africa.

Reed Warbler (*Acrocephalus scirpaceus*). This bird has the upper parts brown tinged with chestnut and the underparts buffish white. It ordinarily inhabits beds of reeds and attaches its deep nest to a number of reed stems, but sometimes nests in other situations. It is a summer visitor to the greater part of Europe and western Asia, wintering in Africa, but in the British Isles is confined to England and Wales.

AVES (ORDER PASSERIFORMES)

[T. M. Fowler.
SPOTTED FLYCATCHER (*Muscicapa striata*).
A well-known summer visitor to the British Isles, conspicuous from its habit of perching on posts or rails in the open.

Marsh Warbler (*Acrocephalus palustris*). This closely resembles the Reed Warbler, but is not so chestnut above and rather yellower below. It inhabits osier-beds and thickets and in summer is distributed over Central and Southern Europe, wintering in tropical Africa. In the British Isles it breeds only in southern England, principally in the Severn Valley.

Sedge Warbler (*Acrocephalus schoenobaenus*). This bird has the upper parts rufous, mottled with dark brown, a broad yellowish-white stripe over each eye and the underparts buff. It occurs in summer throughout Europe and western Siberia, wintering in tropical and southern Africa. In the British Isles it is almost universally distributed, chiefly frequenting the tangled vegetation on the banks of lakes, rivers and streams.

Muscicapidae (*Flycatchers*). The Flycatchers include numerous small insect-eating birds with flattened bills, wide at the base, which is surrounded by bristles. As in the Thrushes, the feathers of the nestlings are mottled. They are confined to the eastern hemisphere, where they are plentiful in Africa, tropical Asia, the Malay Archipelago and Australia some occurring in New Zealand and the Pacific islands and a few visiting Europe and northern Asia in the summer.

Spotted Flycatcher (*Muscicapa striata*). This bird is brown above and dull white below, with dark streaks on the breast. It is found in summer throughout Europe, including the British Isles, and western Asia, wintering in central and southern Africa. The birds commonly perch on the rail of a fence, a post or a bare bough from which they have a clear view, flying out at intervals to capture an insect with an audible snap of the bill and usually returning to the same perch. The nest is a slight cup, generally built on a ledge or bough against a wall or tree trunk, and the eggs are greenish with reddish-brown spots.

566

FLYCATCHERS, VIREOS AND WAXWINGS

Pied Flycatcher (*Muscicapa hypoleuca*). This Flycatcher is also a summer visitor to Europe and western Asia from tropical Africa, but in the British Isles is almost confined to northern England and Wales. The male is black above, with white on the forehead and in the wings and tail, and with white underparts. The female is mainly brown above. The nest is built in a hole in a tree or wall and the eggs are pale blue without spots.

Vireonidae (*Vireos or Greenlets*). This family includes a considerable number of small birds, mostly found in tropical America, some of them visiting temperate North America in summer. They have rather stout, notched bills, higher than broad at the base, hooked at the tip. Their upper plumage is generally greenish.

Red-eyed Vireo (*Vireosylva olivacea*). This bird is found in summer almost throughout North America and winters in South America. Its head is grey, bordered by black, with a white line over the eye ; the upper parts are olive-green and the underparts white, whilst the eye is red. The cup-shaped nest is suspended from a forked branch and the three to four eggs are white, with a few dark spots at the larger end.

Bombycillidae (*Wax-wings*). The Waxwings include only three species, one found in North America, one in north-eastern Asia, and the third breeding in high northern latitudes in both hemispheres and wandering southward in winter. Waxwings have short, thick bills, wide at the base and slightly hooked at the tip ; long crests ; long wings ; short tails and very short legs.

Bohemian Waxwing (*Bombycilla garrulus*). This is the third of the species mentioned above. Its plumage is cinnamon-

[*J. E. Ruxton.*

PIED FLYCATCHER (*Muscicapa hypoleuca*).
In the British Isles this species is almost confined to the wooded valleys of Wales and northern England.

brown, varying to brownish-grey and to chestnut, relieved with black, white and yellow. The tail is black, tipped with yellow. In old birds the secondaries, and occasionally also the tail-feathers, have the tips of the shafts projecting beyond the barbs and somewhat enlarged, coloured bright 'sealing-wax' red. This species is a very erratic migrant, large flocks appearing in winter in various parts of the United States and Europe, including the British Isles, at intervals of years. At this season they feed greedily on berries.

Ptilogonatidae (*Silky Flycatchers*). This family consists of a few small, arboreal birds, distributed from the south-western United States to Costa Rica. They have small, broad bills, very wide at the base, which is surrounded by bristles. Their wings are rather short and rounded; their tails long and fan-shaped; and their plumage silky, with plain but often handsome, blended colours.

Dulidae (*Palm-chats*). This family includes one or two species found in Haiti. They have short, stout, curved, compressed bills; rather long, rounded wings; short tails and strong feet. Their plumage is olive-brown above, yellowish-white below, with conspicuous dusky streaks. Their food consists of fruits and insects, and they chiefly frequent palm-trees, in which they construct enormously bulky nests of sticks, said to be utilized jointly by several pairs.

Artamidae (*Wood-swallows* or *Swallow-shrikes*). The Wood-swallows include a number of small birds, mostly found in Australia, extending through the Malay region to India and also to the Fiji Islands. They have longish, pointed, slightly curved grey-blue bills, wide at the base; long, pointed wings; short tails; and short, stout legs. In most of the species grey is the predominant colour, often varied with areas of black and white. Their food consists almost entirely of insects captured on the wing, and they either sail about in the air like swallows or fly out from a perch like flycatchers. They build rather slight, cup-shaped nests, and lay from two to four greenish or pinkish eggs, with dark markings. They are very sociable birds, almost always found in flocks, and many pairs often nest in close proximity.

Dusky Wood-swallow (*Artamus cyanopterus*) This bird, of southern Australia and Tasmania, has the strange habit of roosting in clusters, some birds hanging on a branch and many others clinging on to them in a compact mass like a swarm of bees.

Vangidae (*Madagascar-shrikes*). This family includes a few birds found in Madagascar, with stout, curved, strongly-hooked bills. Most of them are mainly black and white in colouring.

Grallinidae. This family contains only the Magpie-lark (*Grallina cyanoleuca*) of Australia and an allied species from New Guinea. The Magpie-lark is a moderate-sized black and white bird, with a yellow bill and exceptionally long legs, which spends much of its time running about on the ground feeding on snails and insects. It has a curious flapping flight, somewhat resembling that of the Lapwing, and a loud call-note which earns it the name of " Peewee " in some localities. It builds a large, bowl-shaped nest of mud, generally on the bare horizontal limb of a tree, and lays three or four pinkish eggs marked with red and purple.

Prionopidae (*Wood-shrikes*). The Wood-shrikes include a number of

[*Oliver G. Pike.*

RED-BACKED SHRIKE (*Lanius collurio*).
One of the handsomest of the smaller English birds with its blue-grey head, chestnut back, rosy white breast, black wings and black and white tail.

birds with slightly hooked bills and dull plumage, mainly black, grey or brown. They are found in Africa, tropical Asia, the Malay Archipelago, Australia and some of the Pacific Islands, where they mostly frequent forest country.

Grey Shrike-thrush (*Colluricincla harmonica*). As its name implies, this is a grey bird about the size of a thrush. Its song is loud and melodious. It builds a large, cup-shaped nest near the ground, and lays from three to four pearly-white eggs, spotted with grey and greenish.

Aerocharidae. This family contains only the Helmet-bird (*Aerocharis prevosti*), restricted to north-eastern Madagascar. It has a long, compressed bill, with the upper mandible hooked at the tip and very much elevated and dilated at the base. The sexes are similar in colour, the head, neck and underparts being glossy black, the upper parts mainly chestnut.

Cyclarhidae (*Pepper-shrikes*). The Pepper-shrikes include a few tropical American birds with short, stout, compressed bills, somewhat curved and slightly hooked at the tip. Their plumage is greenish above and yellowish below, with a brownish or greyish band on the crown, bordered by stripes of reddish or cinnamon colour.

Vireolaniidae (*Shrike-vireos*). In this family are a few small birds, found in tropical America. They have large, elongated bills with hooked tips ; rather short, rounded wings ; short tails and rather long legs. Their plumage is green above, yellow or white below.

Streperidae (*Crow-shrikes*). The Crow-shrikes include a number of fairly large

[R. T. Littlejohns.

YELLOW SHRIKE-ROBIN (*Eopsaltria australis*).
A familiar and confiding bird in eastern Australia, with grey head, greenish-brown back and lemon-yellow breast. It always decorates its nest with hanging strips.

[*Robert McLeod.*

GREAT TIT (*Parus major*).
Also known as Ox-eye, from the large white patches on the cheeks. This species is common in most parts of the British Isles.

perching birds with strong bills, slightly hooked at the tip. They occur in Australia and New Guinea.

Black-backed Magpie (*Gymnorhina tibicen*). This bird is widely distributed in eastern and northern Australia. It is a black and white bird as large as a Jackdaw, sometimes called the " Piping Crow " from its fine flute-like warblings.

Laniidae (*Shrikes or Butcher-birds*). The Shrikes include moderate-sized birds with strongly-hooked, hawk-like bills, rounded wings, fairly long tails of twelve feathers and rather short legs. They are numerous in Africa and tropical Asia, and a few occur in Europe, northern Asia and North America. Their food consists of large insects, frogs, reptiles, small birds and small mammals, and they have the curious habit of impaling their victims on thorns, whence they are often called Butcher-birds.

Red-backed Shrike (*Lanius collurio*). This is a summer visitor to Europe and western Asia, wintering in Africa. In the British Isles it breeds in England and Wales, but is only an occasional visitor to Scotland and Ireland. The male has the crown and nape blue-grey, the sides of the head with a black band, the back chestnut-red, the wings black, the tail black with white edges and the underparts rosy white. The female is brownish-grey above and dull white below. Its rather large, cup-shaped nest is

571

placed in a bush and the eggs vary in ground-colour from greenish to salmon, with violet and brownish spots.

Regulidae (*Kinglets and Gnatcatchers*). This family includes a number of very small, arboreal birds, with thin, slender bills and comparatively long wings, rounded at the tip. They are found in Europe, northern Asia and North and South America.

Golden-crested Wren (*Regulus regulus*). This is a very small bird with greenish upper parts and greyish underparts tinged with yellow. In the centre of the crown there is a broad yellow stripe, orange in the centre in the male, bordered with black on each side. The Goldcrest is found throughout Europe and northern Asia, frequenting forests and woods of coniferous trees. In winter the northern forests are deserted and large numbers appear in the southern part of its range. It builds a hanging nest of moss, lined with feathers, suspended from the bough of a fir or yew-tree, and lays from seven to ten or more tiny, buffish-white eggs, with fine spots of brown at the larger end.

Chamaeidae contains only the Wren-tit (*Chamaea fasciata*) of California and Oregon. It is a small bird, with a short, curved, compressed bill with bristles at the base ; short, rounded wings ; a fairly long tail, commonly carried erect ; and comparatively long legs. Its plumage is brown above and buffish below. It inhabits thickets, where it lives much on the ground, and builds an open nest of twigs and grass in a low bush, laying from three to five greenish-blue eggs.

Paridae (*Titmice or Tits*). The Tits comprise a large number of small birds, with short, stout rounded bills and fairly long, rounded wings in which the fourth or fifth primary is the longest and the first is small, sometimes rudimentary. They are found in all parts of the world except South America, the Pacific Islands and New Guinea, though it seems doubtful whether the Australian and New Zealand birds generally placed in the family are really related to the typical Tits.

Great Tit (*Parus major*). This bird occurs throughout Europe and northern Asia and in north-west Africa. It has the crown, the sides of the neck, the throat and a broad line down the centre of the breast, black ; the cheeks, white ; the back, yellowish-green ; the rump, grey ; the wings and tail, greyish-black, with some white markings, and the breast, yellow. It is a lively and active bird, inhabiting woods, orchards and gardens, clinging to the boughs and twigs of the trees in any position which enables it to scan the bark or the foliage for the small insects on which it chiefly feeds. Its nest is built in a hole in a tree or wall, and it lays from six to ten white eggs, spotted with red.

Blue Tit (*Parus coeruleus*). This is a smaller bird, with very similar habits. Its head is blue and white and its rump and breast yellow, the rest of its plumage resembling that of the Great Tit. It occurs throughout Europe, in western Asia and in north-western Africa.

572

TITMICE OR TITS (PARIDAE)

Coal Tit (*Parus ater*).   This is still smaller than the Blue Tit, and has the head black with white patches on the cheeks and nape.   Its back is grey and its breast dull white.   It inhabits forests and woods throughout Europe, a great part of Asia and northern Africa and is widely distributed in the British Isles, where it is specially partial to pine-woods and plantations.

Marsh Tit (*Penthestes palustris*).   This bird has the crown and nape glossy black, the upper parts greyish-brown, the chin black and the underparts buffish white.   It occurs throughout northern and central Europe and in western Asia and Siberia.   In the British Isles it is confined to England, and frequents woods and hedgerows as well as swampy localities.

Willow Tit or Chickadee (*Penthestes atricapillus*).   This closely resembles the Marsh Tit, but the crown is dull black instead of glossy, and in most parts of its range its back is greyer.   It is widely distributed in Europe, northern Asia and North America, but in the British Isles is comparatively scarce, though found in many parts of England and Scotland.

[M. H. Crawford.
BLUE TIT (*Parus coeruleus*).
These birds are readily attracted to fat, coconut or monkeynuts hung out for them.

Crested Tit (*Lophophanes cristatus*).   This bird is an inhabitant of pine-forests in most parts of Europe, but in Britain is confined to those of the Spey Valley and adjacent parts of Scotland.   The head is mottled with black and greyish-white, the feathers of the crown being elongated to form a conspicuous crest, the throat and upper breast are black, the upper parts brown and the underparts dull white.

Long-tailed Tit (*Aegithalos caudatus*).   This Tit has an extremely small body and a very long tail in proportion.   Its plumage is mainly black and white, but some races, especially that inhabiting the British Isles, have a

573

rosy tinge. It occurs throughout Europe and northern Asia. Its domed nest is a large ovoid structure of moss and lichens, lined with feathers, with a small entrance near the top, and is placed in a shrub or tree.

Bearded Tit or Reedling (*Panurus biarmicus*). This bird has a blue-grey head and whitish cheeks and throat, most of the rest of the plumage being russet, varied with some black and white. The male has a black moustache-mark on each side of the face. It inhabits reed beds in many parts of Europe and northern Asia, but in the British Isles is now only found in Norfolk. Its round nest of dead reeds and dry grasses is built near the base of the reeds.

[T. M. Fowler.

NUTHATCH (*Sitta europaea*).
This bird nests in holes and if the entrance is too large it partly blocks it up with mud, leaving a hole of suitable size.

Hypositittidae. This family contains a single species confined to Madagascar, the Coral-billed Nuthatch (*Hypositta corallirostris*). It has a short, stout beak, somewhat hooked at the tip, with stout bristles at the base. Its plumage is mainly blue and its bill, coral-red.

Sittidae (*Nuthatches*). The Nuthatches include a number of small birds, with rather long, stout, straight bills ; longish wings ; short tails ; short legs and large feet, the toes with large, laterally-compressed claws. They are found in Europe, Asia, Australia and North America, in forests and wooded regions, running actively about on tree trunks and branches, indifferently upwards, sideways or downwards, holding on to the irregularities of the bark by their strong feet. They feed largely on nuts, which they fix into crevices of the bark and split open to get at the kernels by hammering the shells with their powerful beaks, but insects and berries are also eaten.

Common Nuthatch (*Sitta europaea*). This bird has the upper parts blue-grey and the underparts buff or white, with chestnut flanks. It is found

574

throughout most of Europe and northern Asia, but in the British Isles is almost confined to England, only occasionally visiting Scotland and never found in Ireland.

Certhiidae (*Creepers*). This family comprises a few small birds found in all parts of the world except South America, Madagascar, New Zealand and the Pacific Islands. They have long, slender bills, usually somewhat curved ; their legs are short ; the toes are unequal in length, the outer much longer than the inner ; and the claws are very strong, that of the hind toe as long as the toe itself.

Common Tree-creeper (*Certhia familiaris*). This is an inconspicuous little bird, whose plumage is mottled brown above and white below. It climbs up the trunks of trees searching for insects in the crevices of the bark, helping to support itself by its tail, the feathers of which are stiff and pointed as in the Wood-peckers. It is found in woodland districts of Europe (including Britain), northern Asia and North America.

Zosteropidae (*White-eyes or Silver-eyes*). This family includes numerous species of

[*T. M. Fowler.*

LONG-TAILED TIT (*Aegithalos caudatus*).
This little bird builds a wonderfully neat domed nest of moss and lichen, warmly lined with feathers.

very small birds found in Africa, southern Asia and Australia, and in most of the islands of the Indian and Pacific Oceans. Their plumage is alike in both sexes and is either brown or green above, white or yellowish below, and a conspicuous ring of small white feathers surrounds each eye. They are Tit-like in habit and feed on insects and berries, build slender, cup-shaped nests in trees or bushes and lay pale blue unspotted eggs.

Grey-backed Silver-eye (*Zosterops halmaturina*). This bird, of south-eastern Australia and Tasmania, is noteworthy because in 1856 it appeared in the South Island of New Zealand ; it soon spread throughout that island

and into the North Island, and subsequently spread to the Chatham Islands.

Dicaeidae (*Flower-peckers and Diamond-birds*). This family includes some very small birds, mostly brilliantly coloured, inhabiting tropical Asia, the Malay Archipelago and Australia. The majority have short, broad, flattened bills ; longish wings and short tails. They are mainly arboreal in habits, feeding on insects, spiders, berries and seeds. Their nests are generally domed, sometimes suspended from boughs and sometimes placed in holes, and their eggs are usually white.

Promeropidae. This family contains only the Long-tailed Sun-bird (*Promerops cafer*) of South Africa. It is a small bird, with a long, curved bill ; a grooved tongue with frayed edges ; and a very long tail. Its plumage is greyish-brown above, mottled white below, the vent is yellow. It usually congregates in small parties on flowering trees, especially Proteas, to obtain the honey from the blossoms. It builds an open, cup-shaped nest and its eggs are creamy-white, marked with wavy lines of purplish colour.

Nectariniidae (*Sun-birds*). The Sun-birds include numerous small birds with long, slender, curved bills and long, protractile tongues which end in a tube, bifid at the tip. They have brilliant metallic colours in their plumage and are sometimes regarded as representing Humming-birds in the Old World, being frequently called ' Humming-birds ' in India. Sun-birds are found throughout tropical and southern Africa, including Madagascar, and in tropical Asia and the Malay Archipelago, east to New Guinea, one species extending to north-eastern Australia. The family is also represented by single species in Baluchistan and southern Persia, Arabia and the Jordan valley in Palestine. Sun-birds flit rapidly about among flowering trees and shrubs, extracting honey from the flowers, also feeding largely on small spiders and insects. They build woven, domed nests, felted together with cobwebs, suspended from boughs, and lay eggs (two) with a greyish ground-colour, freckled or spotted with reddish-brown, purplish or dusky.

Meliphagidae (*Honey-eaters*). The Honey-eaters include a large number of small, or moderate-sized, birds, found in Australia, New Zealand, the eastern part of the Malay Archipelago and many of the Pacific Islands. Their bills are always somewhat curved, usually fairly short, but sometimes very long ; their tongues are extensile, divided at the tip, each half broken up into a brush of horny fibres. They vary greatly in size, form and appearance, but nearly all are lively, pugnacious birds, frequenting trees or bushes, feeding on berries, insects and honey obtained from the flowers by means of their brush-like tongues. Their nests are almost always rather slight, cup-shaped structures, suspended by their edges in the fork of a bough, and their eggs are salmon-pink or white with reddish, grey or black markings.

Blood-bird (*Myzomela sanguinolenta*). This is a small species found in eastern Australia, with a long, curved bill. The male has the head and body brilliant scarlet, with black wings and tail ; the female is brown.

Red Wattle-bird (*Acanthochaera carunculata*). This bird of southern Australia is one of the largest species, fourteen to fifteen inches in length. Its plumage is greyish-brown streaked with white, with a patch of yellow on the abdomen, and on each cheek it has a blood-red lobe or wattle of pendulous skin, from which it derives its name.

Parson-bird or Tui (*Prosthemadera novae zealandiae*). The Tui of New Zealand and the Chatham Islands is another of the larger forms, about twelve inches in length. Its plumage is bluish or greenish-black, with metallic reflections ; there is a white spot on each wing, and the throat has two extraordinary tufts of white, curly feathers.

Mniotiltidae (*American or Wood Warblers*). The Wood Warblers include about one hundred and fifty species of small birds, mainly arboreal in habits, found only in America. Their bills are usually slender and sharply pointed ; the first primary is well-developed, being nearly, or quite, as long as the second and third ; and the tail is usually square but sometimes rounded. Though green and yellow tints predominate in their

[*D. Seth-Smith.*
SPINY-CHEEKED HONEY-EATER (*Acanthagenys rufogularis*). This member of the family of Honey-eaters, found throughout Australia, has a tuft of curious stiff feathers on each cheek.

plumage some are brilliantly coloured, and in their breeding plumage most of the males exhibit some bright colours. Wood Warblers are almost entirely insectivorous, and in winter most of the species retire to the tropics, but in the spring and early summer immense numbers travel northwards in mixed flocks to breed in the forests of the United States and Canada. Several species have fine songs, but the majority have only feeble voices. The majority build cup-shaped nests in trees or bushes and lay from two to six eggs, usually with a creamy ground-colour, more or less spotted or blotched with reddish-brown, grey or black.

Black and White Creeper (*Mniotilta varia*). This bird is streaked with black and white above and below. It is found in summer throughout eastern North America, wintering in the tropics. It runs up the trunks of trees and hangs from the branches with the agility of a creeper and a tit combined.

AVES (ORDER PASSERIFORMES)

Myrtle Warbler (*Dendroica coronata*). This Warbler is bluish-grey, streaked with black, above ; and white below, with black marks on the breast ; the crown, rump and a patch on each side of the breast are yellow ; there are two white bars in the wing and white spots on the outer tail-feathers. It breeds from Alaska throughout Canada to New England, and though the majority winter in the West Indies and Central America, many remain in the United States, feeding on the berries of bayberry and myrtle.

Drepanididae (*Hawaiian Honey-eaters*). This family includes a number of species, many of them now extinct, only found in the Hawaiian Islands. Their bills differ extraordinarily in form, but all have a more or less tubular tongue, split or frayed at the end. Many of the males have brilliant plumage and their feathers were formerly used to make the wonderful feather-cloaks and other ornaments of the Hawaiian chiefs. The females are gener-ally duller in plumage. They are chiefly inhabitants of the mountain forests, where they creep about on the trees, probing crevices for insects and sucking honey from the flowers. Many also feed on berries. Little is known of their breeding habits.

Enicuridae (*Fork-tails*). The Fork-tails include a few small birds with black and white plumage and long, forked tails. They frequent the moun-tain streams of tropical Asia from the Himalayas and China to the Malay Peninsula, Sumatra, Java and Borneo. They build large nests under a stone or fallen tree close to the water, and lay greenish-white eggs freckled with rusty brown. They are constantly in motion, flitting from rock to rock by the sides of the torrents.

Motacillidae (*Pipits, Wagtails, etc.*) This family comprises small birds with thin, slender bills ; wings with only nine primaries, and secondaries nearly as long as the primaries ; and long tails of twelve feathers. They are chiefly terrestrial in habits, running on the ground instead of hopping, and generally keeping the tail in constant up-and-down motion. Their nests are open and cup-shaped, either placed on the ground or in a hole in a bank or wall, and their eggs are spotted. They are represented in almost all parts of the world, but in North and South America, Australia and New Zealand only by Pipits, members of the genus *Anthus*.

Meadow Pipit (*Anthus pratensis*). This bird, often called the " Tit-lark," much resembles the Skylark in colouring, but is a smaller, more slender bird, without a crest, and its song and call-notes are very different. It is an inhabitant of Europe and western Asia, breeding in moorlands, mountain pastures and rough commons, and in winter visiting fields and wet places in the lowlands, or migrating south to the Mediterranean countries. Very similar species, frequenting similar habitats, are found in almost all parts of the world.

Rock Pipit (*Anthus petrosus*). This bird is slightly larger than the Meadow Pipit and its plumage is darker. It inhabits the coasts of north-western Europe, including the British Isles, in summer frequenting

[A. H. Willford.

PIED WAGTAIL (*Motacilla yarrelli*).
The long tail of the " Water Wagtail " is perpetually in up-and-down motion. The hen bird here seen is much lighter on the back than the cock.

cliffs and rocks, but in winter also visiting salt-marshes and muddy estuaries.

Tree Pipit (*Anthus trivialis*). This Pipit is almost identical with the Meadow Pipit in plumage, but has a short curved hind claw, whilst that of the Meadow Pipit is long and straight. Its name is derived from its habit of singing in or from a tree, but like its congeners, it feeds and nests on the ground.

Pied Wagtail (*Motacilla yarrelli*). This is a small black and white bird, with a long tail which is perpetually in motion. It is an inhabitant of the British Isles and western Europe, some wintering as far south as Morocco. It frequents lawns, meadows and river banks.

Grey Wagtail (*Motacilla cinerea*). This Wagtail is somewhat larger and with an even longer tail. In summer the male has the head and back blue-grey, the throat black and the underparts bright sulphur-yellow. The female is duller, and in winter both sexes have the throat white. In summer it is found throughout Europe and northern Asia in suitable localities, and many migrate south to winter in tropical Africa and Asia. It frequents almost exclusively the neighbourhood of rivers and streams in hilly or mountainous country, finding its food on the damp rocks by the water-side.

579

Yellow Wagtail (*Motacilla flava*). This is a summer visitor to Europe, northern Asia and Alaska, wintering in tropical Africa and Asia. The upper parts are olive-brown tinged with yellow, the tail blackish-brown with white edges and the underparts bright yellow. The species includes a large number of races which differ chiefly in the colouring of the head of the male. In the race which breeds in England the forehead, crown and eyebrow of the male are bright yellow. The Yellow Wagtail frequents meadows and pastures chiefly in the vicinity of water.

[*T. M. Fowler.*

YELLOW WAGTAIL (*Motacilla flava*).
A summer visitor to England which breeds in water-meadows and hayfields near rivers.

Alaudidae (*Larks*). This family includes terrestrial birds inhabiting open country —cultivated land, pasture or desert. They are numerous in Africa and Asia, few in Europe, and represented by only one or two species in North America and Australia. The claw of the hind toe is straight, sharp and often very long. Their bills vary greatly, in some species being fairly slender and pointed, in others very stout. Larks are mostly brown or sandy in colour, often being very inconspicuous when on the ground, where they run instead of hopping. Most of them rise into the air to sing and the majority rarely or never settle in trees. Their nests are almost always open, cup-shaped structures on the ground, and their eggs have a whitish ground-colour, generally almost hidden by a profusion of spots and freckles of grey or brownish.

Skylark (*Alauda arvensis*). This is a brown bird, lighter below, and with white margins to the tail. The plumage is more or less streaked with darker colours, and the feathers of the top of the head are elongated, forming a low crest. It is one of the commonest birds throughout large parts of

580

[A. H. Willford.

MEADOW PIPIT (*Anthus pratensis*).
Perhaps better known as the " Titlark," this dull-coloured terrestrial bird is probably the most widespread species in the British Isles.

[T. M. Fowler.

TREE PIPITS (*Anthus trivialis*).
A summer visitor to the British Isles, the male sings either in a tree or in the air during his descent with wings and tail spread.

581

Europe and Asia, those which breed in the more northerly portions migrating south in autumn. During the winter it is found in temperate Europe and Asia and south to India and North Africa. The song of the Skylark, uttered whilst it circles round in the air with rapidly-beating wings, sometimes so high as to be almost invisible, is remarkable more for its continuity and the rapidity with which the loud notes succeed one another, than for sweetness or variety of the notes, but it has inspired some of the finest poems in the English language.

Woodlark (*Lullula arborea*). This is similar to the Skylark in colouring but somewhat smaller, without a crest and with a very short tail. It is found throughout most of Europe, in western Asia and in north-western Africa, but in the British Isles is only found locally in the South of England. It does not inhabit woods, but prefers open country with plantations or scattered trees. Its song is sweeter than that of the Skylark, but less prolonged and may be uttered while the bird is flying or when perched in a tree.

Fringillidae (*Finches, Sparrows, Buntings, etc.*). This is a very large group of small birds, represented in all parts of the world. In Australia and New Zealand none is indigenous, but several European species have been acclimatized. Finches have conical, rather short beaks, with the nostrils close to the feathers and either partly concealed by them or by a membrane. There are only nine primaries in the wing; the tail-feathers number twelve. The sexes are almost always different, the young resembling the females. Almost all, except the Sparrows, build open, cup-shaped nests. The eggs vary in ground colour, but are nearly always spotted, speckled or streaked.

Members of this family are predominantly seed-eaters, but they feed their young largely on insects. Many have pleasing songs.

Hawfinch (*Coccothraustes coccothraustes*). This bird is remarkable for its very stout bill. Its plumage is mainly rufous-brown, with some black and white. It occurs throughout Europe and the greater part of Asia, but its shy habits lead to its being overlooked. Its great partiality for peas often leads to its destruction by gardeners.

Greenfinch (*Chloris chloris*). The Greenfinch has a stout bill and green plumage, with patches of yellow in the wings and tail. It is found throughout Europe, in north-western Africa and western Asia, being very common in the British Isles.

Cardinal (*Cardinalis cardinalis*). This bird occurs throughout eastern North America. The male is bright rosy-red, with some black on the face and a conspicuous crest; the female is dull red and brownish.

Crested Cardinal (*Paroaria cucullata*). This Cardinal is a native of Brazil, Uruguay and Argentina, and is a very common cage bird. The Crested Cardinal is grey above and white below, the head, crest, throat and breast being brilliant scarlet.

FINCHES (FRINGILLIDAE)

Goldfinch (*Carduelis carduelis*). This is one of the most brightly-coloured small birds found in the British Isles, and is a favourite cage-bird. It occurs also throughout Europe, in north-western Africa and western Asia. The face is crimson, the cheeks white and the back of the head and sides of the neck black ; the back is amber-brown ; the breast, white, with a buffish and yellowish band ; the wings are black, barred with bright yellow, and the tail black, with white at base and tip.

Siskin (*Carduelis spinus*). This bird is found in summer from Scotland across northern Europe and Asia to the Pacific, breeding in pine woods,

[*T. M. Fowler.*

SKYLARK (*Alauda arvensis*).
It has been estimated that this is the most plentiful of all European birds.

and migrates southward for the winter, when it is not uncommon in England. Its plumage is predominantly greenish above and yellowish below, and the male has the crown and chin black.

Redpoll (*Carduelis flammea*). This is a small finch with brownish colouring, the feathers being more or less edged with white, and the breast and rump more or less red in the breeding season. The forehead is blood-red and the chin black. Various races of this species occur in high northern latitudes, breeding in birchwoods to the limit of their distribution in the Arctic, whilst the smallest race breeds in the British Isles and the mountain ranges of Europe.

Mountain Linnet or Twite (*Carduelis flavirostris*). This breeds in northern Europe and Asia on high moorlands or near the coast. In the British Isles

583

it is found in Scotland, northern England and Ireland. In winter many
migrate southwards. The plumage is mottled with various shades of brown
and the male has the rump rose-red.

Linnet (*Carduelis cannabina*). In winter this is a comparatively dull
bird, mottled with grey and brown, but in the breeding season the male
has crimson on the head and breast and chestnut-brown mantle. It inhabits the greater part of Europe and south-western Asia, many migrating
southward for the winter. In the British Isles it is a common bird at all
seasons.

Chaffinch (*Fringilla coelebs*). The Chaffinch occurs throughout Europe,
in north Africa and in western Asia. The male has a blue-grey head,
reddish-brown back, yellowish-green rump and pink breast ; the wings are

[*T. M. Fowler.*

GOLDFINCH (*Carduelis carduelis*).
This lovely finch commonly builds its nest in fruit trees. The one here seen is in a pear tree.

blackish, with two conspicuous white bars and the tail, blackish, with
white edges. The female is yellowish-brown above and yellowish-grey
below, with wings and tail like those of the male.

Brambling or **Bramble-finch** (*Fringilla montifringilla*). In summer this
inhabits the sub-Arctic forests of northern Europe and Asia and has occasionally nested in Scotland. In winter it travels southwards in flocks,
and in some seasons is plentiful in the British Isles, its winter range extending
to North Africa, Asia Minor, northern India and Japan. The plumage
is orange-brown with black markings, the rump and a bar on the wing are
white. In the breeding season the male has a black head.

Bullfinch (*Pyrrhula pyrrhula*). This bird, found throughout Europe
and northern Asia, has a short and very stout beak. The male has the top
of the head black ; the back, blue-grey ; the rump, white ; and the cheeks

CROSSBILL (*Loxia curvirostra*).
The crossed mandibles of this finch help it to extract the seeds from fir-cones.

and breast bright red ; the wings and tail are black. In the female the back is brownish-grey and the breast, pinkish-brown, otherwise she resembles the male.

Crossbill (*Loxia curvirostra*). The Crossbill is an inhabitant of the pine - forests of Europe, northern Asia and North America, remarkable for the fact that the curved tips of the mandibles are crossed. The plumage of the male is mostly dull crimson, with brown wings and tail ; the female is greenish-orange and the young, green with dark streaks. The birds climb about in trees like parrots, using the bill as well as the feet, and the bill also serves to extract the seeds from the cones of pine, spruce or larch. The Crossbill breeds very early, often in February, and the birds from northern Europe in some seasons travel south in flocks in the middle of summer, often appearing in numbers in the British Isles and south-western Europe.

In recent years some of these nomads have established breeding colonies in various localities in England and Ireland, but these tend to disappear after a few years, unless reinforced by another invasion from the north.

Serin Finch (*Serinus canarius*). This is a streaked greenish-brown bird, with yellow rump and breast. It is an inhabitant of central Europe and the countries round the Mediterranean, also of

Photos]   *[T. M. Fowler.*
LINNET (*Carduelis cannabina*).
Variously known as the Grey, Red or Brown Linnet, according to its plumage, which changes with the season.

585

the Azores, Madeira and the Canary Islands. This species is undoubtedly the ancestor of the domesticated *Canary*, which from its name was presumably originally brought from the Canary Islands, though its origin is as obscure as that of most other domesticated animals. In confinement a considerable number of varieties have been produced, and variation began early, since in 1587 the canary-bird was described as almost wholly yellow. The different breeds vary in size, the Lancashire being much the largest ; in form, the Scotch and Belgian fancy canaries and the crested canary are the most remarkable ; in colour, the variation is from a plumage resembling that of the wild Serin to pure yellow and to the colours of the Cinnamon and Lizard canaries ; and there is also great difference in capacity for song, for which the Norwich, and particularly the German roller, canaries are the most celebrated.

[*Stanley Crook.*
SISKIN (*Carduelis spinus*).
Chiefly known in England as a winter visitor from the North, but breeding in pinewoods in Scotland.

House Sparrow (*Passer domesticus*). This bird is too well-known to require description. It is found throughout the greater part of Asia and most of Europe, but is everywhere more attached to human dwellings than any other bird, and nowhere thrives away from towns, villages and farms. It has been introduced into North and South America, South Africa, Australia and New Zealand and is steadily spreading over the settled districts of those countries, so that in time it will probably be almost as cosmopolitan as man. In Italy, however, it is replaced by the nearly allied Italian Sparrow (*Passer italiae*), and in parts of Spain, Sicily and North Africa by the Spanish Sparrow (*Passer hispaniolensis*). The bulky, untidy, domed nests of Sparrows resemble those of Weaver-birds and are unlike those of the true Finches, and some authorities consider that the genus Passer should be placed in the family Ploceidae.

Tree Sparrow (*Passer montanus*). This differs from the House Sparrow in having the crown chestnut and a black spot on the cheek, and in the fact that the cock and hen are similar. In many parts of Eastern Asia it takes the place of the House Sparrow, and is familiar from its constant representation by Japanese artists, but in Europe, including the British Isles, it usually inhabits copses, hedges or trees on river-banks.

Common, or Corn, Bunting (*Emberiza calandra*). This is a heavily-built finch, whose plumage is mottled with various shades of brown. It is

586

[Reginald Gaze.

YELLOWHAMMER (*Emberiza citrinella*).
The female here seen on her nest, lacks the bright yellow head of her mate.

[Ian H. Thomson.

BULLFINCH (*Pyrrhula pyrrhula*).

[*Oliver G. Pike.*

CHAFFINCH (*Fringilla coelebs*).
The commonest finch in the British Isles and the builder of a wonderfully neat nest
of moss, lichen and wool.

common in the British Isles and in many parts of Europe, western Asia, and northern Africa.

Yellow Bunting or Yellowhammer (*Emberiza citrinella*). This has the head and under-parts lemon-yellow, the rump chestnut and the remaining plumage mottled brown. It is very common in almost all parts of the British Isles, frequenting hedge-rows and furzy commons, and its range extends through central and eastern Europe to Siberia.

Cirl Bunting (*Emberiza cirlus*). This bird has a more southerly range than the Yellowhammer, extending from South Wales and western and southern England through the countries on both sides of the Mediterranean to southern Russia and Asia Minor. The male has a black throat, yellow collar, greenish band across the breast, yellow belly and chestnut flanks. The rest of his plumage is mottled with various shades of brown, whilst that of the female is almost entirely of this colour.

Reed Bunting (*Emberiza schoeniclus*). This is an inhabitant of reed-beds and bushes growing in marshy localities throughout Europe and northern Asia, many migrating to Africa and India in winter. The male in breeding plumage has the head and throat black, a broad, white collar, the upper parts mottled with reddish-brown and dark brown, and the underparts whitish. The female, and the male in winter, has the plumage

588

mottled with various shades of brown. Both sexes have conspicuous white patches on the outer tail-feathers.

Snow Bunting (*Plectrophenax nivalis*). This breeds in the Arctic and sub-Arctic regions of both hemispheres, a few nesting near the summits of mountains in the Highlands of Scotland. In winter large numbers travel south to the British Isles, Central Europe, Asia and the United States, frequenting high ground or the neighbourhood of the coast. In breeding plumage the male is white with black on the back, wings and tail, but in winter his upper parts are mainly chestnut with large patches of white in the wing. The female has the upper parts greyish-black, the underparts and secondaries being white.

Catamblyrhyn-chidae. This family includes only the Plush-capped Finch (*Catamblyr-hynchus diadema*), found in the Andes, from Colombia to Peru. It is a finch-like bird, but with a stout, very much flattened, broad bill, and the plumage of its forehead and crown is dense, erect and plush-like.

Coerebidae (*Quit-quits* or *American Creepers* and *Sugar-birds*). This family includes a number of small birds allied to the Tana-gers, inhabiting tropical America

[G. K. Yeates.
REED BUNTING (*Emberiza schoeniclus*).
The female is here seen on a hot day shading her young with outspread wings.

589

By courtesy of]   [the *American Museum of Natural History.*
SCARLET TANAGERS (*Piranga erythromelas*).

and the West Indies, many of them brilliantly coloured. Their bills are conical or slender and they have a long extensible bifid tongue, frayed at the end. They climb about in the trees, somewhat like Tits, and extract honey from flowers, and catch insects. They build domed nests of grass, moss and fibres, and lay from two to four eggs, white or greenish-blue, with brown or reddish spots.

Procniatidae. This family contains a single species, *Procnias viridis*, found throughout the forested regions of tropical South America. It has a very wide bill, and lays white eggs in a hole, in a tree or in the ground, lined with roots and stems.

Thraupidae (*Tanagers*). The Tanagers include a large number of finch-like birds, chiefly found in tropical America, a few extending to the United States and Canada in the north and Argentina in the south. Their bills are conical and pointed, and the nostrils are exposed. Most of the species have brilliant plumage and the sexes are frequently differently coloured. They are chiefly forest-frequenting birds, wandering through the jungles in small parties, feeding on berries, flowers and insects.

Scarlet Tanager (*Piranga erythromelas*). This is a summer visitor to eastern North America, wintering in the tropics. The females and young birds, and the adult males in winter, are greenish above and yellowish below, with dark wings and tail, but the adult male in summer is bright scarlet, with black wings and tail. The nest is a rather slight structure of fine twigs and weed stalks, usually placed near the end of a branch, and the three or four eggs are bluish, with numerous reddish-brown markings.

Ploceidae (*Weaver-birds*). The Weaver-birds include a large number of small birds, nearly allied to the Finches, with similar conical bills, but with the first primary developed, though usually small. They are most plentiful in Africa, but occur also in tropical Asia, the Malay Archipelago, Australia and some of the Pacific Islands. The males usually have brilliant plumage, often with strikingly contrasted patches of colour, whilst the females are generally plainer. Almost all the species build large, untidy nests of grasses more or less woven together, domed and sometimes with a projecting tubular entrance. The nests are often close together in colonies. Most species lay white eggs, but in some they are blue or green, and in some they are also speckled or spotted.

Java Sparrow (*Munia orizivora*). This bird is indigenous in Java, Sumatra and Malacca, but has been naturalized elsewhere and is one of the best-known cage-birds. It has a slate-grey body and black crown and usually also white patches on the cheeks. The bill is pink. A white variety is also commonly kept in cages. The sexes are alike. In the wild state it is often very injurious to crops of rice or other grain.

Long-tailed Widow-bird (*Chera progne*). This bird, also called Whydah, is an inhabitant of eastern South Africa, where it inhabits swampy ground and reed-beds. The female is a mottled brown bird with an orange patch on the shoulders, but the male is glossy black, with the shoulder-patch buff and crimson. In the breeding season

[*M. H. Crawford.*
REDPOLL (*Carduelis flammea*).
The smallest of the British finches feeds largely on the seeds of the alder during the winter.

591

the tail-feathers of the male are enormously elongated, becoming about twice the length of the body, and the bird can only fly with some difficulty. In wet weather or against a strong wind it cannot fly at all. The nest is built among long grass on the ground.

Sociable Weaver (*Philaeterus socius*). This Weaver, of South Africa north of the Orange River, constructs an umbrella-shaped mass of sticks and straw among the branches of a tree, in the flat under-surface of which holes are constructed for nests. Sometimes as many as three hundred pairs breed together in one of these structures. The birds are among the dullest members of the family, being brown, buff, black and white.

Icteridae (*Troupials, Hang-nests, American Orioles, Meadow-larks, Grackles and Cowbirds*). This family includes over one hundred and fifty species distributed throughout America, very various in colouring and occupying very diverse habitats — forests, prairies and swamps. They have long, pointed bills and the upper mandible extends backwards to a greater or less extent, dividing the feathers of the forehead. The nostrils are free

By courtesy of]   [the American Museum of Natural History.
PURPLE GRACKLE.

and there are no bristles at the base of the bill. The first primary is as long as the second and third.

Baltimore Oriole (*Icterus galbula*). This bird is found in summer throughout eastern North America, wintering in Central America. The male is largely rich reddish-orange in colour, with a black head, throat, upper back and wings, and a black band across the tail. In the female the orange colouring is much duller and the black markings are replaced by brownish. The nest is a pensile structure, woven of soft materials, entirely by the female, and the eggs are white, curiously scrawled with dark lines. This species frequents woods and orchards.

Meadow-lark (*Sturnella magna*). This is a terrestrial bird inhabiting grassy fields and swamps throughout eastern North America. In this species the sexes are similar, the upper parts mainly black and the underparts largely bright yellow, with a black crescent on the breast. The nest is built of grasses, on the ground, and the eggs are white, speckled or spotted with rufous.

Grackle (*Quiscalus quiscula*). The Grackle is also called the Crow-Blackbird, and is a black bird with brilliant purple, green or steel-blue gloss on the feathers and a rather long, rounded tail. Found in the eastern United States, it is sociable in habits, breeding in colonies, and placing its bulky, compact nest of mud and coarse grasses, generally at some height, in coniferous trees.

Black Cowbird (*Molothrus ater*). This bird is found throughout North America and lives a nomadic life, wandering about in small parties. The males are chiefly glossy black, with metallic reflections, the head and breast being coffee-brown. The females are dark brownish-grey a b o v e , lighter below. They lay their eggs in the nests of smaller birds, and the young, when hatched, grow faster than the rightful occupants, obtaining most of the food brought by their foster parents. The other young birds are thus crowded out or starved and the young Cowbird remains alone, continuing to be fed by the fosterers for some time after it has left the nest.

By courtesy of]   *[the American Museum of Natural History.*
MEADOW-LARK (*Sturnella magna*).

Oriolidae (*Orioles*). The Orioles are medium-sized birds, with ten primaries, of which the first is well-developed, being about half the length of the second, and twelve tail-feathers. The bill is fairly long and straight, with fine, short bristles at the base, and the nostrils are partially covered by a membrane. Orioles are found in tropical Africa, Asia, the Malay Archipelago and Australia, one species visiting Europe in summer. The

[*Major Buxton.*
GOLDEN ORIOLE (*Oriolus oriolus*).

birds called "Orioles" in America belong to the family *Icteridae*. Orioles build hammock-like nests of soft material suspended by their edges from two or more forking twigs. They lay white or pinkish eggs (from three to five), with purplish or brown spots or streaks. The s e x e s are differently coloured, the males usually being largely yellow and the females greenish, while the young have striped breasts.

Golden Oriole (*Oriolus oriolus*). This is the species already mentioned as a summer visitor to Europe. Its range includes southern England, where it would probably breed regularly if the brilliantly-plumaged males were not almost always shot on their arrival. They are chiefly golden-yellow, with black on the face, wings and tail ; the bill is dark pink ; the eye crimson, and the legs and feet slaty-black.

Buphagidae (*Ox-peckers*). The Ox-peckers include only two species of starling-like birds, found in small flocks throughout Africa. They are greyish-brown in colour and live almost exclusively on the bots, ticks and other external parasites of cattle and other large animals. In search of their food they climb over the bodies of the animals in almost the same way as do woodpeckers on trees.

Graculidae (*Glossy Starlings*). This family includes birds closely related to the Starlings, but having bristles round the base of the bill, and laying spotted eggs. They are found in tropical and southern Africa, tropical Asia, the Malay Archipelago and the Pacific Islands, one species visiting northern Australia in summer.

Sturnidae (*Starlings*). The Starlings constitute a small group of birds found in Europe, Asia and Africa. They have fairly long, nearly straight bills, with exposed nostrils, and no bristles at the base. There are ten primaries in the wing ; but the first is very small. They breed in holes and lay unspotted eggs, and the young birds differ in plumage from the adults.

Common Starling (*Sturnus vulgaris*). This bird occurs naturally throughout Europe, north Africa and the greater part of Asia, and has been introduced into North America and Australia, in both of which continents its increase and spread have been rapid. The plumage in both sexes is blackish with metallic reflexions, the tips of the feathers are buffish or whitish in winter, giving the birds a spotted appearance, but these tips wear off, so that in summer the birds are darker and more glossy. The eggs are very pale blue. Starlings are sociable birds and in winter they congregate to roost in reed-beds, shrubberies or plantations in immense swarms.

Rose-coloured Starling (*Pastor roseus*). This Starling has the body rosy pink, the head and neck, wings and tail being glossy black. It has a large black crest. It inhabits south-east Europe and western Asia, commonly visiting India in winter and frequently also wandering westward, sometimes reaching the British Isles. It breeds in large colonies in holes in rocky ground, in a very erratic fashion, selecting regions where locusts or grasshoppers are specially abundant. Its eggs are very pale bluish-white.

Dicruridae (*Drongos*). This family contains representatives in Africa, tropical Asia and the Malay Archipelago east to the Solomon Islands. One species is a summer visitor to Australia. Drongos are mostly black in both sexes, the feathers usually having a metallic sheen. They mostly have a stout bill with a hooked tip; long wings; long, forked tails of only ten feathers; short legs, and small feet. They are insectivorous birds, capturing part of their food on the wing; they are noisy and pugnacious, driving away much larger birds from the vicinity of their nests. The best-known species is the King-crow (*Buchanga atra*), of India, Burma and Indo-China.

[*Charles Reid.*

STARLINGS (*Sturnus vulgaris*).
Probably the most abundant bird in the British Isles, especially in winter, when large numbers which breed on the Continent are present.

[E. N. A.
BOWER, OR COVERED RUN, OF AN
AUSTRALIAN SATIN BOWER-BIRD.
Built of twigs and stiff grass and arranged to form a
kind of tunnel among the bushes. It is used as a sort
of playground and adorned with flowers and feathers,
usually blue in the case of this species.

Ptilonorhynchidae (*Bower-birds*).
The Bower-birds are very closely
related to the birds of paradise, but
their bills are usually stouter and
shorter, and though the males of
many species are brilliantly coloured,
they do not develop specially-modified plumes. They obtain their name
from their habit of constructing
structures of various kinds, composed
of sticks, round which they collect
brightly-coloured objects, and in and
about which they spend a great deal
of time arranging their treasures,
courting and playing. These structures, built by the males on the
ground, and generally called bowers,
are quite distinct from the nests,
which are of the ordinary cup-shaped form, and are built in trees and bushes.
The family contains about twelve species, found in Australia and New Guinea.

Green Cat-bird (*Ailuroedus crassirostris*). This bird, of eastern New
South Wales and south-eastern Queensland, obtains its name from its
extraordinary cat-like notes. It is exceptional in not making any sort
of bower. It lays plain, cream-coloured eggs.

Satin-bird (*Ptilonorhynchus violaceus*). The Satin-bird inhabits coastal
forests throughout eastern Australia. The adult male is entirely blue-
black in colour, with bright blue eyes. He constructs a platform of sticks,
towards the centre of which two parallel rows of sticks are fixed vertically,
to form a short passage with a stick-hedge on each side. On the platform
he collects flowers, either blue or pale yellow in colour, yellowish leaves,
snail-shells and blue feathers, together with any other blue objects he can
find, such as blue-bags, bits of blue paper or blue china.

Spotted Bower-bird (*Chlamydera maculata*). This bird inhabits the
inland regions of eastern Australia, and constructs a bower very similar
to that of the satin-bird, but with a longer passage. Both sexes are brownish,
spotted with yellowish-white, and have a patch of pink feathers on the
back of the neck, larger in the male. This species ornaments its bower
with green berries, white bones and anything shining that it can find, such
as bits of metal or broken glass. The eggs are pale green, covered with
brown and black scrawled lines.

Gardener-bird (*Amblyornis inornata*). The Gardener-bird of New
Guinea builds a bower round a sapling in the form of a hut, and in front of
the entrance spreads a lawn of moss, on which he arrays bright flowers,
berries and beetles. In this species both sexes are olive-brown above,

596

paler below, but the male is distinguished by a bushy crest of soft, orange-yellow feathers.

Paradiseidae (*Birds of Paradise*). This family includes birds akin to the Crows, but with the nostrils either free or partially covered by scale-like feathers, not by bristles. The adult males usually differ greatly from the females, and young birds of both sexes resemble the latter. In the brilliance of their plumage the adult males of this family are equalled only by the humming-birds, and in no other group of birds is there such a development of plumes and modified feathers of extraordinary length and form.

Birds of Paradise are found mainly in the jungles of New Guinea, a few species occurring in the Molucca and Aru Islands, and along the east coast of Australia south to New South Wales. They feed on jungle fruits and insects, but comparatively little is known as to their nests and eggs. In some species the males assemble and indulge in dances on the trees, displaying their marvellous feather ornaments. About seventy species are known, a considerable number of them only from one or two specimens, and there is little doubt that future exploration in New Guinea will discover additional forms.

Great Bird of Paradise (*Paradisea apoda*). This bird inhabits the Aru Islands and southern New Guinea. The adult male is rich brown above and purplish below ; the head and neck are pale yellow and the face and throat metallic green, and from the sides spring tufts of long, soft, golden-orange feathers tipped with brown. The female is entirely reddish-brown, darker on the head and lighter below.

Red Bird of Paradise (*Paradisea rubra*). This bird is somewhat similar to the bird described above in its plumage, but the tufts of plumes on the sides of the male are deep red. It inhabits Waigeu, Batanta and Gemien islands off the west end of New Guinea.

King Bird of Paradise (*Cicinnurus regius*). This is one of the smallest

[*James's Press.*]

MYNAH (*Acridotheres tristis*).
An Indian member of the Starling family, which frequently learns to talk when kept in captivity.

[*James's Press.*
LESSER BIRD OF PARADISE (*Paradisea minor*).
The male of this species has brown plumage, yellow head and neck and the long ornamental plumes of a straw-yellow colour.

species, only about seven inches long, but one of the most remarkable. The male is glossy crimson above and white below, with a metallic green band on the fore-neck. On each side it has a tuft of grey plumes, tipped with green, which it can expand into fans. The shafts of the two central tail-feathers extend as stiff curved " wires " some inches beyond the other tail-feathers, and end in spirally-coiled green discs. The bill is orange, and the legs and feet are cobalt-blue. This is, perhaps, the most widely distributed species, being found throughout New Guinea, in Salawati, Jobi and Misol, and in the Aru Islands.

Paradise Rifle-bird (*Ptiloris paradisea*). This bird, of southern Queensland and Northern New South Wales, is the only member of the family found outside the tropics. The male has black plumage, which in different lights appears rich purple, steel-blue, or coppery-green ; on his throat he has a patch of brilliant metallic feathers, burnished green and purple. The female is brown above and buff below, mottled and barred with black. This is one of the few Birds of Paradise whose breeding habits are known. The nest is a rather slight, open cup, built in a tangle of creepers ; it is chiefly remarkable for the fact that the cast skin of a snake is almost always twined round the outside. The eggs are flesh-coloured, boldly streaked longitudinally with reddish and purplish-brown.

Creadiontidae (*Saddlebacks*). This family contains only two species of arboreal birds, found in New Zealand. They have long, sharp-pointed bills ; rather short, rounded wings ; fairly long tails ; long, strong legs ; and a long claw on the hind toe. The general colour of the plumage is black and a fleshy, orange-coloured wattle depends from the gape on each side. Their nests are placed in hollow trees.

Saddleback (*Creadion carunculatus*). This bird was formerly common in the forests of both islands of New Zealand, but is now very scarce except on a few islets off the coasts. The sexes are alike and their black plumage is relieved by bright chestnut colouring on the back, wing-coverts and tail-coverts, forming a saddle-shaped patch. It is about the size of a Blackbird.

Huia (*Heterolocha acutirostris*). The Huia formerly inhabited the forests on some of the mountain ranges in the North Island of New Zealand, but is now probably extinct. It was as large as a crow, and its plumage was black, glossed with green, with a broad white band across the tip of the tail. It differed from all other birds in having the bill differently shaped in the two sexes. In both it was ivory-white, but while in the male it was stout and nearly straight, in the female it was much longer, more slender and strongly curved. The food consisted of fruits, spiders and insects, particularly the larvae of insects which bore into wood. To obtain these the male used his stout bill to chisel away soft wood or tear off the bark, whilst the female inserted her flexible bill into holes in wood too solid for the male to attack.

Callaeadidae (*Wattled Crows*). This family includes two species inhabiting respectively the North and South

[W. S. *Berridge.*

KING BIRD OF PARADISE (*Cicinnurus regius*).
A small species with orange bill, cobalt feet, plumage crimson and white, with green throat and ornamental feathers in wings and tail.

Islands of New Zealand, and a third found in eastern Australia. They have short, stout, strongly-arched, blunt bills ; short, rounded wings ; and rather long tails. Their plumage is mainly dark grey, with blackish wings and tail. The species found in New Zealand have fleshy wattles on the gape, orange in colour in the South Island form, bright blue in that of the North Island. They associate in small parties, and progress largely by hopping about on the ground or among the branches of trees, a habit which has given the Australian bird the familiar name of Grey Jumper. The nest is a large, bowl-shaped structure, built in a tree ; those of the New Zealand species being of sticks and moss, that of the Australian species, of mud. The eggs are greyish, with purplish and brownish spots ; it is known that in the Australian species several females lay in the same nest.

Corvidae (*Crows, Magpies, Jays, etc.*). This family includes the largest " perching-birds." They have fairly long, but powerful, bills and their nostrils are covered by bristles directed forwards. There are ten distinct

[*Arthur Brook.*

RAVEN (*Corvus corax*).
This largest member of the Crow family still holds its own in most of the wilder parts of the British Isles.

[*Arthur Brook.*

CARRION CROW (*Corvus corone*).
Smaller than the Raven and distinguished from the Rook by its stouter bill with feathered base, this Crow is widespread in England and southern Scotland.

primaries, of which the first is always much shorter than the second. The young birds in their first plumage resemble the adults.

Members of this family are found in almost all parts of the world. Species of the genus *Corvus* (Crows) are absent only from South America, and from most of the Pacific Islands. Birds allied to Jays represent the family throughout South America.

Crows and their allies are probably the most intelligent of birds. Their omnivorous food-habits bring them at times into conflict with farmers and fruit-growers, but they are mostly wary enough to hold their own, and in many countries are among the commonest of birds. Their nests are usually stout, cup-shaped structures of sticks, strengthened with earth and lined with fine twigs, rootlets, etc. Many species usually place them in trees, others generally in holes, or on ledges of cliffs. The eggs are usually from three to six in number, greenish or bluish in colour, with dark spots or mottlings.

Raven (*Corvus corax*). The Raven is the largest of all " perching-birds," and is entirely black, and has a very stout bill. It is found in Europe, north Africa, northern Asia and North America, chiefly in the wilder regions. Its occasional attacks on lambs or sick animals have led to its extirpation in most farming districts of Europe and North America.

601

[L. J. Langford.

ROOK (*Corvus frugilegus*).
Noteworthy from its gregarious habits and usually nesting in trees in towns or adjacent to buildings.

Its deep, hoarse croak is very characteristic, and its intelligence makes it an amusing bird in confinement ; and it is one of the birds capable of learning to imitate human speech.

Carrion Crow (*Corvus corone*). Like the Raven, this Crow is entirely black, but is decidedly smaller, and has a less massive beak ; it is found in western Europe, including England and southern Scotland, and in North-eastern Asia.

Hooded Crow (*Corvus cornix*). This bird has a grey body, with black head, wings and tail. It inhabits Ireland, northern Scotland, northern and eastern Europe, the countries round the Mediterranean, and south-western Asia. It is a common visitor in winter to eastern England and parts of western Europe. It differs from the Carrion Crow only in colour, and where their breeding ranges adjoin or overlap, the two species frequently interbreed, so that some authorities regard these two kinds of Crow as merely colour phases of one species.

American Crow (*Corvus brachyrhynchos*). This Crow closely resembles the Carrion Crow, but is more sociable in habits, and during winter very large flocks congregate to roost together. Very similar entirely black crows occur also in Asia and Australia.

Rook (*Corvus frugilegus*). The Rook of northern Europe and Asia, also has entirely black plumage, but its bill is more pointed, and in the adult bird the area of the face round the base of the bill is devoid of feathers, the naked skin being white. Rooks are sociable at all seasons of the year, breeding together in rookeries, many nests being built in close proximity in the same tree, and often also in many adjacent trees.

Jackdaw (*Corvus monedula*). The Jackdaw is smaller than the Rook, with which it commonly associates, and has a shorter bill, and a patch of grey on the nape. It is common in the British Isles, occurring also in various parts of Europe, north Africa and western and northern Asia. It breeds in holes in trees, cliffs, or buildings.

Nutcracker (*Nucifraga caryocatactes*). This bird has chocolate-brown plumage, with white spots. It inhabits coniferous forests in northern Europe and Asia, and the principal mountain ranges of the two continents. It appears occasionally in the British Isles.

Cornish Chough (*Pyrrhocorax pyrrhocorax*). The Chough is about the size of the Jackdaw, with black plumage, red legs, and a long, slender, curved, bright red bill. It inhabits the mountain ranges of Europe and northern Asia, and is also found in some localities on sea-cliffs, including those of Ireland, Wales and south-western England.

[*Reginald Gaze.*

JAY (*Garrulus glandarius*).
Though noisy at other times, the Jay is very silent when nesting and thus manages to elude the gamekeeper.

AVES (ORDER PASSERIFORMES)

Alpine Chough (*Pyrrhocorax graculus*). This bird inhabits the chief mountain ranges of central and southern Europe, and of western Asia, east to the Himalayas. Like its congener, it is black with red legs, but its bill is shorter and bright yellow.

Magpie (*Pica pica*). The Magpie occurs in Europe, north Africa, northern Asia, and western North America. It has a very long, rounded tail and black and white plumage, the black portions having a beautiful gloss of metallic green, blue or purple. It covers its nest with a dome of sticks, nearly always thorny, leaving a comparatively small opening at one side, and lays from five or six to eight or even ten eggs.

Jay (*Garrulus glandarius*). The Jay has rufous-brown body plumage, with a white rump, and a black tail. The elongated black and white feathers of the crown form an erectile crest. The wing quills are black with a patch of white, and the wing-coverts are barred with black, white and light blue. The Jay occurs in Europe, north-west Africa and northern Asia, chiefly in well-wooded regions.

Blue Jay (*Cyanocitta cristata*). This Jay, of eastern North America, has most of the plumage of the upperparts greyish-blue, the underparts whitish. Its forehead and a band extending from the back of the head down the sides of the neck and across the breast are black, and the wing-quills are broadly tipped with white. Its head is crested.

[*Stanley Crook.*

YOUNG MAGPIES (*Pica pica*).
The long tail, so characteristic of the adult bird, is not developed when the young first leave the nest.

MAMMALIA
BY
R. I. POCOCK, F.R.S.

INTRODUCTION

The Mammals or Mammalia, a name derived from the presence in the female of milk-glands for the nourishment of the young, constitute a well-defined class distinguished from the Reptiles, its ancestral stock, not only in the possession of these glands, but in their hairy covering and warm blood, this last character being shared by Birds.   There are many other differences connected with the skull and the anatomy of the soft parts, but these need not be considered.

The range of structural variation within the class is greater than in any other class of vertebrated animals, except perhaps the Fishes ; and by these variations the Mammals are classified into a large number of subsidiary groups, called Orders.   Some of these, like the whales, bats and elephants are isolated, and easy to define owing to the total extinction of their ancestral forms.   Their descent can be inferred only from their structure and development, and from a study of the extinct fossil species which preceded them in time.   But many of the Orders are difficult to define owing to the survival of primitive species ; and the primitive species tend to converge to a common type pointing to the characters and habits of the immediate ancestor of the class.   A comprehensive survey of all the Orders, backed by the knowledge of their remote reptilian descent, helps us to picture what this ancestor was like.

It was a comparatively small, hairy, long-tailed quadruped with five nearly equal, sharp-clawed toes on the feet and with the brain and sense-organs better developed than in reptiles.   The keener auditory sense, due in a measure to the more elaborate structure of the inner ear, was augmented by the presence of an external ear (*the pinna*), subservient to catching and guiding sound-waves.   The sense of smell was increased by the development in the nasal passages of scrolls of delicate bone (*the turbinals*), over which the ends of the olfactory nerves were spread, and of an area of naked, moist skin round the nostrils, which was sensitive to wind and changes of temperature.   Delicate organs of touch took the form of tufts of long bristles on the muzzle, cheeks and eye-brows, and of sensitive, naked pads on the tips of the toes and the soles of the feet.   The mouth was provided with fleshy lips, a well-developed tongue and numerous teeth.

This hypothetical little creature could run, leap, climb, burrow and swim. Its diet consisted mainly of insects and other small animals ; but although the female retained the reptilian habit of laying eggs, it hatched them, as a bird does, by the heat of its body, suckling them thereafter by means of its milk-glands, opening on the ventral surface, possibly in a pouch, and probably using a crevice or burrow as a nursery.

Comparison of this type with the higher, or as they are generally called more specialized, types of mammals shows how profoundly they have deviated from it in most respects in the course of their evolution in adaptation to a great variety of environments and modes of life.

The hair may be turned into spines or horny plates, or entirely lost. The tail may be adapted for swimming, prehension and other purposes or may disappear. In the head the eyes, the external ear and the tactile bristles may be enlarged, reduced or obliterated. But the organs most affected are the limbs and mouth, which are subservient respectively to two of the most important activities of life, namely locomotion, upon which the finding of food, escape from enemies and capture of prey largely depend, and feeding, which involves the picking up of food and dealing with it by mastication or otherwise before it is swallowed. And since the modifications of the limbs and mouth are more useful for the classification of mammals than those of other organs, it is necessary to give a few details regarding them to explain the meaning of some of the technical terms unavoidable in a treatise of this kind.

Since the limbs of man are familiar and in many respects primitive, they may be selected for description. The fore-limb or arm consists of an upper single long bone, the *humerus*, jointed above to the shoulder blade and below to the lower arm, which is composed of two long bones, the *radius* and the *ulna*. The wrist, or *carpus*, consists of several small bones to which the hand or *manus* is jointed. The hand, excluding the fingers, is made up of five longish bones, the *metacarpals*. To these the fingers or digits are jointed. The thumb, known technically as the first digit or *pollex*, consists of two bones or *phalanges*, the remaining four of three phalanges, the nails being supported by the terminal *phalanx*.

The hind limb or leg is like the arm in its main bones, but they are differently named. The thigh bone is the *femur*, the shin bones the *tibia* and *fibula*, the ankle is the *tarsus*, and the foot, without the toes, is composed of five *metatarsals*, the first digit, the ' great toe ' in man, being called the *hallux*.

Apart from certain minor differences connected with the *hallux* and *pollex*, the conversion of the claws into nails and the loss of the pads, the limbs of man resemble in essentials those of our hypothetical mammalian ancestor.

When standing upright, man plants the entire sole of the foot on the ground. Apes and bears, when they assume that attitude, do the same. They are called *plantigrade*. But most mammals, generally in the interests of speed and spring, have the feet, especially the hind feet, lengthened, with the wrist and ankle raised off the ground so that they walk on their digits, the pads beneath forming a cushion for support. They are known as

606

digitigrade, dogs and cats being typical examples. But even the rhinoceros and elephant are digitigrade, the elephant being an instance of a short-footed, slow-moving beast with this type of gait. The extreme modification of the digitigrade type is seen in those mammals, like sheep, which walk on hoofs encasing the enlarged terminal bone of the digits. They are *unguligrade*. In digitigrade and unguligrade mammals there is a marked tendency for the middle digits to monopolize the function of support at the expense of the others, which dwindle in size or disappear, four digits being retained in the pig, two in the giraffe and only one in the horse.

[*James's Press.*

TRICERATOPS : A PREHISTORIC MONSTER.

There are many other modifications of the feet. In the swimmers, like the otter and beaver, the digits of the hind feet are lengthened and webbed. In diggers, the fore-feet are usually widened and are always armed with large claws, as in the mole. Only one other point requires notice here. The hind-limbs throughout the mammals are much more variable than the fore-limbs. Being the principal organs of locomotion, they are usually larger and more specialized ; but all visible trace of them may be lost, as in the whales. The fore-limbs, on the contrary, never disappear ; they reach their maximum of development in the wings of bats.

607

MAMMALIA

The teeth, called collectively the dentition, are also very important organs for the classification of mammals, since they vary almost infinitely with diet. Usually they differ in shape and function in accordance with their position in the mouth. The teeth of the dog, which are well-known and tolerably primitive, will serve for illustration. In the upper jaw on each side there are three small front teeth, the incisors, lodged in a small bone, the *premaxilla*. Behind these is a long tooth, the *canine*, which is the first tooth of the series in the main bone of the jaw, the *maxilla*, the rest, six in number and extending to the back of the mouth, are the cheek-teeth. These are divided into two categories. The first four are distinguished by having, like the canines and incisors, what are called milk predecessors. They are known as *premolars*. The last two, which have no predecessors and are absent in young puppies, are the *molars*. A similar set of teeth is found in the lower jaw, except that there is one additional molar. But the dog has lost one upper molar. If this were present, the animal would have possessed what is usually assumed to be the numerically typical mammalian dentition represented by the formula $i, \frac{3}{3}$ $c, \frac{1}{1}$ $pm, \frac{4}{4}$ $m, \frac{3}{3}$ making a total of forty-four teeth in all.

Although two sets of teeth, varying in shape and function are usual in mammals, the full complement is seldom retained. Occasionally, however, it is exceeded, very considerably indeed in some of the whales, which are also unusual in having the teeth of one set only and all alike.

The adaptations of teeth to diet are very remarkable. Normal teeth, like those of the dog, are composed of hard, bony dentine, the crown being covered with still harder enamel, and they are lodged in the jaw by one or more roots which are closed at the bottom when the tooth is complete so that it never grows subsequently. Cheek-teeth of this kind, with simple cusped or tubercular crowns, are characteristic of most carnivorous and insectivorous mammals. But the cheek-teeth of species which feed on tough vegetable fibre may meet the wear and tear of mastication in two ways. The roots remain open so that growth of the tooth continues until age is far advanced, and the hard enamel of the crown dips into the dentine in loops and folds and is itself sometimes covered with a layer of *cement*, so that when the crown is worn, its surface exhibits a complicated pattern of alternating ridges of cement, enamel and dentine, well fitted for its grinding purpose. Perfected teeth of this description are found in the horse and elephant. But other mammals may show marked deterioration of the teeth; the armadillos, for example, have lost the enamel. Finally, in some of the anteaters there is not a vestige of a tooth remaining and this defect has been brought about independently in three distinct orders, represented by the South American Anteaters, the Pangolins and the Echidnas.

The last structures frequently used in classification to which reference must be made are those concerned with the development of the young before birth.

[*James's Press.*

THE SIBERIAN MAMMOTH OR HAIRY ELEPHANT.

It was stated above that the primitive mammal was an egg-layer, like most reptiles. But in only two kinds of existing mammals, the duckbill and the echidna, has this habit been retained. In the rest the young are never at any stage enclosed in an egg-shell and are born in a state of greater or less activity, and in all these, except the kangaroos and their allies, the young during its development is attached to the mother by a nutritive mass of blood-vessels called the *placenta*. According to its form and extent the placenta is called diffused, zonary, discoidal or dome-shaped. At birth it either becomes simply detached from the maternal tissues, or it brings away a considerable portion of them welded to it. The latter is called a deciduate and the former a non-deciduate placenta. Species with a placenta are called *placental*, and those, like the kangaroos, without it, *implacental* mammals.

Order MONOTREMATA (Duckbill, or Platypus, and Echidnas, or Spiny Anteaters)

These animals are distinguished from all other mammals and resemble reptiles in having an interclavicle and complete coracoid bones in the shoulder girdle, a single posterior orifice for the alimentary canal, urinary and genital ducts, and by laying tough-shelled eggs. In these respects the

MAMMALIA (ORDER MONOTREMATA)

By courtesy of] [*Australian Trade Publicity.*
DUCKBILL OR PLATYPUS (*Ornithorhynchus paradoxus*).
This animal lives in long burrows in the banks of rivers and streams in eastern Australia and in Tasmania. It spends its active hours in the water.

Monotremes are exceedingly primitive; but the young, after being hatched by the heat of the mother's body, as in birds, are fed by her milk, which exudes from a number of pores on the skin, there being no definite teats. There are two families, confined to Australasia.

Ornithorhynchidae. This family contains the Duckbill or Platypus (*Ornithorhynchus paradoxus*), an aquatic species, with the jaws naked and shaped like a duck's beak, the mouth provided with broad, horny teeth, the eyes small, the ears absent, the body covered with close, beaver-like fur, the tail broad, the legs short and the toes webbed, but armed with strong claws. In the male there is a poisonous spur on the back of the heel.

The Duckbill lives in long burrows in the banks of rivers and streams in eastern Australia and in Tasmania. The burrow has its main entrance below the level of the water and expands into a spacious chamber where the animal rests and rears its family of two; and from this chamber a ventilation shaft is carried to the surface of the ground, its aperture being concealed amongst vegetation. The Duckbill spends its active hours in the water, feeding upon small crustaceans and water-snails which it fetches from the bottom, storing the food temporarily in the cheek pouches, to be eaten at leisure at the surface or on land. When asleep the Duckbill rolls itself up into a ball.

Echidnidae or Tachyglossidae. This family comprises the Echidnas, known also popularly as the Spiny or Porcupine Anteaters. They have a long, narrow, beak-like snout terminating with the nostrils and small

[*W. S. Berridge.*
ECHIDNA OR SPINY ANTEATER (Family *Echidnidae*).
Echidnas feed mainly after dark, lying up during the day in burrows or rock crevices. When alarmed, they roll up into balls, like hedgehogs.

610

ECHIDNAS OR SPINY ANTEATERS

aperture of the mouth, through which the extensile worm-like tongue is protruded ; there are no teeth, the ear is absent, the tail is conical and short, the back is armed with mostly white spines, and the feet are broad and provided with strong claws for digging and tearing open the earth mounds of the ants and white ants upon which these animals feed. The male has a spur like that of the duckbill ; and the female is provided with a pouch in which she places her single egg and in which the young one after hatching suckles.

Echidnas feed mainly after dark, lying up during the day in burrows or rock crevices ; and when at rest or alarmed, they roll up, like hedgehogs, presenting an array of spines, their only means of defence, to the enemy.

There are two principal kinds. The Five-toed Echidna (*Echidna aculeata* or *Tachyglossus aculeatus*) has five toes on each foot, short legs and longish, more numerous spines. It is found in Papua, Australia and Tasmania, each of these districts having its peculiar race, the one inhabiting Tasmania being remarkable for the conceal-ment of the spines be-neath a coating of long

[*W. S. Berridge.*
NEW GUINEA ECHIDNA OR BLACK SPINED PORCUPINE ANT-EATER (Family *Echidnidae*).
Echidnas have long, narrow, beak-like snouts terminating with the nostrils and the small aperture of the mouth, through which the extensile, worm-like tongue is protruded.

hair. The Echidnas are about one and a half feet in length.

The Three-toed Echidna (*Proëchidna* or *Zaglossus bruijnii*) has usually only three visible toes, shorter and fewer spines, but considerably longer legs. When standing erect upon these, the animal, with its long curved snout, looks like a miniature elephant. It is a larger species than the last, measuring from two to two and a half feet long and standing some eight inches high. It is found in Papua but not in Australia.

611

Order MARSUPIALIA (Pouched Mammals)

The Marsupials are principally distinguished from other mammals by the development of the young, which during prenatal growth are not connected with the mother by the tissue of interlocking blood-vessels that is called the placenta. They are implacental mammals. After birth the young instinctively crawls in search of a teat and takes hold of it; the portion of the teat within the mouth thereupon swells so that the young one, unable to loose its hold, hangs inertly to it, milk being periodically pumped into its stomach by the contraction of muscles associated with the mammary glands of the mother. In most cases the teats and young are surrounded or completely covered by a flap of skin forming the pouch from which the order takes its name.

The Marsupials are arboreal or terrestrial, rarely aquatic mammals, exhibiting great diversity of structure, the extreme forms being as different from each other as some of the orders of placental mammals, like the rodents and carnivores, which they adaptively resemble in general appearance. But they are all linked together by numbers of intermediate types and there is no agreement about their classification, some authors relying on the teeth, others on the feet for the division of the order into suborders. Usually they are classified by the teeth into two suborders, the *Polyprotodontia*, which have many small incisor teeth, and the *Diprotodontia*, which have the two front lower incisors much larger than the others when present. But a more satisfactory division is based on the hind feet; these supply a character admitting of no exceptions.

The following is the classification of the Order MARSUPIALIA :

Suborder Eleutherodactyla
Family *Didelphyidae* (American Opossum)
  ,,   *Dasyuridae* (Tasmanian Wolf, etc.)
  ,,   *Notoryctidae* (Pouched Moles)
  ,,   *Caenolestidae* (Selvas)

Suborder Syndactyla
Family *Peramelidae* (Bandicoots)
  ,,   *Macropodidae* (Kangaroos)
  ,,   *Phalangeridae* (Australian Opossums)
  ,,   *Phascolarctidae* (Koala)
  ,,   *Phascolomiidae* (Wombats).

Suborder Eleutherodactyla
The second and third digits of the hind feet are not united and are similar to the fourth and fifth in structure and usually in length. The teeth are variable, being usually insectivorous or carnivorous in type, with the upper canine and usually the lower, longer than the incisors. Hence the

dentition is typically " polyprotodont," the median lower incisors being small. This character, however, fails in one family, the Caenolestidae.

Four families, the *Didelphyidae*, *Dasyuridae*, *Notoryctidae* and *Caenolestidae*, belong to this suborder.

American Opossums (Family *Didelphyidae*). Distinguished by having the first toe of the hind foot large and typically prehensile, and five pairs of incisor teeth in the upper jaw. The canine teeth are large and

[W. S. Berridge.
AZARA'S OPOSSUM, FROM BRAZIL.

trenchant and the incisors are small and subequal. The tail is usually prehensile and the pouch may be present or absent.

These Opossums range from the United States to the Argentine and there are many different kinds, but they are mostly similar in habits.

The largest is the Common or Virginian Opossum (*Didelphys marsupialis*), characterized by its very soft black and white underfur being covered with long grey or black hairs. The head is usually white, with black stripes; the tail hairy at the root, nearly naked elsewhere and prehensile; and the pouch is present. Large specimens measure from one and a half to two feet from the nose to the root

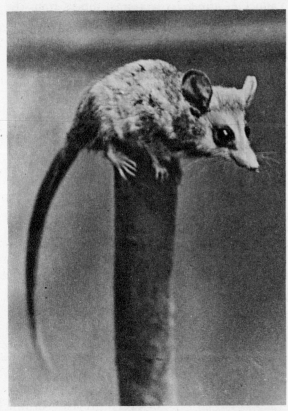

[D. Seth-Smith.
ELEGANT OPOSSUM.

613

of the tail, the tail being about fourteen inches in length. This Opossum ranges from the United States to Brazil. In habits it is nocturnal, sleeping by day in a hollow stump or hole and wandering by night about the trees or ground in search of any food it can find ; birds, eggs, crabs, insects, carrion, nuts and fruit. It is a great pest to poultry-keepers. It is extraordinarily tenacious of life and when mauled, lapses into a state of coma, called " death-feigning." Hence the phrase " playing 'possum." Two or three litters of from six to a dozen young are born in the year and the mother may have two families at a time under her charge, one clinging to her body, the other, newly born, in the pouch. The Crab-eating Opossum belongs to this species.

One of the smallest is the Murine Opossum (*Marmosa murina*), which, like the last, has large ears and a long tail, but is uniformly furry and has no pouch. It is greyish-brown in colour, with dark rings round the eyes. The head and body are about six and the tail eight inches in length. It ranges from Mexico to Brazil, and is not uncommonly imported into this country in bunches of bananas from Demerara and elsewhere.

The Water Opossum or Yapock (*Chironectes minimus*) differs from the arboreal species in having the five toes of the hind feet webbed and cheek-pouches in the mouth. The colour is varied black and grey, the sides being marked with four very broad black stripes extending from the back. The head and body are about one foot in length, the tail a little longer. Its range is from Guatemala to Brazil. This Opossum frequents the banks of streams and rivers and feeds upon shrimps, water insects and small fishes.

Australian Carnivorous Marsupials (Family *Dasyuridae*). These are distinguished from the Didelphyidae by the small size or absence of the first digit of the hind foot and by the presence of four pairs of upper incisor teeth. The pouch, when developed, opens backwards, but it may be represented by two ridges of skin, or may be absent. The family is restricted to Australasia.

The Tasmanian Wolf (*Thylacinus cynocephalus*), one of the largest of the marsupials, takes its name from its superficial likeness to a wolf. It is, however, greyish brown, with a number of dark

[*W. S. Berridge.*
TASMANIAN WOLF (*Thylacinus cynocephalus*).
This is one of the largest of the marsupials. It is greyish-brown in colour and the coat is short and smooth. It stands one and a half feet at the shoulder.

stripes on the hind quarters, is short coated and has a smooth, thick, tapering tail and weak loins. Nevertheless, it is digitigrade, and has a dog-shaped head with large, erect ears, and stands about one and a half feet in height, and has a tail one and a half feet in length. It is now restricted to Tasmania, where it

[D. Seth-Smith.

TASMANIAN DEVILS (Sarcophilus harrisii).

These are much smaller than the Tasmanian Wolf and somewhat badger-like in build and size. The hair is short, jet black and usually varied with a fair amount of white.

is sometimes called the " Hyæna " or " Tiger " ; but it formerly inhabited the mainland of Australia. Although very rare, it is still found in hilly, timbered country, where it hunts at night for birds and small mammals, including wallabies, which it catches by persistent tracking. In the settled districts it has been killed out, owing to its depredations on farmers' livestock. The litter consists of four young ones, which are carried in the pouch till they outgrow it. Thereafter the mother hides them in the scrub or a cave until they are big enough to look after themselves.

The Tasmanian Devil (Sarcophilus harrisii) is much smaller than the Wolf, and is short-legged and plantigrade, with the head disproportionally large as compared with the body. It is somewhat badger-like in build and size, but is short-haired, jet black, usually varied with a certain amount of white. In habits and diet it closely resembles the wolf, feeding on any birds or small mammals it can pounce on unaware, and frequenting any kind of country supplying necessary cover and food. It is highly predacious and capable of killing even wallabies ; but it is not the savage animal its name suggests, being susceptible to taming, especially if taken young. The young, usually four to the litter, are born in May, and apparently stay in the pouch for about four months, when the mother provides a nest for them in some secluded spot.

The Australian Native Cats (Dasyurus) are less clumsily built than the Devil, and have the feet adapted for climbing and running, and a much longer, bushier tail. Except for being spotted with white, they are rather like genets. The pouch is apparently developed only at the breeding season.

There are many species found in New Guinea, Australia and Tasmania. The largest is the Spotted-tailed Dasyure or " Tiger-Cat " (Dasyurus maculatus), the head and body measuring about two feet, and the tail one and a half feet. It inhabits eastern Australia and Tasmania, usually in wooded

615

[W. S. Berridge.

COMMON DASYURE OR AUSTRALIAN NATIVE CAT
(*Dasyurus viverrinus*).

or bush country. It is capable of killing even wallabies, is a pest to poultry-keepers, and is such a savage fighter that one has been known to get the better of a big tom-cat.

The rest of the species are smaller and have the tail unspotted. The Common Native Cat (*D. viverrinus*), in which the head and body measure about one and a half feet and the tail less than one foot, is usually olive-grey, with white spots, but black specimens are not uncommon. It is distinguished by the absence of the first digit on the hind foot. In habits it is like the larger species, feeding at night on small animals and lying up by day in hollow logs, holes or rock crevices, where the young, from four to seven in number, are reared after leaving the pouch. Formerly the most plentiful of all the Native Cats in eastern Australia, this species is now rare, owing to its decimation by an epidemic at the beginning of the century.

To this family also belong a large number of mainly insectivorous marsupials occurring in New Guinea, Australia and Tasmania, which from their small size are popularly designated Pouched Mice or Pouched Rats, and are referred scientifically to the genera *Phascogale, Dasycercus* and *Sminthopsis*. Some of them occasionally climb trees ; but for the most part they are terrestrial, living in burrows or rock crevices. One of the most curious is the Jerboa Pouched Mouse (*Antechinomys laniger*), which has very long hind feet and hops like a Jerboa. Although only a little over three inches long, the tail measuring five inches, it can cover no less than six feet with a jump. It frequents principally the rocky or sandy plains of central Australia.

The Banded Anteater (*Myrmecobius fasciatus*) is a representative of this group, highly modified in adaptation to its diet of ants, its tongue being long and extensile, its cheek-teeth bluntly cusped, and the tactile facial bristles greatly reduced. The general colour is reddish-grey, but the back is black, relieved with white stripes ; the tail is long and bushy, the pouch is absent, the head and body measure about nine inches, and the tail six or seven. Now very rare, this animal inhabits south-western Australia, in timbered country where ants, which it licks up with its tongue, are to be found, and where it can shelter among fallen logs or under the roots of trees. As many as seven young have been found clinging to the under-side of the mother.

Pouched Moles (Family *Notoryctidae*). This family contains a single species, the Pouched Mole (*Notoryctes typhlops*), a type very highly modified in relation to subterranean life. In general form it is very like a mole, having no external ears, vestigial eyes, and short, thick legs; but it has a blunt muzzle covered with a horny shield, and a short, horny knob-tipped tail; its feet are adapted in very different ways for burrowing, only the two outer claws of the fore foot being enlarged, whereas the hind foot is broad and is also adapted for excavation. The female has a pouch with two teats. The colour is white and the length about six inches. The animal lives in the deserts of South Australia and feeds on worms and insects, which it devours with the voracity of a mole. It does not appear to be a deep burrower, but travels along just beneath the surface of the sand in search of food, and is not known to live in burrows. It has, at all events, been found under grass-clumps, and certainly comes to the surface of the ground during and after rains.

Selvas (Family *Caenolestidae*). These little rat-like marsupials are interesting in a scientific rather than a popular sense. Their kinship, on the whole, is clearly with the Dasyuridae, which they resemble in the structure of the feet, but in having the median pairs of lower incisor teeth converted into long projecting tusks they resemble the next suborder. One or two species have been discovered, but the best known is the Sooty Selva (*Caenolestes fuliginosus*), which is about the size of a rat, and very similar in appearance, except for its sharper snout. It inhabits Colombia and Ecuador at heights from 5,000 to 11,000 feet; but, except that it lives on the ground, is nocturnal and eats animal food, very little is known of its habits.

Suborder Syndactyla

Here the second and third digits of the hind feet are small, fused to their tips so as to resemble one short digit with two sharp claws; the third digit is typically considerably the largest and in the middle line of the foot. The dentition is typically "diprotodont," the median lower incisors being enlarged; but this character fails in the Bandicoots.

This suborder, restricted to Austra-

[*W. S. Berridge.*

RABBIT-EARED BANDICOOT (*Paragalia lagotis*).
This is greyish-fawn in colour, with the end of the tail white. It inhabits south and west Australia.

lasia, contains five families, the *Peramelidae* (Bandicoots) ; the *Macro-podidae* (Kangaroos and Wallabies) ; the *Phalangeridae* (Australian Opossums, Sugar Squirrels, etc.) ; *Phascolarctidae* (Koala or Australian Bear), and the *Phascolomiidae* (Wombats).

Bandicoots (Family *Peramelidae*). The Bandicoots are distinguished by having all the incisor teeth small and the canines trenchant, as in the Dasyuridae ; but their limbs are like those of the Kangaroos. They live on the ground, nesting in hollows or burrows in the bush or plains, and are omnivorous, eating small animals, especially insects, as well as bulbs, roots, and berries.

The Rat Bandicoots have short ears, five toes in the fore feet, and the tail uncrested. Gunn's Bandicoot (*Perameles gunni*) has no spines in the fur and has the rump banded with dark ' light stripes. The head and body measure eight inches, the tail three and a half inches. It inhabits Victoria and Tasmania.

The Short-nosed Bandicoot (*Isoodon obesula*) has spines mixed in the fur and the colour tolerably uniformly greyish-yellow. The head and body are eleven inches in length, the tail about five inches. It is found in Southern Australia and Tasmania. There are many other species, differing from these in minor particulars.

The Rabbit Bandicoots have long ears, the tail crested above, and longer hind legs. The best-known species is the Common Rabbit Bandicoot (*Paragalia lagotis*) ; this is greyish-fawn in colour, with the end of the tail white ; the head and body are about nine, and the tail five inches in length. It inhabits South and West Australia.

The Pig-footed Bandicoot (*Choeropus castanotis*) also has large ears, but is distinguished by having only two functional toes on the fore foot. It is greyish in colour ; the head and body measure about ten and the tail four inches in length. It inhabits the grassy plains of the greater part of Australia.

Kangaroos and Wallabies (Family *Macropodidae*). This family differs from the Bandicoots in the teeth ; the canines, when present, are never trenchant or larger than the incisors, and the front pair of lower incisors is long and projecting. But the hind feet are like those of the Bandicoots, although longer and adapted for hopping, the first toe being absent, or small and thin, and the fourth enlarged and provided with a hoof-like nail. The tail is long.

Kangaroos and Wallabies (*Macropus*) differ in size, the smaller species being called Wallabies. Their general form is well known. They have the head and forequarters lightly built and the hindquarters massive and strong, with powerful hind legs and a long, muscular tail, which is used as a fifth leg or prop when the animal is walking or standing upright. When grazing and moving slowly, they progress on all fours, supporting the body on the fore legs and tail and swinging the hind legs forwards ; but when going at speed, they cover the ground with a succession of leaps, using the

[G. Morey (Mondiale).

GREAT GREY KANGAROO IN FLIGHT.

A big Kangaroo, when chased and hard pressed, can bound twenty-five feet or more and can clear obstacles five or six feet high.

By courtesy of]   [the Commonwealth of Australia.

RED KANGAROO (*Macropus rufus*).

This is even larger than the Great Grey Kangaroo, and has a woolly coat and longer fore limbs.   It inhabits the open plains of central Australia.

hind legs only, with the body inclined forwards and the tail stretched out behind to balance it. A big Kangaroo, when chased and hard pressed, can bound twenty-five feet or more and clear obstacles five or six feet high, if not more. They are adapted to all kinds of country, the Kangaroos being found in the open plains, forests or hillsides ; the Wallabies usually keeping to the bush and scrub, feeding on grasses and low-growing vegetation.

[Dorien Leigh.
GREAT GREY KANGAROO (*Macropus giganteus*), WITH YOUNG. This sometimes stands nearly six feet in height, is typically grey in colour, and inhabits well-timbered country in west and east Australia, also Tasmania.

But a few Kangaroos are arboreal and subsist mainly on foliage.

The pouch is large, with its orifice opening upwards or forwards. There seems to be no definite breeding season ; and the young, usually one but occasionally a couple, are at first tiny and naked, but in about four months become covered with hair and afterwards may be seen looking out of the pouch and even attempting to nibble grass. When about a quarter grown, they venture forth and exercise by the mother's side, but on a hint of danger scramble back to the pouch for safety, making use of it until they have outgrown its dimensions.

Big male Kangaroos, which are larger than the females, are redoubtable antagonists when brought to bay, defending themselves by kicking with their hind legs. They frequently indulge in " sparring " matches, standing up and scratching at each other's heads with their fore paws and kicking with the hind legs, standing on the tail and one leg while the other delivers its strokes. This natural habit has been taken advantage of by showmen in what is called " training "

Kangaroos to " box." Kangaroos and Wallabies are far less plentiful than they used to be. They are a nuisance on the grazing grounds of sheep-farms ; but the great factor in the reduction of their numbers is the value of their skins to the fur trade.

They are found in New Guinea and Tasmania, as well as all over Australia, except in the desert parts.

Only a few of the best known of the many

[W. S. Berridge.

RED-NECKED WALLABY AND YOUNG.

species can be noticed. The Great Kangaroo (*Macropus giganteus*), the " Old Man " of the earlier colonists, can stand nearly six feet high. It is typically grey in colour and inhabits well-timbered country in west and east Australia and also Tasmania, where it may be reddish in tint. The Red Kangaroo (*M. rufus*) is even larger than the last and has a woolly coat and longer fore limbs ; the male is usually red and the female greyish. It lives in the open plains of central Australia. Both these species are gregarious, but the Wallaroo (*M. robustus*), a smaller but more heavily-built species, varying locally from blackish to red, is found solitary or in pairs on forested hillsides in western and eastern Australia.

Of Wallabies, or small Kangaroos, there are a great many species, varying in habitat as much as the Kangaroos, one of the largest and most familiar being the Black-tailed Wallaby (*M. ualabatus*), which is partial to damp, bushy gullies, and was

DERBIAN WALLABY.

[James's Press.

formerly abundant in south-eastern Australia. The head and body measure between two and a half and three feet and the tail about one and a half feet in length.

The Fawn Nail-tailed Wallaby (*Onychogalea unguifera*) is distinguished by having a horny spur at the tip of the tail. It is fawn in colour, the head and body measure about three feet in length and the tail one and a half feet. It inhabits Western Australia. Other species are found elsewhere, but in habits they resemble ordinary Wallabies.

The Brush-tailed Rock Wallaby (*Petrogale penicillata*) differs from the others in having the claw of the large toe short and blunt. It is about the size of the Black-tailed Wallaby, and is found in eastern Australia, frequenting the mountain ranges and displaying extraordinary agility in hopping about on boulders and rocky ledges.

[*W. S. Berridge.*

URSINE TREE-KANGAROO (*Dendrolagus ursinus*) FROM NEW GUINEA. Tree-kangaroos have the hind legs comparatively short, and although adapted to tree climbing, frequently descend to the ground, on which they can run with considerable speed.

The Tree-kangaroos (*Dendrolagus*) differ from the preceding in having the hind legs comparatively short, only a little longer than the fore legs, which are strongly made. Although adapted by their limbs for tree climbing, these Kangaroos, of which there are some dozen species, found in New Guinea and Queensland, are by no means restricted to arboreal life, frequently descending to the ground, on which they can run with considerable speed, but they ascend trees if pursued. They are about the average size of the larger Wallabies. The Ursine Tree-kangaroo (*D. ursinus*), of north-western New Guinea, and Bennetts' Tree-kangaroo (*D. bennetti-anus*), of north-eastern Queensland, may be cited as examples.

The Rat-kangaroos or Bettongs (*Potoroinae*) are distinguished by their prehensile tails and the large size of the three middle claws of the fore feet. They are about the size of rabbits and lie up during the day in burrows or nests made of grass, which they carry in bundles to the spot by means of their tails. They were

[*W. S. Berridge.*
RAT-KANGAROO (Family *Potoroinae*).
This is about the size of a rabbit and lies up during the day in a burrow or nest made of grass, which it carries in bundles to the spot by means of its tail.

formerly abundant and a great pest to farmers, but are being exterminated by the imported foxes. They are widely distributed in Australia, the commonest being the Rufous Rat-kangaroo (*Aepyprymnus rufescens*) of eastern Australia and the Brush-tailed Bettong (*Bettongia penicillata*), found in Southern Australia.

The Musk Rat-kangaroo (*Hypsiprymnodon moschatus*) differs from the rest of the family and resembles the next in having a distinct, though small, first toe on the hind foot, which otherwise is like that of the Kangaroos. It also has a naked, scaly tail. The colour is rusty-grey ; the head and body are about ten and the tail six and a half inches in length. It inhabits Queensland and lives in damp scrub, feeding on insects as well as vegetables.

Australian Opossums, Phalangers, Sugar Squirrels, etc. (Family *Phalangeridae*). These are distinguished from the Kangaroo family by having the hind feet short and adapted for climbing, instead of for hopping or running, the first toe, or hallux, being large, thick, and prehensile, and the fourth of ordinary length. The tail is long and generally prehensile. The muzzle is short and broad and the tongue not extensile.

The Vulpine Opossum (*Trichosurus vulpecula*), the best-known member of this family, is a heavily-built, thick-furred animal, with short legs, a long tail, bushy throughout except at the tip beneath, where it is prehensile ; and none of the digits of the fore foot is opposable. The colour is usually grey, but varies locally to red, brown or black. The size is also variable, the head and body measuring from about one foot to nearly two feet in length and the tail from ten inches to fourteen inches. It is found practically throughout Australia and in Tasmania, wherever eucalyptus trees, upon the foliage of which it mainly feeds, grow. But it also eats the leaves and fruits of cultivated plants. The single young one, born in the winter, stays in the mother's pouch for two months and is subsequently carried on her back until able to fend for itself.

AUSTRALIAN RING-TAILED OPOSSUM (*Pseudochirus*)
These Opossums have the tail tapering and short-haired towards the end. They are skilful climbers.

The Ring-tailed Opossums (*Pseudochirus*) are lighter and smaller than the Vulpine, have the tail tapering and short-haired towards the end, and the first and second digits of the fore foot separated from the rest and opposable to them. A large number of species is known, most of them living in New Guinea, the others in Australia. In diet and habits they closely resemble the Vulpine Opossum, but are more skilful climbers, the most active being the Lemur-like Opossum (*P. lemuroides*) found in Queensland, which descends trees by means of long leaps from branch to branch. Its general colour is greyish-brown, and its length is about fifteen inches, the tail being some three inches shorter. As in some other species, the female constructs a large nest of twigs and leaves interwoven with the branches of the scrub.

The Cuscuses (*Phalanger*) differ from the Ring-tailed Opossums principally in having the end of the tail naked above and below. There are many species, found mostly in the islands to the north of Australia. The best-known are the Black Cuscus (*Ph. ursinus*) of Celebes, which is blackish-brown in colour, the two sexes being alike and the Spotted Cuscus (*Ph. maculatus*), found in New Guinea and North Australia, which is irregularly mottled with white, black and red in the male, the females being typically grey and black, and larger than the males. These are large, heavily-built species, the head and body being over two feet long and the tail some one and a half feet. They are all comparatively slow climbers, spending the day curled up in the branches of trees and bushes.

Photos]   [W. S. Berridge.
AUSTRALIAN OPOSSUM (Family *Phalangeridae*).

The Striped Phalangers (*Dactylopsila*) may be known by their pattern of broad, longitudinal black and white bands and by having the fourth toe of the fore foot much longer than the others. The average length is about ten inches, the tail being either longer or shorter than the head and body. There are several different kinds, found

[W. S. Berridge.
SPOTTED CUSCUS (*Phalanger maculatus*).
The male is irregularly mottled with white, black and red, the female being typically grey and black, and larger than the male. They spend the day curled up in the branches of trees and bushes.

mostly in New Guinea, the typical species being the White-footed Phalanger (*D. trivirgata*). These Phalangers are largely insectivorous and use their thin, long fingers for extracting grubs from holes and crevices in trees.

The Opossum-mice, or Dormouse-phalangers (*Dromicia*), are well named from their general mouse-like appearance and size and their habit of sleeping through the winter, lying up in nests and subsisting on an accumulation of fat stored mostly in the tail during the autumn. They are widely distributed, the most familiar being the Dwarf Opossum-mouse (*D. nana*), found in Victoria and Tasmania.

Very distinct from the typical Phalangers, of which it is a specialized offshoot, is the little Honey-mouse (*Tarsipes spenserae*), characterized by its very long snout, extensile tongue and defective back teeth. Its colour is greyish, ornamented with three dark stripes on the back ; the length is about three inches, the tail being a little more. It is found only in Western Australia, and feeds mainly on small insects, but is very partial to honey, which it extracts from flowers by means of its long tongue.

[F. W. Bond.
LESSER FLYING PHALANGER (*Petaurus*).
In these " Sugar Squirrels " the flight-membrane extends from the wrist to the ankle. The mother carries the young one on her back after it has been two months in the pouch.

MAMMALIA (ORDER MARSUPIALIA)

Flying Phalangers and Sugar Squirrels. Several Phalangers resemble Flying Squirrels in gliding from tree to tree, supported on a flap of membrane extending along the sides of the body.

[*Dorien Leigh.*

KOALA OR NATIVE BEAR OF AUSTRALIA (*Phascolarctos cinereus*).
This has cheek pouches and no visible tail, the feet being well adapted for grasping. It feeds by night on the foliage of eucalyptus trees.

In the larger Flying Phalanger (*Petauroides volans*) the membrane runs from the elbow to the knee. It has large ears, the head and body measure about one and a half feet in length and the bushy tail a few inches more ; the colour is blackish-grey above, whitish below. It inhabits eastern

626

Australia, and feeds on eucalyptus leaves at night. The longest measured flight was eighty yards from the top of one tree to the foot of another.

In the smaller Flying Phalangers or Sugar Squirrels (*Petaurus*), the membrane extends from the wrist to the ankle. The commonest species is the Short-headed Flying Phalanger (*P. breviceps*),

[*D. Seth-Smith.*
AUSTRALIAN PIGMY FLYING PHALANGER
(*Acrobates pygmaeus*).
This little animal has a very narrow flight-membrane, but a feather-like tail, and broad pads on the tips of the toes.

which is grey above and white below, the head and body being about seven inches and the tail eight inches in length. The mother carries the young one on her back after it has been two months in the pouch. Its natural home is eastern Australia, but it is abundant in Tasmania, where it was introduced.

The Pigmy Flying Phalanger (*Acrobates pygmaeus*) has a very narrow membrane, but a feather-like tail, and broad pads on the tips of the toes. The colour is fawn-grey above, white below. The head and body measure only two and a half inches and the tail three inches in length. It feeds on insects, and inhabits eastern Australia.

The Koala or Native Bear (Family *Phascolarctidae*). The Koala (*Phascolarctos cinereus*) differs from the phalangers in having cheek pouches and no visible tail. Its ears are large and hairy, its nose prominent and rounded, its fur thick, and the feet of its powerful limbs are well adapted for grasping. It attains a length of about two and three quarter feet. It is restricted to eastern Australia, and lives in eucalyptus trees, feeding on the foliage by

[*Dorien Leigh.*
COMMON HAIRY-TAILED PHALANGER (*Trichosurus vulpecula*),
KNOWN AS THE OPOSSUM IN AUSTRALIA.

627

night and sleeping curled up in a forked branch by day. The single young one, born in mid-winter, stays in the pouch for about three months. For the next three months the mother carries it on her back. The scarcity of this animal is due to persecution by the fur-trade, and to decimation by epidemics.

The Wombats (Family *Phascolomiidae*). The Wombats (*Phascolomis*) are distinguished by having the teeth and mouth modified for gnawing exactly as in the rodents. They are terrestrial, the paws being adapted for burrowing, with the first digit of the hind foot greatly reduced in size. In appearance they resemble gigantic guinea-pigs. In habits they are nocturnal, lying up in deep burrows by day and feeding on grasses, roots and bark by night. A single young one is born in the winter and is independent of its mother when about six months old. There are two species. The Ursine Wombat (*Ph. ursinus*) has coarse black or grey fur and a naked nose, and measures from three to four feet in length. It is found in Australia and Tasmania. The Hairy-nosed Wombat (*Ph. latifrons*) has soft grey fur and a hairy nose. It inhabits the drier, more inland districts of eastern Australia.

Order EDENTATA (Sloths, Anteaters and Armadillos)

The mammals of this order are principally distinguished from the Pangolins (*Pholidota*) and the Aard-Varks (*Tubulidentata*), formerly associated with them, by having accessory interlocking processes on some of the vertebrae of the hinder part of the back. Teeth, when present, are defective in enamel, and the front of the mouth is always toothless. The order includes several gigantic prehistoric species, but space will not permit of their description here.

The order is restricted to America and is divisible into two suborders, the Pilosa or Hairy Edentates and the Loricata or Armoured Edentates.

Suborder Pilosa
(*Hairy Edentates*)
Members of this suborder are distinguished by the genital and urinary ducts and the intestine opening close together on a common eminence or in a saccular fold of the

[*W. S. Berridge.*

WOMBAT (*Phascolomis mitchelli*).
Wombats resemble in appearance gigantic guinea-pigs. They lie up in deep burrows by day and feed on grasses, roots and bark by night.

628

skin. The skin is thickly clothed with hair, and in existing species has no bony plates imbedded in it. This suborder is subdivided into two very distinct tribes, the *Tardigrada* or Sloths and the *Vermilingua* or Anteaters.

Sloths (Tribe *Tardigrada*). In animals belonging to this tribe the head is short and globular, with an abbreviated muzzle, massive jaws and a short,

[*W. S. Berridge.*

TWO-TOED SLOTH (*Choloepus didactylus*).
There are two toes only on the fore feet, and the soles of the feet are entirely naked. This Sloth inhabits Brazil.

broad tongue; the mouth, which has a tolerably long gape, is provided at the sides with simple, peg-like teeth; the tail is short or vestigial; the limbs are elongated and slender, the feet narrow and long, alike on all four limbs and never have more than three digits, which are tightly tied together and armed with very long sub-equal claws; and the coat is long and shaggy.

There are two well-marked genera of Sloths, the Two-toed Sloth or Unau (*Choloepus*) and the Three-toed Sloth or Ai (*Bradypus*), both being commonly assigned to the family Bradypodidae.

The Two-toed Sloth (*Choloepus*) has two toes only on the fore feet, the soles of the feet are entirely naked, the tail is vestigial, the nostrils are large and thick-rimmed, the ears are valvular, the hair on the crown grows backwards, the front tooth of each jaw is large and canine-like, and there are six or seven vertebrae in the neck. The common species (*C. didactylus*), with seven neck-bones, inhabits Brazil; and the related form, Hoffman's Sloth (*C. hoffmanni*), with six neck-bones, extends from Ecuador to Costa Rica.

The Three-toed Sloth (*Bradypus*) has three toes on the fore foot. The soles of the feet are almost entirely covered with long hair, the tail is quite distinct, the nostrils are small, the ears not valvular, the hair on the crown grows forwards, fringing the face, the teeth are all alike, and there are nine neck-bones. These Sloths range from Brazil northwards to Nicaragua, but the species are not well understood, the best known being the typical species (*B. tridactylus*), which has between the shoulders a curious patch of soft, short hair, black in the centre and yellow at the edges, and the Collared Sloth (*B. torquatus*), which is ornamented with a black band round the neck.

629

MAMMALIA (ORDER EDENTATA)

The Sloths are so completely adapted to arboreal life that they are practically helpless on the ground, to which they never voluntarily descend. In trees, however, they are perfectly at home, although slow, deliberate climbers. They move along the underside of branches, suspended by their claws, with the back towards the ground, and sleep in that attitude, with the head thrown forwards on the breast. They are absolutely defenceless, but are admirably concealed by the abundant growth on the hairs of a microscopical alga-like plant which makes them look like tufts of greenish moss. They feed on foliage, using the long, hooked claws of their fore legs to pull the leaves within reach of the mouth. The newly-born young, of which there is but one, clings to its mother by clasping her with its limbs after the manner of a baby monkey.

[*D. Seth-Smith.*

THREE-TOED SLOTH (*Bradypus tridactylus*).
In this Sloth there are three toes on the fore feet and the soles of the feet are almost entirely covered with long hair. The tail is quite distinct.

Anteaters (Tribe *Vermilingua*). In the members of this tribe the head is elongated into a slender snout and the jaws are very weak ; the mouth is toothless and tubular, with a small gape, and the tongue is exceedingly long and worm-like ; the tail is nearly as long as the head and body ; the limbs are stout, comparatively short, and the fore and hind feet are dissimilar, the hind foot having four or five sub-equal toes, whereas in the fore foot the third toe is much larger than the second and has a huge falcate claw ; the hair of the body is not long and shaggy.

There are three well-defined genera : *Myrmecophaga, Tamandua* and *Cyclopes,* forming the family Myrmecophagidae. In the Great Anteater (*Myrmecophaga tridactyla*) the snout is very long ; the tail is rigid and provided with a crest of long, stiff hairs above and below ; the legs are tolerably long ; the hind foot has five short, separated toes and the whole sole is naked and applied to the ground ; the fore foot has four toes, the first and fourth being short, the second and third larger and armed with long claws ; on the outer side of the foot there is a big, cushion-like pad, on which the Anteater rests when walking, the claws being turned inwards. The general colour is blackish-grey, relieved by a broad black stripe, with white margins on the shoulder, and grey fore legs. The standing height is about two feet. Its habitat is the forests of South and Central America. It is purely terrestrial, spending the day sleeping on the ground curled up with its great tail spread over the body, the long hairs sloping on each side, like a roof, to throw off the rain. At night it wanders abroad in search of ant-hills and termite mounds, which it rips open with the claws of its powerful hind limbs to get at the insects it licks up by means of its long, wormlike tongue, rendered sticky with saliva. It is an inoffensive creature, but when attacked defends itself boldly by striking savagely at its assailants with its muscular fore legs, while standing with its back to a tree, its vulnerable snout tucked down on its breast. Inexperienced dogs get severely

[*F. W. Bond.*

LESSER ANTEATER OR TAMANDUA (*Tamandua tetradactyla*).
This is much smaller than the Great Anteater. Its colour varies considerably, the general hue being reddish-yellow, varied more or less with black patches.

lacerated by its claws ; and it is said that even a puma is cautious about coming to close quarters with the animal at bay. The female produces only one young at a time ; and this she carries on her back until capable of looking after itself.

The Lesser Anteater or Tamandua (*Tamandua tetradactyla*) is much smaller than the last-named, is covered all over with short hair, has a flexible, prehensile tail, a much shorter snout and a considerably larger pad on the outside of the fore foot. Its colour varies considerably, the general hue being reddish-yellow, varied more or less with black patches. The total length is about three and a half feet and the height about eight inches. Except that the Tamandua is an expert climber and spends most of its time in trees, it resembles the Great Anteater in habits ; and like that animal is found in South and Central America.

The Two-toed Anteater (*Cyclopes didactylus*) is distinguished by having two toes only on its fore feet and four on its hind ; its tail is prehensile, and this animal is more thoroughly adapted for arboreal life than the Tamandua, never voluntarily coming to the ground. It is covered with silky yellow fur, is only about the size of a rat, and inhabits the forests of Central and South America.

Suborder Loricata (*Armoured Edentates*)

This suborder, containing the Armadillos (Family *Dasypodidae*), differs essentially from the Pilosa in having the vent separated from the genital and urinary orifices, and the skin, which is typically scantily hairy, provided with a protective coating of bony scales, which, however, vary considerably in development.

The head is conical with the muzzle narrowed ; the mouth has a large gape, numerous teeth and a moderately long tongue, the legs are short and the tail long or of medium length. The bony armour, extending from the snout to the end of the tail, is absent from the lower side. It is usually divided into a head-shield, a scapular shield, covering the shoulders, and a pelvic shield, covering the rump, these latter two shields being separated by a varying number of movable bands of scales enabling the body to be more or less rolled into a sphere. Armadillos are purely terrestrial, living in burrows in the forests or plains and feeding mostly upon insects, but eating other food as well. They are more widely distributed than the sloths and anteaters, ranging in America from Texas to Patagonia. There are many different kinds, differing in a variety of ways ; but only the principal types can be mentioned.

Only two closely-related species, namely the Six-banded Armadillo (*Dasypus sexcinctus*) and the Peludo (*D. villosus*), are commonly imported alive to this country. They are about sixteen inches long, with the tail about half that length, and have from six to eight movable bands on the back, the muzzle conical, the ears short and far apart, and five toes on each

By courtesy of] [Carl Hagenbeck's Tierpark, Stellingen.
GREAT ANTEATER (*Myrmecophaga tridactyla*).
The general colour is blackish-grey relieved by a broad black stripe, with white margins on the shoulders, and grey fore
legs. The height is about two feet. Its habitat is the forests of South and Central America.

foot, the claws of the fore feet, as in all Armadillos, being long, for the
purpose of digging. The Six-banded Armadillo is found in Brazil and
Paraguay, and the Peludo, which is the hairier, in the Argentine. They
feed upon insects, snakes, the eggs of ground-nesting birds, and on
carrion and even on grain and green vegetables when animal food fails.
The litter consists of from two to four young, which are born and reared
in the burrow.

The Giant Armadillo (*Priodontes gigas*) differs from the foregoing in
having as many as twelve or thirteen movable bands, much bigger claws
on the third and fourth toes of the fore foot, and the scales on the base of
the tail irregularly arranged and not disposed in bony rings. As its name
indicates, it is a relatively large animal, as big as a small pig, the head and
body measuring nearly a yard long and the tail about one and a half feet.
It lives in the forests of Brazil and Guiana.

In the Three-banded Armadillos, the Apar (*Tolypeutes tricinctus*), for
example, there are only two or three movable bands, the tail is very short,
the fore foot may have only three toes and the claws of the hind foot are
flattened and nail-like. They walk on the tips of the claws of the fore feet
and can roll up more completely than any other species. The head and body
measure a little over one foot and the tail is about two inches in length.
They inhabit the pampas of the Argentine and Buenos Ayres. The Pebas or
Nine-banded Armadillos (*Tatusia novemcinctus*) have from six free bands

633

in the young to nine in the adult ; the ears are long and set close together on the back of the head, and the snout and tail also are long. This Armadillo is also distinguished by having a pair of teats on the abdomen as well as the pair on the breast, and by producing a litter of from six to twelve young ; and it is the only Edentate in which the permanent teeth are preceded by milk-teeth. The head and body may measure one and a half feet in length, and the tail is over one foot. There are one or two closely-related species, ranging from Texas to the Argentine ; the hairy Peba (*T. pilosa*) of Peru being remarkable for the thick coating of hair which completely covers the scales.

Very different from all the preceding is the Pichiciago (*Chlamyphorus truncatus*), so-called from the truncated shape of the hinder end of the body due to the pelvic shield forming a vertical semicircular plate. It is also distinguished by the sides of the face and the lower surface being covered with silky hair, by the minute size of the ears, by the scales on the back forming a continuous series of movable bands passing over the neck, and by the spatulate tail, but above all by the armour of the back forming a loose cloak attached to the body only along the spine. This, the smallest of the Armadillos, measuring only about six inches long, lives in very sandy districts in the Argentine and Chile. It digs with great rapidity and uses the flat hinder end of the body to block its burrow.

Order PHOLIDOTA (Scaly Anteaters or Pangolins)

The Scaly Anteaters or Pangolins, the only known representatives of this order, are of unknown ancestry and occupy an isolated position in the class Mammalia. They were formerly classified with the South American Anteaters in the Edentata ; but it is now known that the characters they have in common, namely a toothless mouth, with a small orifice, a long, elastic tongue, and enlarged glands for the copious secretion of saliva, as well as powerful limbs and claws for tearing down the nests of white ants, are merely adaptive resemblances, also independently acquired by the Spiny Anteaters or Echidnas

[*W. S. Berridge.*
PEBA OR NINE-BANDED ARMADILLO (*Tatusia novemcinctus*).
The head and body may measure one and a half feet in length and the tail is over one foot.

(see page 610), due to similar feeding habits, their diet being ants, termites and worms.

The most striking peculiarity of the Pangolins is the protective coating of large, rigid, overlapping but erectile and sometimes spiny scales, formed of consolidated hairs, which cover the crown, the whole of the body above, the outside of the limbs and the tail above and below, the underparts being soft and hairy. To these scales, coupled with the

[W. S. Berridge.

WHITE-BELLIED TREE PANGOLIN (Family *Manidae*).
Pangolins have a protective coating of large, rigid, overlapping but erectile and sometimes spiny scales. Like hedgehogs, these animals roll into a compact ball when attacked.

emission of nauseous secretions, the Pangolins, otherwise defenceless, comparatively inactive and unintelligent, owe their survival. When attacked, they seldom attempt to escape, but, like hedgehogs, roll into a compact ball, presenting to the enemy an impenetrable armour of horny plates and emitting at the same time their obnoxious odour.

Pangolins (Family *Manidae*) are confined to the warmer parts of the old world. By skeletal and external differences they fall into two natural groups, one Asiatic, the other African. Of the African group there are two types. One (genus *Smutsia*) contains the giant Pangolin of Central Africa and the Short-tailed or Temminck's Pangolin of South Africa, which are about the size of pigs, with the tail shorter than the head and body, and are terrestrial, living in burrows ; the other (genus *Phataginus*) also contains two species, which are about as big as rabbits, have the tail prehensile and much longer than the head and body, and are arboreal, living in the forests of West Africa. The Asiatic species, ranging from the Himalayas and south China to Ceylon and Java, are intermediate in size and habits between the two African types, being climbers as well as burrowers. The best known are the Thick-tailed Pangolin of India, where it is commonly known as the Armadillo, and the Eared Pangolin (genus *Manis*), inhabiting Nepal and China.

Pangolins are said to produce from one to three young at a birth, but nothing is known of their longevity, since they never survive long in captivity.

635

Order ARTIODACTYLA (Cloven-hoofed Mammals)

This order is the first of the series of Hoofed Mammals, which were formerly associated as the Ungulata. But it is now agreed that the superficial resemblances in shape between such creatures as Cattle and Horses, or Hippopotamuses and Rhinoceroses, are adaptations to habits independently acquired along different lines of development from primitive stocks distinguished at a comparatively early period in the evolution of Placental Mammals; and there is evidence that the Artiodactyla were an offshoot from the branch which also gave rise to the Carnivora.

The order is essentially distinguished by the structure of the feet, in which there are never more than four toes, the first being absent, the third and fourth the largest and symmetrically paired, the median axis of the limb passing between them. The second and fifth, generally functionless or absent, are, when present, also alike and symmetrically placed outside or behind the main digits, which are almost always unguligrade. The stomach is usually complex and there is no dilatation of the intestine known as the caecum. The order is divided by the pattern of its teeth and the structure and mechanism of its stomach into two main suborders, the *Bunodontia* or

[*W. S. Berridge.*
Javan Wild Boar (*Sus vittatus*).

Non-ruminantia and the *Selenodontia* or *Ruminantia*. The various genera are again classified into tribes and families as follows :

Order ARTIODACTYLA
Suborder BUNODONTIA or NON-RUMINANTIA
Family *Suidae* (Pigs)
   ,,   *Hippopotamidae* (Hippos)
Suborder SELENODONTIA or RUMINANTIA
Tribe **Tylopoda** (Camels and Llamas)
Tribe **Tragulina** (Chevrotain [Mouse Deer])
Tribe **Pecora.**
   Family *Bovidae* (Cattle, Antelopes and Sheep)
     ,,   *Antilocapridae* (Prongbucks)
     ,,   *Giraffidae* (Giraffes)
     ,,   *Cervidae* (Deer).

Suborder BUNODONTIA or NON-RUMINANTIA

This suborder, containing the Pigs (Family *Suidae*) and the Hippopotamuses (Family *Hippopotamidae*), is essentially distinguished by the crowns of the cheek teeth being studded with tubercles, and by the comparatively simple, non-ruminating stomach. The bones between the wrist or "knee" and the ankle or "hock" and the digits are not united.

INDIAN WILD BOAR (*Sus cristatus*).
In this animal the crest on the neck and shoulders is greater than in the European species.

Pigs (Family *Suidae*). The pigs are adapted for terrestrial life and are unguligrade. The snout is unlike that of any other family of Artiodactyla, the nostrils opening on a flat, disk-shaped plate which terminates the muzzle, and is supported by a special bone which aids its function for rooting the soil. The mouth is always armed with tusk-like canines of permanent growth.

In habits pigs are gregarious, living in forest or bush, and are omnivorous in diet, eating any small animals they come across, although feeding mainly on roots, tubers and other vegetable substances.

They are found in temperate and warm countries of both the Eastern and Western Hemispheres and are divided into two sub-families, the *Suinae* or Old World Species and the *Pecarinae* or New World Species.

The Wild Pigs of the Old World (Suinae). The Wild Pigs of Europe, Asia, and Africa have the upper canines growing upwards or outwards, a simple stomach, no gland on the back, and four toes on the hind as well as on the fore feet.

The best-known member of the group is the European Wild Boar (*Sus scrofa*) from which our domesticated breeds of pigs were derived. It formerly inhabited Great

Photos]   [*W. S. Berridge.*
BABIRUSSA (*Babirussa babyrussa*).
In this animal the upper canines grow upwards through the skin of the muzzle and curve backwards towards the forehead. It is a native of Celebes.

MAMMALIA (SUBORDER NON-RUMINANTIA)

Britain and still survives in the wilder parts of Europe. The colour is dusky-brown or blackish-grey, and the coat consists of coarse bristles overlying thick underwool. The head is long, the neck short and the body powerfully built. The head and body measure about four and a half feet in length and the standing height is nearly three feet. The tusks of the boar project beyond the upper lip, and with these formidable weapons, and aided by quickness and strength, the boar is more than a match for any animal its own size. The nearly-related Crested Wild Boar (*S. cristatus*), of India, has, when attacked, been known, indeed, to kill tigers. These animals, however, are seldom aggressive unless provoked. The boars usually live apart, the herds or " sounders " consisting of sows and young. They are prolific animals, often producing litters of half-a-dozen twice in the year. The period of gestation is four months, and the young are light brown, with dark stripes. The duration of life is twenty years or more.

[*W. S. Berridge.*
WART-HOG (*Phacochoerus aethiopicus*).
The most grotesque of all the Wild Swine. It frequents the open plains and veldt of Africa.

Many other species are found in Asia as far eastward as Japan and Celebes, the Bearded Wild Boar (*S. barbatus*) of Borneo and Sumatra being remarkable for its very long head and small ears. The Pigmy Wild Hog (*Porcula salvania*), found in Nepal and Bhutan, is interesting from being the smallest of the family. It is only one foot in height, has a shorter tail, and only two instead of six pairs of teats.

Very distinct from the preceding is the Babirussa (*Babirussa babyrussa*) of Celebes, in which the upper canines grow upwards through the skin of the muzzle and curve backwards towards the forehead, the lower canines, unique in the family for not being kept sharp and short by wearing against the upper, being very long. The colour is greyish-brown and the skin is nearly naked and wrinkled. The litter consists of two young only.

In Africa south of the Sahara there are three distinct kinds of Wild Swine. The Bush-pig (*Potamochoerus porcus*) is distinguished from *Sus* by its longer, tufted ears and by the presence in the male of bony bosses on the skull supporting two pairs of gristly warts on the muzzle. There are several local races, the most interesting being the typical form found in Madagascar, where it is the only indigenous representative of the Artiodactyla ; the Common Bush-pig (*P. p. koiropotamus*), the Bosch Vark of the Boers, very similar to the last and inhabiting East and South Africa ;

and the Red Bush-pig or River-hog (*P. p. porcus*), found in the forests of West Africa, which is distinguished by its redder colour and shorter, smoother coat. These Pigs are about two feet high ; but in habits and the colouring of the young they resemble *Sus*.

[*Sport & General*.
WEST AFRICAN BUSH-PIG (*Potamochoerus porcus*).
This has long, tufted ears and, in the male, bony bosses on the skull supporting two pairs of gristly warts on the muzzle.

The Forest-hog (*Hylochoerus meinertzhageni*), which, owing to its secluded life in the forests of Central Africa, was not discovered until 1904, is bigger, more bristly and blacker than the Bush-pigs, the boar standing up to two and three-quarter feet, and further differs in its greatly-expanded nose-disk, and in the tip of the upper tusk not being sharpened by the lower. The sow has only two pairs of teats and the young are striped.

The Wart-hog (*Phacochoerus aethiopicus*), called Vlackte Vark by the Boers, is the most grotesque of all the Wild Swine. The snout and nose-disk are even more expanded than in the Forest-hog, and the tusks are longer and the skin nearly naked, except for a mane of long bristles along the back. The boar is between two and two and a half feet in height, and the young, usually four or six to the litter, are unstriped. This species frequents the open plains and veldt of Africa, often sheltering in the burrows of the Aard Vark (page 729), and associating in the open with antelopes and zebras. When running, it has the peculiar habit of carrying the tail erect, with the tufted end curled backwards.

The American Wild Pigs, or Peccaries (Subfamily *Pecarinae*) are distinguished by the downward direction of the upper tusks, the saccular stomach, the loss of the outer small hoof on the

[*W. S. Berridge*.
EAST AFRICAN BUSH-PIG.

By courtesy of]   [Carl Hagenbeck's Tierpark, Stellingen.
COLLARED PECCARY (*Pecari tajacu*).
This animal takes its name from the white stripe on each shoulder, the general
colour being blackish-grey.

hind foot, and by the presence of a large scent gland on the back. The commonest kind is the Collared Peccary (*Pecari tajacu*), which ranges from Texas to Patagonia. It takes its name from the white stripe on each shoulder, the general colour being blackish-grey. The other kind, the White-lipped Peccary (*Tayassu pecari*), has no collar, is brown in tint above, and whitish below. It is slightly larger, standing about one and a half feet in height. It ranges from Mexico to Paraguay. Although comparatively small, Peccaries are formidable, fearless animals in the herd and have been known to kill and eat the Jaguar.

Hippopotamuses (Family *Hippopotamidae*). Hippopotamuses are amphibious, equally at home in the water and on land. Their feet, adapted for walking on muddy soil, are digitigrade, and are provided with a large pad-like sole behind the two median digits. The muzzle has no disk-like termination, but is broad and rounded, with the nostrils on its summit and in line with the similarly high-set eyes and ears. Thus the animal can breathe, smell, see and hear with only the top of its head at the surface and the rest of it immersed ; the skin is smooth, hairless or nearly so : the body is long and bulky, the tail short, and the legs short and stout. In addition to the tusk-like canines, the central pair of lower incisors also form a pair of forwardly-directed tusks of permanent growth.

Hippos are now restricted to Africa ; but the discovery of extinct species in late Tertiary times in Europe, including England, and in India, shows that the group is a northern one, which has survived

[W. S. Berridge.
HIPPOPOTAMUS (*Hippopotamus amphibius*).
The hippo is restricted to Africa. There are several local races, differing very
slightly in appearance and habits.

only in its present African home. But it must have entered Africa at a comparatively early period, judging from the finding of remains of extinct species in Madagascar.

Common Hippopotamus. This species (*Hippopotamus amphibius*) is distinguished by its huge size, long body, big head, with bulging eyes and short legs with compact feet. A good-sized bull stands from four and a half to five feet at the shoulder and the head and body measures twelve feet or so in length, the weight being over 8,000 lbs., between three and four tons. The age to which they attain can be known only from captive

[*Aerofilms.*

HIPPOPOTAMUSES IN AN AFRICAN RIVER.
Formerly hippos were plentiful in all the big rivers of Africa, but sportsmen and native hunters have contributed to lessening their numbers.

specimens. A bull, named " Obaysh," which was captured when only a few days old in the Upper Nile in July, 1849, died in the Zoological Gardens in March, 1878, when close upon thirty years old ; and a female, named " Guy Fawkes," of which Obaysh was the sire, was born on November 5th, 1872, and died on March 20th, 1908, when nearly thirty-five and a half years old.

Several local races of this hippo, differing slightly from each other in size and in some minor cranial characters, have been named, but they are all very similar, both in appearance and habits.

Formerly hippos were plentiful in all the big rivers of Africa, even in the lower Nile. But European sportsmen, who covet their tusks as trophies, and native hunters who kill them for their hides and flesh, have contributed to lessening their numbers. Nevertheless, they are still abundant in some places. But in the settled districts they are becoming annually scarcer because of the practical impossibility of cultivating land near the rivers where they occur. Not content with the natural supply of vegetable food, they raid fields of corn or other produce at night, and some idea of the loss a farmer may suffer from a visit of a single hippo may be gathered from the circumstance that "Obaysh," in his prime, required a daily allowance of one hundred pounds weight of corn, hay, roots and green food. Added to this, a hippo will trample down and destroy in a night as much food as he eats, possibly more.

With its broad muzzle, abbreviated tail and stumpy limbs, the hippo is clearly not a swift swimmer. It is merely adapted for lying immersed with its organs of special sense above the surface to warn it to sink altogether on detecting danger, for slow paddling or for walking along the bottom in shallow water and for browsing on subaqueous plants, which it uproots with its tusks. Sportsmen estimate that the animal stays under water for about five or ten minutes ; but it is capable of much longer submergence. A specimen in the Zoological Gardens, for instance, which was frightened by a dog entering its house, was timed to stay down twenty-nine minutes. And to illustrate the difference in temperament between animals of the same kind, it may be added that another hippo was so enraged by the intrusion of a stray dog entering its pond for a swim, that it plunged into the water and killed the dog with one snap of its great jaws.

Despite its bulk and weight, the hippo is much more active on land than its appearance suggests and can descend even steep banks with surprising ease. As a rule it spends the day drowsing in the rivers or lying out on their banks and shoals, and starts to feed on weeds or forest vegetation after nightfall. In habits it is gregarious and its voice is a succession of snorting roars, which can be heard for miles.

The males are pugnacious and frequently fight amongst themselves and are dangerous to attack from small boats or canoes ; but the females, which are much smaller, are more timid, unless they have young to defend. The period of gestation is from eight to nine months and the mother comes ashore to give birth to her calf, of which there is as a rule only one, rarely two. It is soon capable of following her to the water and at times suckles beneath the surface ; and while it is quite small, she carries it on her back, out of the water, when swimming any distance.

Pigmy Hippopotamus. This species (*Choeropsis liberiensis*) looks like the young of the larger species. In conformity with its more terrestrial habits, it is less heavily built, the body being relatively shorter, the back more arched, the head smaller, the legs less stumpy, with the toes more loosely united so as to be capable of greater expansion. The height is only about two and a half feet and the weight about four hundred pounds. The period of gestation is the same as in the larger species ; and from records of specimens kept at the Zoological Gardens, the span of life is probably also the same.

This species is restricted to Liberia and Sierra Leone in West Africa and is found in the forest near water, to which it retreats when alarmed. But it is on the whole less aquatic in habits and more active on land than its larger ally.

Suborder Selenodontia or Ruminantia

The first name for this section is taken from the folding of the surface of the grinding teeth into crescent-shaped ridges, a further dental peculiarity being the invariable absence, at least in the adult, of incisor teeth in the front of the upper jaw, their place being taken by a pad of hardened gum. With these features is associated the habit of " chewing-the-cud " or ruminating, which is dependent upon the structure of the stomach. In its most highly - developed

[G. P. A.

PIGMY HIPPOPOTAMUS (*Choeropsis liberiensis*).
This is more terrestrial than the larger species and is less heavily built. The height is only about two and a half feet. The species is restricted to Liberia and Sierra Leone.

form, possessed by Cattle, Sheep, Deer, and others, the stomach consists of four compartments communicating by narrower passages. The first is a huge sac, called the rumen or " paunch," which has its lining membrane covered with close-set papillae. The second, known as the reticulum or " honey-comb," has its membrane developed into a network of ridges like a honey-comb. The third, still smaller, is a sieve, called the psalterium or " manyplies," because its lining membrane is raised into a number of closely-packed plates, like the leaves of a book (psalter), the edges of which nearly meet in the middle of its cavity. The fourth, the abomasum or " reed," is an elongated sac with its membrane raised into a number of longitudinal folds. It is in this fourth compartment that gastric juice is secreted and true digestion of food takes place. It represents the true stomach of ordinary Mammals, the other compartments being expansions of the oesophagus or throat, which opens into the stomach at the junction of the paunch and honey-comb and from its orifice a channel with muscular walls passes along the upper wall of the honey-comb to the "manyplies."

The "cud-chewing" action of this stomach is as follows : fresh food, after mastication, is swallowed and passes into the paunch, where it lies for some time to soak and soften. By the contraction of the paunch it is then regurgitated and again masticated. When swallowed a second time, it passes along the channel to the "manyplies" and makes its way between the plates of this compartment to the "reed," where it is digested.

The Selenodont or Ruminant Artiodactyls are divided into three tribes : the *Tylopoda* (Camels and Llamas), *Tragulina* (Chevrotains), and *Pecora* (Oxen, Sheep, Antelopes, Giraffes and Deer).

Camels and Llamas (Tribe *Tylopoda*). These Ruminants are distinguished by having a tusk-like outer incisor tooth, as well as a canine, in the upper jaw, and a tusk-like canine separated from the incisors in the lower jaw. The mouth, thus armed, is used for fighting in a way unknown in other Ruminants. The feet are digitigrade, consisting of only two digits provided with a thick pad beneath and tipped with nail-like hoofs. The stomach has three compartments only, and the walls of the paunch are furnished with small pouches, the orifices of which can be closed by a circular muscle.

The tribe contains a single family, *Camelidae*, containing the Camels and the Llamas.

Camels. The Camels (*Camelus*) are distinguished by their large size, short rounded ears, humped backs, the union of the digits to form a broad foot, and their longish tails. There are two species, the Arabian one - humped Camel or "Dromedary" (*C. dromedarius*) and the Bactrian two-humped Camel (*C. bactrianus*), which also differs in having shorter legs. All the dromedaries are domesticated animals ; but although there are wild examples of the Two-humped Camel in Central Asia, these,

[*W. S. Berridge.*
BACTRIAN OR TWO-HUMPED CAMEL (*Camelus bactrianus*).
This has shorter legs than the Arabian One-humped Camel, or Dromedary.

like some of the wild horses of the same districts, may be the descendants of specimens escaped from captivity. The Bactrian Camel is adapted to life in the steppes of Central Asia, whereas the Dromedary is fitted to the sandy plains of Arabia and North Africa. They are essentially desert animals, exceedingly hardy, and capable of withstanding great privations and extremes of heat and cold. They naturally feed on coarse, desert vegetation ; and, living in districts where food may be scarce or difficult to find, they are provided with the humps

[W. S. Berridge.

DROMEDARY AND YOUNG (*Camelus dromedarius*).
A sturdy camel can carry some six hundred pounds, going thirty miles a day, although the walking pace is only three miles an hour.

of fatty tissue for sustenance when their natural diet fails. That is the reason why the humps may be reduced to mere bags of skin in poorly-fed beasts.

It is frequently stated that the cells of the stomach are reservoirs for water especially designed for these animals living in deserts, where droughts are likely to occur. That is not the case. In well-fed camels these cells are always packed with food. In a starved camel, no doubt, when the contents of the stomach are fluid, the cells will be filled with it ; and there is, perhaps, no reason to reject the well-known stories of Arabs threatened with death from thirst, killing their camels for the fluid in their stomachs.

The broad, flat, leathery-soled feet enable the camel to traverse loose sand, in which a horse would sink at every step. But there are other characters attesting adaptations to a desert habitat. Compelled habitually to sleep or rest in the open on hard ground, the camel has its chest, knees and thigh joints shielded with horny pads to prevent abrasion of

645

the skin against the rough or gritty soil. These are present in the newly-born calf. Other modifications obviate the discomfort and danger of sandstorms. The sides of the tail, for instance, are fringed with hairs to protect the underlying parts and the bare skin on the inside of the thighs from the wind-driven grains; the small ears can be tucked down out of harm's way, and the nostrils are valvular and lined with hairs to exclude the particles of flying grit.

Camels vary in colour from dark brown to dirty white, but are never piebald like most domesticated animals. The part played by the camel in inter-tribal trade in remote times can only be inferred from historical records and from its usefulness at the present time. But it is known that the wealth of chiefs and tribes was measured by their herds of camels, and its value depended upon its provision of flesh, milk, leather, wool, labour and transport power, in districts where sheep, cattle and horses are difficult to feed and keep.

By reason of their great size and strength, sturdy camels can carry some six hundred pounds, going thirty miles a day, although the walking pace is only three miles an hour. But there is a lightly-built breed of dromedary not used for heavy bales, which will carry its rider at about twice that speed and cover double the distance in the same time.

Although the usefulness of the camel to man's service has earned for it the title " Ship of the Desert," the animal has defects of temper which at times render it exceedingly troublesome. It has gained a reputation for stupidity and obstinacy from its resolute refusal to budge when it wishes to lie down and rest; and during the rutting season the males are excessively quarrelsome, not only fighting amongst themselves, but savagely biting their owners or anyone who ventures near them.

Llamas. The Llamas (*Lama*) have no hump, are smaller and more lightly built than camels; they also have longer, pointed ears, a short, bushy tail, a thick fleece of wool and narrow feet, with the digits only joined for half their length. They are not adapted for desert life; but are found up to the snow-line in the Andes of South America, their feet being fitted for traversing rocky hill-sides and the thick coat protecting them from the severe cold of those altitudes. They live in herds of over a hundred individuals sometimes and are comparatively defenceless, trusting to their agility to escape from enemies. But when exhibition in a menagerie has taught them fearlessness of man, they may be dangerous at times, charging their keepers, striking them down with their fore feet and biting them severely with their sharp teeth. They also have the well-known and annoying habit of spitting when upset. There are two wild species, the Huanaco or Guanaco (*Lama huanacus*) and the Vicugna (*Lama vicugna*).

Huanaco. This animal is considerably the larger of the two, standing from three and a half to four feet at the back, and having a relatively longer head. Its general colour is a pale yellow-brown, with an ashy-grey head, and white below. It also has a wider geographical distribution and a more varied habitat, occurring not only in the Andes of Peru and Bolivia, but throughout the plains of the Argentine and Patagonia and even in Tierra del Fuego. It is fearless of water and has been observed swimming

By courtesy of]   [*Carl Hagenbeck's Tierpark, Stellingen.*
VICUGNA (*Lama vicugna*).
This is a wild species, standing less than three feet in height. It is tawny in colour, and inhabits higher altitudes than does the Huanaco.

from island to island in the neighbourhood of Cape Horn. In Patagonia, it is not uncommon to find great accumulations of the skeletons of these animals in one spot, showing that it is the custom of sick or old individuals to seek a particular place wherein to die.

Vicugna. This species is less than three feet in height, and has a shorter head of the same tawny hue as the body. It inhabits the Andes of Southern Ecuador, Peru and Northern Bolivia at higher altitudes than the Huanaco, and is not found in the Pampas region farther south.

Since llamas are the only hoofed animals indigenous to South America, except some deer and peccaries, it is not surprising that the earliest settlers in the country, the Incas, domesticated them as the Tartars and Arabs domesticated the camels. When the Spaniards conquered South America, llamas were the only beasts of burden the natives possessed. They kept vast herds of them

[*W. S. Berridge.*
LLAMA (*Domestic breed*).
The llama is capable of carrying about one hundredweight. Its feet are fitted for traversing rocky hill-sides, the thick coat protecting the animal from the severe cold of high altitudes.

647

HUANACO OR GUANACO (*Lama huanacus*).
This is a wild species and stands from three and a half to four feet at the back. In general colour it is a pale yellow-brown, with an ashy-grey head, and white below.

and employed them, not only for transport, but for their hides, wool, flesh and milk. There are two distinct breeds, the typical Llama and the Alpaca.

Alpaca. This is the smaller of the two, and was especially kept for the luxuriance of its wool, which is famous for its quality the world over. This breed was not used for transport, that being the duty of the stronger llama, which is capable of carrying about one hundredweight, and was largely employed for fetching ores from the mountains, the removal of household goods and merchandise, and even for riding. But the introduction into South America of sheep, horses, asses and, more particularly of mules, which are as sure-footed and hardy and much more powerful than llamas, has largely deprived these animals of their usefulness.

Llamas and Alpacas vary in colour from black or brown to white or a piebald mixture of the two. It is generally supposed that both these breeds are descendants of the wild Huanaco, which on account of its superior size would naturally be preferred to the Vicugna for domestication. But there are certain differences between the wild and the tame animal which suggest the possibility of the descent of the domesticated breeds from a third species now wholly reclaimed from a wild state.

Photos] [W. S. Berridge.
ALPACA.
Before the introduction into South America of sheep, this animal was especially kept for the luxuriance of its wool. This breed was not used for transport.

648

CHEVROTAINS OR MOUSE-DEER

WATER CHEVROTAIN (*Hyemoschus aquaticus.*)
This animal is found near water, and is a good diver and swimmer. It is a native of West Africa.

Chevrotains or Mouse-deer (Tribe *Tragulina*). The Chevrotains or Mouse-deer (Family *Tragulidae*), the smallest of the Artiodactyls, resemble the next tribe, the Pecora, in the structure of their front teeth and feet; but the bones supporting the third and fourth digits are less completely united to form a " cannon-bone," and the corresponding bones supporting the second and fifth digits are entire, the whole limb being much more primitive and approaching that of the pigs. In the stomach, the third compartment, well developed in the Pecora, is rudimentary. The absence of horns is made good by the large, tusk-like upper canines.

The Chevrotains are dainty little creatures about the size of hares, inhabiting the jungles and forests of tropical Asia and Africa. Being timid and defenceless, they lie up by day in sheltered places, only venturing out at dusk to feed. One or two young are born at a time.

The species of the typical Chevrotains (*Tragulus*), represented by the Kanchil (*T. kanchil*) and the Napu (*T. javanicus*), are uniformly coloured, usually chestnut-red. They inhabit south-eastern Asia from Burma to Borneo, and the Philippines. The Indian and Ceylonese Chevrotain (*Moschiola meminna*) is brown, ornamented with white spots and stripes. The West African or Water Chevrotain (*Hyemoschus aquaticus*) also has a pattern of white marks, but is a larger, thicker-legged

Photos]   *[W. S. Berridge.*
NAPU OR JAVAN CHEVROTAIN (*Tragulus javanicus*).
The Chevrotains, or Mouse-deer, are dainty little creatures about the size of hares, inhabiting the jungles and forests of tropical Asia and Africa.

species, found near water, into which, being a good diver and swimmer, it plunges to escape danger.

True Ruminants (Tribe *Pecora*). In this tribe there are no incisor teeth in the upper jaw; the canines of the lower jaw lie alongside the incisors and resemble them in structure and function. The feet are unguligrade, the hoofs of the third and fourth digits alone resting on the ground and having their inner surfaces flattened so that they fit together to form the so-called " cloven hoof," and the two long bones (metacarpals and metatarsals) lying respectively between the wrist or " knee " and the ankle or " hock," which are raised high off the ground, are fused to form a single " cannon " bone. The stomach is as described above.

This tribe is found all over the world, except Australasia and Madagascar, from the Arctic regions southwards.

There are four families: the *Bovidae* (Cattle, Sheep, Goats, Antelopes and Gazelles); the *Antilocapridae* (Prongbuck); the *Giraffidae* (Giraffes); and the *Cervidae* (Deer).

Cattle, Sheep, Goats, Antelopes and Gazelles (Family *Bovidae*). In this family the horns, present at least in the males, consist of a solid, bony growth from the skull, encased in a sheath of true horn, which is neither branched nor shed and is of continuous growth, like claws or hoofs.

Nearly all the species of this family are found in Europe, Asia and Africa.

[James's Press.

SPANISH CATTLE (*Bos taurus*).

[F. W. Bond.

CHARTLEY BULL AND COW (*Bos taurus*).

These so-called wild park cattle are descendants of domesticated breeds kept true to the fancied colour by the elimination of calves which revert to the ancestral type in tint. There are no genuinely wild species.

A few only inhabit North America and there is none in South America. It is divided into a large number of intergrading subfamilies, most of which are comprehensively called "Antelopes"; but that term does not symbolize a natural group.

Cattle and their Allies. The Bovine section contains the cattle and their allies. They are mostly large, always heavily-built animals, in which the horns are nearly equally developed in both sexes, are never twisted, and never have pronounced ridges or crests; the tail is long or moderately long, and the skin has no special scent glands. The muzzle is broad and is adapted for grazing.

True Cattle (Bos). Of these there are no genuinely wild species, the so-called wild park cattle of Chillingham, Cadzow, Chartley (formerly) and elsewhere being the descendants of domesticated breeds kept true to the fancied colour by the elimination of calves which revert to the ancestral type in tint. This fancied colour is white, with a black or red rim round the muzzle, black or red ears and sometimes spots of those hues on the legs. They are of considerable historical interest and are greatly prized by their owners. In build they resemble the typical, domesticated breeds of Europe (*Bos taurus*), which have no hump on the shoulder, and the croup high and in line with the back. There is little doubt that the

MYSORE BULL (*Bos indicus var.*), INDIA.

ancestor of these breeds was the Aurochs or Urus (*Bos primigenius*), a huge wild bull which inhabited the forests of Europe and became extinct as a wild animal in the sixteenth century, or perhaps a little later.

Humped Cattle or Zebus (*Bos indicus*), originally known from India, whence they have been exported to many tropical countries, are probably also descended from the Aurochs, although more altered from that type than our cattle. There are many breeds of them ; but they all differ typically from European breeds in having a fatty hump on the shoulder and the croup sloping.

Of the wild species the two most nearly akin to the domesticated breeds just described are the Gaur (*Bibos frontalis*) and the Banteng (*B. banting*). They are, however, distinguished by their shorter tails, " white-stockinged " legs and the elevation of the withers, especially in the bulls.

Gaur. This is often called the " Bison " by sportsmen, and is, perhaps, the handsomest of all wild cattle. The coat is sleek and brownish in hue ; the forehead is hairy and typically arched between the horns, which are massive and curved, and the withers are so elevated that the bull may surpass six feet in height, the cow being about a foot shorter. Gaur are found in India, but not in Ceylon, in Indo-China, Burma and the Malay Peninsula, where they are called Seladang. They live, as a rule, in small

Photos]   *[W. S. Berridge.*

GAYAL.

This is a tame or semi-wild form of the Gaur, being formerly regarded as a distinct species. It is found in India, Assam and adjoining countries.

herds both in the plains and hills, ascending the latter to a height of six thousand feet in warmer districts. Despite their size, they are shy of man, although dangerous when wounded.

In Assam and adjoining countries there is a tame or semi-wild form, the *Gayal* or *Mithan*, which usually has a flat forehead, and was

BANTENG (*Bibos banting*).
This wild species is distinguished from the domesticated Humped Cattle by its shorter tail, " white-stockinged " legs and the elevation of the withers.

formerly regarded as a distinct species. It is, however, almost certainly a domesticated race of the Gaur which in places has run wild.

Banteng or *Tsaine*. This differs from the Gaur in being smaller, having a larger dewlap, a longer tail, a white patch on the buttocks and the area between the horns in the bulls naked and roughened. The colour varies from pale brown in cows and young bulls to nearly black in old bulls. The height is from five to five and a half feet, the withers not being so elevated. It ranges from Indo-China to Java and Borneo, and, in the last two countries at least, is domesticated by the natives.

Bison. The true Bisons have the withers elevated as in the Gaur ; but the hair, at least of the head and neck, is developed into a mane and on the rest of the body is thick and woolly in the winter ; the horns are short

Photos]   [*W. S. Berridge.*

HUMPED CATTLE OR ZEBU (*Bos indicus*).
These differ typically from European breeds in having a fatty hump on the shoulder and the croup sloping.

and there are fourteen pairs of ribs instead of thirteen as in the Gaur and domesticated cattle. There are two species, the European (*B. bonasus*) and the American (*B. bison*), both being uniformly brown in colour.

The European Bison or Wisent, sometimes but wrongly called the Aurochs, is the larger of the two, has the mane less well developed and the hind quarters considerably higher, thus approaching the Gaur, which it rivals in size, a bull standing about six feet high, and weighing up to about two thousand pounds.

The species is now nearly extinct. A few still survive, it is said, under strict protection in the forests of Lithuania ; and there are one or two herds in the Caucasus, otherwise the species is represented by examples in Zoological Gardens or private parks like the Duke of Bedford's at Woburn.

The American Bison, called Buffalo in the States, has a more voluminous and extensive mane, a more sloping croup, and carries its head lower than the European. The height does not exceed five and three-quarter feet, but the weight may be over two thousand pounds.

[*W. S. Berridge.*
YAK (*Poephagus grunniens*).
The colour of the wild animal is deep brown, the height from five to five and a half feet and the weight up to one thousand two hundred pounds.

In times gone by this Bison lived in vast herds in the prairies of North America to the east of the Rockies. Its extermination started by wholesale slaughter by the Indians as soon as they got horses from European settlers, and was nearly completed by the latter before measures were taken to protect the few that remained in the Yellowstone Park and in Canada, where there is now a flourishing herd. It has never been domesticated, but when crossed with imported cattle, it produces a fertile hybrid, the Cattalo.

Yak (Poephagus grunniens). The Yak, with the same number of ribs as the Bisons and elevated withers, is a relatively long-bodied, short-legged species, with a thick fringe-like mane on the throat and belly, a long, thick tuft on the tail, and long horns. The colour of the wild animal is deep brown, the height from five to five and a half feet and the weight up to one thousand two hundred pounds. Its natural home is the high plateau and mountains of Tibet and Western China, where it ascends the mountains to a height of 15,000 or 20,000 feet in summer. It is very hardy and surefooted, and was domesticated generations ago by the natives for its flesh, milk, and as a beast of burden. The tame animal is smaller, variously coloured, and the cows are often hornless.

By courtesy of]   [Canadian Pacific Railways.

AMERICAN BISON (*Bison bison*).

[*D. Seth-Smith*.

EUROPEAN BISON OR WISENT (*Bison bonasus*).
The European Bison is larger than the American, has the mane less well developed and the hind quarters considerably higher.
The species is now nearly extinct.

MAMMALIA (SUBORDER RUMINANTIA)

Buffaloes. The cattle, hitherto described, have the horns circular or oval in section, and the wild species will cross with European domesticated breeds; but in the Buffaloes the horns are typically flattened in front, at least basally, and are more or less triangular in section. These animals have never been known to breed with domesticated cattle. There are two distinct groups of them.

African Buffaloes (*Syncerus caffer*). These have shorter heads, larger, fringed ears, and the hairs along the spine directed backwards.

They are found in suitable localities all over Africa south of the Sahara and are represented by many local races, the extreme modifications being so distinct that they were regarded as separate species. The typical race, known as the Cape Buffalo, is black, stands about five feet high, and the horns, which are close together on the summit of the head, where they form a helmet-like mass, curve at first downwards and backwards close to the ears, then upwards. It inhabits the open bush country, generally near rivers in South Africa, and is represented by nearly-related races in similar districts in East Africa. It is considered by sportsmen to be one of the most dangerous of the big game animals of Africa.

[*W. S. Berridge.*

AFRICAN DWARF BUFFALO (*Syncerus caffer*).
There are many local races found in open bush country, generally near rivers, all over Africa south of the Sahara.

Dwarf Buffalo. This is a very distinct race, and is sometimes called the Bush Cow. It inhabits the Congo forest area, and is considerably smaller than the African Buffaloes, its height being only about three and a half feet. It is typically red, although bulls, at least, turn black with advancing years; its horns also are smaller, hardly expanded at the base and not curved downwards above the ears. But between these two extremes there appear to be races intermediate in size, colour and horn development.

Asiatic Buffaloes. In these the head is relatively longer, the ears are smaller and unfringed and the hairs along the spine are directed forwards. There are three distinct species. The Common Indian Buffalo (*Anoa bubalis*) is a big beast, bulls being from five to five and a half feet high and

[British Museum (Natural History)

AFRICAN BUFFALO (Syncerus caffer)

By courtesy of]

ROAN ANTELOPE (Hippotragus equinus)

" WATER-BUFFALO " (*Anoa bubalis*).
Bulls are from five to five and a half feet high and usually black in colour. These buffaloes live in herds, usually in swampy districts.

usually black. The horns project laterally from the sides of the forehead, where they are widely separated, and may be of immense length, the span from tip to tip being as much as eight or nine feet. These buffaloes live in herds, usually in swampy districts and from their habit of mud-wallowing and lying for hours immersed, only the head above the surface, are frequently called "Water-buffaloes." They are courageous animals with little fear of man and when banded together will attack and kill tigers. The period of gestation is ten months. This buffalo was domesticated generations ago. It is used for draught purposes and milk, and has been introduced into many countries including Italy and Australia.

Tamarau or Philippine Buffalo (*A. mindorensis*). This is a smaller species, standing about three and a half feet high, and has short, massive horns growing backwards from the forehead and almost in contact at the base. In a great measure it connects the big Indian Buffalo with the typical Anoa (*A. depressicornis*) of Celebes, a still smaller and more lightly-built species, a little over three feet in height, but with the thinner horns growing backwards in the same way. This little buffalo is of particular interest because it links the cattle with the next group of the family, the Tragelaphine antelopes, particularly the Elands, evidence of this kinship being seen externally in the direction of the horns, their presence in both sexes,

Photos]   [*W. S. Berridge.*
ANOA (*A. depressicornis*).
A lightly-built little buffalo, a little over three feet in height. It is interesting because it links the cattle with the Tragelaphine antelopes.

By courtesy of]   [*Field Museum of Natural History, Chicago.*

BONGO (*Boöcercus eurycerus*).
The Bongo is four feet high, chestnut in colour with about twelve white stripes. It lives in the forested districts of Central Africa.

the tufted, or " bovine " tail and in the presence in some specimens of white patches above the hoofs, two white spots on the cheeks and a white bar low down on the throat, marks which are known as " tragelaphine " from their prevalence in these antelopes.

Tragelaphines. This group contains a large number of species with hardly a single invariable character in common except some of the " tragelaphine " markings above referred to ; but the horns are never provided with knobs, are usually spirally twisted and keeled in front, and the feet, as in cattle, never have glands opening just above the hoofs. The group is found in Africa and India.

Elands (*Taurotragus*). These are the largest of the group and differ from cattle in having the horns spirally twisted, like a gimlet, and glands between the lateral hoofs of the hind feet. Bulls have a mat of hair on the forehead.

There are two species. The Common Eland (*T. oryx*) is brighter or paler fawn, with the neck the same colour as the body ; the ears are narrow and the dewlap begins on the throat. A large bull stands nearly six feet in height and weighs about one thousand two hundred pounds. This Eland ranges from Kenya Colony to South Africa and Angola. East African specimens which inhabit bush country are brighter in colour and have a few white stripes on the body ; but in the Kalahari the colour is dun unrelieved by stripes.

Lord Derby's Eland (*T. derbianus*) is distinguished by its reddish colour, more numerous white stripes, blackish neck and larger ears and the dew-

658

By courtesy of] [Carl Hagenbeck's Tierpark, Stellingen.

ELAND (*Taurotragus oryx*).
A large bull stands nearly six feet in height and weighs about twelve hundred pounds.

lap beginning at the chin. It inhabits more wooded country than the Common Eland and ranges from Senegambia to the Soudan and Portuguese Guinea.

Bongo (*Boöcercus eurycerus*). This animal is nearly allied to the Elands, but has no dewlap or frontal mat, and the massive horns have an open spiral of about one complete twist. It is four feet high, is chestnut in colour, with many white stripes (usually about twelve), and lives in the forested districts of Central Africa.

Kudus (*Strepsiceros*). These are distinguished from the preceding by having the tail uniformly hairy, by the horns being absent in the female and forming an open corkscrew spiral in the male. There are two species. The Greater Kudu (*S. strepsiceros*) is the handsomest of all antelopes. The height is close upon five feet, the colour greyish-brown, with white stripes on the body, and there is a long fringe on the throat. It ranges

[F. W. Bond.

YOUNG FEMALE LESSER KUDU (*Strepsiceros imberbis*).
The Lesser Kudu, only about three feet in height, is restricted to Somaliland and Kenya.

from Abyssinia to South Africa, and usually frequents wooded hill-sides.

The Lesser Kudu (*S. imberbis*), restricted to Somaliland and Kenya, is only about three feet in height and has no throat-fringe.

Bush-bucks (*Tragelaphus*). These are the most plentiful of all the group, and differ from the Kudus in their less-twisted horns. The largest is the Mountain, or Buxton's, Bush-buck (*T. buxtoni*), which is about four and a half feet high, brownish in colour, with hardly a trace of stripes, and inhabits the mountains to the south of Abyssinia.

Nyala (*T. angasi*). This differs sexually in colour, the male being slate-grey, with a white spinal crest and a fringe on the throat and belly, the female bright red, with white stripes and no fringe. The height is about three and a half feet. This species is found in Zululand, and adjoining countries and

[W. S. Berridge.

- MARSH-BUCK (*Limnotragus spekii*).
This antelope is semi-aquatic, frequenting reed beds in Central Africa, and often lying immersed in water, with only the nostrils above the surface.

frequents jungles along river banks.

The smallest species, the Common Bush-buck (*T. scriptus*), which is from two and a half to three feet high, is found nearly all over Africa south of the Sahara, some two dozen local races being distinguished, the handsomest being the *Harnessed Antelope*, in which both sexes are red, with white stripes.

Marsh-bucks, or Situtungas, (*Limnotragus spekii*) differ from the Bushbucks in having the feet very long, with

[E. Schneider.

NYALA (*Tragelaphus angasi*).
The male is slate-grey, with a white spinal crest and a fringe on the throat and belly ; the female bright red, with white stripes and no fringe.

[W. S. Berridge.
NYLGHAIE (*Boselaphus tragocamelus*).
This big and ungainly antelope is common in Central India,
but is not found in Ceylon.

the hoofs widely separable, an adaptation for walking on muddy banks. The height is about four feet. This antelope is semi-aquatic, frequenting reed beds in Central Africa and often lying immersed in water, with only the nostrils above the surface.

There are two Tragelaphines in India, the Nylghaie and the Four-horned Antelope. They differ from the African species in having a gland in front of the eye and the horns, present only in males, not spirally twisted.

Nylghaie, or *Blue Bull*, (*Boselaphus tragocamelus*). This big and ungainly antelope, about four and a half feet high, has a mane on the neck and the tail fringed. In the male the colour is iron-grey, the throat is tufted and the horns are short, curved spikes. The female is fawn and has no throat-tuft. Common in Central India but not found in Ceylon, the Nylghaie occurs in small herds in the plains or low hills covered with thin bush.

Four-horned Antelope (*Tetracerus quadricornis*). This takes its name from the usual presence of a pair of additional small horns in front of the ordinary pair, which are short spikes. It is a small antelope of India, about two feet in height, is reddish fawn in colour, and lives mostly in bush or thin forest, but is not gregarious.

Kobines. This group, containing the Water-bucks. Kobs and Reed-bucks of Africa, is related in some respects to the Tragelaphines, but the horns, present only in males, are untwisted, typically

By courtesy of]   [Carl Hagenbeck's Tierpark, Stellingen.
DEFASSA WATER-BUCK (*Kobus defassa*).
This is also known as the Sing-sing; its range embraces parts of
West as well as East Africa.

lightly curved and strengthened by thick transverse ridges.

Water-bucks. The largest species are the typical so-called Water-bucks (*Kobus ellipsiprymnus* and *K. defassa*), in which the height is over four feet. The former, distinguishable by the white ring on the rump, set off by the dark brown hue of the body, inhabits the plains and hills of

[*W. S. Berridge.*

YOUNG HARNESSED ANTELOPE.
Both sexes are red with white stripes.

East Africa as far south as the Zambesi. The other, known as the Singsing, has no rump-ring, is usually paler and has a wider range, which embraces parts of West as well as East Africa.

The term "Water-buck" is inappropriate for these two antelopes, but is more suitable for two related species, the typical Lechwe (*K. leche*), which is typically fawn in colour and frequents swampy districts of the Zambesi, and to Gray's Lechwe (*K. megaceros*), which is about the same size, over three feet high, dark brown in colour, with a white patch on the back of the neck, and lives in the swamps of the Upper Nile. The Kobs (*Kobus kob*) resemble the large Water-bucks in habits, but are much smaller, about three feet high, are mostly fawn in colour, and are widely distributed.

The Reed-bucks or Riet-boks (*Redunca arundinacea*, etc.), also

[*James's Press.*

HARNESSED ANTELOPE.
(*Tragelaphus scriptus*).
This is the handsomest of the Common Bush-bucks, of which there are some two dozen local races.

663

widely distributed, and of medium size, differ from the foregoing in having the tail bushy, not tufted. The Vaal-rhebok (*Pelea capreolus*), with a similar tail, but greyish in tint and only two and a half feet high, is the most primitive type of this section, the horns being simple, straight spikes. Its habitat is rocky hills of South Africa.

Aepycerines. This group contains the Impala or Palla (*Aepyceros melampus*) and is distinguished from the preceding by the absence of lateral hoofs and by the presence of a pair of glands, covered with black hair, above the fetlocks of the hind legs. The horns, absent in the female, are long, lyrate and knobbed ; the colour is reddish-brown and the height over three feet. This elegant antelope lives in the bush country of East and South Africa.

Bubalines. This group contains the Hartebeests and Wildebeests or Gnus, large African antelopes with long faces, swollen muzzles, valvular, hairy nostrils, large pocket-like glands on the fore feet and horns of equal size in both sexes. They are gregarious and live in the open plains of Africa.

Wildebeests or Gnus.

[*W. S. Berridge*.
WHITE-TAILED GNU (*Connochaetes gnou*).
This is rather like a small buffalo, brown in colour, with a white, bushy tail. It is now probably extinct as a wild animal.

These have the horns unridged and directed downwards then upwards ; the muzzle is very broad, the face coarsely hairy and the neck maned. There are two kinds ; the White-tailed Gnu, or Black Wildebeest, (*Connochaetes gnou*) is brown, with a white, bushy tail, a high croup and horns bent sharply down before curving upwards. It is a savage-looking animal, rather like a small buffalo, and standing 4 feet high. It was formerly abundant on the flats of South Africa, but is now probably extinct as a wild animal.

The Brindled Gnu or Blue Wildebeest (*Gorgon taurinus*) is a larger antelope, nearly four and a half feet high, and greyish in colour, brindled with brown stripes on the neck and forequarters, the tail being black. It has a wide range, from Kenya to the Zambesi and Angola.

Hartebeests. In these animals the horns are ridged and directed upwards, the face is smooth and the neck without a mane.

664

GNU OR BLUE WILDEBEEST (*Gorgon taurinus*).

There are two kinds of Gnu : the White-tailed Gnu, or Black Wildebeest, and the Brindled Gnu, or Blue Wildebeest, somewhat larger, nearly four and a half feet in height.

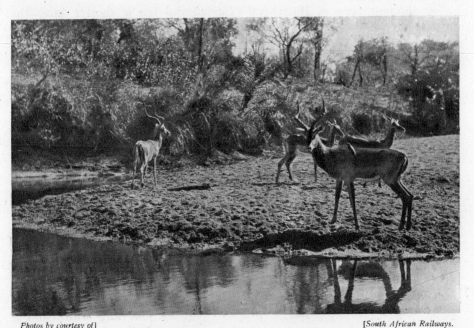

Photos by courtesy of]   [*South African Railways*.

IMPALA OR PALLA (*Aepyceros melampus*).

The height of this elegant antelope is over three feet, the colour being reddish-brown. Habitat, bush country of East and South Africa.

MAMMALIA (SUBORDER RUMINANTIA)

The typical Harte-beests (*Bubalis*) have long, narrow faces and the horns, which are raised on an eminence, exhibit a sharp angular bend before the point. There are a great many species, differing in colour, the shapes of the horns, etc., and the range covers practically the whole of Africa. The most northerly form, the Bubal (*B. buselaphus*), inhabiting Morocco and Tunis, is a pale fawn in colour and about three and a half feet high. The

[W. S. Berridge.

BLESBOK (*Damaliscus albifrons*).
This Hartebeest is brownish, with a white blaze on the face. It stands about three feet in height.

most southerly, the Kaama (*B. caama*), from Cape Colony, is reddish-brown, with the face mostly black, the height being about four feet.

A different type of Hartebeest (*Damaliscus*) has a shorter face, the horns not elevated and without the angular bend. The earliest-known kinds were the Bontebok (*D. pygargus*) and the Blesbok (*D. albifrons*), which are about three feet high and brownish, with a white blaze on the face. The Bontebok, distinguished by its white rump, is now represented by a single herd preserved to the south of Cape Town; the Blesbok, by a few protected herds north of the Orange River. Related species without any white and a little larger range through East Africa

[F. W. Bond.

ARABIAN ORYX (*Oryx leucoryx*).
In these large antelopes the straight, spike-like horns are present in both sexes.

666

YOUNG GEMSBOK (*Oryx gazella*).
The Gemsbok is found only in South Africa.

Photos]   [*W. S. Berridge.*
BONTEBOK (*Damaliscus pygargus*).
This Hartebeest is distinguished by its white rump, and is now represented by a single herd preserved to the south of
Cape Town.

to Senegambia, the Sassaby (*D. lunatus*) being found in Mashonaland; the Tiang (*D. korrigum*) ranging from Kenya Colony westwards, the Topi Antelope (*D. korrigum topi*) occurring in Uganda, and Hunter's Hartebeest (*D. hunteri*) inhabiting Jubaland.

Gazellines. This group is nearly akin to the last, but has the face shorter, the muzzle narrower, a pocket-like instead of a nearly solid facial gland and large glandular clefts on the hind, as well as on the fore feet. The horns of the male are like the Blesbok's, but in the female they are small or absent. These antelopes live in open, often desert country, are mostly of medium or small size and have slender legs.

[*Wide World Photos.*

GRANT'S GAZELLE (*Gazella granti*) AND EAST AFRICAN ORYX (*Oryx beisa*).

Gazelles. The typical gazelles (*Gazella*) have the horns curving backwards, the neck not unusually long, and conspicuous glandular pads on the knees. There is a great variety of species and races, ranging from central to south-western Asia and thence all over North Africa into British East Africa. Most of them, like the Dorcas Gazelle (*G. dorcas*) of the northern Sahara, and the Arabian Gazelle (*G. arabica*) of Arabia, are very much alike, being generally sandy-brown in colour, with black and white bands on the face and usually on the flanks and buttocks. They are of small size, the height being about two feet. Much larger species, very variable locally in colour, are Soemmering's Gazelle (*G. soemmeringi*) from the deserts near

Abyssinia, and the Mhor Gazelle (*G. dama*) from Morocco, Gambia and the Soudan, in which the height is about three feet. Nearly as large and remarkable for the great length of the horns is Grant's Gazelle (*G. granti*) from British East Africa.

Black-buck (*Antilope cervicapra*). This differs from the gazelles in having the horns spirally twisted and in the colour-contrast between the sexes, the

BLACK-BUCK OR INDIAN ANTELOPE (*Antilope cervicapra*).
The females are fawn and the males assume a black livery in the breeding season.

females being fawn and the males assuming a black livery in the breeding season. The height is about two and a half feet. It inhabits the plains of central and north-western India.

Springbok (*Antidorcas marsupialis*). This resembles the typical gazelle in its horns, shape and colouring, but differs in having a large white dilatable patch of glandular skin on the hinder part of the back and no knee pads. The height is about two and a half feet. This antelope replaces

Photos]   [*W. S. Berridge.*
SPRINGBOK (*Antidorcas marsupialis*).
The height of this little gazelle is about two and a half feet.

669

GAMBIAN ORIBI ANTELOPE.

[*James's Press.*

the gazelles in Africa, south of the Zambesi, where it periodically migrates in vast hordes.

Gerenuk. An aberrant member of this section is the Gerenuk, or Waller's Gazelle, (*Lithocranius walleri*), which is remarkable for the extreme length of its neck and legs and small but extraordinarily heavy head, whence its name meaning "stone-headed." The height is about three and a quarter feet and the species occur in Somaliland and British East Africa.

Africa is also the home of large numbers of familiar small or medium-sized antelopes with short, spike-like horns, a scent gland between the digits, and usually in front of the eyes. They represent several distinct groups.

Duikers. The Cephalophine group, containing the Duikers, is distinguished from all antelopes by the ducts of the face-glands opening by a series of pores. There is a large number of species spread all over central and southern Africa, differing greatly in colour and size. One of the largest, Jentink's

[*W. S. Berridge.*

COMMON DUIKER ANTELOPE.
The name "duiker," meaning diver, is given to these antelopes because of their manner of plunging into the undergrowth.

670

[James's Press.

THE EDMI OR CUVIER'S GAZELLE (*Gazella cuvieri*) FOUND IN N.W. AFRICA.

[W. S. Berridge.

ADDAX ANTELOPE.
This antelope, with long and spirally-twisted horns, inhabits the desert regions of Northern Africa.

Duiker (*Cephalophus jentinki*), which inhabits Liberia, is two and a half feet high and whitish on the body, black on the head and neck. The Blue Duiker (*C. monticola*), of South Africa, is about one foot high, and greyish-brown in colour. The name "duiker," meaning diver, is given to these antelopes because of their manner of plunging into the undergrowth.

Oribis. The Neotragine group, of which the Oribis (*Ourebia*) are the best-known representatives, differs from the Duiker group in having the pores of the face-glands scattered and typically sunk in a pocket. The Oribis, of which there are many species, are the largest, standing about one and a half feet in height, and are fawn in colour, with a patch of bare skin under the ear and tufts on the knees. The common Oribi (*O. ourebi*), of Cape Colony, and the Black-tailed Oribi (*O. nigricaudata*), of

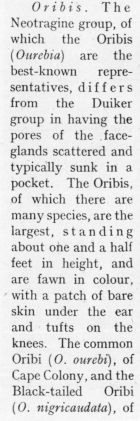

[F. W. Bond.

EAST AFRICAN BOHOR REEDBUCK (*Redunca redunca*).

672

By courtesy of]   [*Richard T. Doonor, Philadelphia, and the Academy of Natural Sciences of Philadelphia, U.S.A. (founded 1812).*

SABLE ANTELOPES.

Both male and female carry horns, which in the male may reach a length of over sixty inches. These antelopes are usually found in herds of from one to two dozen.

[*W. S. Berridge.*

WHITE-FACED GAZELLE (*Gazella marica*).
This gazelle inhabits the desert regions of S. Arabia.

GRYSBOK (*Nototragus melanotis*).
The colour of this little animal is rich red, sprinkled with white hairs. It inhabits Cape Colony.

Senegambia are examples.

Grysbok (*Nototragus melanotis*). This animal of Cape Colony, differs from the Oribis in having no patch below the ear and no knee pads. The colour is rich red, sprinkled with white hairs. The Steinbok (*Raphicerus campestris*), also found in Cape Colony, differs from the Grysbok in having no lateral hoofs. The Royal Antelope (*Neotragus pygmaeus*), inhabiting Guinea, differs from the preceding in having the horns, which are only one inch long, inclined backwards. This antelope, which is reddish-fawn in colour, is the smallest of all antelopes, standing only ten inches high.

Klipspringers. The Oreotragine group contains only the Klipspringer (*Oreotragus oreotragus*), which is probably related to the foregoing, but is distinguished by its harsh, pithy coat, the absence of foot-glands, and the structure of the hoofs, which, instead of being pointed, are blunt at the end, the animal walking upon the extreme tips, with the heels elevated. By means of its feet, this antelope is able

Photos] [*W. S. Berridge.*
KLIPSPRINGER (*Oreotragus oreotragus*).
The hoofs, instead of being pointed, are blunt at the end, and the animal walks upon the extreme tips, with the heels elevated. It is thus able to climb about the rocky precipices of the mountains, where there is apparently no foothold.

to climb about the rocky precipices of the mountains it frequents, where there is apparently no foothold. It is brownish or yellowish in colour, a little over one and a half feet in height, and ranges from Nigeria to Abyssinia and Cape Colony.

Dik-diks. The Madoquine group, popularly known as Dik-diks, are elegant little antelopes, differing principally from the Oribi group in the structure of the muzzle, which forms a thickened kind of proboscis, clothed with hair to the very edge of the nostrils. There are many species, ranging from Abyssinia to Cape Colony, Salt's Dik-dik (*Madoqua saltiana*), from Abyssinia, and the South African Dik-dik (*Rhynchotragus damarensis*), both about fourteen inches high, being representatives. The Beira (*Dorcotragus megalotis*), inhabiting Somaliland, is a specially - modified type with short hoofs, like those of a goat, adapted for rock climbing.

Chiru and *Saiga*. In Central Asia there are two aberrant antelopes, each the representative of a special group. The Pantholopine group contains the Chiru

[*W. S. Berridge.*
PIGMY OR ROYAL ANTELOPE (*Neotragus pygmaeus*).
This antelope, which is reddish-fawn in colour, is the smallest of all antelopes, standing only ten inches in height.

[*Wide World Photos.*
YOUNG DIK-DIK ANTELOPE (*Rhynchotragus*).
In these elegant little antelopes, the muzzle forms a thickened kind of proboscis clothed with hair to the very edge of the nostrils.

675

(*Pantholops hodgsoni*), which differs from the gazelles with which it was formerly classified by the absence of face-glands and foot-glands, its compact sheep-like feet, inflated nostrils and other characters. The horns, present only in the males, are long, erect and strongly ribbed ; the coat is coarse and close, the tail short, the colour fawn and the height a little over two and a half feet. This antelope lives in herds to the north of the Himalayas in Tibet, up to an altitude of 18,000 feet.

[*W. S. Berridge.*

Dama Gazelle (*Gazella dama*).

The Saiga (*Saiga tatarica*), the only representative of the Saigine group, is distinguished by the immense inflation of the nose into a proboscis with the nostrils opening downwards ; the horns are erect, ridged and amber-coloured as in some sheep. The animal has other sheep-like characters and seems, in a measure, to connect the group with the gazelles. The colour is yellowish in the summer, whitish in winter, and the height is about two and a half feet. The Saiga inhabits the steppes of South Russia and western and Central Asia.

Chamois. The Rupicaprine group, typified by the Chamois, links in a measure the preceding Gazelline with the following Caprine section, but differs from both in having the horns equally well - developed in both sexes, generally smooth and never ridged. In other respects the genera vary greatly. They inhabit mountainous districts of Europe, Asia and North America.

CHAMOIS.
The Chamois is found at high altitudes in the principal mountain ranges of Europe, from the Pyrenees to the Caucasus, and also in Asia Minor.

The Chamois (*Rupicapra rupicapra*), has the horns short, vertical and hooked at the tip. There is a well-developed gland on the head, just behind them, which becomes greatly swollen in the rutting season in the males. The general colour is brown and the height about two and a half feet. The Chamois is found at high altitudes in the principal mountain ranges of Europe, from the Pyrenees to the Caucasus, and also in Asia Minor.

Gorals and *Serows.* Differing from the Chamois in having the horns sloped backwards and not hooked, in the absence of the gland on the head, and in the presence of flask- or sac-like glands in the feet, and a naked, moist nose, are the Gorals (*Naemorhedus*) and the Serows (*C a p r i c o r n i s*), found mostly in the

Photos]　　　　　　　　　　　　　　　　　*[W. S. Berridge.*
HIMALAYAN GORAL (*Naemorhedus*).
This is a relation of the Chamois and Takin, differing from the former in having the horns sloped backwards and not hooked.

ROCKY MOUNTAIN GOAT (*Oreamnos americanus*).
The white coat is very long and shaggy in winter. This animal ranges through the northern portion of the Rockies from British Columbia to Alaska.

Himalayas and the mountains of China, although the typical Serow (*C. sumatraensis*), which is between three and three and a half feet in height, ranges as far south as Sumatra.

Rocky Mountain Goat (Oreamnos americanus). This resembles the Serow in the shape and direction of its horns, but has a head-gland and no definite foot-glands as in the Chamois. The legs are short below the knees and hocks and the colour is white, the coat being very long and shaggy in the winter. The height is about three and a half feet, and the range is the northern portion of the Rockies from British Columbia to Alaska.

Takin (Budorcas taxicolor). The Takin is heavily built, with a low croup and short limbs, as in the Rocky Mountain Goat; but it is distinguished by the horns being thickened at the base and growing outwards, slightly downwards and then upwards at the point. The height is three and a half feet or over. The range is from Bhutan in the Himalayas to Central China. In Bhutan the Takin is brown with a light saddle; but in Shensi in China it is golden-brown all over.

Musk-ox. In the Musk-ox (*Ovibos moschatus*), the horns are an exaggeration of the type

Photos]   [*W. S. Berridge.*
TAKIN (*Budorcas taxicolor*).
The range of this animal is from Bhutan in the Himalayas to Central China.

seen in the Takin, being still thicker at the base and growing downwards close to the face before turning upwards at the tip. The build is heavy, the tail very short and the legs are short and strong as in the Takin ; but the croup is high and, as a protection against cold, the coat is coarse and shaggy, falling almost to the fetlocks, and the h o o f s are broad, with hair projecting between them, as an aid to crossing slippery snow and icefields. The general colour is brown, and the height about four feet. The scent of musk

[*W. S. Berridge.*

HIMALAYAN SEROW, OR GOAT ANTELOPE
(*Capricornis sumatraensis*).
These animals are found mostly in the Himalayas and the mountains of China.

By courtesy of]   [*Carl Hagenbeck's Tierpark, Stellingen.*

MUSK-OX (*Ovibos moschatus*).
The Musk-ox, which is about four feet in height, inhabits north-eastern Canada, Greenland and some of the adjoining Arctic Islands.

from which the ani-
mal takes its name is
not secreted by any
special glands but per-
vades the flesh and is
especially noticeable
during the rutting sea-
son. The Musk-ox
feeds on the sparse,
coarse vegetation of the
countries it inhabits,
namely, north-eastern
Canada, Greenland and
some of the adjoining
Arctic Islands.

CAUCASIAN IBEX, OR TUR (*Capra caucasica*).
The horns are comparatively short and curve outwards and backwards close to the neck.

Goats and Sheep, Ibexes, Markhors and Thars (*Caprinae*). These are assigned to the Caprine section, and are not easily definable from the Rupicaprines except by the sexual inequality in the size of the horns, which are well developed in the males and small or absent in the females. The two groups are also alike in inhabiting mountainous districts of the northern hemisphere.

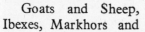

Photos]   *[W. S. Berridge.*
MARKHOR (*Capra falconeri megaceros*).
The horns are spirally twisted, either like a corkscrew or gimlet.

The typical repre-
sentatives of the sec-
tion, the Goats and the
Sheep, are very distinct
from one another ; but
they are to a greater
or less extent linked
together by interme-
diate types, which,
according to fancy, may
be called by either
name.

Goats (*Capra*). In
the Goats, the wild
species of which are
usually called Ibex, the
horns are inclined up-
wards and backwards
and there are no scent
glands on the face,
groin or feet ; but the
lower side of the tail is

CRETAN IBEX (*Capra hircus*).
This is the wild species from which domesticated goats are descended. It is still found indigenous in Crete.

glandular, and the males have a beard and the characteristic "goaty" odour. They are confined to Europe, North Africa and Central Asia, and are represented by the Ibexes of Spain (*C. pyrenaica*) and the Alps (*C. ibex*) in Europe ; of Nubia (*C. nubiana*) and Abyssinia (*C. walie*) in Africa ; and of the Caucasus (*C. caucasica*), the Tur ; of Asia Minor and Persia (*C. hircus*), the Pasang or Wild-goat ; of Central Asia and the Himalayas (*C. sibirica*) ; and of Afghanistan, etc. (*C. falconeri*), the Markhors. These species vary considerably in size, colour, curvature and structure of the horns and other characters. Typically, the horns form a bold, nearly semi-circular curve upwards and backwards ; but in the last of the list, the Markhor, they are spirally twisted, either like a corkscrew or gimlet. Of special interest as being the wild species from which domesti-

cated goats are descended is the Persian and Asia Minor species, still found indigenous in Crete. One of the smallest species is the Spanish Ibex, about two and a half feet in height ; the largest being the Caucasian and Siberian species, which may reach three and a half feet.

Tur (*Capra caucasica*). In some of the Caucasian Ibexes, called Tur, the horns are comparatively

Photos]　　　　　　　　　　　　　　　　[*W. S. Berridge.*
HIMALAYAN BHARAL OR BLUE SHEEP (*Pseudois nayaur*).
This differs from typical goats in being without a beard and in having no strong odour.

681

[*James's Press.*

"Nilgiri Ibex" (*Hemitragus hylocrius*).
This is one of the Thars, and inhabits the hills of southern India.

short and curve outwards and backwards close to the neck. In this respect they approach the Bharal (*Pseudois nayaur*), often erroneously called the Blue Sheep, which further differs from typical goats in being without a beard and in having no strong odour. It is grey in colour, with black marks on the legs, is about three feet in height, and inhabits the Himalayas at an average altitude of about 13,000 feet.

Another species, closely akin to the goats, is the so-called Barbary Sheep or Udad (*Ammotragus lervia*), which has horns very like those of the Bharal and the odour of goats, but is distinguished by a longer tail and a mane of long hair on the throat and upper part of the fore legs. The colour is fawn and the height about three and a quarter feet. It is found in Barbary and Kordofan in North Africa.

Thars (*Hemitragus*). These are beardless goats with short, evenly-curved horns. Their distribution is

[*Clarke and Hyde.*

Nubian Goat.
The colour of these goats is sometimes black, sometimes brownish-red and spotted.

peculiar in its discontinuity. The typical species (*H. jemlahicus*) is a shaggy-coated animal, brown in colour, about three and a quarter feet high, and found in the Himalayas; the second (*H. hylocrius*), known as the " Nilgiri Ibex," about the size of the last but shorter coated and thicker horned, inhabits the hills of southern India ; the third (*H. jayakari*), the smallest of all

[*W. S. Berridge.*
THAR
(*Hemitragus jemlahicus*).
This beardless goat is shaggy-coated, brown, about three and a quarter feet in height and found in the Himalayas.

the goats, being only two feet high, is found in south-eastern Arabia.

Sheep (*Ovis*). These are distinguished from the rest of the group by having a pair of pocket-glands on the face and groin, flask-like glands in all the feet ; no glands on the under side of the tail, and the horns in the rams directed outwards and downwards at the tip and then in nearly all cases forwards on each side of the face, with a marked spiral

[*Charles Reid.*
BARBARY SHEEP OR UDAD (*Ammotragus lervia*).
This animal, fawn in colour and about three and a quarter feet in height, is found in Barbary and Kordofan in North Africa.

683

twist. Apart from one isolated species in Corsica and Sardinia, they range from Cyprus, Asia Minor and Persia through Central Asia and through the Rocky Mountains in North America.

There are many different kinds, both species and local races, the latter generally restricted to particular mountain ranges. The Mouflon

By courtesy of]   *[Canadian Pacific Railway.*
BIGHORN OR ROCKY MOUNTAIN SHEEP (*Ovis canadensis*).
There are more than a dozen local races, varying in colour from brownish as in the typical race from British Columbia, to white in the Yukon race.

(*O. musimon*) of Sardinia and Corsica is a small species about two and a quarter feet high, dark brown in colour, with a white saddle. The Asiatic species are paler and vary greatly in size and in the massiveness and length of their horns. The Red Sheep (*O. orientalis*), inhabiting Cyprus, Asia Minor and Persia, is the smallest, being only slightly larger than the Mouflon, the points of the horns turning inwards towards the neck. The largest is the Argali (*O. ammon*), ranging from the northern slopes of the Himalayas to Kamtchatka. It may be as much as four feet high and typically has long, massive horns, curving forwards on each side of the face, and is fawn in colour. The best-known races are the typical form from the Altai, Marco Polo's Sheep (*O. a. poli*) from the Pamirs and Hodgson's Sheep (*O. a. hodgsoni*) from Tibet

By courtesy of]   *[Carl Hagenbeck's Tierpark, Stellingen.*
URIAL OR PUNJAB WILD SHEEP (*Ovis vignei*).
This sheep ranges from Sind, the northern Punjab and Persia to Tibet.

and Kashmir. Intermediate between the Red Sheep and Argali in distribution and size, but with the horns curved as in the Argali, is the Urial or Gad (*O. vignei*), which is nearly three feet high and ranges from Sind, the northern Punjab and Persia to Tibet. The Bighorn or Rocky Mountain Sheep (*O. canadensis*) is smaller than the Argali, the height seldom much exceeding three feet, and has smaller horns. There are more than a dozen local races, varying in colour from brownish as in the typical race from British Columbia to white in the Yukon race.

Domesticated Sheep are probably descended from the Mouflon, with a possible strain of the Red Sheep and the Urial. The fleece has been

[W. S. Berridge.
HAUSSA OR AFRICAN LONG-TAILED SHEEP.
This domesticated race has a hairy coat like a goat's.

685

developed by selective breeding, but there is no explanation of the long tail seen in European breeds, all the wild species having short tails. Some domesticated breeds, however, like the Haussa sheep of West Africa, have short tails and no fleece. Except for the horns they are

[W. S. Berridge.
UNICORN SHEEP FROM NEPAL.
In this domesticated breed the two horns are artificially joined.

goat-like and their general appearance is probably responsible for the view of the existence of hybrids between goats and sheep. There is, however, no evidence of the two interbreeding.

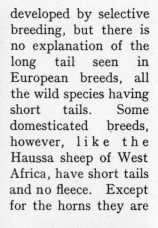

[W. F. Taylor.
FAT-TAILED SHEEP.
This eastern breed has an accumulation of fat on its long tail.

Family Antilocapridae (*The Prongbuck or Pronghorn.*)

The sole representative of this family is the Prongbuck (*Antilocapra americana*), known in the United States as the antelope because it is the only animal resembling an antelope in

[W. S. Berridge.
DUMBA OR FAT-RUMPED SHEEP.
In this breed the fat is on the buttocks.

habits and appearance found in that country. The horns, indeed, resemble those of the antelopes and cattle (*Bovidae*), in consisting of a bony core encased in a horny sheath; but they

[*W. S. Berridge.*
MERINO SHEEP.
The fleece of this sheep supplies merino wool.

differ in two respects, the sheath being two-pronged and periodically shed and replaced. There is, however, no connection

James's Press.
FOUR-HORNED SHEEP.
In this domesticated breed each horn is split into two.

between this casting and regrowth of the sheath and the casting and regrowth of the antlers of deer. In the latter the bone itself is shed and redeveloped.

The horns, usually present only in the bucks, rise vertically above the eyes, generally to a height of

[*W. S. Berridge.*
MOUFLON (*Ovis musimon*).
This wild sheep inhabits Sardinia.

687

about twelve inches. The tip of the main prong is hooked and the accessory prong projects forwards. The colour is brown above, white on the belly, throat and cheeks ; and there is a conspicuous blaze of erectile hair on the rump, which acts as a guide mark to keep the members of the herd together at night. The tail is quite short and the legs are long and slender. The height is about three feet.

Prongbuck were formerly found in large herds in the prairies of temperate North America, to the west of the Mississippi ; but the species is now on the verge of extinction, owing, apparently, to its susceptibility to a disease known to veterinary surgeons as " fossy-jaw." Its chief enemies, apart from man, are wolves. But there are stories of does, with fawns to defend, killing small prairie wolves by cutting them to pieces with strokes of their sharp hoofs. The fawns, usually two in number, are born in the spring, and until strong enough to follow the doe, lie up in clumps of prickly cactus in clearances made by the mother for their use.

[*W. S. Berridge.*

YOUNG PRONGBUCK (*Antilocapra americana*).
This animal was formerly found in large herds in the prairies of temperate North America, to the west of the Mississippi, but is now on the verge of extinction.

[*Underwood.*

GIRAFFES AND ZEBRAS.
There are several local races of giraffe, differing from each other in pattern and colour. They are found in suitable localities all over Africa, south of the Sahara.

The Family Giraffidae (*Giraffes and Okapi*)

This family is distinguished from the rest of the Pecora by the presence of a deep cleft in the crown of the outer tooth, the canine, in the front of the lower jaw and by the nature of the horns, which are always short, covered for the greater part of their length, or entirely, by hairy skin, and are developed in the skin of the head as separate nodules of bone which, as growth proceeds, become firmly attached to the skull. Other characters common to the two representatives of the family are the possession of a long, extensile tongue and prehensile lips, both adaptations for plucking foliage, and the absence of all trace of lateral hoofs.

Giraffe. The Giraffe (*Giraffa camelopardalis*) is distinguished by its immense stature, due to the excessive length of the neck, which in the adult is about as long as the body, and of the limbs, and to the height of the fore quarters, the withers being much higher than the croup, so that the back is steeply sloped. The horns, which are present in both sexes, are quite short and tipped with hair, not with naked bone, the ears are comparatively small, the lips are long and mobile, and the tail is longish and provided with a terminal tuft reaching considerably below the hocks. The colour, as the specific name, meaning "spotted camel," indicates, consists of brownish spots on a pale ground. The bull, which is bigger in every way than the cow, may measure, with the neck erect, over eighteen feet from the crown to the sole of the foot. Such a beast will be about twelve feet at the withers and is able to pluck foliage twenty feet or so from the ground, and a man of average stature can easily stand between his fore legs. The cow is from two and a half feet to three feet shorter. The period of gestation is between fourteen and fifteen months and only one calf is born at a time. It is the same colour as the parent, but has the neck relatively much shorter and the horns indicated by a pair of tufts of hair.

Giraffes are found in suitable localities all over Africa south of the Sahara, excluding the thickly-forested districts of the Congo ; and they are represented by several local races, differing from each other in pattern and colour, and by the development in the bulls of a median bony elevation on the forehead in front of the two horns. Such giraffes have been called " three-horned." Occasionally, also, there is an additional pair of smaller bosses on the back of the head behind the horns, making so-called " five-horned " giraffes. The handsomest of all the races is the Somaliland Netted Giraffe (G. c. *reticulata*), which has large dark brown spots separated by a network of whitish lines. The typical Soudanese and Nubian form (G. c. *camelopardalis*), which extends across North Africa, has paler, more widely-separated spots. In the Tanganyika Giraffe (G. c. *tippelskirchi*) the spots are stellate, with indented edges. In these northern kinds, the additional horn-like bosses on the head are of common occurrence in adult bulls, and the legs are almost without spots ; but in the dark-spotted Cape Giraffe (G. c. *capensis*), which formerly extended as far south as the Orange River, only the two normal horns are present and the legs are spotted to the hoof.

The habits of giraffes are similar wherever they are found. They frequent open bush country, often dry localities, where acacias, upon the foliage of which they principally feed, are to be found. Deep forest, thick jungle and marshy ground, are quite unsuited to them. They live in herds, often associating with zebras, ostriches and antelopes, and are exceedingly difficult to stalk by reason of the wide range of vision their great stature gives them. Many sportsmen, too, have testified to the protective value of their colour and pattern, which blends with the chequered background of branches and foliage. Feeding on green leaves, they are able to go a long time without water, but apparently drink freely when opportunity offers ; and lions, their only enemy besides man, lie in wait for them at the pools. When drinking, they are compelled to straddle their fore legs wide apart to enable the mouth to reach the ground. As might be guessed from their build, they have a most ungainly gallop, but can cover the ground at considerable speed ; and when traversing wooded country, they carry the head low, dipping it under branches which threaten to check their progress. Their means of defence are limited to striking with the head, which in the bull is extraordinarily heavy, and kicking with their powerful feet. As many people must have noticed in the Zoological Gardens, they have a peculiar odour, particularly the bulls. Another peculiarity about them is their silence. It has been stated, indeed, that they are dumb, although their vocal organs are known to be normally constructed ; but one of the game wardens in East Africa records hearing a cow call, the sound being compared to the bleat of a sheep.

Okapi. Although the body of the Okapi (*Okapia johnstoni*) is short and plump and its limbs and neck tolerably long, it has none of the exaggerated height and elongation of the neck seen in the giraffe. It is also much smaller, the female, which, unlike the female giraffe, is hornless and bigger than the male, standing only between five and five and a half feet at the withers. Its ears, too, are much larger, and its lips shorter ; the horns, which may be five inches long, do not appear before maturity, and ultimately acquire a naked, bony point ; and the colour is quite peculiar, the body and neck a rich, dark brown, the head largely buffish-white, and the hind-quarters striped black and white from the root of the tail to the hock and the fore limbs from below the shoulder

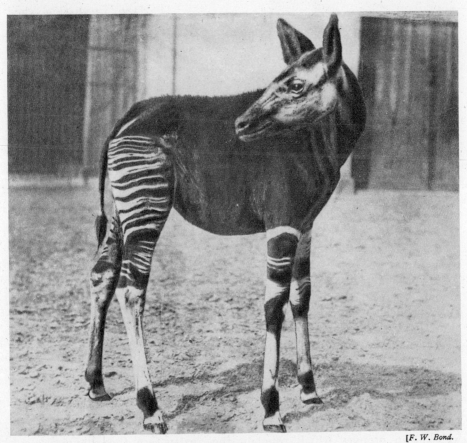

[*F. W. Bond.*

THE OKAPI (*Okapia johnstoni*).
The Okapi inhabits the Semliki and Ituri forests of the Upper Congo and feeds solely upon leaves.

to the knee, the lower portion of the limbs being white, with a thick black fetlock ring.

The Okapi inhabits the Semliki and Ituri forests of the Upper Congo and feeds solely upon leaves, there being no grass under the thick canopy of branches and foliage overhead. It avoids swampy ground and is very difficult to stalk on account of the keenness of its scent and hearing, its large ears compensating for the restricted range of vision imposed by the darkness and vegetation of its habitat. When alarmed it slips quietly away or makes off at a gallop, carrying its head, like a giraffe, stretched forwards in a line with the back. It is solitary or found in pairs and only one calf, a clumsily-built little creature, resembling its parents in colour, is born at a time. The Okapi is said to be even stronger than a buffalo and a very vicious kicker.

[W. S. Berridge.
RED DEER (*Cervus elaphus*).
This deer is typically reddish-brown in summer, greyer in winter, and paler below, with a buff patch on the rump.

Family Cervidae (*Deer*)

The Deer are distinguished from the other families of the Pecora by the presence in the males of either characteristic horns, called antlers, or of long, tusk-like upper canines; occasionally antlers and tusks coexist, and only very rarely are antlers absent.

Antlers differ from the horns hitherto described in growing from the summit of a bony, skin-covered stalk or pedicle and in consisting, when functional, of dead, naked bone which is periodically shed and replaced. In cold and temperate latitudes where the seasons of the year are well marked and the breeding time fixed, the shedding and replacement are annual. But in the tropics there is no fixed period. As soon as the antler is shed, the bud of the new one, covered with soft, hairy vascular skin, the "velvet," appears on the summit of the pedicle. The bud grows rapidly and, becoming ossified, gradually assumes the form characteristic of the species, covered the while by the "velvet" and nourished by the blood contained in the vessels. At the base of the antler there is a bony swelling, the "burr," and at this point, when the antler is full sized the blood-supply is cut off. The velvet consequently dies and finally peels away in long strips, leaving the antler cleaned or "burnished." The well-known grooves which roughen the antlers are the channels along which the blood vessels passed. Antlers are exceedingly variable in size, shape and the number of branches, or "tines," they bear. They are found usually only in stags and are primarily used in rival combats for the hinds or does. But such contests seldom end fatally for either combatant. It is not to the advantage of the species that they should do so, and the function of the tines is probably to act as guards to prevent the infliction of fatal wounds.

DUKE OF BEDFORD'S DEER.

Deer are mainly woodland or forest animals and are found in suitable localities all over Europe, Asia and America, but are absent from Africa, apart from Barbary, where the Red Deer occurs.

By the skeleton of the feet the deer are divided into two groups. In the first the long bones (*metacarpals*), which in "lower" families of Artiodactyls, like pigs (page 637), run from the wrist, or "knee," to the lateral digits of the fore foot, are, when present, represented by their upper ends only. This group, called *Plesiometacarpalia*, is almost restricted to Europe and Asia, only one species, the Wapiti, wandering into North America. A complete gradation can be traced in this group from highly-

Photos]

[James's Press.

PERSIAN RED DEER OR MARAL.

organized species as large as a horse, with huge, many-branched antlers and no upper canine teeth, to more primitive species, no bigger than spaniels, with tiny, spike-like antlers and long, tusk-like upper canines.

In the second group, the *Telemetacarpalia*, the bones in question are represented by their lower ends only, which support the lateral digits of the fore foot.

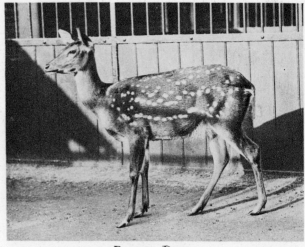

FORMOSA DEER.
This deer is found in the mountains of the island of Formosa. The coat is rather paler than that of the Japanese Deer (*Sika*), of which it is a local race.

Plesiometacarpalia.

To the Plesiometacarpal section belong the typical Stags (*Cervus*), of which the common Red Deer and the Wapiti are the best-known representatives.

Red Deer (*C. elaphus*). This is still found in Great Britain and Ireland and is more abundant on the Continent. It is typically reddish-brown in summer, greyer in winter and paler below, with a buff patch, involving the tail, on the rump. The height of the stag is about four feet and the weight about three hundred pounds and upwards. The antlers, which grow in the summer and are in use in the winter, carry usually six tines on the "beam," and since the names given to these tines are applied to those of other deer, they must be mentioned. The lowest is the " brow," the second the " bez," the third the " trez," the remaining three forming a cup at the summit being the "surroyals." A stag with six tines on each antler is called a "twelve-pointer " or a "royal hart."

Photos]   [*James's Press.*
THAMIN OR ELD'S DEER.

RED DEER (CERVUS ELAPHUS)

By courtesy of] [*Canadian National Railway.*
A HERD OF WAPITI AT WAINWRIGHT, ALBERTA.
This is a much bigger stag than the Red Deer, is paler and more fawn in colour, with a much larger patch on the rump.

In the breeding season, in the autumn, the full-grown stags engage in fierce contests for the possession of as many hinds as they can collect, and at this time they are very noisy, their incessant roaring resounding through the forest. The period of gestation is about eight months : and the fawn, which, like that of most deer, is spotted with white, is dropped in heather or bracken, where it remains concealed and is visited periodically to be suckled by its mother, who never strays far from the spot. The duration of life is usually about twelve years, but occasionally considerably more.

There are several races of the Red Deer, the best defined being the Maral (*C. e. maral*) of Northern Persia, which is considerably larger than European specimens.

[*W. S. Berridge.*
JAPANESE OR SIKA DEER (*Sika nippon*).
These are brown in winter, reddish and spotted in summer, and stand some three feet in height.

695

MAMMALIA (SUBORDER RUMINANTIA)

Wapiti (C. canadensis). This is a much bigger stag than the Red Deer, is paler and more fawn in colour, with a much larger patch on the rump and a shorter tail. The height is as much as five feet, or more. The antlers, also, are different, the fourth tine being very long and the end of the antler bent abruptly backwards. In North America, where this stag is known as the " elk," there are several local races and others are found in Central Asia.

Other stags related to the Red Deer and the Wapiti found in Asia are the Hangul (*C. hanglu*) of Kashmir and the Shou or Wallich's Stag (*C. wallichi*) of Nepal and Sikkim. In these the hair on the rump is white and the tip of the antler is typically forked.

By courtesy of]   [*Carl Hagenbeck's Tierpark, Stellingen.*
AXIS OR SPOTTED DEER (*Axis axis*).
This deer is reddish in colour and has white spots at all ages and seasons.

Japanese Deer. In Central Asia there is another group of Deer distinguished from *Cervus* by their smaller size, longer tails, simpler antlers, with the " bez " tine absent, and by the coat being spotted, at least in summer. From its introduction into various parks in the British Isles, where it has been crossed with the Red Deer, the Japanese Deer (*Sika nippon*) is a familiar example. It is brown in winter, reddish and spotted in summer, and stands about three feet in height.

Swamp Deer. In tropical Asia there are several larger and smaller species not so closely akin to Cervus. The Swamp Deer or Barasingha (*Rucervus duvaucelii*) is distinguished by its large ears, bright red colour, and by the shape of its antlers. It inhabits the open forest and grassy plains, not swamps as its name suggests, of Northern India, congregating in vast herds during the breeding season.

696

Thamin or Eld's Deer (Panolia eldi). This is, on the contrary, generally found in swampy plains in Burma, Siam and the Malay Peninsula. It is brown in colour and has peculiar antlers, the brow tine and beam forming a continuous curve.

Indian Sambar (Rusa unicolor). This deer, sometimes called Elk by Indian sportsmen, is rather larger than the Red Deer, is brown throughout life, and has massive three-tined antlers, which may be carried for several years. It is usually found in wooded, hilly districts in India and Ceylon; but related races extend through the Malaysian Islands to Borneo.

WAPITI (*Cervus canadensis*).
In North America this stag is known as the "Elk."

Chital or Axis Deer. A very handsome stag smaller than the Sambar, the height being only about three feet, and further differing in its reddish colour and white spots at all ages and seasons, is the Chital or Axis Deer (*Axis axis*), which mostly inhabits the jungles in the alluvial plains of India and Ceylon.

Hog Deer. A second species, the Hog Deer (*Axis porcinus*), is much smaller than the Chital, only about two feet high, and browner in tint and only indistinctly spotted when full grown. It ranges from Ceylon to Siam, and is typically solitary or found in pairs.

Several small species of deer related to the Hog Deer and Sambar are found in the Philippines and other islands of the East.

Photos]   [*W. S. Berridge.*
AXIS OR SPOTTED DEER (*Axis axis*).
Also known as the Chital, this deer mostly inhabits the jungles in the alluvial plains of India and Ceylon.

Fallow Deer (*Dama dama*). This deer, which is commoner in English parks than either the Red or Japanese Deer, is like the latter, an imported alien, its original home being the Mediterranean countries. It has very characteristic antlers with the summit spread, flattened (palmated), and armed with several small tines. Its height is about three feet, and the colour of the typical variety is fawn, decorated with white spots in summer, and greyish in winter. But a dark blackish-brown variety is almost equally common.

KASHMIR DEER.
[*D. Seth-Smith.*]
This fine stag may stand over four feet at the shoulder, and the horns may reach this same length.

Milu or David's Deer (*Elaphurus davidianus*). This is as large as the Red Deer and is the only species with a longish, tufted tail. The antlers, too, are peculiar, being of large size, and two-forked, the stout, long brow tine growing nearly vertically upwards and the thinner beam backwards, close to the back. The only known examples of this stag are preserved by the Duke of Bedford at Woburn. These are the descendants of specimens originally kept in the Royal Park in Pekin.

Muntjacs or Barking Deer (*Muntiacus*). These are represented by many species ranging from India to China and Borneo. They are small deer distinguished by the association in the males of long, tusk-like upper canines with antlers which are short, two-pronged and supported on very long pedicles. The Muntjacs are small deer with short legs, large ears and a longish tail, and mostly inhabit thick jungle or bush, creeping stealthily about in the undergrowth, and living singly or in pairs. The young, one or two in number, are spotted. The best known is the Common Muntjac

(*M. muntjak*), known to sportsmen from its call as the "Barking Deer." Its colour is mahogany-red a n d its height a little over one and a half feet.

Tufted Deer (*Elaphodus cephalophus*). This deer and its allies inhabits central and southern C h i n a, and is so named on account of a tuft of hair on the crown. They are distinguished from the Muntjacs by the antlers consisting of a single minute spike.

[*James's Press.*

SAMBAR DEER (*Rusa unicolor*).
This is rather larger than the Red Deer.

Telemetacarpalia. The second division of the Deer family, defined above (page 694), is mainly American, only the Roebuck, the Chinese Water Deer and the Musk Deer being confined to the Old World and the Elk and the Reindeer occurring in both the Eastern and Western Hemispheres:

As in the first division (page 693), a gradation can be traced from large, highly - organized species with well-developed, many-tined antlers and no canines, to small more p r i m i t i v e species with spike-like antlers or without antlers but large, tusk-like canines.

Elk or Moose (*Alces alces*). This is the largest and least elegant of all Deer, the legs being very long, the body, tail and neck short

[*W. S. Berridge.*

SWAMP DEER OR BARASINGHA (*Rucervus duvaucelii*).
This deer inhabits the open forest and grassy plains, not swamps as its name suggests, of Northern India.

699

and the muzzle greatly swollen. The antlers are sometimes simple and erect, but typically are many-tined, palmated, and project laterally from the sides of the head. The colour is brown, with the legs pale. The height may be nearly seven feet and the weight over one thousand pounds. It inhabits the northern forested districts of North America, Asia and Europe; but

MUNTJAC OR BARKING DEER (*Muntiacus muntjak*).
This deer is mahogany-red in colour and a little over one and a half feet in height.

is now very rare in Europe. In America, where the finest specimens are found, it is called the Moose. Its diet consists of foliage, twigs, mosses, lichens and aquatic plants, in search of which it wades into marshes and lakes; but on account of its long legs, short neck and swollen muzzle, it is unable to graze on short pasture. It is fond of the water and during hot weather frequently stays for long periods immersed in rivers and lakes. The pairing season, when the bulls are very pugnacious, is in the autumn, and the calves, from one to three, are born about eight months later. The Elk is not truly gregarious, small family parties, which occupy clearings in the forest called "moose-yards," being the most that are found together.

Reindeer or Caribou (*Rangifer tarandus*). This is the only member of the Deer family in which antlers are present in both sexes. They are

Photos]   [*W. S. Berridge.*
FALLOW DEER (*Dama dama*).
The colour of the typical variety is fawn, decorated with white spots in summer and greyish in winter.

700

similar in plan to those of the Old World deer, but the brow tines, one of which is usually larger than the other, and the trez tines carry supplementary prongs. Otherwise the modifications of the Reindeer are mostly adaptations to its habitat. The lateral hoofs reach the ground and the main hoofs are very broad so as to facilitate movement over snow and swampy ground; the coat as a protection against cold is very thick and the nose is overgrown with hair. The ears and tail are short, the colour is brownish with lighter areas, the height is about four feet or a little over and the average weight of males is from three hundred to three hundred and fifty pounds, the females being one h u n d r e d pounds less.

By courtesy of]   *[Canadian Pacific Railway.*
AMERICAN ELK OR MOOSE *(Alces alces).*
This is the largest of all deer; the height may be nearly seven feet and the weight over a thousand pounds.

The distribution of the Reindeer coincides in latitude with that of the Moose, but extends northwards t o t h e borders of the Arctic Ocean. The species is not, however, restricted to snowy wastes. In North America and Siberia the northern herds m i g r a t e southwards in winter to districts where vegetation is available; but in Spitzbergen and other Arctic islands where their movements are more restricted, they are at times hard pressed for food at that season and may be reduced to eating cast-up seaweed, and to get at grasses and lichens they scrape away the covering of snow with their feet, antlers and noses.

There are several different kinds, two in North America, where they are known as Caribou, being particularly well defined. The Barren-ground Caribou, inhabiting the tundras, is a smaller race, with thinner antlers than the Woodland Caribou, which is found even to the south of the St. Lawrence.

In Lapland the Reindeer has long b e e n domesticated and is to the natives what the camel is to the nomads of Asia and the Sahara, supplying them with milk, flesh, hides and means of transport. Herds of this small European race have, within recent years, been imported into North America, where they serve the same purposes as in their native home.

REINDEER OR CARIBOU (*Rangifer tarandus*).
This is the only member of the deer family in which antlers are present in both sexes.

Roebuck (*Capreolus capreolus*). This, although small, is an interesting representative of this group as still being a member of the British fauna. It is found in Scotland, whence specimens were brought to Dorsetshire and turned loose. The colour in summer is reddish, in winter greyish-brown, with a large white patch on the rump. The legs are long but the tail is vestigial. The height is about two feet, the weight fifty pounds or more. The antlers, usually about eight inches long, have typically three prongs rising from a long erect basal stalk. They are shed generally in December and the new ones are functional by March, dates very different from those of the antler-change in the Red Deer. The fawns, sometimes two in number and born in May, are spotted with white. Roebuck live in small herds and feed on grass and foliage in the early morning

Photos]   [*W. S. Berridge.*
MILU OR DAVID'S DEER (*Elaphurus davidianus*).
This is the only species with a long, tufted tail.

DEER (FAMILY CERVIDAE)

ROEBUCK (*Capreolus capreolus*).
The colour in summer is reddish, in winter greyish-brown, with a large white patch on the rump. Height about two feet.

and evening. This Roebuck is found all over central and south Europe in suitable localities and allied races occur as far eastward as China.

White-tailed or Virginian Deer, Mule Deer and Black-tailed Deer. In addition to the Wapiti, Moose and Caribou, North America has three species of deer, about the size of Fallow Deer, each having many local races. The White-tailed or Virginian Deer (*Odocoileus virginianus*) is the most beautiful of all deer in the summer coat of red, ornamented with white spots, but in winter it is grey-brown and spotless. The species ranges from Canada to Peru and Bolivia, and as it is traced southwards its size decreases, its colour changes and its antlers become simplified. The related Mule Deer (*O. hemionus*) has larger ears, a black-tipped tail and is more restricted in range, occurring from British Columbia to Mexico. Here too, the size is smaller and the antlers are simpler in southern races. The Black-tailed Deer (*O. columbianus*), ranging from Alaska to New Mexico, has the whole of the upper side of the tail black and the ears smaller than in the Mule Deer.

Marsh Deer, Pampas Deer and Pudus. In South America there are several species, the largest being the Marsh Deer (*Blastocerus dichotomus*), which is red in colour, nearly as large as the Red Deer and inhabits the forests of Brazil and the Argentine. Smaller and yellowish-brown in colour is the Pampas Deer

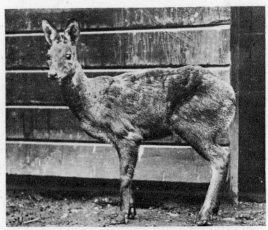

Photos]   [W. S. Berridge.
MUSK DEER (*Moschus moschiferus*).
These deer live at high altitudes in Central Asia, occurring in the Himalayas up to 12,000 feet.

703

(*B. bezoarticus*), found in the Pampas of the Argentine and Patagonia. These two species have branched antlers. But in the Andes of Peru and Chili there are species with simple, two-pronged antlers and in the forested districts of Central and South America there are others about the size of Muntjacs, with spike-like antlers. The tiniest of all the American Deer are the Pudus (*Pudu pudu*), which are about one foot in height, have spike-like antlers, and hardly a trace of the tail. They inhabit the cordilleras of Ecuador, Peru and Chili.

Chinese Water Deer (*Hydropotes inermis*). This is a primitive type of this division, having no antlers but large upper canine tusks. It resembles the Muntjacs in size and shape, and is found in China and Korea, frequenting riverside reed beds, where the does give birth to their fawns, from three to six in number.

Musk Deer. Still more primitive than the Water Deer, although resembling it in having long canine tusks and no antlers, is the Musk Deer (*Moschus moschiferus*), which takes its name from the presence in the male of a scent gland near the middle of the belly, which secretes the musk of commerce. The male also has a pair of scent-glands on the tail, which is nearly naked except for a terminal tuft of long hairs. The coat is harsh and pithy. The colour is brown, speckled with grey or buff and the height is about one and a half feet. The legs are long and powerful, the four hoofs being also long and widely separable. The period of gestation is five months, one fawn, as a rule, being produced at a time.

Musk Deer live at high altitudes in Central Asia, occurring in the Himalayas up to 12,000 feet. They are essentially adapted to districts where the cold of winter is severe, and their feet are well fitted for traversing snow-covered hill-sides. They are solitary in habit, feeding in the morning and evening on lichens, grass and foliage, and lying up during the day in brushwood.

[*Major A. Radclyffe Dugmore.*

A FIGHT BETWEEN TWO CARIBOU STAGS.

Order PERISSODACTYLA (Rhinoceroses, Tapirs and Horses)

Although provided with " hoofs " like the Artiodactyla, the members of this order differ from them in being " odd-toed," the third digit being in the middle of the foot and symmetrically flanked by the second and fourth when these are present. There are other anatomical differences in the skeleton, and the intestine has a large saccular dilatation, the caecum. They appear to have been evolved from a different primitive type of mammal, their stock being the same as that from which the elephants and several other orders, described later, arose.

Family Rhinocerotidae (*Rhinoceroses*)

The Rhinoceroses are superficially so unlike Horses that no one would suppose them to be related. They are huge, ungainly, digitigrade beasts, the feet being broad and compact, composed of three equal toes, and provided with a horny sole ; the limbs are short and stout ; the hide is thick, at most scantily covered with hairs ; the head is large, with a con-cave forehead, and the muzzle carries one or two horns, which grow through life and are composed of consolidated dermal fibres without a bony core. In the dentition the incisors are variable but are never more than six in number, above and below, and are not used for biting ; the canines are absent and the six large cheek teeth are much less complicated in their ridges and loops of enamel than those of horses.

Rhinoceroses are now found in tropical Asia, from India to Borneo, and in East and South Africa. Their habits vary in details according to the species, but, being exclusively vegetarian in diet, and of great size, they must live where there is abundance of food, foliage, grasses and the like, and water. They are not gregarious, like the Equidae, at most two or three being usually found together. They have, therefore, no need of a loud call to keep a herd together, the voice being merely a grunt, snort or squeal, uttered under the stimulus of fear or anger. They have the reputation of being dull-witted creatures, with poor eye-sight but acute hearing and smell. When wounded or cornered, they will charge blindly at an assailant ; but on the whole they are timid and inoffensive and prefer escape to fighting. Despite their size and bulk they can travel at con-siderable speed and there is something peculiarly horse-like in their swinging gallop. The single young one which is born at a time is able to follow its mother soon after birth.

The Asiatic species, three in number, differ in several important respects from the two African species, especially in possessing a pair of tusk-like incisor teeth in the upper and lower jaws. The lower projects forward on each side of the front of the mouth and is kept sharp by grinding against the upper. This tusk, not the horn, is the animal's weapon when charging and it is capable of inflicting a severe gash. For the lodgment of the upper tusk, the bone that carries it is comparatively large. Also the skin of the

Asiatic species is thicker and to facilitate movement is jointed or creased where the limbs and neck are attached to the body.

Indian One-horned Rhinoceros. The best and longest-known species of the Asiatic group, referred to the genus *Rhinoceros*, is the large Indian One-horned Rhinoceros (*R. unicornis*), which, as its name indicates, has a single horn on the nose. The hide is very thick, hairless, studded with rounded tubercles and jointed by great folds on the neck, in front of the shoulder and behind it and also in front of the hips and above the legs, but the fold in front of the shoulder does not pass over the back part of the neck. The height at the shoulder of a good specimen may be five feet or over but is usually about five feet six inches, and the weight is about four thousand pounds. The horn, which in wild specimens is present and equally long in the two sexes, is usually less than one and a half feet over the front curve, the record being two feet, with the basal circumference about the same ; but in captive specimens it is frequently reduced to a mere stump by rubbing against the bars and walls of cages. Although at one time widely distributed in India, this Rhinoceros is now restricted to Nepal, Bhutan and Assam. It lives in the thick jungles of the alluvial plains, frequently in marshy places and is partial to wallowing in the mud.

Lesser One-horned Rhinoceros. Related to the last, but differing from it superficially in the mosaic pattern of fine scratches on the skin (which also lacks the tubercles), by the extension of the neck fold over the back, by its lighter build, and by its smaller head, is the Lesser One-horned Rhinoceros (*R. sondaicus*), sometimes but very inappropriately called the Javan Rhinoceros. In actual height, there seems to be little to choose between the two ; but the male of this species has a comparatively small horn, seldom over ten inches along the curve, whereas the female is nearly or quite hornless. This species ranged from the Sanderbans of Bengal through Burma and the Malay Peninsula to Java. But its habitat is more varied than that of its larger ally, since, in addition to the swampy Sanderbans, it frequents forests, sometimes at considerable altitudes. It is now almost extinct.

Sumatran or Asiatic Two-horned Rhinoceros (*Ceratorhinus sumatrensis*). This differs from both the preceding species in having, as its name indicates, two horns, a larger in front and a smaller behind. Its skin, moreover, is covered, although not thickly, with coarse hair and is less jointed, having but one complete fold behind the shoulder. The size is comparatively small, the standing height being only up to about four and a half feet and the weight two thousand pounds. The front horn is occasionally over two feet six inches, but usually it is only about one foot over the curve, whereas the back horn is commonly from about three to six inches. The habits appear to be similar to those of the Javan Rhinoceros. This is a very widely-ranging species, extending from Bhutan to Assam through the Malay Peninsula to Sumatra and Borneo, but not occurring in Java. A few local

[Major A. Radclyffe Dugmore.

AFRICAN BLACK RHINOCEROS.
Rhinoceroses are now found in tropical Asia, from India to Borneo, and in East and South Africa. They are exclusively
vegetarian in diet.

races have been described, but the differences between them are too trivial to notice.

African Rhinoceroses. The two African species, both of which are two-horned, differ from the Asiatic in having no incisor teeth in either jaw. This defect has reacted on the jaws, the lower being shorter in front and the premaxillary bones of the upper small and functionless. Thus deprived of tusks for defence, these animals depend upon their horns, which are larger than in the Asiatic species, and to give support to the front horn, the principal weapon, the nasal bones which support it are much broader and rounder at the end. The skin, moreover, is sufficiently thin to dispense with the conspicuous jointed folds observable in the Asiatic species. On account of these differences, the African species are referred to a distinct genus, *Diceros.*

[James's Press.
SUMATRAN TWO-HORNED ASIATIC RHINOCEROS *(Ceratorhinus sumatrensis).*
In this rhinoceros the skin is covered, although not thickly, with coarse hair, and is less jointed than in the Indian species.

Although both are of nearly the same dark leaden hue, they are popularly called the Black and White Rhinoceroses.

Black Rhinoceros (*D. bicornis*). This is the commoner and better known of the two and may be at once distinguished by the pointed, prehensile upper lip, narrower ears and the position of the eye, which is more under the back horn. The usual height is between five and six feet ; but the recorded weight of a specimen which scaled rather less than three thousand pounds, indicates a more lightly-built animal than the big Indian Rhinoceros. The front horn varies in length from less than two feet, to over four feet and is sometimes thin and almost blade-like from wear. The back horn is occasionally almost as long as the front, but is usually considerably shorter.

The Black Rhinoceros lives in the open plains of Africa, from Abyssinia southwards. It was formerly plentiful in Cape Colony, but has been for the most part killed out in districts to the south of the Zambesi. It feeds, for the most part, on scrub, using its upper lip to pluck the foliage. It is the swiftest and generally the most active of all Rhinoceroses, and consequently the most dangerous when provoked to charge. It carries its head high when on the move ; and the calf follows at the heels of its mother.

White Rhinoceros (D. simus). This is distinguished from all other Rhinoceroses by its square-cut upper lip, lacking the prehensile lobe. It also has the head relatively larger than in the Black, the ears more spread and the eye farther back in relation to the hinder horn. It stands as much as six and a half feet in height and is the largest land mammal next to the Elephant and Giraffe.

[*Photopress.*
AFRICAN BLACK RHINOCEROS (*Diceros bicornis*).
There are two species of African Rhino, called popularly, the Black and the White, both of which carry two horns.

The horns vary much in length, the front one being usually about three feet, but sometimes as much as five feet ; the rear horn is usually about half the length of the other.

In times past, this Rhinoceros may have spread through East Africa from the Soudan to the Orange River. But it has only been found in the region of the Upper Nile and between the Zambesi and Orange Rivers. In South Africa it was almost exterminated by the end of the last century, the sole survivors being a few individuals in the Umfulosi Reserve, Zululand. The existence of the species near the source of the Nile and Wele River was a comparatively recent and unexpected discovery. Less alert and slower in movement than the Black, it is easily killed, even with spears, and the final extinction of the species, unless rigorously protected, will probably soon be accomplished.

Unlike the Black Rhinoceros, which is a browser, the white species is a grazer, as the shape of the upper lip indicates. It generally frequents fairly open country, but may be found in heavily-timbered bush. When on the move, the animal carries its head low, by reason of its great weight, with the muzzle close to the ground ; and the calf is said to precede the mother, guided by her forwardly-directed long horn. In colour, the " white " Rhinoceros is a light, dirty brown.

[*Underwood.*
INDIAN ONE-HORNED RHINOCEROS (*R. unicornis*).
In captive specimens the horn is frequently reduced to a mere stump by rubbing against the bars and walls of cages.

MAMMALIA (ORDER PERISSODACTYLA)

Family Tapiridae (*Tapirs*)

The Tapirs are short-legged and digitigrade like the rhinoceroses, but have four toes on the fore feet. The toes, which have long, narrow hoofs, are capable of being spread. Also, the body is covered with short hair, the tail is very short, and the snout and upper lip are developed into a short but thick, flexible trunk used for hooking foliage into the mouth. In association with the trunk, the nasal openings in the skull are situated far back, instead of being terminal as in rhinoceroses and horses.

In the dentition, the incisors and canines are complete as in the horses ; but the lower canine is set forwards and with the outer upper incisor forms a pair of short tusks on each side of the mouth. The crowns of the cheek-teeth are low and simple in structure, and carry four conical cusps.

Tapirs are timid, inoffensive creatures, browsing on forest foliage and dashing away through the undergrowth when alarmed, or, being expert swimmers, plunging into rivers to escape danger. They are mostly nocturnal and solitary, two or three at most being found together. The young, of which only one is born at a time, differs remarkably from the parents in colour, being deep brown with a pattern of longitudinal white stripes and spots which disappear in about six months' time.

[D. Seth-Smith.

EAST INDIAN OR MALAY TAPIR AND HALF-GROWN YOUNG (*Tapirus indicus*).
This species is distinguished by its peculiar colour, the head, forequarters and legs being black and the loins white. The young differs remarkably from the parents in colour, being deep brown with a pattern of white stripes and spots.

[*Keystone.*

BRAZILIAN TAPIR (*Tapirus terrestris*).
The American species, four in number, are tolerably uniformly brown in colour, and considerably smaller
than the Malay Tapir.

Tapirs are the only members of the Perissodactyla indigenous in America, which is now their headquarters; but there is an outlying member of the family found in the East Indies. This discontinuous distribution is explained by the extension of the family in former times over a wide area of the Northern Hemisphere and its survival in the two widely-separated countries above mentioned.

East Indian or Malay Tapir (*Tapirus indicus*). This is distinguished by its peculiar colour, the head, forequarters and legs being black and the loins white. It is also the largest of the species, standing close on four feet high. It inhabits the jungles of the Malay Peninsula, Sumatra and Borneo.

American Tapirs. The American species, four in number, are tolerably uniformly brown in colour and considerably smaller than the Malay Tapir, standing between three and three and a half feet high. Of these, the most widely distributed and best known is the Brazilian Tapir (*T. terrestris*), which is frequently imported to this country. It inhabits the lowland forests of the Amazon and its tributaries, and may be known by the crest on its forehead and neck. Its chief enemy, apart from man, is the jaguar. The Pinchaque or Roulin's Tapir (*T. roulini*), which has the neck rounded and not crested, is found in the mountain forests of Ecuador and Colombia up to about 8,000 feet. The other species, Baird's Tapir (*T. bairdii*), and Dow's Tapir (*T. dowii*), inhabiting Central America are distinguished from the rest by certain cranial characters, but nothing of note is known of their habits.

MAMMALIA (ORDER PERISSODACTYLA)

Family Equidae (*Horses, Asses and Zebras*)

The Horses, the highest types of this order, are distinguished by being " unguligrade " and single-toed ; that is to say, they walk upon the terminal bone of the third digit only, this bone being encased in a large, compact hoof, the wrist, or " knee," and the ankle, or " hock," being raised high off the ground. The teeth consist of six strong incisors above and below, the canines, when present, are always small and the cheek teeth, neglecting the first premolar, which is of no functional importance and generally absent, consist of a similar series of six above and below in each jaw, each tooth being massive, prismatic, deeply imbedded and of persistent growth till old age is reached, the grinding surface, when worn, exhibiting an intricate pattern of loops and ridges of cement, enamel and dentine.

[Gambier.

DAPPLE-GREY SHIRE OR CART HORSE.

The limbs are clearly adapted for swift running over hard ground and the teeth for cropping and masticating the coarse grasses and other herbage of the open country these animals frequent. They are gregarious, and breed once in about every two years, a single foal being born at a time. The genuinely wild species assigned to the genus *Equus*, and popularly known as Horses, Asses and Zebras, are found only in Asia and Africa.

Horses and Ponies. The various breeds of domesticated Horses and Ponies (*Equus caballus*) are familiar to all ; and in different parts of the world, in the Argentine Pampas, the North American Prairies and in the Steppes of Siberia, there are herds of " feral " horses, that is to say, wild horses descended from specimens which escaped from captivity. There is, however, one genuinely wild type known as Przevalsky's Horse (*E. caballus przewalskii*) and regarded as a race of the domesticated breeds. It is a sturdily-built pony, standing about twelve hands at the withers, with a massive head, small ears, heavy jaws and big teeth, its general colour being dun, with a mealy muzzle, a black stripe on the back and some black below the knees and hocks. In the short summer coat, the mane forms an erect crest and the tail is tufted ; but in the long, thick winter coat, the mane tends to fall over to one side and some longish hairs grow on

SUFFOLK PUNCH " WHIRLWIND."

the upper part of the tail. It inhabits Mongolia. Nothing of interest is known of its habits ; but it associates and interbreeds with the feral ponies of the district and many of these hybrids have been imported to Europe and exhibited as genuine wild horses.

Asses. These differ from horses in one or two particulars. The hind legs never have a trace of the " chestnut " which is typically found b e l o w the hock on the hind leg in all horses ; the voice is a " bray " instead of a " neigh," and the period of gestation is about twelve months, one month more than in the horse.

Asiatic Wild Asses. Wild Asses belong to two distinct types, one found in Asia, the other in Africa. The Asiatic species are more horse-like than the African, their ears being smaller and their general hue sandy or dun above instead of slate grey. The voice, too, is distinct. It may be described as a stifled bray, since it consists of a squealing inhalation followed by a guttural exhalation ; but it has none of the volume of the bray of the African species. The largest and handsomest is the Kiang (*Equus kiang*) of Tibet, where it is found at elevations up to about 16,000 feet. Apart from the crested mane and a stripe down the back, which, like the tail tuft, are black, the upper side is pale chestnut in summer, rather darker in winter when the coat is long and thick ; but the muzzle, a large area of the neck below, the belly, legs and the backs of the thighs are creamy-white. Kiangs are powerfully built and stand from twelve to thirteen hands at the withers.

Photos] ARABIAN STALLION. *[Gambier.*

They live in small herds, and when grazing are guarded by one of their number which watches the surrounding country at a distance of some two hundred yards from the rest and gives the alarm when danger threatens. They are swift of foot and strong swimmers, fearlessly crossing even rapid rivers.

In the deserts of north-western India, Persia, Syria, Tartary and as far to the north as Mongolia, there is a second species (*Equus hemionus*), which is smaller and more lightly built than the Kiang but resembles it in all essential habits. Having a wide geographical range, it is represented by several local races, the Mongolian race being known as the Dziggetai and the Persian and Indian race as the Ghorkar or Onager (*E. onager*).

[*W. S. Berridge.*
AFRICAN WILD ASS (*Equus asinus*).
It is from the African Wild Asses that our domesticated breeds are derived.

African Wild Asses. African wild asses (*Equus asinus*) are of particular interest because they are the stock from which our domesticated breeds were derived. They are restricted to Nubia, the eastern Sudan and Somaliland, but are now rare everywhere. They differ from the Asiatic asses in having much longer ears and narrower hoofs ; their voice is the loud familiar bray and they are grey in colour above, white below, on the muzzle and round the eyes. They are handsome, strongly-built animals, considerably larger than the common domesticated donkey. They live in small herds in desert districts, and are remarkable for the great speed and sure-footedness with which they can traverse rough country. There are one or two local races, the best marked being the typical Nubian form, which has a black patch at the base of the ear, a black stripe down the back and one across the shoulders and only faint stripes on the legs, marks which persist as tell-tale signs of descent in the domesticated type ; and the Somaliland race, which has no black patch on the ear, at most a trace of the spinal and shoulder stripes, but strong bars on the legs.

Zebras. In East and South Africa, the asses are replaced and represented by the Zebras and Quaggas. Zebra, however, is merely a popular name for fully-striped members of the horse-tribe and does not indicate the kinships of the animals that bear it. The three very distinct species which pass under that name are merely linked together by the possession of stripes, a character inherited from the common ancestor from which the horses and asses, which have lost the stripes, are also descended.

KIANG AND FOAL (*Equus kiang*).
This is the largest and handsomest of the Asiatic Wild Asses, being found in Tibet at elevations up to about 16,000 feet.

The largest, and some think the handsomest of the striped species, is Grévy's Zebra (*E. grevyi*), which stands about thirteen hands at the withers, the mare being as big as the stallion, if not bigger. It may be distinguished by its long, expanded and round-tipped ears, very small warts, and by its pattern, the stripes on the neck being broad, on the body, narrow ; the spinal stripe is, however, very broad on the croup, where it is separated from the adjoining stripes on the upper part of the quarters, which are vertical. The voice is a bray, unmistakably like that of the donkey. This species is found in the lowlands of Abyssinia, Somaliland and the northern parts of Kenya. It lives in open, scrub-covered plains, never in thick bush.

The Mountain Zebra (*Equus zebra*) is a very different looking animal from Grévy's Zebra. The ears, although large, are pointed and asinine in shape, and the head is more elegantly shaped and there is a small dewlap on the throat. The stripes are as complete as in Grévy's Zebra, those of the flanks passing on to the belly, but the spinal stripe is exceedingly narrow and in contact with the body stripes to the root of the tail. On the thighs they are remarkably broad, few in number and longitudinal, and the uppermost of them defines an area on the croup, covered with short, transverse stripes and called the " gridiron " from its fancied resemblance to that implement. The legs, which are delicately formed, have very narrow hoofs; but the " chestnut " is represented by a large, oval area of naked skin.

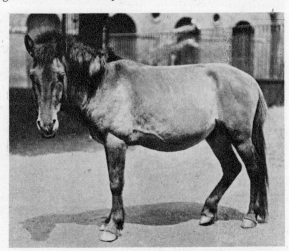

Photos]   *[W. S. Berridge.*
MONGOLIAN WILD HORSE (*Equus caballus przewalskii*).
The general colour is dun, with a mealy muzzle, a black stripe on the back and some black below the knees and hocks.

715

MAMMALIA (ORDER PERISSODACTYLA)

By courtesy of]   *[South African Railways & Harbours.*
CHAPMAN'S QUAGGA.
This Quagga is found in Bechuanaland.

This zebra, the smallest of all, stands about ten and a half hands at the withers. It is an unusually silent animal. There are no trustworthy records of the nature of its voice in the wild state and in captivity it seldom utters more than an angry squeal.

The typical race of this zebra was at one time plentiful in the mountainous parts of Cape Colony and early attracted the attention of sportsmen by its beauty and the speed and precision with which it could traverse rocky, precipitous hill-sides. But indiscriminate slaughter, chiefly in the interest of the hide-trade, has brought it to the verge of extinction in that part of South Africa, a few herds only remaining, now happily under strict protection. It extends, however, through what was formerly German South-west Africa into Angola ; but this western race, known as Hartmann's Mountain Zebra, differs from the Cape Colony race in being a little bigger and much lighter in colour owing to the widening of the white and the narrowing of the black stripes.

Quaggas. More nearly akin to the Mountain than to Grévy's Zebra is the third species (*Equus quagga*), known by a number of trivial and scientific names in accordance with its local variations. It differs from the Mountain Zebra in its smaller ears, broader hoofs, absence of the lappet of skin, or dewlap, on the throat, backwardly-growing hairs on the spine, and also in pattern. The stripes from about the middle of the flanks sweep boldly backwards at their upper ends and pass over the loins and croup, the stripes on the latter not forming a " gridiron " pattern. Average specimens stand about eleven and a half hands at the withers and their general appearance is more

By courtesy of]   *[Carl Hagenbeck's Tierpark, Stellingen.*
GRÉVY'S ZEBRA (*Equus grevyi*).
In this species the stripes on the neck are broad, on the body narrow ;
the spinal stripe is, however, very broad on the croup.

QUAGGAS (EQUUS QUAGGA)

equine and less asinine than that of the Mountain Zebra. The voice is very distinct, at least from that of Grévy's Zebra. It has been well described as a repetition of the syllables " qua-ha-ha," which suggested the name " Khoua Khoua," used by the Hottentots and converted into " quagga " by the Boers, for the South African race, which was first made known to Europeans. This, the typical race, now extinct, had no stripes on the legs or hind-quarters below the tail, and

By courtesy of]   [Carl Hagenbeck's Tierpark, Stellingen.
HARTMANN'S MOUNTAIN ZEBRA (*Equus zebra hartmannae*).
In the Mountain Zebras the stripes on the thighs are remarkably broad, and few in number.

the stripes on the flanks were generally indistinct and more or less confluent, resulting in a mottled, brownish tint. But, judging from old pictures, there was a great deal of individual or local variation both in the general hue and the distinctness of the stripes. This Quagga, nevertheless, was a very different looking animal from those found in East and North Africa, which are completely and boldly striped all over with black and cream. Grant's Quagga of Kenya Colony and Crawshay's Quagga of Nyasaland are instances. But south of the Zambesi there are several races exhibiting a gradual evanescence of the stripes on the limbs and hind-quarters, and completely connecting the two extremes in pattern and colour described above. The best known of these intermediate races are Chapman's Quagga of Bechuanaland and Burchell's Quagga of Griqualand West. The latter, which most resembles the typical Quagga, is, like it, now extinct. There is no known explanation of this singular and striking change in the South African races of the species, which is essentially an inhabitant of the open plains and veldt of Africa.

[W. S. Berridge.
CHAPMAN'S QUAGGA (*Equus quagga chapmanni*).
The existing races of Quagga can be distinguished by having the stripes from about the middle of the flanks sweeping boldly backwards at their upper ends.

717

Order PROBOSCIDEA (Elephants)

Elephants differ from all other mammals in appearance and in many anatomical characters. Their most noticeable peculiarity is the lengthening of the nose and upper lip into a long, muscular, flexible trunk, with the upper and lower rims of the terminal nostrils formed into two lobes, or lips, capable of picking up even small particles of food. The head is very massive and short as compared with its height, the eyes very small, the ears large and flap-like, and the neck so short that the movements of the head are greatly restricted. The legs are long, thick and columnar, and the feet short and broad. The animal, however, is digitigrade, resting on a large pad behind the hoofs of the five toes, the wrist and heel being raised off the ground. Another character of the limbs is the setting of the bones in a nearly upright line. This gives the peculiar swing to the hind limb when the animal is walking and enables it to kneel with the foot projecting backwards, a feat quite beyond the powers of most mammals, with the exception of man. The tail is long and fringed at the end with very stout, long bristles ; but, except in the young, there are hardly any hairs on the skin, which is thick and wrinkled.

The shape of the head, with its large forehead, gives the elephant a sagacious look, suggesting a big brain. The brain, however, is quite small ; but the bones of the skull are very thick, although full of air-cells, to lighten the weight ; and the expansion of the head is to give attachment to the great muscles of the neck which have to support the weight of the trunk and teeth, especially of the two tusks, or "ivories," of the upper jaw, when these are of large size. The tusks are the only incisor teeth the elephant possesses. They grow throughout the animal's life and owe their commercial value to being composed of dentine or ivory, the enamel being absent. Canines are not developed ; but the cheek-teeth are remarkable in a variety of ways. They are huge blocks, so huge that there is only room for one complete tooth, or parts of two, to be functional at a time above and below in the shortened jaws. There are six of them altogether. They are not, however, all developed at once, but successively, one behind another during about the first half of the animal's life. Each tooth, as it comes into use, has open roots and continues to grow for a considerable time to counteract the wear. But the wear is faster than the growth, and as the crown is ground down, the roots close and become absorbed, and the tooth, greatly reduced in size as it travels along the mouth, with its successor behind it, reaches the front of the jaw, where its remnant is ultimately shed. These teeth are also very elaborately made, consisting of a number of plates of dentine and enamel, united by cement, set one in front of the other. But the joining of the plates is secondary, each of them being developed from its own pulp quite separately from those before and behind it.

Indian and African Elephants.—There are two kinds of elephants, the Asiatic or Indian (*Elephas maximus*) and the African (*Loxodonta africana*), which differ in many ways. The Indian has a high, bulging forehead, comparatively small ears covering the sides of the neck, and the tip of the trunk provided above with a finger-like lobe which closes down on the square-cut, lip-like lower rim. The African has a rounded, sloping forehead, enormous ears meeting on the top of the neck and covering a large part of the shoulder, and the upper and lower rims of the nostrils produced into two larger, more similar lips. The differences in the trunk are associated with differences in the way of picking up food. If a pile of soft bran or half a loaf is given to an Indian Elephant, the animal picks them up by coiling the end of its trunk round them. The African picks up as much of the bran as it can between the lips of its trunk, and, if it finds the bread too large to be grasped in that way, presses the end of the trunk against it and by exhausting the air from its nostrils, lifts it from the ground by suction. Small pieces of food, like biscuits or leaves, are picked up between the lips of the trunk by both species alike ; and so delicate are these implements that the common belief in an elephant's ability to pick up a pin is probably not far from the truth.

By courtesy of]   *[Carl Hagenbeck's Tierpark, Stellingen.*
YOUNG AFRICAN ELEPHANT (*Loxodonta africana*).
The African Elephant has a rounded sloping forehead, enormous ears meeting on the top of the neck and covering a large part of the shoulder, and the upper and lower rims of the nostrils produced into two nearly similar lips.

A more important difference between the two species lies in the structure of the cheek-teeth, which are much more elaborate in the Indian Elephant. The plates composing them are narrow and flattened, so that a large number are packed together to build up the tooth. The number progressively increases from four in the first tooth in the young calf to over twenty in the last tooth, which comes into use at mid-life. In the African Elephant the plates are lozenge- or bow-shaped, expanding from the edge to the middle of the crown and are not nearly so numerous, the number for the first and last tooth, as indicated above, being respectively three and ten, the last having only about half as many as in the Indian Elephant. These differences are very clearly shown on the worn tooth by the alternating lines of cement, enamel and dentine ; and the name *Loxodonta*, meaning " bow-toothed," was given to the African Elephant on account of the pattern of the cheek-teeth.

Distribution of Elephants. The Asiatic Elephant ranges from the foot-hills of the Himalayas southwards through India and Ceylon and eastwards through Burma, Siam and the Malay Peninsula to Sumatra and Borneo. Slight differences exist between the typical elephant of India and those of Ceylon, the Malay Peninsula and Sumatra, but they are too trivial to call for further notice.

A century or so ago the elephant of Africa was found all over the continent, south of the Sahara, in the forests as well as in the plains, wherever the bush was thick enough to afford shelter and food. But in the southern districts to the south of the Limpopo River they have long since disappeared, apart from an isolated herd found in the Addo bush near Port Elizabeth. The ivory-hunters were the great factor in their exter-mination, and were it not for the imposition of legal restrictions upon the trade, a similar fate would have overtaken the elephants in every part of Africa occupied by Europeans. Some idea of the extent and rapidity of the slaughter may be gathered from Selous's estimate that in the three years preceding 1875 not less than one hundred thousand pounds weight of ivory was traded from Matabeleland alone, and a few years ago it was computed that the tusks imported annually into Antwerp alone represented over eighteen thousand elephants.

Several different kinds of African Elephants, representing local races, have been named on the evidence of alleged differences in the shape of the ears of mounted Museum Specimens. There appear, however, to be only two well-defined types, the big ordinary kind, with long, pointed ears, found in the more open plains from Abyssinia southwards through East Africa, and a smaller kind with shorter, rounder ears, found in the Congo forest. From the shape of its ears this African Elephant was called *Loxodonta africana cyclotis*.

Size and Weight of Elephants. The African Elephant is, on the average, rather larger than the Indian ; but the height seldom exceeds eleven feet, a bull of that size being considered a real prize by sportsmen. The biggest specimen ever seen in this country, the still famous " Jumbo," formerly exhibited in the Zoological Gardens, was estimated to be between ten and a half feet and eleven feet. It is a very big bull Indian Elephant that reaches ten and a half feet, although there are dubious records of specimens reaching eleven feet. Cows of both species are always smaller, from seven to nine feet being about their height.

A rough and ready, although not strictly accurate, method of estimating the height of an elephant is practised in India by taking the circumference of a fore foot, which, surprising as it may seem, is about half the height,

720

AFRICAN ELEPHANTS (*Loxodonta africana*)

By courtesy of]   [*British Museum (Natural History)*

ELEPHANTS—" At the River-side "

sometimes more. In the African Elephant, the foot is relatively smaller, its circumference being less, sometimes considerably less, than half the animal's height.

The difficulties of weighing elephants are obvious. There are, however, a few records. A bull measuring ten feet, killed in South Africa, was said to be nine thousand eight hundred and sixty pounds. Of Jumbo's

[Lt. Col. F. D. S. Fayrer.

An Indian Elephant (*Elephas maximus*) with Unusually Long Tusks.
The biggest pair, from an Asiatic elephant, of which there is a trustworthy record, measured eight feet nine inches and eight feet six and a half inches respectively, with a basal girth of about twenty-two inches and a combined weight of two hundred and twenty-two pounds.

weight there are two discrepant records, namely eight thousand nine hundred and sixty, and fourteen thousand five hundred and sixty pounds! An Indian bull and cow in New York turned the scale at six thousand eight hundred, and four thousand five hundred pounds respectively; but these must have been immature animals. Another bull eight feet high weighed just under six thousand four hundred pounds, and a cow seven and a half feet high, a little over five thousand seven hundred pounds.

Tusks. The tusks in bulls are always larger on the average than those of cows; but they may be short, and slender and project only a few inches beyond the jaw in both sexes, especially in Ceylonese and Indian Elephants ; and they are usually better developed in the African than in the Asiatic species. They are also subject to individual variation in size from use, one being frequently longer than the other. In the Asiatic Elephant good tusks run from six to eight feet long, measured along the convex curve, with a combined weight of from one hundred to two hundred pounds. The biggest pair of which there is a trustworthy record measured eight feet nine inches and eight feet six and a half inches, respectively, with a basal girth of about twenty-two inches and a combined weight of two hundred and twenty-two pounds. In the African Elephant, the longest known pair were eleven feet five and a half inches and eleven feet, with a girth of eighteen and a half inches, and a combined weight of two hundred and ninety-three pounds. But another pair with a length of about nine feet had a girth of twenty-five and twenty-three and a half inches, and a combined weight of three hundred and seventy-two pounds ! The measurements, it may be added, are taken after extraction from the jaw, the imbedded root amounting to one foot or more.

Age. Elephants are slow breeders, the period of gestation being twenty or twenty-one months, and only a single calf, as a rule, is born at a time. The calf is soon capable of accompanying its mother and suckles with its mouth, the teats of the mother, two in number, being between her fore legs. Maturity is reached in about twenty-five years, and the natural duration of life is probably about the same as in man, say seventy years, although it was formerly believed to be anything from one hundred and fifty to two hundred years. The old saying that an animal is as old as its teeth expresses the idea that it is dependent on them for its existence. Now the sixth and last tooth of an elephant comes into use when the animal is about forty years old—that is to say, five teeth have been disposed of during that period of the creature's life. The last tooth, it is true, is the largest and doubtless the longest in use of the set, but it is impossible to believe it can endure for a century or more to carry the creature to the great age at one time claimed for it.

A particular case may be cited to illustrate this point. An Indian Elephant presented by King Edward VII to the Zoological Gardens died in 1917, when she was known to be about fifty years old. Her last tooth had then been in use about ten years and about one-third of it had been worn away, although throughout her life she had been fed upon hay, bran and other foods much softer than the woody fibre she would have eaten in a wild state. If she had lived and the rate of wear above stated had continued, her last tooth would have come to an end, and her life probably with it, in another twenty years. She would then have been only about seventy and would have died of old age. Hence it may be inferred that three score years and ten is the approximate span of an elephant's life. It must be added, however, that the life of a tame and toothless elephant

722

might be artificially prolonged by feeding it on soft food requiring no mastication. This may, perhaps, account in part for the stories of excessive longevity based upon captive specimens in India, where elephants are often held sacred and are always greatly prized.

Habits. Apart from a few minor differences, the habits of African and Indian Elephants are very similar.

Like most herbivorous mammals, they are gregarious, the herds being composed of a varying number of individuals, from about a dozen up to fifty or sixty, according to the suitability of a locality, but the huge herds

[*Aerofilms.*

AFRICAN ELEPHANTS IN A SWAMP STAMPEDING AT THE APPROACH OF AN AEROPLANE.
The herds are composed of a varying number of individuals, from about a dozen to fifty or sixty, according to the suitability of the locality.

of a hundred or more that used to be reported are seldom encountered nowadays. Solitary bulls are not infrequently met with ; and about these " rogues," as they are called in India, much has been written and considerable difference of opinion prevails. Some maintain that they are undesirables expelled from the herd and compelled to live a life of solitude, which has soured their tempers and made them vicious. Others think they are merely bolder individuals, which, regardless of the safety which lies in numbers, have voluntarily separated themselves temporarily from their companions. They have the reputation of being more dangerous to man than bulls in a herd, and are said often to attack without provocation.

Being vegetable feeders needing plenty of food and water, elephants

723

are always found in jungle, forest or bush, never far from rivers, streams or pools, sometimes at considerable altitudes, sometimes in the plains, and they frequently pass from one watering place to another, travelling long distances through the woods and plains, as occasion demands.

When on the move, the herd marches, as a rule, in single file and keeps to beaten tracks. Wherever, indeed, these animals have sojourned, the country is traversed in all directions by " elephant-paths," known to sportsmen by their hard, smooth surface, the result of the passage year after year of hundreds of feet over them. Since elephants are fearless of water and excellent swimmers, rivers are no barrier to their progress ; and when crossing a river, they sink deep below the surface with only the top of the head and the end of the trunk above it. One obstacle they cannot cross, on account of their inability to leap, is a deep ditch too wide to stride across.

The ease with which they climb up and down steep slopes is surprising considering their bulk and ungainly build, and they will sometimes descend a smooth decline, sliding on their bellies with their legs stretched out in front and behind.

More surprising still is the silence with which they can travel even through the bush. Over open ground they can walk without a sound, so soft and light is the tread of the cushion-like pads of the feet.

Sportsmen with experience of elephants in the wild are agreed regarding their general timidity and the alacrity with which they make off the moment danger threatens. Their hearing and sight are comparatively poorly developed, but their power of scent is unusually keen. Stalking them with success is, therefore, exceedingly difficult unless the wind is in the right direction. But pacific as elephants are as a rule, a wounded bull is one of the most dangerous beasts in the world ; and the cows, when calves are with them, are apt to charge when quite unmolested.

The habitual method of drinking of elephants is unique. Water is sucked up into the trunk and blown down the throat from the back of the mouth. By this means they can get the water required from a shallow pool or stream to which they cannot lower their heads. But at times they slake their thirst by wading into a river and gulping the water with the mouth.

Food. Their food consists of foliage, grass, canes, fruit, bark, tubers and the like. Branches and foliage can be stripped at a height of twelve or fifteen feet from the ground, and bark is pulled off in long strips with great precision by the trunk. The tusks, helped sometimes by the fore feet, are also used for turning over and loosening the soil for tubers. But much rich foliage and tempting fruit grows out of reach ; and to secure it, entire trees are felled by pressing with the head after the roots have been broken or exposed by means of the tusks. Usually, it seems, the right tusk is used, but sometimes the left, and the preference of one or the other as a tool accounts for the discrepancy in the length of the two tusks above described. Not infrequently the tusks get broken off by being used for that purpose. Elephants with one or both tusks fractured are often shot

[W. F. Taylor.

INDIAN ELEPHANTS (*Elephas maximus*) AT HOME.
The Indian Elephant has a high, bulging forehead, comparatively small ears covering the sides of the neck, and the tip of the trunk provided above with a finger-like lobe, which closes down on the square-cut lip-like lower rim.

and now and again hunters have found pieces of tusk a foot or more in length jammed in the ground under an obstinate root.

It is impossible to find out how much food and water a wild elephant takes daily. This can only be inferred from experience with captive specimens. A big elephant in captivity, fed upon dry food, like hay, bran and grain, will drink forty or fifty gallons of water a day, and requires a minimum ration of about one hundred and fifty pounds weight of food to keep it in fair condition. But tame elephants in India will daily consume from six hundred to seven hundred pounds of green food, which weighs much more than dry hay.

Voice. With the help of the trunk elephants utter a great variety of sounds, blowing that organ to clear it being the simplest. The loudest is a shrill blast called " trumpeting." The roar produced in the throat somewhat resembles that of the lion. There is also a deep, growling rumble sounding as if produced far down in the chest.

Intelligence of Elephants. The elephant has a world-wide fame for its capabilities as a servant and companion of man, and for the extraordinary development of its intellectual faculties. They are, admittedly, exceedingly tractable and can probably be more easily and rapidly tamed than any other wild animal ; and they can be readily educated to respond to words and gestures of command and to perform actions which suggest complete understanding of what they are about or what is required of them. But in the wild state, according to the records of sportsmen, they evince no more intelligence than other wild beasts, their wariness of man or method of felling trees being indications merely of particular instincts conducive to success in their natural environment ; and when these instincts, coupled with innate skill in the use of the trunk, tusks and feet for a variety of purposes, are transferred to the new conditions of captivity, the capabilities and general behaviour of elephants have earned for them their reputation for cleverness. The caution, for instance, with which they test a frail-looking bridge before venturing on it has been ascribed to intelligence ; but it is nothing more than obedience to an instinct prompting them to tread warily on strange, untested ground lest it yield like a pitfall to their weight.

But although their intelligence is not of so high a standard as has sometimes been claimed, a considerable measure of it cannot be denied them. An illustration may be observed any day in the Zoological Gardens. If a visitor drops a piece of bread between the barrier and the cage and out of his own and the elephant's reach, the beast with his trunk will blow the piece, if necessary more than once, towards the visitor's feet, knowing, apparently, that the gift of it will be his reward. The elephants have not been taught this trick. They have found it out for themselves. And since it is difficult to imagine circumstances in the life of wild elephants that could implant the instinct to behave in that way, intelligent seems the only suitable term to apply to the action.

Domestication. Elephants were trained for man's service at an early historic period ; and this applies both to the Indian and African species, as is attested by ancient coins and medals. The African was employed for warfare and other purposes at the time when it inhabited the northern part of the Continent; and it was this elephant that Hannibal took with him across the Alps in his invasion of Italy from Spain. Later the long-continued importation of specimens to Italy for processions and wild beast contests in the amphitheatres, and the incessant demand for its ivory, were probably accessory factors in its extermination in the countries to the south of the Mediterranean. With its disappearance from those countries, it ceased to be a domesticated animal; and until recently it was commonly believed by Europeans in Africa to be untameable, despite the evidence to the contrary supplied by menagerie specimens that it is as docile as its Indian relative. The Belgians in the Congo were the first to take it in hand and are now training it for work which no beast of burden can do so effectively in that country.

In the East the Indian Elephant from times immemorial has played an important part in human affairs, for warfare in the past and at the present time for haulage, vehicular work, processions, tiger-shooting, forest-clearing and so forth. Good and showy elephants have always been prized by their owners; but the most valued of all, even to this day, is the "white elephant," which seems to be of commoner occurrence in Burma and Siam than elsewhere. The albino variety was regarded with the greatest veneration; and it is said that the coveted possession of one in Siam in the seventeenth century kept three nations at constant war for nearly a century and caused the death of five kings and thousands of soldiers.

Some Extinct Elephants. The two kinds of elephants now living are the sole survivors of a great population of these huge beasts that in comparatively recent times roamed over the greater part of the northern hemisphere, in Europe and Asia, and invaded even North America. Their remains, indeed, are frequently found in the Thames gravels and elsewhere in England. The best known of these is the Woolly Mammoth, first cousin to the Indian Elephant, but a little smaller in the body, with weaker quarters, and a shorter tail, although the head was relatively larger to support the gigantic tusks which curved forwards and inwards in front of the head, their points sometimes actually crossing so that they could not be used for uprooting trees. The tusks, indeed, were not required for that purpose because this elephant inhabited the grassy tundras of Siberia, as far north as the shores of the Arctic Ocean, where the trees are mostly stunted or scrub-like. The Mammoth carried in winter a coat of woolly fur covered with coarse hair, sometimes a foot-and-a-half long, long enough almost to sweep the ground, and under the skin was a layer of fat some three inches thick; and as a further provision against the winter, when the grass and low herbage on which he fed was buried deep under frozen snow, he laid up in the autumn stores of fodder, sufficient, with the

727

fat which was gradually absorbed, to carry him through the long, cold period. Such stores of food and splendidly-preserved skeletons, with portions of the skin and hair adhering, have been found in Siberia, buried in ice. So abundant was this elephant that since the dawn of history its tusks have been valuable commercial commodities for the peoples who lived near his home.

Some of the extinct elephants of recent geological times were bigger even than the African Elephant, standing thirteen feet or more at the shoulder'; but in Cyprus and other Mediterranean islands, there were dwarfed elephants, representing the African type, no taller than small ponies.

Evolution of the Elephant. The wonderful story of the evolution of the elephants may be briefly told. As their skeletons are traced back in time, all the peculiarities of the type gradually disappear. The huge bulk and globular head dwindle, the jaws lengthen, the teeth become simplified, until finally we reach an animal somewhat resembling a tapir in build, with tusks in the front of both jaws and molar teeth like those of ordinary herbivorous hoofed mammals ; and this creature, evolved in Africa, showed many points of resemblance to the order shortly to be described, the Hyracoidea.

Order SIRENIA (Manatees and Dugongs)

The singularly inappropriate term for the ugly, ungainly mammals of this order, an offshoot from the stock of the Elephants and Coneys, is derived from the belief that the Dugong of the Indian Ocean was responsible for the ancient fables of mermaids and sirens.

In adaptation to aquatic life, the sirenians are surpassed amongst Mammals only by the Cetaceans, which they resemble in shape, in the absence of hind limbs, flipper-like fore limbs, the presence of a horizontal tail-fin, small eyes and loss of the ear-conch. In other respects, however, the head is very different from a Cetacean's, the muzzle being rounded and blunt and provided with a cleft, muscular, bristly upper lip by means of which water-weeds, on which these animals feed, are plucked from the bottom and passed backwards into the mouth to be masticated by broad-crowned cheek teeth. In the Manatee (*Trichechus*) there are eleven of these teeth and they succeed one another along the jaw, as in elephants, six, as a rule, being functional at a time.

Sirenians are surprisingly skilful in the use of their flippers, employing them not only to direct food to the mouth and to paddle and balance in the water, but also for holding the solitary helpless young to the breast to suckle, the teats, as in Elephants, being close to the fore limbs. This human method of nursing was one of the inspirations of the mermaid fable.

The Manatee inhabits the Atlantic rivers of tropical Africa and America, the African species (*T. senegalensis*) and the Common American species

728

(*T. americanus*) being the best known. In these animals the tail is rounded, there are no front teeth and the jaws are not bent downwards. The length is about eight feet.

The Dugongs (*Halicore dugong* and *H. australis*) inhabit respectively the Indian Ocean and the Australian Seas. They are never found far from shore and feed on seaweeds. They differ from the Manatees in having the tail shaped like a whale's flukes and the jaws bent downwards to accommodate a pair of tusks, which in the male have a sharp cutting edge and grow through life, like those of an elephant. Dugongs are about the same size as Manatees.

Order TUBULIDENTATA (Aard-vark)

The Aard-vark (*Orycteropus*), also known as the African Ant-bear, is a strange beast whose organization suggests its descent from the same ancient stock as that which gave rise to the Elephants and Sirenians. It is not related to the American Anteaters, with which it was formerly classified.

It is an ungainly beast, with a long, narrow head, a pig-like snout, donkey-like ears, a muscular tail, and strong legs armed with powerful digging claws ; with these it demolishes the white-ant mounds to feed upon the insects, which it licks up with its long, extensile tongue. The mouth has no front teeth, but the cheek-teeth

[*W. S. Berridge.*
AARD-VARK OR AFRICAN ANT-BEAR (*Orycteropus*).
With its powerful digging claws, the animal demolishes white-ant mounds and feeds upon the insects, which it licks up with its long, extensile tongue.

are quite unlike those of any other Mammal, being composed of a number of closely-packed denticles, each with a pulp cavity and radiating tubules.

There are several species found in different parts of Africa south of the Sahara, the best known being the typical Aard-vark (*O. afer*) of Cape Colony, which is yellowish-brown in colour, its head and body measuring four and a half feet and the tail two feet. It is solitary and nocturnal, lying up by day in its own deep burrows, sometimes hollowed out in a white-ant mound. Although very powerful, it is quite defenceless, depending for safety upon the quickness of its hearing and a speedy retreat to shelter the moment danger threatens.

Order HYRACOIDEA
(Coneys)

There is no popular name for the animals of this Order except the biblical term Coney, which belongs by rights to the rabbit, an animal which they super-ficially resemble in size, colour and shape, apart from their short ears. By their teeth

[W. S. Berridge.
ROCK-CONEY OR HYRAX (*Procavia capensis*).
This lives on the Kopjes and hill-sides of the open districts of Africa and south-western Asia.

and other characters Coneys belong to the stock to which the elephants trace their descent, a lineage no one would suspect from their appearance and habits. They have a complete set, which no rodent possesses, of large cheek-teeth, like those of the rhinoceros, and tusk-like incisors in front of the mouth, but no canines ; their feet are naked beneath and the toes, except one, have hoof-like nails, the exception being the inner toe of the hind foot, which carries a claw used as a scratcher to clean the fur. There also is a large scent-gland on the back marked by a patch of black or whitish hair.

There are two distinct kinds, the Rock-coney (*Procavia*) and the Tree-coney (*Dendrohyrax*), forming the Family *Procaviidae*, found in Africa, Arabia and Syria.

The Rock-coneys, resembling Marmots in habits except that they shelter in crevices and not in their own burrows, live on the Kopjes and hill-sides of the open districts of Africa and south-western Asia and feed on leaves and shoots of small shrubs. They are skilful climbers and extra-ordinarily active and wary. The young, usually three in number, are born in the shelters the parents occupy. There are many different species, the most commonly imported being the Cape Coney (*P. capensis*), known to the Dutch of South Africa as the " Dassie." The Syrian Coney (*P. syriaca*) is now very rare.

The Tree-coneys live in the lofti-est trees of the forests of Central Africa, and shelter in holes in the trunks. Their loud, weird cries at night carry for miles through the forest. As a rule, they are short-lived in captivity even in Africa, and one species only, the Gold Coast Tree-coney (*D. dorsalis*), has been imported.

[D. Seth-Smith.
TREE-CONEY (*Dendrohyrax dorsalis*).
This animal lives in the loftiest trees of the forests of Central Africa, and shelters in holes in the trunks.

Order RODENTIA (Gnawing Animals)

The Rodents differ essentially from the Insectivora (page 824), which they approach in their generally low organization, by the structure of the mouth and teeth. There are never more than two functional incisor teeth in the upper and lower jaws and these are of large size, chisel-like, adapted for cutting hard substances, of permanent growth, and separated by a long space from the cheek-teeth, there being no canines. This space is filled by flaps of skin, growing inwards from the cheek, which can be separated for swallowing but serve to prevent indigestible, gnawed fragments passing back to the throat.

The Rodents have successfully adapted themselves to the most varied conditions, and exhibit great diversity in structure and habits. They are found practically all over the world and, apart from the Bats, are the only indigenous placental mammals found in Australia.

The Order is divided into two suborders, the *Duplicidentata* (Double-toothed Rodents) and the *Simplicidentata* (Single-toothed Rodents).

[A. H. Willford.
Rabbit (Wild) (*Oryctolagus cuniculus*) at Home.

CLASSIFICATION OF THE RODENTIA.

Suborder DUPLICIDENTATA [DOUBLE-TOOTHED RODENTS] (Hares and Rabbits).

Suborder SIMPLICIDENTATA (SINGLE-TOOTHED RODENTS).
1. **Squirrel Tribe** (Squirrels, Marmots, Beavers, etc.)
2. **Mouse Tribe**
    Family *Muscardinidae* (Dormice)
    Family *Muridae*, Murines (Rats and Mice), Cricetines (Hamster), Microtines (Voles, Lemming)
    Family *Spalacidae* (Mole Rats)
3. **Jerboa Tribe**
    Family *Jaculidae* (Jerboas, Jumping Mouse)
    Family *Anomaluridae* (African Flying Squirrels)
    Family *Pedetidae* (Cape Jumping Hare)
4. **Porcupine Tribe** (Porcupines, Chinchillas, Cavies, Agutis and Capybara).

731

Suborder DUPLICI-DENTATA (Hares, Rabbits and Picas)

These Rodents are distinguished by the presence in the upper jaw of a pair of minute incisors behind the large pair, and the enamel of the latter is not restricted to the front edge. The soles of the feet are always hairy and the tail is short or absent.

DUTCH RABBIT.

There are two families, the Picas (*Ochotonidae*) and the Hares and Rabbits (*Leporidae*).

The Picas (*Ochotona*), sometimes called Mouse-hares or Calling-hares, which are not unlike guinea-pigs, have short ears, no tails and no scent glands in the groin. They are gregarious, living in burrows and rock crevices in cold districts of Central Asia and North America, and have a peculiar piping call. For the winter they lay up stores of food, but do not hibernate. The young, about six to the litter, are born naked, as in rabbits. There are many species. Royle's Pica (*O. roylei*) from the Himalayas, the Siberian (*O. alpina*) and the Rocky Mountain Pica (*O. princeps*) may be cited as examples.

In the Hares and Rabbits (*Fam. Leporidae*) the ears are stalked, the tail is present, and there is a pair of scent glands in the groin. The family is widely spread in all the continents, from the Arctic southwards, but it is not found in Madagascar or Australia.

Photos]   [*Sport & General.*

ANGORA RABBIT.

There are many different kinds to which the names Rabbit and Hare are indiscriminately applied.

Common Rabbit (Oryctolagus cuniculus). This species is gregarious, typically living in extensive burrows, called " warrens " in which the numerous young, naked and helpless at birth, are born. It is found in Central and Southern Europe, but its general appearance is too well known to need description. It has been introduced into several countries, notably Australia and New Zealand, where it has proved an unmitigated pest to farmers, although considerable revenue is derived from its skins, which are dressed in imitation of more valuable furs, the suffix or prefix " coney " indi-cating their real nature. The wild rabbit is the source of all domesticated breeds, of which the so-called " Belgian Hare " is the largest.

Several exotic species are regarded as Rabbits rather than as Hares, notably the North Ameri-can " Cotton-tail " (*Syl-vilagus floridanus*, etc.), which produces naked young in burrows.

Hares differ from Rab-bits in habits. They are not gregarious and do not burrow, but lie up in a kind of nest, called the " form," in which the small litters of young, covered with hair and with the eyes open, are born. For safety they depend largely on speed of foot and endurance, requiring the intake of large volumes of air. Hence the nasal passages are much more spacious than in Rabbits, which bolt to their burrows when

[*Charles Reid.*

COMMON ENGLISH HARE (*Lepus europaeus*).
This hare entered Great Britain from Western Europe and spread to Scot-land, but failed to reach Ireland, although it has been artificially introduced there.

chased. In the Hares the ears and hind limbs are also much longer than in the Rabbits.

English Hare (*Lepus europaeus*). This Hare is much larger and has longer ears and legs than the Rabbit. Its summer coat is also redder ; but frequently turns grey in winter. It entered Great Britain from Western Europe and spread to Scotland, but failed to reach Ireland, although it has been artificially introduced there.

[*Capt. Knight (Mondiale)*.
BRITISH RED SQUIRREL (*Sciurus vulgaris*).
This ranges from Ireland into Asia, and is the only indigenous species in the British Isles.

Scotch or Mountain Hare (*L. timidus*) is smaller, browner and has shorter ears and tail. Being somewhat intermediate in appearance between the English Hare and the Rabbit, it has been mistaken for a hybrid between these two species, which, however, never interbreed. It entered Scotland from the north and was originally confined to the Highlands, but has been introduced into the Lowlands, where it sometimes crosses with the English Hare. It is a race of the North European species, known as the Blue Mountain, or Variable Hare, which typically turns white in winter, the tips of the ears alone remaining black.

Irish Hare (*L. t. hibernicus*). This represents another race, and is larger and redder than the Scotch Hare and seldom shows signs of turning white in winter.

Another species besides the Variable Hare turns white in winter, namely the Prairie Hare (*L. campestris*), one of the North American White-tailed " Jack Rabbits." The Polar Hare (*L. arcticus*), of the same continent, seems, on the other hand, to be white all the year round. Other Hares from the States, known as the Swamp Rabbits (*Limnolagus aquaticus* and *L. palustris*) are interesting from their habitat being marshy localities. In this respect they offer the greatest contrast to the Arabian Hare (*L. arabicus*), which frequents sandy deserts. Many other species, resembling the English Hare in habits, are found in India and Africa.

Suborder SIMPLICIDENTATA (Single-toothed Rodents)

This suborder includes Rodents with only one pair of upper incisor teeth, in which the enamel is restricted to the front edge.

There is a large number of families and subordinate groups mainly distinguished by technical characters in the skull, which cannot here be described ; but as a matter of convenience, the species may be assigned to four sections : the Squirrel Tribe, the Mouse Tribe, the Jerboa Tribe and the Porcupine Tribe.

The Squirrel Tribe

It will be understood that the Squirrels form a very large group and that it will be possible to mention here only a few of the more interesting and representative species.

Arboreal Squirrels. The typical Squirrels, which have long, bushy tails, are expert climbers, although quite at home on the ground. They are diurnal, active throughout the year, feeding mainly on fruits, nuts, buds and seeds, varied with eggs, young birds and sometimes insects. The young, usually three or four in number, are born in nests of leaves lodged in a hole or forked branch of a tree. There are many different kinds found to the limits of tree-growth all over the world except Australia and Madagascar.

Common Red Squirrel (Sciurus vulgaris). This ranges from Ireland into Asia, and is the only indigenous species in the British Isles. In this country it is foxy-red in winter, with tufted ears ; but in summer the tufts are moulted and the colour becomes greyish-brown, the tail at all seasons being

[*Charles Reid.*

NORTH AMERICAN GREY SQUIRREL (*Sciurus carolinensis*).
This was imported into Great Britain some years ago, and is proving a great pest by destroying the eggs and fledglings of our song-birds.

735

paler. The head and body measure about nine inches and the tail seven inches. It was formerly much more plentiful than now ; and its disappearance has been ascribed, not altogether justly, to the larger North American Grey Squirrel (*S. carolinensis*), which was imported some years ago and is steadily spreading all over the country and proving a great pest by destroying the eggs and fledglings of our song-birds. Many tropical Squirrels are beautifully coloured, a particularly handsome species, and the largest of all, being the Great Indian Squirrel (*Ratufa indica*), which is nearly three feet long from the snout to the tip of the tail and offers the greatest contrast to the pretty little Palm Squirrel (*Funambulus palmarum*), which is less than one foot in total length and is brown, banded with white.

[James's Press.
AMERICAN GROUND SQUIRREL OR CHIPMUNK (*Tamias*).
This squirrel lives in burrows in woods, and differs from ordinary squirrels in having cheek-pouches.

Ground Squirrels. Rather similar to the Palm Squirrels in pattern and size are the Chipmunks, or Striped Gophers (*Tamias asiaticus*, etc.), found in eastern Asia and North America. They live in burrows in woods, and differ from ordinary squirrels in having cheek-pouches. The Sousliks (*Citellus citellus*, etc.) are allied to the Chipmunks, but live in the open plains of Europe, Asia and North America.

Marmots. The Sousliks connect the Squirrels with the Marmots, which may be regarded as heavily-built Ground Squirrels with short, not bushy tails. They inhabit Central Europe and Asia and North America and live in colonies in burrows, coming out, usually in the morning and evening, to feed. When abroad they are extremely wary, one or more of the company acting as sentinels to warn the rest of the approach of danger. The species frequenting cold districts sleep through the winter. Of the typical Marmots there are many different kinds, perhaps the best known being the Alpine Marmot (*Marmota marmota*), in which the head and body measure about two feet and the tail six inches ; and the North American Woodchuck (*M. monax*), which has the tail of about the same length but the head and body only one foot long. Closely related to the true Marmots and resembling them in habits is the " Prairie Dog " or Prairie Marmot

736

(*Cynomys ludovicianus*), which inhabits the North American Prairies, sometimes occurring in such numbers that their burrows cover acres of land, constituting what is called a " town."

The Arboreal Squirrels, Ground Squirrels and Marmots constitute the family *Sciuridae*.

Flying Squirrels. The Flying Squirrels form a second family (*Petauristidae*), distinguished by

[W. S. Berridge.

EUROPEAN SOUSLIK (*Citellus citellus*).
The Sousliks are allied to the Chipmunks, but live in the open plains of Europe, Asia and North America.

the presence of a wide flap of skin stretching between the fore and hind limbs on each side and supported in front by a rod of cartilage jointed to the back of the wrist. By means of this parachute they are able to glide some distance through the air from tree to tree. These are not so active either in trees or on the ground as ordinary squirrels and further differ from them in being purely nocturnal. Otherwise their habits and diet are very similar. They are found in Europe, Asia and North America and are represented by a large number of different kinds varying in size and other respects, those from tropical Asia being the largest. For instance, the large brown Indian Flying Squirrel (*Petaurista philippensis*) may measure one and a half feet long from the nose to the root of the tail, the tail being nearly two feet. It can pass from tree to tree over a distance of sixty or eighty yards. On the other hand, the common North American species (*Glaucomys volans*) and the

[*Chase (Dorien Leigh).*
NORTH AMERICAN WOODCHUCK (*Marmota monax*).
Marmots are extremely wary, one or more of the company acting as sentinels to warn the rest of the approach of danger.

European species (*Sciuropterus russicus*) are smaller, the latter, found in Scandinavia, Russia and northern Siberia, being about one foot in total length, of which the tail is about five inches.

Beavers (Family *Castoridae*). The Beavers form another family and are not unlike huge Marmots; but may at once be distinguished by their wide, scaly, paddle-like tails and fully-webbed hind feet adapting them for aquatic life.

[*W. S. Berridge.*

ALPINE MARMOT (*Marmota marmota*).

Marmots live in colonies in burrows, coming out, usually in the morning and evening to feed.

There are two species, the European Beaver (*Castor fiber*), which still survives in small numbers in the Rhone, Elbe and in Norway and in Central Asia, and the American Beaver (*C. canadensis*), which is widely distributed in North America, although killed out in many places where it was formerly plentiful. The two species are very similar, both being covered with thick, brown fur impervious to water. A full-grown beaver measures about two and a half feet from the nose to the root of the tail, the tail being one foot, and the average weight is about forty or fifty pounds. The span of life is from twelve to fifteen years. The young, generally four in number, are born in the spring in a burrow or lodge.

The European beaver lives, like a water-rat, in burrows in the banks of streams, seldom indulging in the engineering feats for which its American ally is famous. These operations are designed for the protection of the colony from enemies, of which the cougar and wolverine, apart from man, are the most formidable, and as a safeguard against frosts. The most important work is the " dam," which, by blocking the flow of a river, produces a " pond " of deep, still water, sometimes causing it to overflow the adjoining land, forming a "beaver-meadow." The dams are laboriously built-up of logs and branches, plastered with mud to stick them together and fill up interstices. To get the necessary woodwork, the beavers fell the nearest trees by gnawing through the trunk. The tree is then cut up into pieces and transported to the water, small branches being carried and large ones pushed or pulled over the ground. Mud and soil for packing is picked up with the fore paws and carried to the spot, the beaver waddling along on its hind legs and tail. The material is plastered on the dam by means of the fore paws.

When the trees are some distance away, the beavers frequently dig ditches or "canals" from the pond, so that they may themselves travel more safely by water to and from the scene of their tree-cutting and convey the logs more readily by flotation. The "lodges," or homes, are built of the same materials as the dams. Sometimes they are mere piles of branches built over the end of the burrow at the water's edge ; but more often they are separated from the burrow as distinct domiciles erected from the bottom of the pond, with the entrance low down beneath the water and the dwelling chamber high up under the roof, which projects some few feet above the surface. In these lodges, sunk in deep water, beavers can live in comparative safety from all enemies, but man, and in the winter, with stored up food, can defy the cold when the surface of the pond may be frozen hard. Their food consists mainly of the bark of willow, poplars and other trees, but they also eat water lilies, grass, roots and so forth.

[H. Bastin.
BEAVER'S TEETH (INCISORS) :
FRONT VIEW.

Pocket - gophers (Fam. *Geomyidae*) are members of the Squirrel tribe adapted to sub-terranean life and are mole-like in general shape, with powerful digging claws. Charac-teristic of them is a

[W. S. Berridge.
AMERICAN BEAVER (*Castor canadensis*).
A full-grown beaver measures about two and a half feet from the nose to the root of the tail, the tail being about one foot.

739

[F. W. Bond.
COMMON DORMOUSE (*Muscardinus avellanarius*).
The dormouse fattens itself on nuts, beechmast and acorns before retiring for its winter sleep.

capacious food-pouch on the cheeks outside the mouth. They live in extensive underground burrows, the best-known species being the Common Pocket-gopher (*Thomomys bursarius*), which is found in the prairies of the United States. The head and body measure about seven inches and the tail two or three inches.

Mouse Tribe.

These Rodents are more numerous in species, more widely distributed and more varied in habits than the others, but on the average they are comparatively small animals resembling ordinary rats and mice. There are, however, many marked deviations from the usual type. The Rodents found in Madagascar and Australia belong to this tribe.

Dormice (Fam. *Muscardinidae*). These recall diminutive squirrels in their diet, arboreal habits and hairy tails. They are, however, nocturnal and hibernate, at least in cold temperate latitudes. They inhabit Europe, Africa and Central Asia.

The Common English and Continental Dormouse (*Muscardinus avellanarius*) is about the size of a house-mouse, but is fawn in colour and has the tail well haired. It is found in thickets and hedges, and fattens itself on nuts, beechmast, and acorns before retiring for its winter sleep, which is spent in a compact nest of leaves, sometimes on

[James's Press.
SQUIRREL DORMOUSE (*Glis glis*).
This little animal takes its name from its size and bushy tail.

the ground. In the spring the female builds a breeding nest for her young, usually in a bush.

In Europe there are several other kinds of dormice, the largest being the Squirrel Dormouse (*Glis glis*), so named from its size and bushy tail. It has been recently imported and has established itself in Herts and Bucks, where it is known locally as the chinchilla. It is a savage species and usually nests in holes in trees. Two other species are found in Europe and several others throughout Africa and Asia.

Muridae. This family contains an immense number of species known

[*Rudolf Zimmermann (Sächsische Landesbildstelle).*

A FAMILY OF DORMICE.

as Rats, Mice, Hamsters, Voles, etc., which mostly have slender, sparsely-haired, scaly tails and short feet. Only a few of the more interesting can be mentioned.

In our country the species belong to the Murine or Mouse Group and the Microtine or Vole Group; but the names "rat" and "mouse" are applied indifferently to both.

Murine Group. The most familiar members of this group, characterized by rooted, cusped cheek-teeth, are the House-rats and House-mouse.

House-rats. We have two species of House-rats, popularly known as the Brown or Norway Rat (*Rattus norvegicus*) and the Black or Old English Rat (*R. rattus*). But none of these titles is appropriate, because the Brown Rat may be black and Norway was not its original home;

741

and the Black Rat may be brown and is not Old English in the sense of being indigenous to this country. The Brown Rat reached England from Central Asia about 1730, and proceeded to supplant the Black Rat, which had established itself several centuries earlier and is still to be caught in dockside warehouses of our seaport-towns. Both species are destructive, costly aliens, and may be the carriers of the organism,

[John J. Ward.
BROWN OR NORWAY RAT (*Rattus norvegicus*).
This rat is a little larger, has shorter ears and tail, a smoother coat and is much less active than the Black Rat.

which, when transmitted to human beings by their fleas, causes bubonic plague. The two may be readily distinguished. The Brown Rat is a little larger, has shorter ears and tail, a smoother coat and is much less active. Its tint varies from brown to black or fawn, and it is the original of the tame piebald and white rats of the animal

[W. S. Berridge.
CAIRO SPINY MOUSE.

trade. The Black Rat is more elegantly built, and in addition to its much longer tail and larger ears, has long hairs jutting from the shorter coat. The typical colour is not black but slaty-grey; but the brown variety, known as the Alexandrine Rat, is not uncommon. It is an Oriental species and was brought to us in connection with commerce.

House-mouse (*Mus musculus*), which needs no description, is another alien believed to have come from Central Asia, but the date of its importation is unknown. All

[W. S. Berridge.
BLACK OR OLD ENGLISH RAT (*Rattus rattus*).
The Black Rat is more elegantly built than the Brown Rat and has long hairs jutting from the shorter coat.

our breeds of fancy mice were derived from it. Except when fighting, House-mice are vocally silent animals ; but, now and again, individuals called " singing mice " from the piping notes they utter are recorded. This is due to some pathological affection of the organ of voice.

Another peculiar type, called " waltzing mice " from their peculiar twisting antics, is especially popular in China and Japan. The habit, which is transmitted to offspring, does not seem to be due to any defect in the brain or ear.

Wood or Long-tailed Field-mouse. Of the two indigenous wild mice found in England, the commoner is the Wood or Long-tailed Field-mouse (*Apodemus sylvaticus*), which is abundant in Great Britain and Ireland. It sometimes invades houses, but may be distinguished from the House-mouse by its larger size, reddish back and white belly. It lives in burrows in woods and

[*James's Press.*

HARVEST-MICE (*Micromys minutus*).
In these mice the tail is partially prehensile and the fore feet are modified for climbing.

hedgerows and lays up stores of food for winter use.

Harvest-mouse (*Micromys minutus*). This is like the Wood-mouse in colour but very much smaller and is further distinguished by its partially-prehensile tail and the modification of its fore feet for climbing. It is unknown in Ireland, but is locally distributed throughout Great Britain.

743

Meadows and cornfields are its usual habitat. For breeding purposes, in summer it constructs a compact nest the size of a cricket ball by tightly weaving grass-blades together. This is frequently attached to growing corn-stalks a foot or so from the ground.

Cricetine Group. This second group, though unknown in Great Britain, is important from its wide distribution elsewhere, occurring in Central Europe, Asia and Africa, and in Madagascar and America taking the place of the Murines, from which it differs in having the cusps of the cheek-teeth arranged in two, not three rows. As an example may be taken the European and Asiatic Hamster (*Cricetus cricetus*), a large rodent nearly a foot long, with the tail only two inches in length ; it is reddish above but black on the belly. It lives in companies in elaborate burrows containing store-rooms and nurseries. It sleeps through the winter ; but, being abundant and prolific, is a great pest to farmers, and it carries food to its burrows in its large cheek-pouches, which it fills with its fore paws. Its skins are extensively used for lining cloaks and overcoats.

[*W. S. Berridge.*

BANK-VOLE (*Clethrionomys glareolus*).
This resembles the Field-vole in size, but is redder in colour.

[*Sächsische Landesbildstelle.*

EUROPEAN AND ASIATIC HAMSTER (*Cricetus cricetus*).
This rodent, a foot or so in length, is a great pest to farmers, and carries its food to its burrows in its large cheek-pouches, which it fills with its fore paws.

White-footed Mouse (*Peromyscus americanus*). This mouse, of North America, although in habits and appearance closely resembling our Wood-mouse, belongs to this group. So also does the curious Fish-rat (*Ichthyomys stolzmanni*), which is about as big as a Brown Rat, has webbed feet and a head like an otter's. It inhabits mountain streams in Peru, and feeds on fish.

Microtine Group. The species of this group may

be distinguished superficially by their small eyes and ears and short tails, and fundamentally by their flat-crowned, unrooted cheek-teeth. The group is not found in Ireland.

Water-rat or Water-vole (Arvicola amphibius), which is much the same colour as a Brown Rat but rather smaller, is the largest British species. It lives in burrows in the banks of streams, is a good diver and swimmer and feeds on roots and a variety of green stuff.

Field-vole or Short-tailed Field-mouse (Microtus agrestis). This is about the size of a House-mouse. It lives in meadows and makes a nest for its young in the grass. It is very prolific, producing three or four litters of some four or five young ones in the season. A peculiarity of this vole, and of its Continental allies, is the occasional prodigious increase in their numbers, causing "vole or mouse plagues"; but in a year or two the normal number for the district is re-established.

Bank-vole (Clethrionomys glareolus). This, the third British species, is commoner than the Field-vole, which it resembles in size, but is redder in colour. It has larger ears, a longer tail, and is more omnivorous in diet.

Of the many exotic species of this group only two of popular interest can be mentioned.

[*Stanley Crook.*

SHORT-TAILED FIELD-VOLE (*Microtus agrestis*).
This vole is very prolific, producing three or four litters of some four or five young ones in the season.

Lemming (Lemmus lemmus). This, in its size, tortoiseshell colouring and very short tail, resembles a half-grown guinea-pig. It is found in Scandinavia, usually in the mountains, where it lives in burrows, and in winter in runs under the snow. Periodical swarms of millions of Lemming are not unusual. At such times they migrate in hordes, keeping a course across country as if impelled to go in one direction, undeterred by crevices, streams or other obstacles. If they reach the coast, blind instinct drives them into the sea to be drowned by the thousand. No satisfactory explanation of this strange behaviour has been given.

Musquash or Musk-rat (Ondatra zibethica). This is the largest of the

Voles, the head and body measuring one foot and the tail a little less, the colour being rich brown. It inhabits cold temperate parts of North America and is aquatic, its tail being flattened from side to side for swimming. In diet it is omnivorous, eating mussels and fish, as well as vegetable food. Usually it lives in burrows in the banks of streams; but occasionally in still water it builds " huts,"

ZECH'S MOLE RAT (Family *Spalacidae*).
Mole-rats have no visible eyes, or external ears, and the feet are enlarged for digging.

which, like the " lodges " of beavers, project above the surface. Musquash fur is of considerable value; and the animal has been imported into England and the Continent to constitute Musquash-farms. But they have everywhere escaped from confinement and become a menace to the countryside by the weakening of the waterways by their extensive burrows, attempts to keep them in check costing thousands of pounds annually.

Mole-rats (Family *Spalacidae*). These are representatives of the Mouse tribe thoroughly adapted to subterranean life. The body is cylindrical, covered with soft, mole-like fur, there is no tail, no trace of a neck, the large, wedge-shaped head has no visible eyes, or external ears, and the feet are enlarged for digging. Mole-rats live in underground burrows, feeding on bulbs and roots, and are found in south-eastern Europe and the adjoining parts of Asia and Africa. The Mountain Mole-rat (*Spalax monticola*), from Hungary, Turkey, etc., is brownish in colour and measures about nine inches long.

Photos]   *[W. S. Berridge.*
MUSQUASH OR MUSK-RAT (*Ondatra zibethica*).
The fur is of considerable value; and the animal has been imported into England and the Continent to constitute Musquash-farms.

746

Jerboa Tribe

The Jerboas (*Jaculidae*) are about the size of rats, but are distinguished by their very long hind legs and long, tufted tails, the tuft being black-and-white, whereas the colour is otherwise sandy or pale brown to harmonize with the steppes of central Asia and the deserts of south-western Asia and North Africa, where these animals live, usually in companies. They are nocturnal, lying up in burrows during the day and feeding at night on a variety of vegetable and animal food. In gait they are habitually bipedal, either trotting along on their hind legs or travelling at great speed by means of prodigious leaps several yards in length. There are many species distinguished mainly by the length of their ears and the numbers of toes on the hind feet, these varying from five to three. Two species of North African Jerboas (*Jaculus jaculus* and *Scirtopoda orientalis*), each with three toes, are commonly imported, less well known being the Asiatic five-toed Jerboas (*Allactaga indica* and *Euchoreutes naso*).

The North American Jumping Mouse (*Zapus hudsonius*) in size and appearance is intermediate between the Jerboas and typical Mice. It inhabits woods, plains and even marshland and, although mouse-like in size, can hop eight or more feet.

[D. Seth-Smith.

ASIATIC FIVE-TOED JERBOA.
These little animals can travel at great speed by means of prodigious leaps several yards in length.

African Flying Squirrels (Family *Anomaluridae*). Although resembling the real flying squirrels (page 737) in habits and in having a flight-membrane, these are not related to them and may be distinguished by the presence of two rows of large, pointed scales at the root of the tail below and by the attachment to the elbow, instead of to the wrist, of the rod supporting the membrane. The scales are used to support the animal when it is resting on a vertical tree trunk ; they are, indeed, used as " climbing-irons." There are many species found in the forests of Central Africa, the largest being the Red Flying Squirrel (*Anomalurus fulgens*) from the Gaboon and the Black (*A. peli*) from Guinea. The head and body measure about fifteen inches and the tail seven or eight inches.

Pedetidae. The Cape Jumping Hare (*Pedetes cafer*), known to the Dutch as the Spring Haas, is the sole representative of the Family Pedetidae.

747

Although related to the African Flying Squirrel, this animal is very different in habits and appearance, resembling a small, long-eared, bushy-tailed Kangaroo. The colour is brown; the head and body measure about two feet and the tail one and a half feet. It is gregarious and nocturnal, lying up in burrows by day and feeding on roots, grass, etc., at night. When

[W. S. Berridge.

DEGU (*Octodon degus*).
This rodent is a native of South America.

alarmed, it leaps away at great speed after the manner of jerboas and kangaroos.

Porcupine Tribe

The typical Porcupines (Family *Hystricidae*) are distinguished by the armature of long, erectile, smooth, black-and-white spines on the back, by possessing a rattle made of quills or thickened bristles on the tail and by their terrestrial habits, their feet being adapted for running and digging. They are nocturnal and herbivorous, lying up by day in burrows, rock crevices or other sheltered places, and the young, two to four in number, are born, as apparently in all the species of this tribe, with their eyes open, and are soon capable of looking after themselves. They inhabit Africa and southern Asia and a few places in Europe.

[D. Seth-Smith.

CAPE JUMPING HARE (*Pedetes cafer*).
The head and body measure about two feet and the tail one and a half feet.

Crested Porcupine (*Hystrix cristata*). This is found in North Africa, Sicily and Italy, and may be taken as an example of a number of superficially very similar species. The head and body measure two feet, but the tail, without the rattle, which is composed of hollow, inflated quills, is only two or three inches. The spines on the

748

BRAZILIAN TREE PORCUPINE (*Coendou prehensilis*).
(Family *Erethizontidae*.)
In the Tree Porcupines the feet are adapted for climbing, and the spines are shorter and thinner than in the terrestrial species.

back, which are very stout, sharp and easily detached from the skin, measure from three to twelve inches. They are very efficient defensive weapons ; and porcupines surpass even skunks in the arts of self-advertisement. Roaming about in the dusk they are conspicuous by reason of the whiteness of their quills ; they emit a pungent odour like that of concentrated human perspiration, and they make as much noise as they can by grunting and shaking the rattles in their tails. Their attributes appeal to the sight, hearing and scent of possible enemies, and are sure marks of identity, warning predacious beasts to beware of attacking them.

HODGSON'S LONG-TAILED PORCUPINE.
Porcupines are nocturnal and herbivorous.

Photos]   *[W. S. Berridge.*
AFRICAN CRESTED PORCUPINE (*Hystrix cristata*).
These animals emit a pungent odour like that of concentrated human perspiration.

Tree Porcupines (Family *Erethizontidae*). These differ from the preceding in being arboreal, with the feet adapted for climbing. The spines, too, are much shorter and thinner and are beset with reversed barbs so that, when they become detached and stick in the skin of an attacking foe, they work inwards and set up festering sores. These porcupines

MEXICAN TREE PORCUPINE (*Coendou mexicanus*).
(Family *Erethizontidae.*)

are American. The North American species (*Erethizon dorsatum*), found as far north as Canada, has a short, spiny tail with which it strikes when attacked. The best - known South American species, or Coendus (*Coendou prehensilis, C. setosus*, etc.), have long, scaly prehensile tails. The quills of these Tree Porcupines are conspicuous when erected, and the animals have the same odour as those of the Old World ; but there is no record of their noisiness.

As in the case of the Tree Porcupines, South America is the headquarters of most of the remaining Rodents of this tribe, one or two only, such as the Cane-rat (*Thryonomys swinderianus*) and the Rock-rat (*Petromys typicus*), being African. In South America there are many different species, some of which, like the Degu (*Octodon degus*), closely resemble ordinary rats and mice in size and habits. Others, also of small size, such as the Tucotucos (*Ctenomys magellanicus*, etc.) are like the Mole-rats in being subterranean.

Coypu or Beaver-rat (*Myocastor coypus*). This animal belongs to this rat-like section, and is something like a small beaver in appearance, with webbed feet but a rat-like tail, one foot in length, the head and body measuring two feet. It is aquatic, and common in the Argentine, living usually in burrows in the banks of streams and lakes. The young, usually about six to the litter, are soon capable of following the mother into the water, where as many as can find room ride on her back. The teats are set high up on the flanks so that the young can suckle while in the water. Coypu fur, known in the trade as Nutria, is a good imitation of Beaver. Enterprising showmen have sometimes profitably exhibited this animal as a sample of what London can produce in the way of Sewer-rats.

Photos by courtesy of]   [*Carl Hagenbeck's Tierpark, Stellingen.*
COYPU OR BEAVER-RAT (*Myocastor coypus*).
Coypu fur, known in the trade as Nutria, is a good imitation of Beaver.

750

Chinchillas and Viscacha. The next series contains a number of different kinds in which the hind feet are digitigrade, the hock being raised well off the ground. The digits, moreover, exhibit the perissodactyle arrangement, the third toe being median and symmetrically flanked by the second and fourth, which are shorter. There are two main divisions with this type of foot, represented respectively by the Chinchillas, the Cavies and their allies.

The Chinchillas (Family *Chinchillidae*) are distinguished by having moder-

CHINCHILLA (*Chinchilla laniger*) (Family *Chinchillidae*).
Chinchillas have moderately long, thick tails, with short hairs below and long hairs above, forming a kind of brush.

ately long, thick tails, with short hairs below and long hairs above, forming a kind of brush. The Common Chinchilla (*Chinchilla laniger*), well known for the value and beauty of its exquisitely soft silver-grey fur, is about the size of a large squirrel, the head and body being some ten inches long and the tail about five. It is gregarious, lives in burrows and crevices in the Andes of Chile and Bolivia, and is extraordinarily active, racing over the rocks with amazing speed and precision. It was formerly very abundant, but is now comparatively scarce from persistent persecution by fur traders.

Cuvier's Chinchilla (*Lagidium peruanum*) resembles the last in habits but is as large as a rabbit. It inhabits the Andes up to 15,000 feet. Its fur is not so valuable.

The Viscacha (*Vizcacia viscacia*), inhabiting the pampas of the Argentine, is a big-

Photos]   [*W. S. Berridge.*
VISCACHA (*Vizcacia viscacia*).
This gregarious rodent lives in warrens called "Viscacheras," which are often adopted by birds, a Little Owl being the commonest lodger.

751

headed, heavily-built rodent, the head and body measuring nearly two feet and the tail about seven inches. The third digit of the hind foot has a thick brush of stiff bristles used as a fur-cleaner. The general colour is mottled grey and black, but the face is banded black and white. This animal is mostly nocturnal and gregarious, living in warrens called " visca-cheras," which are often

WEST INDIAN AGUTI (*Dasyprocta cristata*).
Agutis are mainly nocturnal, lying up by day in burrows under tree roots or other sheltered spots.

adopted by birds, a little owl being the commonest lodger. Viscachas have a curious habit of piling up near their burrows heaps of food-rubbish, stones, cattle-bones or other objects they find on the pampas.

Agutis, Paca, Cavies and Capybara. The rodents grouped under these headings differ from the Chinchillas in having the tail short or absent. Each type represents a special family.

Agutis (Family *Dasyproctidae*). These are about as large as rabbits, measuring some one and a half feet long, but stand high on their slender legs. Their technical name is derived from the long, rather bristly hair on the hindquarters. They are swift-footed forest dwellers and mainly nocturnal, lying up by day in burrows under tree roots or other sheltered

Photos]   *[W. S. Berridge.*
SOOTY PACA OR SPOTTED CAVY (*Cuniculus paca*).
This is found in the forested districts of all the northern countries of South America.

spots. Only one or two young are born at a time. They have a wide range and there are many different sorts, such as the Red-rumped Aguti (*Dasyprocta aguti*) from Brazil, the Mexican (*D. mexicana*) from Central America, the West Indian (*D. cristata*), and others, differing principally in colour, which varies from speckled red to speckled black.

GUINEA-PIG OR RESTLESS CAVY.
This animal was introduced into Europe from Dutch Guiana in the sixteenth century.
[F. W. Bond.

Cavies. The Sooty Paca or Spotted Cavy (*Cuniculus paca*). This represents the Family *Cuniculidae*, and measures about two feet long and in habits and appearance resembles a large heavily-built Aguti, with a head shaped like a cart-horse's; and it may be further distinguished by its pattern of white spots and longitudinal stripes on an otherwise dark brown coat. It is found in the forested districts of all the northern countries of South America.

The size and general appearance of the typical Cavies (Family *Caviidae*) are familiar from the tame variety known as the Guinea-pig, a name which is no doubt a corruption of Guiana-

PAMPAS CAVY.
[W. S. Berridge.

PACA RANA OR FALSE PACA (*Dinomys branickii*).
[W. S. Berridge.

pig. The wild species, of which there are many distributed over the greater part of South America, are very like the smooth-haired domesticated variety, except that they are never parti-coloured but of a tolerably uniform grizzled olive or brown hue. The animal was introduced into Europe from Dutch Guiana in the sixteenth century, the

PATAGONIAN CAVIES (*Dolichotis magellanica*).
This cavy stands about one foot in height and measures three feet in length.

wild species probably being Cutler's Cavy (*Cavia cutleri*), known to have been domesticated by the Incas of Peru.

The Patagonian Cavy or Mara (*Dolichotis magellanica*), sometimes known locally in the Argentine as the "hare," is a very different-looking animal, standing about one foot high and measuring three feet long. It has long legs, longish ears and is greyish or yellowish in colour, with a conspicuous white patch on the rump. It lives, usually in parties of a dozen or so, in the pampas of the Argentine and the stony wastes of Patagonia, and is diurnal, feeding and basking in the sun by day and sheltering in burrows by night. It is remarkably swift and trusts to its speed to escape the pursuit of wild dogs and other enemies.

The Carpincho or Capybara (*Hydrochoerus hydrochoeris*), the sole representative of this family, the *Hydrochoeridae*, is the largest of the rodents, being comparable in size to a pig, which it further resembles in its scanty clothing of coarse hair. The colour is yellowish-brown, the length about four feet, and the weight up to one hundred pounds. Its feet are very like those of the tapir, and it is very similar to those animals in habits, living in the forests and lowlands of Brazil and adjoining countries, always near water, into which, being an expert diver and swimmer, it plunges when alarmed. Its chief enemies on land are the jaguar and the puma and in the water the anaconda and cayman. The food consists of grass and other vegetable matter and water-weeds.

Photos]   [W. S. Berridge.
CAPYBARA OR CARPINCHO (*Hydrochoerus hydrochoeris*).
This rodent always lives near water, being an expert diver and swimmer.

754

Order CARNIVORA (Flesh-eating Mammals)

This order contains such familiar mammals as cats, dogs, bears, seals and others. The digits, five, rarely four, in number, are armed with claws. The general organization of the brain and other parts is of a high type. The front teeth are stable in number and arrangement, consisting usually above and below of six incisors set in a lightly-curved or straight line between two tusk-like canines, with the outer incisor larger than the inner; two of the cheek-teeth, the fourth or last premolar above and the first molar below, which work against one another, very commonly have their main cusps high, blade-like, and adapted for cutting flesh; hence they are called the sectorial or carnassial teeth. But many members of the order, showing the inappropriateness of its name, are mainly herbivorous; and in these the sectorial teeth lose their characters.

By the structure of their feet, it is customary to divide the carnivora into two suborders, the *Fissipedia*, or cleft-footed species, like Cats, Dogs, Bears, etc., and the *Pinnipedia*, or fin-footed species, comprising the Seals and Walruses, in which the limbs are converted into paddles.

CLASSIFICATION OF THE ORDER CARNIVORA

Suborder **FISSIPEDIA** (Normal-footed)
    Tribe **Aeluroidea** (Cat-like)
        Family *Hyaenidae* (Hyaenas)
          ,,   *Cryptoproctidae* (Fossa)
          ,,   *Herpestidae* (Mongooses)
          ,,   *Viverridae* (Civets, Genets, etc.)
          ,,   *Felidae* (Cats, Lions, Tigers, Lynx, Cheetah, etc.)
    Tribe **Arctoidea** (Bear-like)
        Family *Canidae* (Dogs, Wolves, Jackals and Foxes)
          ,,   *Mustelidae* (Weasels, Martens, Skunks, Badgers and Otters)
          ,,   *Procyonidae* (Raccoons, Coatis, Cacomistles, Kinkajous, etc.)
          ,,   *Aeluridae* (Pandas)
          ,,   *Ursidae* (Bears)

Suborder **PINNIPEDIA** (Fin-footed)
    Family *Otariidae* (Sea-lions)
        ,,   *Odobaenidae* (Walruses)
        ,,   *Phocidae* (Seals).

Suborder FISSIPEDIA

The term cleft-footed means that the digits, whether webbed or not, can be spread and separated from each other during locomotion, whether it be for running or swimming. Also in this group the cheek-teeth, with rare exceptions, are not all alike, but varied in shape and function.

This suborder is itself divided into two main groups, the *Aeluroidea* or cat-like, and the *Arctoidea* or bear-like, which unfortunately cannot be distinguished by any external feature, although they differ, in some anatomical respects, particularly in the bones of the skull connected with hearing and smelling.

[*Major A. Radclyffe Dugmore.*
SPOTTED HYAENA (*Crocuta crocuta*).
This is distinguished from the other species by its larger size, more rounded ears, shorter, softer coat, and by its pattern of dark spots on a yellowish-tawny ground.

Aeluroid Carnivores or Cats and their Allies

In this group the nasal passages in the skull are almost filled by two scrolls of spongy bone which arise from the back of the passages and reach nearly to the nostrils; and on the lower side of the skull, beneath the ear, there is a hollow, bony swelling, called the *bulla*, which in this group consists of two bones, an outer and an inner, joined together, and from the line where they meet arises a bony shelf dividing the cavity of the bulla into two chambers.

These characters are common to the Hyaenas (Family *Hyaenidae*), the Mongooses (Family *Herpestidae*), the Fossa (Family *Cryptoproctidae*), the Civet Cats (Family *Viverridae*) and the Cats (Family *Felidae*).

It is noteworthy that, with the exception of the Cats, none of these families is represented in America.

756

TRIBE AELUROIDEA (CAT-LIKE)

Hyaenas (Family *Hyaenidae*)

Although from their appearance Hyaenas are popularly regarded as akin to the dogs, they belong in reality to the cat tribe and resemble the mongooses and the fossa in having a large, saccular scent-pouch beneath the root of the tail. They are especially distinguished by their long, digitigrade, dog-like legs and feet, which have only four toes, and by their powerful jaws and massive teeth adapted for cracking thick bones, big pieces of which they are capable of swallowing and digesting. Their general shape is ungainly owing to their long neck and legs, short body and weak, sloping hindquarters. They are, indeed, not built for leaping or speedy running. At most, they achieve a shambling gallop, seldom employed for chasing living prey. Their food consists very largely of the dead bodies of big game, and they share with vultures and jackals the distinction of being the chief scavengers of Africa and southern Asia. Nothing, however, comes amiss to them in the way of animal food, carrion or otherwise ; and they will eat any small creatures they can kill, even children at times, and are often a pest to farmers by taking sheep, goats, small house-dogs and other livestock.

[*W. S. Berridge.*
STRIPED HYAENA (*Hyaena hyaena*).
This hyaena is smaller and more lightly built than the Spotted Hyaena.

There are two well-marked types represented by the Striped and Spotted Hyaenas.

The Striped Hyaena (*Hyaena hyaena*) has a long, shaggy, greyish coat, relieved by black stripes. It is a smaller, more lightly-built animal than the Spotted, standing a little over two feet at the shoulder ; and further differs in the shape of its teeth and in the young resembling the mother in colour at birth. It is found in India, south-western Asia and over a large part of North Africa, generally frequenting open, dry country, lying up by day in burrows or caves on the hill-sides and coming out at night to search for food, which it finds by scent, discovering by this means the freshly-interred human bodies. Notoriously a cowardly, skulking beast, it seldom bites when attacked, the instinct of self-defence in an animal with such powerful jaws being strangely suppressed.

757

In Africa south of the Zambesi, this species is represented by the Brown Hyaena (*H. brunnea*), or Strand Wolf, a larger species, blackish-grey in colour and striped on the legs only. Its habits, however, seem to be identical, but on the coast of south-western Africa it is said to haunt the beach to feed on crabs, fish or even whales that may be washed ashore.

The Spotted Hyaena (*Crocuta crocuta*) may be distinguished at a glance from the other species by its larger size, more rounded ears, shorter, softer coat, and by its pattern of dark spots on a yellowish-tawny ground colour, the legs being usually brown, particularly in immature individuals. The cubs are entirely brown all over and gradually acquire more and more of the tawny-yellow tint the older they get. The height of the adult is about two and a half feet. This Hyaena is found only in Africa south of the Sahara, although not in the Congo forest. Its habits closely resemble those of the other species, but it is less solitary and more venturesome, boldly invading the camps of travellers and the huts or villages of natives at night in search of food, clearing away the refuse it finds and carrying off any livestock it can kill, sometimes even attacking sleeping human beings.

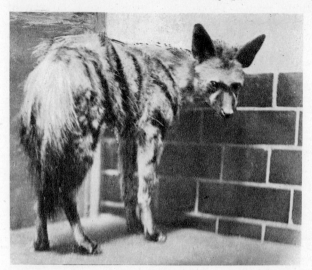

[*W. S. Berridge.*
AARD WOLF (*Proteles cristatus*).
This animal is seldom seen, because it lies up in burrows during the day and ventures out to feed only at night.

On this account it is very much feared, and exaggerated accounts of its depredations, appearance and size, promulgated by natives, have given rise to the belief of the existence in East Africa of a strange unknown mammal known to English settlers as the " Nandi Bear."

Aard Wolf, or Maned Jackal (*Proteles cristatus*). This must be regarded as a degenerate representative of the Hyaena stock, adapted to a different diet. In appearance it is very like a half-grown Striped Hyaena ; but it differs from all the Hyaenas in having the " dew-claw " on its fore feet, which the Hyaenas have lost, and more particularly in its comparatively weak jaws and diminutive, widely-spaced cheek-teeth, quite unfitted for the mastication of ordinary flesh. It feeds, indeed, upon soft carrion to a certain extent, but mainly upon white-ants. It is restricted to Africa, where it ranges from Somaliland to the Cape Province. It is,

758

MARSH MONGOOSE.

[F. W. Bond.

however, seldom seen, because it lies up in burrows during the day and ventures out to feed only at night.

Mongooses
(Family *Herpestidae*)

In having six cheek-teeth above and below on each side, the Mongooses resemble the Civets and Genets. Their claws are long, non-retractile, and used for digging, and they have a scent-gland beneath the root of the tail. They are typically long-bodied, short-legged, long and bushy-tailed animals rather small in size, covered with coarse, usually grizzled hair, the head being broad, with a pointed muzzle and short rounded ears. In habits they

[W. S. Berridge.
INDIAN OR GREY MONGOOSE (*Herpestes nyula*).
This little animal is capable of killing most carnivores of its own size, or even larger.

are terrestrial, living in burrows or natural holes and are for the most part active, predatory little creatures, feeding on small mammals, birds, eggs, reptiles. frogs crabs, insects or even fruits, partiality for this or that kind of food depending on the species. The family is very widely distributed almost all over Africa,

[W. S. Berridge.
KUSIMANSE (*Crossarchus obscurus*).

759

one species being found in Spain, and over southern Asia from Persia to the Malay Islands. It is in Africa that the greatest diversity in the structure and habits of Mongooses occurs, all the Asiatic kinds being tolerably similar. About thirty species are known, only a few of which can be mentioned here.

Of these the best known is the Common Indian Mongoose (*Herpestes nyula*), which is widely distributed in the country and varies locally in colour from grey to reddish grey, the head and body measuring about one and a half feet, the tail being a little less. Although easily tamed and turned into a household pet, this Mongoose is naturally a savage, courageous, sanguinary little beast, capable of killing most carnivores of its own size, or even larger. It lives solitary or in pairs in thickets, fields, hedgerows, seldom in thick jungle, and lies up and breeds in burrows. It preys upon rats, mice, birds, frogs, indeed, upon any animals it can find and is famous

[*W. S. Berridge.*

FOSSA (*Cryptoprocta ferox*).
When attacked, the Fossa is said to emit a skunk-like odour from its scent glands.

for its hostility to snakes, fearlessly attacking even the most venomous kinds. Many stories have been told of its combats with the deadly cobra. At one time it was supposed to be immune to the venom of this snake; but experiments have shown that this is not so. The Mongoose, indeed, takes the greatest care not to be bitten, avoiding the strokes of the snake by active side-leaps and watching for the chance, when the reptile has missed, to spring upon it and, if possible, grip it by the neck, close to the head. Failing in this, it bites the back and leaps clear before the snake can recover. Thus the contest is continued, until the cobra, baffled and exhausted by the activity of its opponent, offers the chance for a quick pounce and firm grip behind the head, either by attempting to escape or by delaying too long to recover its defensive attitude. Almost equally famous is this Mongoose for clearing ships and houses of rats; and many years ago it was introduced into the West Indies to keep down these rodent pests, which destroyed the sugar-canes.

Some of the African Mongooses differ in no respects in habits from the Indian species. But others are less predacious, less active, and prey to a greater extent upon insects, and are gregarious, living in companies, in burrows or old termite mounds, and sometimes combining to attack their prey. Well-known examples are the Banded Mongoose (*Mungos mungo*), distinguishable by its black stripes, and the Meerkat (*Suricata suricatta*), a small, fawn-coloured, sharp-nosed little animal, not much larger than a big rat. These gregarious species have the habit of squatting upon their haunches outside their burrows, watching for enemies and ready to dart underground at a warning cry from one

LARGE INDIAN CIVET (*Viverra zibetha*).
This species has feet like a cat's, with protected, retractile claws. It ranges from Northern India to China and Malaya.

of the sentries. The Egyptian Mongoose is one of the largest species, and is interesting from its food consisting largely of the eggs and young of the crocodile.

Fossa. In Madagascar, a home of primitive mammals, there are a few mongoose-like and civet-like species which serve in a measure to link those two families together. The largest and most interesting of these is the Fossa (*Cryptoprocta ferox*), the sole representative of the family *Cryptoproctidae*. This animal combines the scent gland of the Mongooses with the feet of the Palm Civets and the teeth of the Cats. But the likeness to the Cats in the teeth has been independently acquired in relation to highly predacious habits and carnivorous diet.

Photos]   *[W. S. Berridge.*
AFRICAN CIVET (*Civettictis civetta*).
In this species the claws are unguarded.

The Fossa is uniformly brown in colour, its head and body measuring a little over two feet and its tail about one and a quarter feet. In habits it is nocturnal and mainly arboreal and when attacked is said to emit a skunk-like odour from its scent glands. The natives of Madagascar, indeed, report that when prowling around their fowlpens at night, it suffocates the poultry with the odour.

761

Civets, Genets and Palm Civets
(Family *Viverridae*)

[W. S. Berridge.
CHINESE MASKED PALM CIVET (*Paguma larvata*).
The Palm Civets are less predatory than the genets and more frugivorous in diet.

This family differs from the Cats in having the head longer, lower and altogether more dog - like, the cheek - teeth less specialized for cutting and less reduced in number, there being typically six cheek-teeth above and below on each side; there is also a perfume gland in the groin. The feet, although never quite so markedly digitigrade as in the Cats, always have the claws sharp and retractile and sometimes protected by lobes of skin as in those animals; but the first toe (hallux) of the hind foot is never absent. None of its members is so predatory in habits or so carnivorous in diet as the Cats, many of them subsisting to a great extent on fruits and other vegetable food. The perfume glands appear to be used for scenting the ground, tree-trunks and other objects to enable the members of the species to find each other in the forest.

Civets or Civet Cats. Of these the Large Indian Civet (*Viverra zibetha*) and the African Civet (*Civettictis civetta*) are the largest and best known. They are nocturnal, terrestrial animals, about the size of a large fox-terrier, and feed upon small mammals and birds and fruits of various kinds. In both the perfume glands are well developed. The Indian species has feet like a cat's, with protected, retractile claws; the general colour of the body is greyish, but the black tail is banded with white, the throat is black and white, and there is a black crest down the back; the fur is soft and thick, making the skin of some

[F. W. Bond.
DONGOLAN GENET (*Genetta dongolana*).
The genets are related to the civets, but are much smaller, with longer tails and shorter legs, being almost exclusively arboreal.

importance in the fur-trade for wraps. The head and body measure two and a half feet, and the tail is one and a half feet long. The species ranges from Northern India to China and Malaya.

There are several smaller, related species in the East. Apart from their furs, these Civets are of some commercial value on account of the use of the secretion of their glands as a basis for perfumes. It smells, when diluted, like the cobbler's substance known as "heel-ball." In some parts of the East the animals are kept in cages and the perfume extracted periodically with a small spoon. The Little Indian Civet (*Viverricula indica*) has even been introduced into Socotra and Madagascar for the sake of its scent.

The African species, found almost all over Africa south of the Sahara, is about the size of the Large Indian Civet, but differs in having its claws unguarded, also in its coarse fur and heavily-spotted body.

Genets (*Genetta*). These are related to the Civets, but are much smaller, with longer tails and shorter legs and are almost exclusively arboreal in habits and extremely active. The colour is generally grey or yellowish-brown, relieved by many small spots or fewer large blotches. Apart from

[*W. S. Berridge.*
INDIAN PALM CIVET OR TODDY CAT
(*Paradoxurus hermaphroditus*).
Its popular name is derived from its supposed fondness for "toddy" or "palm-juice."

one species, the Common Genet (*G. genetta*), which still survives in Spain and the south of France, these animals are confined to Africa, where there are many different kinds, the Blotched and Feline Genets (*G. tigrina* and *G. felina*), of South Africa, and the Pardine Genet (*G. pardina*), of West Africa, being the best known. They vary little in size, the Spanish species measuring : head and body, one foot ten inches and the tail about one foot six inches.

An interesting variation of the Genet type may be briefly referred to as a recent discovery in the heart of Africa. This is the Water Genet (*Osbornictis piscivora*), which is the size of a large Genet, but differs in having sharper teeth, fitted for holding slippery fishes, naked feet for walking on the muddy banks of streams, and in having lost all trace of the pattern, the general colour being reddish-brown relieved by white patches on the head, and a black tail. It is found on the banks of streams in the Belgian Congo.

MAMMALIA (ORDER CARNIVORA)

Palm Civets. These animals, with their long tails, short legs and arboreal habits, superficially resemble Genets, but are more plantigrade in gait, much less active, less predatory in habits and more frugivorous in diet, the cheek-teeth in consequence having broader, more crushing crowns. There are many species, ranging in Asia from India to South China and Celebes, the most familiar being the Toddy Cat (*Paradoxurus hermaphroditus*), its popular name being derived from its supposed fondness for " toddy," or " palm-juice." It has longish, coarse fur, blackish-grey in colour and sometimes spotted and lined with black, the head and body measuring about two feet and the tail one and a half feet. In habits it is nocturnal, sleeping in trees during the day and feeding by night on small animals, eggs, insects, fruit and vegetables. But it often adopts human abodes and lies up in roofs, outhouses and old drains, and may be very destructive to the householders' poultry. It is found in Ceylon, India and Malaya.

Binturong. The curious animal known as the Binturong (*Arctictis binturong*) resembles a large, shaggy Palm Civet with a much shorter muzzle and tufted ears ; but its chief peculiarity lies in the long, powerful tail being as prehensile as in some of the American Monkeys. The colour is wholly black or grizzled-black, the head and body measure about two and a half feet and the tail is over two feet long. It is nocturnal and arboreal, living exclusively in the forest, but although its diet is apparently the same as that of the Palm Civets, its teeth are much smaller and flatter-crowned. As in the case of the Palm Civets, the perfume glands of the Binturong give off a strong odour resembling that of an uncleaned cage of tame mice. The Binturong ranges from Assam to the Philippines.

Otter Civet. A still more remarkable relative of the Palm Civets is the Otter Civet (*Cynogale bennetti*), which, in its brown colour and particularly the shape of the head, as well as in its aquatic habits, resembles a small otter. Its teeth have sharp cusps for holding slippery fishes, its nostrils open on the summit of the muzzle so that the animal can breathe at the surface with its whole body submerged, and the tactile bristles on the muzzle are long and stiff, as in most aquatic mammals. But the tail is comparatively short and the feet unmodified. The animal is evidently not a fast swimmer, and it is known to be a tolerably expert climber. It ranges from Malaya to Borneo.

In the forests of Central Africa there is an animal called the Two-spotted Palm Civet (*Nandinia binotata*), which is very commonly imported to Europe for zoological gardens. In habits, appearance and size it resembles the typical Palm Civets represented by the Toddy Cat, although it has close, thick fur, spotted with black and, on the shoulders, two pale spots, whence its popular name is derived. But some points connected with the skull show that it is a very primitive type, the most primitive of all the existing cat-like carnivores.

From the Film] [" *Africa Speaks.*"

EAST AFRICAN LIONS (*Panthera leo*) AND THEIR KILL.
Lions hunt for food by day as well as by night, preying principally upon antelopes of various kinds, wild pigs, buffaloes, zebras and farm-stock.

CAT FAMILY (Felidae)

This family is the most highly organized and the most completely adapted for predatory life of all the Carnivora. Its members are digitigrade, the first digit of the forefoot being small and raised high off the ground, that of the hind foot absent ; the claws are retractile and, except in the Cheetah, sharp, curved and protected by lobes of skin on the toes. The jaws are short and massive and the cheek teeth are reduced in number to four, or even three, of which two only are functional, above, and three below; their crowns, especially those of the sectorial teeth, form cutting blades, not crushing surfaces.

Cats are distributed all over the great continents of the world from north temperate regions southwards ; but do not extend beyond Borneo in Asia and are absent from Madagascar and Australia. Their habits are very similar wherever they are found. For preference, as a rule, they kill their own prey, which consists mainly of any mammals or birds they can over-come, but many of them will eat reptiles, frogs, fish or even insects and carrion at times. As a rule, they catch their prey by stealthily stalking or by lying in wait for it until within springing distance ; but, owing to the shortness of the jaws, they never secure it with a quick snap, but strike it down or grab it with their paws before seizing it with the mouth.

There are a great many different kinds of Cats, but apart from the common house cat, the best known are the lions, tigers, panthers or leopards and their allies. These species constitute a group, or genus, by themselves, known as *Panthera*, which is distinguished by having the upper end of the windpipe, containing the vocal organs, suspended from the skull by a chain of bones and elastic ligaments so that it can be raised and lowered at will. These great cats roar but never purr. In all the other cats the vocal organs are attached tolerably closely to the skull by a short series of bones. The voice of these cats, although often loud, is never describable as a roar, and pleasure is expressed by purring.

Lion (*Panthera leo*). The Lion is distinguished from the other species of this group by its uniform tawny hue, the presence of a black tuft on the tip of the tail in both sexes and by the usual development of a mane in the male. Both in the loss of the pattern and in the presence of the mane, the Lion is also the most specialized member of the Cat family; and on those grounds alone might deserve the title " King of Beasts "; but the Lions which earned that distinction, deserved it on account of the magnificence of their appearance due to a huge black and tawny mane covering the neck and shoulders, long enough almost to sweep the ground, and passing along the belly as a deep black fringe. But such Lions are no longer known as wild animals. They inhabited Barbary and the Cape, and are believed to be extinct.

Mane. In no existing wild Lions, either in Asia or Africa, does the mane grow over the shoulders or along the belly. It may be full on the neck and largely black; and Lions so adorned are admittedly handsome beasts. But often it amounts to little more than a longer or shorter frill and may be entirely absent, as it is in the Lioness. It is doubtful whether Lions of this description would ever have been regarded as regal or selected as our national emblem. The Lion's mane, indeed, is more variable individually than the human beard, since it may be black or tawny, absent, small or full in the same district. Another peculiarity is its tendency to be fostered in growth by conditions of captivity, Lions in menageries having finer manes than those in the wilds. The reason for this is unknown. The use of the mane is also unknown; but its development on the neck, and sometimes along the belly, suggests that it may safeguard vulnerable parts from the teeth and claws of rivals in their combats for the possession of Lionesses.

Tail-spur. The so-called Spur at the end of a Lion's tail is so often referred to that it calls for passing notice. An imaginative naturalist once suggested, indeed, that the beast uses it to lash his flanks and stimulate his fury. This spur, when present, is nothing but a naked horny piece of dead skin at the extreme tip of the tail and is so enveloped in the tuft that it cannot possibly be brought into contact with the animal's body.

Roar. Most of the Cats are silent animals, except during the breeding season, when they use their voices as a sexual call; but the Lion is notoriously noisy, roaring, often in concert, but for what purpose is unknown, at all seasons of the year, especially after sunset and at night. The roar of the Lioness is similar but not so resonant. In menageries when one Lion starts to roar, the rest take it up and the volume of sound is deafening. But the popular idea that the roaring is stimulated by hunger is a mistake. In the London Zoological Gardens, for instance, although the Lions may roar at any time of the day, they almost always do so as soon as the house is shut after they have been fed.

Distribution. Within historic times Lions were found in Greece, Asia Minor and Syria; but they have long ceased to exist in those countries. They survived until comparatively recently in Mesopotamia and Persia;

[*Major A. Radclyffe Dugmore.*

EAST AFRICAN LION (*Panthera leo*).
The mane is very variable individually, being black or tawny, absent, small or full in the same district.

but it is doubtful whether any now remain there. In North India they formerly extended from Sind to Bengal; but between 1814 and 1880 they were exterminated except in Gujerat, where a few still survive, under strict protection, in the Gir forest. There is no doubt that man was the exterminating factor in Asia, as he also was in the case of the Barbary and Cape Colony Lions above referred to. At the present time Lions, although in rapid process of extinction in all the settled districts, are generally distributed throughout Africa south of the Sahara, apart from the Congo forest, and are still plentiful in many districts where Big Game is abundant. But their predatory habits make them impossible neighbours to white men, and their range is being steadily curtailed as the occupation of the continent proceeds.

767

MAMMALIA (ORDER CARNIVORA)

Habits. Lions hunt for food by day as well as by night, preying principally upon antelopes of various kinds, wild pigs, buffaloes, zebras and goats and cattle near the settlements. But they devour any carcase they come across, and even in places teeming with live game will return time after time to feast on a dead rhinoceros in the last stages of decomposition. They are usually shy of man ; but sometimes attack him unprovoked, and there are well-established cases of them becoming habitual man-eaters. Such Lions are sometimes, but by no means always, old animals which find men easier to catch than wild game.

Lions are not so solitary in their habits as other cats, parties ranging from half-a-dozen to a dozen being more commonly met with than a single individual or pairs. Sometimes, also, they combine in the killing of prey. There is, for instance, a well-known account of three full-grown Lions attacking a wounded bull buffalo, which would have been more than a match for them singly.

Lions are said to be monogamous, although the evidence is not con-clusive. Nevertheless, the male hunts for the female while suckling her cubs; and the cubs, when old enough, accompany their parents in quest of game. The period of gestation is from four to five months, the birth of the cubs, usually from two to five to the litter, taking place either before the eyes are open or after. Unlike their parents, the cubs generally show a distinct pattern of rosette-like spots, which on the back tend to run into looped stripes. This pattern, no doubt that of the Lion's ancestor, attests the close kinship between this animal and the tiger, leopard and jaguar. At two years, a Lion is sufficiently well grown to be able to pull down a zebra, but full development is not reached before four or five years. He may live to be about twenty years, but by that time his teeth are worn, his activity and strength have left him and his usual fate is to be torn to pieces by hyaenas and jackals. A full-grown Lion stands about three feet at the shoulder, and measures ten feet in total length, of which the tail is three feet, and he may reach a weight of five hundred pounds. The Lioness is always smaller, the weight being from two hundred and fifty to three hundred pounds.

Tiger (*Panthera tigris*). Although at once distinguishable from the lion by his bright yellowish-orange colour, vertical, black, generally looped stripes, white underside, white patches over the eyes, and in the absence of a conspicuous mane, the Tiger resembles him closely in average size, strength and other particulars, but the hindquarters are not so well developed and the head is not so flat. The voice of the two animals is so much alike as often to deceive inexperienced ears ; but the roar of the Tiger, a sexual call, is a single deep intonation, probably repeated after an interval of half a minute or so ; the repetitions, however, are never in rapid succession, nor do Tigers roar in concert like lions. But a Tiger starting to call in the Zoological Gardens will often set the lions roaring.

768

Leopard (*Felis pardus*)

By courtesy of] [*British Museum (Natural History)*

Tiger (*Panthera tigris*) " At Toilet "

Photo]   [F. W. Champion, Indian Forest Service, author of " With a Camera in Tigerland.

TIGER (*Panthera tigris*).

Tigers habitually frequent forest and thick jungle, with which their colour harmonizes, not open bush, like lions.

MAMMALIA (ORDER CARNIVORA)

Tigers are found only in Asia, where they occur as far to the north as Mongolia. Thence they spread in a south-westerly direction as far as the Caucasus and southwards as far as Java and southern India. They came originally from the north and migrated southwards, entering India by way of China and Burma; but they

SIBERIAN TIGER.
This local race is typically paler in hue than the Indian, and grows a thick coat in winter.

reached southern India after the isolation of Ceylon and are unknown on that island.

They vary much more in colour and size than lions. Indian specimens are about the same size as lions; but Mongolian specimens are usually larger, standing thirty-eight inches at the shoulder, whereas Sumatran Tigers are much smaller, less than thirty inches. Mongolian Tigers are typically paler in hue and grow a thick coat in winter; Caucasian Tigers are also thick coated at that season, but their stripes are often brown and rather indistinct; the most fully-striped and darkest-tinted specimens come from Sumatra and Java. Black and white lions are unknown; but both these varieties occur as "sports" in Tigers, although black is uncommon. In white Tigers the stripes may retain their dark tint; but sometimes they are obliterated, as in albino tame cats.

Tigers habitually frequent forest and thick jungle, with which their colour harmonizes, not open bush, like lions; and in the tropics they lie up during the heat of the day, and prowl about after sunset, often travelling long distances in search of prey, which consists mainly of deer, wild

Photos]   *[W. S. Berridge.*
INDIAN TIGER (*Panthera tigris*).
. Tigers vary much more in colour and size than lions : Indian specimens are about the same size as lions.

770

pigs, cattle and goats ; but like lions, they will eat carrion and, when hungry, frogs, tortoises, lizards, fish and even insects.

As a rule, Tigers are afraid of man ; but there are many instances of Tigers becoming inveterate "man-eaters" when the stimulus of hunger has overcome their timidity, leading to the discovery that man is naturally defenceless and easily killed.

Tigers are not so gregarious as lions, and usually occur singly or in pairs. When several are seen together, they are, as a rule, a family party consisting

[H. Bastin.

LEOPARD OR PANTHER (*Panthera pardus*).
Leopards are tree climbers and frequently lie in ambush along branches overhanging a forest path on the watch for prey passing beneath.

of the Tigress and her cubs, sometimes, but not often, accompanied by the Tiger. Three or four cubs usually constitute the litter ; and the period of gestation is probably the same as in lions.

Unlike lions, Tigers seldom breed in captivity, although for over a century they have been crossed with lions in menageries, the resulting hybrids, which may favour either parent in general colour, being sterile.

Leopard or Panther (*Panthera pardus*). The Leopard is distinguished from the lion and tiger by its spotted pattern, its relatively longer tail and smaller size. A large male, however, is hardly inferior to the small tigresses

771

[*Gambier Bolton.*

OUNCE OR SNOW LEOPARD (*Panthera uncia*).
The fur in the winter is luxuriant and woolly, a protection against the extreme cold of Central Asia and the high Himalayas.

of Java. The pattern is of the rosetted type, each rosette being composed of four or five solid spots forming a round or angular figure enclosing a pale central area darker than the ground colour and sometimes containing one or more small black spots. But both colour and pattern are subject to much variation. The commonest variety is the Black Leopard met with in Abyssinia and the East Indies.

Although restricted to the Old World, the Leopard exceeds in its range that of the lion and tiger combined. It occurs in Europe to the east of the Black Sea, and is found all over southern Asia, northward to Amurland and southward to Java and Ceylon, its presence in Ceylon showing that it entered India before the tiger. Except in the Sahara, it has established itself almost everywhere in Africa, even in the forested Congo area which the lion does not enter. At one time it was supposed that there were two distinct kinds, the Panther and the Leopard, living side by side in various parts of the world. But this mistake was chiefly due to ignorance of the differences between the sexes, males being called Panthers and females Leopards. Now it is generally agreed there is but one species represented by a number of local races differing in colour in accordance with varied habitats.

772

SNOW LEOPARD OR OUNCE

The dominant type is the ordinary yellowish Leopard of India and East Africa; the Javan Leopard is smaller and more rusty in hue; the Black Leopard replaces the spotted in southern Malaya; the Persian Leopard, inhabiting arid hill tracts, is, on the contrary, almost grey and grows such a luxuriant coat in winter that it has been mistaken for the Ounce.

The voice of the Leopard is like a deep, rapidly-repeated, barking cough, comparable to the sound made by a coarse saw passing through hard wood.

It is needless to discuss the habits of Leopards, since they agree closely with those of lions and tigers, except that Leopards, by reason of their greater activity and smaller size, are tree climbers and frequently lie in ambush along branches overhanging a forest path on the watch for prey passing beneath. They are seldom dangerous to man unless wounded or cornered.

The height of a Leopard is between two and two and a half feet and the total length about seven feet, of which the tail is rather less than three feet.

Snow Leopard or Ounce (*Panthera uncia*). Although about the same size, this is a less powerful animal, with smaller head, weaker jaws, and a longer tail than the Leopard; the rosettes, too, are larger, fewer and on the back form three longitudinal stripes. The colour is typically grey, generally with a tawny wash, and the fur in the winter is luxuriant and woolly. This is a protection against the extreme cold of central Asia and the high Himalayas where the Snow Leopard lives, and its general tint harmonizes with the

[Photopress.

JAGUAR (*Panthera onca*).
The Jaguar can be distinguished from the Leopard by its larger head, shorter tail and more robust build. As a rule, too, the rosettes are larger and fewer.

rocky ground the animal frequents. It preys upon animals ranging in size from wild sheep and hares to the little picas no larger than guinea-pigs. Its skin in the winter coat is greatly prized by furriers.

Jaguar (*Panthera onca*). This is the most powerful of the *Felidae* found in America, where it is the sole representative of the leopard group. It closely resembles the leopard in colour, pattern, voice and habits, but may be distinguished by its larger head, shorter tail and more robust build. As a rule, too, the rosettes are larger and fewer, the skin in consequence being handsomer. Its range is from Texas to the Argentine. In the latter country it is found in the treeless pampas, and preys upon the deer and smaller mammals ; but the forests farther north are its headquarters, and here it occurs both in the low-lying districts of the great rivers as well as in the mountains. Although not so active as the leopard either on the ground or in trees, the Jaguar is a good climber and frequently lies in wait on the branch of a tree for deer, capybaras, or peccaries passing beneath. Fish also it preys upon, scooping them from the rivers with a dexterous stroke of the paw. Fresh-water turtles, too, it takes when they come ashore ; and is said to dig up their eggs buried in the river banks. Like the leopard, the Jaguar is addicted to melanism, especially in the moist Amazonian Valley. A very large male may reach nine feet in total length, the tail being about two and a half feet.

Puma or Cougar (*Puma concolor*). This is the largest of the second group of Cats, and is about the size of a leopard, but, when adult, is uniformly tawny or pale brown in colour. It was formerly, on account of its tint, supposed to be related to the lion ; but the pattern of the cubs, no doubt the pattern of the ancestral form, is entirely different from that of lion cubs ; and there is no close kinship between the two species, the Puma being more nearly allied to the house cat.

The range of this animal in America is almost as extensive as that of the leopard in the Old World. It extends from the confines of Canada to Patagonia, although it has been killed out in all the settled districts of the States. Its adaptability to varied habitats is unusual. In South America, for instance, it lives alike in the low-lying forests of the Amazons, where it chases monkeys in the trees, and up to the snow-line in the Andes, where it preys on the guanaco. It is powerful enough to kill horses ; but nothing comes amiss to it from deer and farm-stock to guinea-pigs and birds of various kinds. Yet it seems to be a well-established fact that this powerful cat never makes an unprovoked attack on man and seldom, if ever, kills even children.

Clouded Leopard or Clouded Tiger (*Neofelis nebulosa*). This big cat is miscalled, as it is not related to the leopard. Next to the leopard and cheetah it is the largest species inhabiting the Old World. It is, however, much less powerful than the leopard. It has a longish head, with great upper canine teeth, short legs and a

774

[F. W. Bond.
CLOUDED LEOPARD OR CLOUDED TIGER (*Neofelis nebulosa*).
This is one of the handsomest members of the Cat family, its colour being greyish-brown, relieved by large, irregular, darker blotches bordered with black.

[H. S. Thorne.
PUMA OR COUGAR (*Puma concolor*).
The Puma extends from the confines of Canada to Patagonia, although it has been killed out in most of the settled districts of the United States.

775

[W. S. Berridge.
EGYPTIAN OR FETTERED CAT (*Felis ocreata*).
An African species tamed by the ancient Egyptians.

very long tail and is one of the handsomest members of the Cat family, its colour being greyish-brown, relieved by large, irregular, darker blotches bordered with black. It is found in south-eastern Asia, ranging from the eastern Himalayas to Borneo and Formosa. In habits it is mainly arboreal, feeding on birds and small mammals. The height is less than one and a half feet, the total length about six feet, the tail being nearly as long as the head and body.

Serval and Ocelot. There are many other species of smaller cats inhabiting temperate and tropical districts of Asia, Africa and America, the best known being the Serval (*Leptailurus serval*) of Africa, a long-legged, rather short-tailed, spotted cat, distinguished by its large, rounded ears, set close together on the top of the head; and the Ocelot (*Leopardus pardalis*) of Central and South America, a strongly-built, savage cat, also rather short-tailed and typically-banded with broad, longitudinal stripes, and further identifiable by its large, pink nose.

Perhaps the most beautiful of the smaller cats is the Golden Cat (*Profelis temminckii*), of eastern Asia. The body is a bright golden-bay and usually unmarked,

[F. W. Bond.
LEOPARD OR BENGAL CAT (*Prionailurus bengalensis*).
This cat of India, Malaya and China is a little smaller than our domestic cat.

SERVAL (*Leptailurus serval*).
This long-legged, rather short-tailed, spotted cat of Africa is distinguished by its large, rounded ears, set close together on the top of the head.

the underparts being white. The eyes are large and pale yellowish-green, and the nose is pink. Striking, also, is the Marbled Cat (*Pardofelis marmorata*), which has the marbled markings on the body only, the tail being spotted and comparatively long. This species inhabits certain parts of the Himalayas, Burma, Malaya and the Dutch East Indies. Its pattern is like that of the Clouded Leopard. The Pampas Cat (*Lynchailurus pajeros*) is a very savage species inhabiting the pampas of the Argentine and Patagonia. The long, yellowish-grey hair of the body is banded obliquely with light brown, the legs being barred with

SCOTCH WILD CAT (*Felis silvestris grampia*)
This cat is now restricted to the northern mountainous parts of Scotland.

Photos]   *[W. S. Berridge.*
OCELOT (*Leopardus pardalis*).
A strongly-built savage cat of Central and South America, identifiable by its large pink nose.

darker brown. This cat is about the size of the European Wild Cat. Some other species are shown in the illustrations.

Common Wild Cat (*Felis silvestris*). This, however, is the most interesting of the smaller species. It was formerly found all over Great Britain, but is now restricted to the northern mountainous parts of Scotland, its

777

[D. Seth-Smith.
PALLAS'S CAT
(*Trichailurus manul*).
This cat has a thick coat of long, soft, yellowish-grey hair. The tail and hindquarters are striped. Its home is central Asia.

range extending through central and south Europe as far as Asia Minor. In size this Cat agrees closely with the domestic cat, but looks a little larger on account of its thicker, longer fur and bushier tail. The general colour is brownish, with vertical black stripes on the flanks and hindquarters, the hinder half of the tail being banded and black-tipped. In Scotland, it makes its home in hollow trees or crannies in the rocks, and feeds on hares, rabbits, field-mice, grouse and other birds. But there is nothing peculiar in its habits. Its chief interest lies in its being, almost beyond doubt, one of the ancestors of our domestic cat, which it closely resembles in all essential characters. There is, however, another very similar

[W. S. Berridge.
GEOFFROY'S CAT (*Oncifelis geoffroyi*).
This is a native of South America.

but shorter-coated and longer-tailed Wild Cat (*F. ocreata*), an African species which was tamed by the Ancient Egyptians and was very possibly brought to Europe and crossed with the indigenous species. At all events, some fifty per cent. of the tame cats in

[*W. S. Berridge.*

VIVERRINE OR FISHING CAT (*Zibethailurus viverrinus*).
This cat lives partly on fish and frequents marshy regions in India and other countries of the East. It is of medium size.

the world, apart from specially-modified breeds, partake of the characters of these two wild species. Typically, these tame cats have vertical black stripes on the flanks, a pattern called "mackerel" by cat-fanciers. But there is another type of tame cat to which the term "tabby" probably belongs by rights, which has a very different pattern of bold, black stripes forming a characteristic curved, often spiral, arrangement on the flanks. It was this tabby which originally received the name *Felis catus*, long misapplied to the European Wild Cat. The origin of this tabby is unknown, but it lives alongside the "mackerel" and the two freely interbreed, but their patterns never get mixed. All our domestic cats, blacks, reds, whites, tortoiseshells, blues, Persians, Manx, and Siamese are traceable

By courtesy of the]   [*Canadian Government, Dominion Parks Branch, Ottawa.*
CANADIAN LYNX (*Lynx canadensis*).
This species is closely allied to the Common or Northern Lynx.

779

either to the "mackerel" or "tabby" type; and no species but the European and North African Wild Cats, so far as is known, were concerned in the ancestry of the "mackerel." These two species are also of interest because they represent a group of Cats from which the Lynxes were derived.

[*W. S. Berridge.*

JUNGLE CAT (*Felis chaus*).
This cat, an intermediate species between the Wild Cats and the Lynxes, has a small tuft of hair on the ears.

Lynxes (*Lynx*). The typical Lynxes differ from the Wild Cats just described in the shortness of the tail, the higher hindquarters, the presence of a whisker-like fringe on the cheek and of a tuft at the tip of the ear and in the circular pupil of the eye when contracted. But they are unmistakably closely related to the Wild Cats and are connected with them by several intermediate species. One of these is the Jungle Cat (*Felis chaus*) of India and Africa, which has a small tuft on the ear and a tail of intermediate length. In one of the typical Lynxes, too, the Bob-tailed Cat (*Lynx rufus*) of North America, the ear tuft is comparatively small and this species has been aptly described as "an overgrown house cat," which it resembles in "mewing, yowling and caterwauling."

Of the true Lynxes the best known is the Common or Northern Lynx (*L. lynx*), which varies locally and seasonally in colour, from reddish to grey, and is sometimes spotted, sometimes not. The head and body

[*Sport & General.*

COMMON OR NORTHERN LYNX (*Lynx lynx*).
This Lynx varies locally and seasonally in colour from reddish to grey and is sometimes spotted, sometimes not.

[W. S. Berridge.
BOB-TAILED CAT (*Lynx rufus*).
This is one of the typical lynxes in which the ear tuft is comparatively small, and which has been aptly described as " an overgrown house cat."

measure about three feet and the tail five inches long. It is a powerful beast, at times killing animals as large as sheep, but preying mostly on smaller mammals and birds. It is now very rare in Europe, but a few may survive in the Alps, Scandinavia and Russia. In central Asia it is more plentiful and in the Himalayas is found at altitudes of 10,000 feet and more. A distinct species, the Southern Lynx (*L. pardellus*), is found in Spain and Asia Minor. The Canadian Lynx (*L. canadensis*) is more nearly allied to the Common Lynx.

Caracal (*Caracal caracal*), always known to sportsmen in Africa, Arabia and India, where it lives, as the Lynx, is a species which connects the true Lynxes with the Wild Cats, having no fringe on the cheek and a tail reaching to the hocks. It is not thick furred like the Northern Lynxes and is a uniform tawny-brown, with blackish ears. The head and body measure about two and a half feet and the tail is about nine inches long. In some parts of India it is trained to catch hares, small deer and other game, and has been described as extraordinarily swift of foot.

Cheetah [Chita] (*Acinonyx jubatus*). This animal is sometimes called the Hunting Leopard, and is distinguished from the typical members of the Cat family by being adapted for running down swift-footed prey

[James's Press.
CARACAL (*Caracal caracal*).
This animal connects the true lynxes with the Wild Cats, having no fringe on the cheek and a tail reaching to the hocks.

781

over hard ground. The head is small and light, the body is compressed to offer as little resistance to the air as possible, the tail is long to aid in rapid turning, the legs are also long and slender, the feet are narrow, and are provided with hard pads and toes capable of being widely spread and armed with strong, straighter claws unprotected by the lobes of skin constituting the sheath. The

YOUNG CARACAL (*Caracal caracal*).

usual height is about two and a half feet and the weight about one hundred pounds. The colour in this species is some shade of sandy-fawn, relieved by numerous close-set, solid spots, with a characteristic black streak passing down the face from the eye, and there is generally a short mane on the nape.

The range is from central India, through Persia, and thence nearly all over Africa except the Congo forest. In India, where this animal was trained by the Rajahs for coursing Black-buck and Gazelles, it is nearly extinct, and specimens have been imported from East Africa to take its place in that sport. The custom is to take the Cheetah, hooded, on a bullock-cart as near a herd of antelopes as possible and then unhood and release it. On sighting the herd, the Cheetah, taking advantage of any scrub providing cover, creeps still closer before launching itself at speed towards its quarry. For a short distance, up to about a quarter of a mile or so, it is said to be the swiftest mammal known. At all events, it can overtake these fleet-footed antelopes, and upon coming up with one, strikes it to the ground with a blow of the paw, then kills it by tearing its throat. Wild Cheetahs, however, usually prey upon smaller game.

In Southern Rhodesia there is another kind, the King Cheetah (*A. rex*), a much handsomer animal in which the spots tend to fuse in large blotches and stripes, especially on the back. This animal was at one time mistaken for a variety of the Common Leopard.

Photos]   [*W. S. Berridge*.
YOUNG AFRICAN CHEETAHS (*Acinonyx jubatus*).
For a short distance, up to about a quarter of a mile or so, the Cheetah is said to be the swiftest mammal known.

DOGS, WEASELS, BEARS and their Allies (*Arctoidea*)

In this, the second Suborder of typically terrestrial carnivores, the forepart of the nasal passages is blocked by a pair of scrolls of spongy bone arising from their side-walls, the scrolls arising from the back of the passages being comparatively short. Also the bulla of the ear is composed of a single bone.

To this Suborder belong : the Dogs and Foxes (Family *Canidae*) ; the Weasels, Badgers, Otters, etc. (Family *Mustelidae*) ; the Raccoons and their Allies (Family *Procyonidae*) ; the Pandas (Family *Aeluridae*), and the Bears (Family *Ursidae*).

[*Fox Photos.*

TIMBER WOLVES.
Most of the big wolves of North America are called Timber Wolves.

Of these, the Raccoons are restricted to America, the Pandas to Asia, the others occurring in both the eastern and western hemispheres.

Dogs, Wolves, Jackals and Foxes (Family *Canidae*)

This family is distinguished from other Arctoid Carnivores by being adapted for swift running in pursuit of prey, the feet being compact and completely digitigrade. The jaws are long, formed for snapping, and are provided with nearly the full complement of teeth, mostly well developed, the carnassials, with one exception, having high cutting blades. The

783

NORTH AMERICAN PRAIRIE WOLF.

species are all terrestrial, none being modified for aquatic or arboreal life.

There are two subordinate groups, the *Canine* (Dogs, Wolves, Jackals) and the *Vulpine* (Foxes). In the Canine Group, the forehead of the skull is swollen with air-cells; in the Vulpine Group it is flat.

Canine or Wolf, Jackal and Dog Group

Wolf (*Canis lupus*). The typical Wolf, although now exterminated in most settled districts, was formerly distributed all over the northern hemisphere, from the Arctic Regions as far south as the Mediterranean, Arabia and India in the Old World and as Mexico in America. It has become adapted to a great variety of environments and climate and is represented by a large number of local races differing in colour, size and thickness of coat, the largest, handsomest and most formidable animals being found in northern, cold districts.

The *European Wolf* has a long, shaggy coat, usually of black and grey or tan hairs overlying a dark underwool, the tail being of the same tint and bushy, but the legs are covered with short tan-tinted hairs; the individual variation, however, is considerable. In the plains of northern India, it is replaced by the *Pale-footed Wolf*, a smaller, greyer animal, with little or no under fur. In northern Siberia the Wolf is larger and nearly white, and a very similar Wolf, called the *Tundra Wolf*, is found

Photos]   [W. S. Berridge.
WOOLLY WOLF FROM TIBET.

784

OCELOT (*Felis pardalis*)

By courtesy of]

[*British Museum (Natural History)*

JAGUAR (*Felis onca*)

in the barren grounds of Canada. But most of the big Wolves of North America are called *Timber Wolves*, some being coloured like the European Wolf, some greyer, the Texan race being known from its tint as the *Red Wolf*; Black Wolves have been recorded from Russia, Tibet, Alaska and Canada. The height of the European Wolf is about two feet four inches.

[*Gambier Bolton.*

AUSTRALIAN DINGO.
This was no doubt introduced into Australia by the Aborigines who came from Asia.

Wolves are essentially predatory and in severe winters of northern countries frequently combine in packs for the pursuit of prey. At such times and when pressed by hunger, they are bold and attack man and in America such formidable game as the Moose, Musk Ox and Bison ; and are liable to inflict great damage on farmers by raiding their live stock. As a rule, they are comparatively solitary, seldom more than two or three being seen together. They pair once a year in the winter and the period of gestation, as in dogs, is nine weeks. Hence the cubs, which are black at birth and usually four or more to the litter, are born in the spring. Full size and strength are reached in about three years.

There is no known structural difference between Wolves and big domesticated dogs, except that dogs have relatively smaller teeth and smoother coats, lacking the long, loose, harsh hairs of Wolves. They have been repeatedly crossed and produce fertile

INDIAN WOLF.

[*W. S. Berridge.*

[W. S. Berridge.

SIBERIAN WILD DOG OR DHOLE (*Cuon javanicus alpinus*).
The rusty-brown coat of this dog turns fawn in winter.

offspring. All the evidence, indeed, points to the conclusion that the Wolf was the main stock whence our domesticated breeds were derived.

Dingo or Australian Wild Dog. This was no doubt introduced into the country by the aborigines who came from Asia. But the first European settlers found it wild and preying upon Kangaroos, Wallabies, etc. It soon, however, took to attacking their sheep and a war of extermination was waged against it in all the settled districts. It crosses readily with European dogs and pure-bred examples are now difficult to obtain ; but from all accounts it was originally fawn in colour, two feet or less in height and resembled domesticated dogs in its smooth coat and small teeth.

Prairie Wolf. In addition to the bigger " Timber " Wolves, there are several smaller kinds ranging in America from southern Canada into Mexico. These are usually known comprehensively as the Prairie Wolf or Coyote (*C. latrans*). It is more addicted to living in burrows and more omnivorous in diet than the Timber Wolf, and by reason of its smaller size, much less destructive, preying mainly on hares, mice, and birds, but sometimes combining in small packs to hunt the prongbuck, which being too fleet for the united pack, is chased in relays.

Jackals. The name Jackal is given to several species which are about the size of a Fox-terrier, but which have thick, coarse coats and bushy tails, like Wolves, and a generally " foxy " aspect. The Common Jackal (*Canis aureus*) still lingers in eastern Europe, whence it extends through southern Asia as far as Burma and is plentiful throughout India and Ceylon. In colour it much resembles the European Wolf. It is omnivorous in diet, feeding on hares, mice, birds and carrion, varied with such vegetable food as sugar-canes, maize and coffee-berries near plantations. It will also take offal and carrion and is a useful scavenger in the East. The Egyptian Jackal (*C. lupaster*), a larger animal standing some sixteen inches at the shoulder, is sometimes called " wolf " in its native country.

The handsomest of the species is the Black-backed Jackal (*C. mesomelas*), found in East and South Africa. It is even more " foxy " in appearance

786

than the Asiatic Jackal on account of its larger ears, but its distinguishing mark is the saddle of black and white hairs covering the back and sharply contrasted with the reddish-brown tint of the flanks and legs.

Wild Dogs. Many species of Wild Dogs, generally called foxes from their appearance and smallish size, one or two only being large enough to be known as wolves, are found in South America, inhabiting the Andes, the tropical forests and the open plains as far south as Cape Horn. The largest, the Red or Maned Wolf (*Chrysocyon brachyurus*), is like a gigantic fox with a very short body and extremely long legs. It lives in the open bush of Brazil and the Argentine and feeds upon rodents, birds, fruit sometimes and, being as big as a wolf, is strong enough to attack sheep. The name " Wolf " was also given to another species (*Dusicyon australis*), although it was only as large as a big jackal, which was restricted to the Falkland Islands but is now extinct. The term " Fox " is generally applied to two groups, each containing several species, represented by Azara's Fox (*Pseudalopex gymnocereus*), which is common in the Argentine pampas and very fox-like in appearance and size but greyer in tint ; and by the Crab-eating Fox (*Cerdocyon thous*), a darker, smaller-eared dog found in the forests of Venezuela and Brazil. Finally, there is a curious little dog, the Bush Dog (*Speothos venaticus*), somewhat badger-like in build, but not so heavy, which on account of its dentition is sometimes regarded as related to the Dholes. It usually frequents the river-sides of Venezuela and Brazil, and eats crabs, cavies and other small animals.

Red Dogs or Dholes (*Cuon*). The Red Dogs, known in India as Dholes, are a small group of Wild Dogs hardly larger than big jackals but more sturdily built, especially in the muzzle, and distinguished by the loss of the last lower molar tooth. There is one species (*C. javanicus*) which ranges from India and Java in the south to the Altai and Amurland in the north. The southern races are comparatively short-coated and uniformly red throughout the year, but the northern races grow a very thick coat and sometimes turn nearly white in winter. These dogs frequent

[*W. S. Berridge.*

JACKAL.
Jackals are about the size of a Fox-terrier and have thick, coarse coats and bushy tails like wolves and a generally " foxy " aspect.

787

forests and hill-sides. They hunt in packs, averaging a dozen or more individuals, and prey upon wild pigs and deer, as large as sambur, instances in India being known of them destroying even tame buffaloes and cattle. In combination, they exhibit great courage and there are recorded cases of attacks by them on bears, leopards and tigers. Mainly nocturnal, they lie up in holes, rock-crevices and thick bush by day; and the pups, born in the early months of the year, are usually from four to six in number.

Hunting Dog (*Lycaon pictus*). This is also called the Hyaena Dog, and is about the size of a small wolf, but has a more massive head and muzzle, much larger, rounded ears and is tortoiseshell in colour, the yellow, black, and sometimes white blotches being variously blended, but it differs from all the other species of the Dog Family, and resembles the hyaenas in having no dew-claw on the fore foot. This animal inhabits the bush and plains of East and South Africa and feeds mainly on buck of various kinds, killing even such large species as the hartebeest, the gnu and the sable antelope. It hunts in packs, usually composed of from fifteen to a score or more individuals. Although seldom attacking man, this dog is a great pest to owners of cattle and sheep. The pups, sometimes a dozen in number, are born in large burrows.

[F. W. Bond.

MANED OR RED WOLF (*Chrysocyon brachyurus*).
This is a wild dog that lives in the open bush of Brazil and the Argentine. It is like a gigantic fox with a very short body and extremely long legs.

Vulpine or Fox Group

Except that the pads of the feet are more hairy and the tail, as a rule, longer and bushier, there is no external feature by which Foxes can be distinguished from wolves, dogs and jackals.

Arctic Fox (*Alopex lagopus*). This species, however, is nearly intermediate between the two groups, but is unmistakably a Fox in its feet and tail, although its ears are shorter and rounder. It inhabits the Arctic Regions as far south as the northern limit of tree—growth in both the Old and the New World. It feeds upon birds and their eggs, arctic hares,

[*W. S. Berridge.*

EAST AFRICAN HUNTING DOG (*Lycaon pictus*).
This dog hunts in packs of from fifteen to a score or more individuals, killing even such large species as hartebeest and sable antelopes.

[*F. W. Bond.*

CRAB-EATING FOX (*Cerdocyon thous*).
This dog is found in the forests of Venezuela and Brazil.

[*Photopress.*

FENNEC FOX (*Vulpes zerda*).
This is a very small, sandy-coloured species with gigantic ears, inhabiting the Sahara.

lemmings, crabs and any animal food it can find ; and in the winter, either migrates southwards where food is to be had or stores up dead lemmings in rock crannies against the time of scarcity. It exhibits two colour phases. The normal type changes its colour seasonally, growing a luxuriant white coat in the winter, whereas in the brief summer months it is short-coated and white only below, the upper parts being brownish and speckled with buff. The other phase is a permanently dark variety, greyish or brownish throughout the year. This phase is known as the " Blue Fox ", in the fur trade, the other as the " White Fox," the skins being of value only in the winter. The number of pups is usually about six, but sometimes as many as eleven.

Common or Red Fox (*Vulpes vulpes*). This Fox may be distinguished in all its numerous races by the black patch on the back of its ears and the white tip or " tag " to its tail or brush. It overlaps the Arctic Fox in its northern distribution, but extends as far south as North Africa, Arabia, India and the southern states of North America, holding its own alike in the barren tundras, in forested and desert districts. It varies locally in size, colour and luxuriance of coat, northern latitudes producing in every way the finest specimens. The smallest and palest race is the *White-footed Fox* of the deserts of the Punjab and Persia. Northern races are richer and darker in tint and frequently exhibit marked individual variation in colour in accordance with the proportion of red, black or grey in the hairs. The best instance is supplied by the Canadian race, where the ordinary

790

Red Fox of the country, hardly distinguishable from the European Fox, occurs in at least two other well-marked phases, known to the furriers as the *Cross Fox*, which is half black and half red, and the *Silver Fox*, which in its most valued type is black, with scattered, silver-tipped hairs. This type is now being successfully bred on " fox-farms " both in America and Europe. Most of the red fox furs worn as wraps come from Australia, where English foxes imported many years ago, to keep down rabbits, have increased beyond all expectations.

The habits of Foxes, wherever found, appear to be similar. They feed upon small mammals, birds, eggs, reptiles and even insects and occasionally eat fruit, the precise nature of their diet varying with the country they inhabit. They are nocturnal and many, like the European Fox, but not all, have eyes like the house cat, with slit-like pupils when contracted. They are extremely wary, quick-sensed and swift, able to cover rough ground at great speed and even to ascend easily climbable trees, if pushed. They lie up at night in burrows, crannies of rocks or in scrub ; and, as is well known, have very highly-developed instincts, regarded by some as intelligence, in avoiding traps, " breaking scent " and in other ways. The cubs, usually four or five in number, are born after a gestation period of

[*W. Cooper.*

COMMON OR RED ENGLISH FOX (*Vulpes vulpes*).
The ground-scent left by the Common Fox is due to glands in the soles of the feet.

791

ARCTIC FOX (*Alopex lagopus*).
This fox inhabits the Arctic Regions as far south as the northern limit of tree—growth in both the Old and the New World.

nine weeks, in the early spring, and are capable of breeding by the autumn of the next year. It may be added that, in spite of a prevalent belief to the contrary, there is no authentic case of the European Fox, or any other, crossing with dogs. Experiments, indeed, have shown that this Fox is sterile with the Arctic Fox. The ground-scent left by the Common Fox is due to glands in the soles of the feet.

There are many other species of Fox living in various parts of the world, all smaller than the Common Fox and without the black ears and white tag. Of these the best known are : the Bengal Fox (*V. bengalensis*) of Hindustan, a small, grey Fox, without the scent of our species ; the Fennec Fox (*V. zerda*), a very small, sandy-coloured species, with gigantic ears, inhabiting the Sahara ; the Silver-backed Fox (*V. chama*) of South Africa, which is the most southern of all the True Foxes and the Kit Fox (*V. velox*), another small species inhabiting the prairies of North America. Another common North American species, called the Grey Fox (*Urocyon cinereo-argenteus*), which is grey and buff in colour, differs from ordinary Foxes in having a crest of stiff hairs along the upper side of its tail. It is the

Photos]   *[W. S. Berridge.*
BENGAL FOX (*Vulpes bengalensis*).
This is a small grey fox without the scent of our species.

By courtesy of]   *[The High Commissioner for Canada.*
BLACK VARIETY OF THE NORTH AMERICAN RED FOX.

only Fox which spreads into South America. In South and East Africa there is a peculiar species known as the Long-eared Fox (*Otocyon megalotis*), which differs from all the other members of the family in the greater number of the cheek teeth and the shape of their sharply-cusped crowns, fitted for masticating white ants, on which the animal principally feeds, although it will eat small mammals, birds, etc., as well. It is not so strongly built as the Common Fox, is generally darkish-grey in colour, and has very large ears.

[F. W. Bond.
NORTH AMERICAN GREY FOX (*Urocyon cinereo-argenteus*).

Weasels, Martens, Skunks, Badgers and Otters (Family *Mustelidae*)

This family differs from the preceding in having shorter jaws, the ears small and rounded, and the limbs shorter, with the feet less compact and never so completely digitigrade. The cheek-teeth, also, are fewer in number.

For popular purposes, the family may be divided into three groups, the *Musteline* (Weasels, Martens, etc.), the *Meline* (Badgers and Skunks) and the *Lutrine* (Otters).

[*Jas. A. Speed.*

STOAT (*Mustela erminea*).
This animal is shown in its summer coat. In the north it always turns white in winter. Its winter coat is known as "Ermine."

In the Musteline Group, the shortening of the jaws and numerical reduction of the teeth reach the extreme in the family, apart from the Otters. The teeth are adapted to carnivorous habits, and the feet for active movement, being semidigitigrade, with short, curved, sharp claws.

The Stoat, Weasel and Polecat (*Mustela*) are typical examples of this section and are members of the British fauna. Apart from size and colour, they are much alike in appearance and habits. The jaws are short, the body long and slender and the feet hairy between the pads. They are predacious, blood-thirsty, active creatures, feeding upon any animals they can kill. Although able to climb, they habitually live and hunt on the ground. The young, usually five or six in number, are born in the spring or early summer in a burrow or any secluded retreat.

Weasel (*Mustela nivalis*). This is one of the smallest of the Carnivora, and found all over Great Britain but not in Ireland. It is brown in colour, with more or less white on the middle of the belly and has a short tail, about two inches long, the head and body measuring six or seven inches.

FERRET OR ALBINO POLECAT.
[W. S. Berridge.
The tame Ferret was probably derived from a North African species of Polecat.

It is common in hedgerows and about farms, where it is a danger to chickens. It feeds, however, mainly on field-mice and is a useful check on these potential pests, but it fearlessly attacks rats despite their superior size. Family parties sometimes hunt in packs, but usually two at most are seen to-gether. It is widely distributed in Europe, and in the north regularly turns white in winter; but this change is very rare in Great Britain.

Stoat (*M. erminea*). This is considerably larger than the Weasel, the head and body measuring about eleven inches and the tail five, the tail being black at the end. Otherwise, the colour of the two

WEASEL (*Musteli nivalis*).
[W. S. Berridge.
The Weasel is one of the smallest of the Carnivora and is found all over Great Britain, but not in Ireland.

animals is much the same except that in the Stoat the more abundant white on the belly is sharply defined from the brown of the flanks; but in the Stoat inhabiting Ireland and the Isle of Man this contrast is not so pronounced. The Stoat, which is as common in Great Britain as the Weasel,

[F. W. Bond.
THE GRISON, A SOUTH AMERICAN REPRESENTATIVE OF THE POLECAT.

is a greater pest, since it kills full-grown game-birds, poultry and hares. Like the weasel, it has a wide distribution in Europe, and in the north always turns white in winter, the tail-tip alone remaining black. It often changes partly or wholly white in England, even as far south as Cornwall. Its winter coat, known as " Ermine," was formerly one of the most valuable furs.

Polecat (*Putorius putorius*). The Polecat is bigger than the Stoat, the head and body measuring about sixteen inches and the tail seven inches. The coat, too, is longer and differently coloured, the legs being blackish and the creamy hair on the back overlain by longer, black or brown-tipped hairs, the head showing a whitish band over the eyes. The species is not found in Ireland, and in Great Britain only lingers in a few wilder parts, a pale variety occurring in Wales. But in Central and South Europe it still holds its own, despite the value of its winter fur, which is known as Fitch or Kolinsky.

[*W. S. Berridge.*
THE TAYRA, A SOUTH AMERICAN REPRESENTATIVE OF THE MARTENS.

The scent glands of the Weasel and Stoat are comparatively inoffensive; but the odour of the Polecat is so objectionable that it was formerly known in England as the " Foulmart." When attacked, it raises the long, blackish hairs of its coat, displaying the creamy-white underfur as a warning mark of identity.

There are many other species of Weasels, Stoats and Polecats found in Europe, Asia and America. From a North African species of Polecat, the tame ferret was probably originally derived. Another close ally of the Polecat is the Mink (*M. lutreola*), a semi-aquatic species with a valuable fur, found in Europe, Central Asia and North America.

Martens (*Martes*). These are the most elegant of the Weasel family. They are larger than the Stoats and Polecats, without their objectionable odour, have longer muzzles, longer, bushier tails and are both terrestrial and arboreal in habits and sufficiently active in trees to catch even squirrels. They are also less strictly carnivorous, varying their normal animal diet with fruit of various kinds. The young, usually four or five in number, are born in hollow tree-trunks or crannies in rocks. Martens are widely distributed in Europe, Central Asia and North America, up to the limits of tree-growth. Many species are known, but the habits of all are similar. Those that are found far north or at high altitudes yield valuable furs in the winter coat.

Pine Marten (*Martes martes*). This still lingers in a few wild parts of the British Isles, and ranges from Ireland into Asia. It is brown, with a yellow throat; the head and body measure about one and a half feet and the tail some nine or ten inches.

Beech or Stone Marten (*Martes foina*). This is not a British species, and differs from the Pine Marten, with which it was formerly confused, in its smaller ears, larger foot-pads and usually whiter throat. It does not extend so far north in Europe or Asia; but at high elevations in the Himalayas it produces a valuable fur.

Sable Marten (*M. zibellina*). Of all the Martens this is the most prized by the furriers. It inhabits northern Europe and Asia. It is nearly allied to the Pine Marten, but differs in the quality of its fur and other minor particulars. Of the North American Martens, the most interesting is the Fisher or Pekan (*M. pennanti*), the largest of the group, rivalling an otter in size. It is said to be more than a match for the Raccoon and to feed in certain districts on the Canadian Porcupine, which few mammals care to interfere with (see page 750).

[*W. S. Berridge.*

WOLVERENE OR GLUTTON (*Gulo gulo*).
The Glutton inhabits the northern forested districts of the Northern Hemisphere, and is mainly terrestrial, but sometimes climbs trees in search of food.

Yellow-throated Marten (*Lamprogale flavigula*). This is akin to the true Martens and inhabits India, China and the Malay Peninsula. It is considerably smaller than the Fisher, but larger than the Pine Marten, and is remarkable for its varied colouring of black, brown and yellow.

Glutton or Wolverene (*Gulo gulo*). The Glutton is unmistakably related to the Martens, although in general appearance more like a small bear with a tail. Its colour is dark brown, with a paler band extending along the sides of the body; the coat is thick and long and the bushy tail is about half the length of the head and body, which may be as much as three feet in length. It inhabits the northern forested districts of the Northern Hemisphere, and is mainly terrestrial, but sometimes climbs trees in search of food. Being comparatively inactive, it catches its prey either by strategy or by digging it from the ground and is said to secure even foxes by this method. Trappers dread its vicinity from its habit of following a line

797

of traps, skilfully overturning them to eat the bait or devouring the captured animal.

Meline or Badger Group (*Melinae*). Here the jaws are typically larger than in the Weasels, the teeth, as indicated by the enlargement and crushing character of the crowns of the molars, are, as in the Bears, adapted for a more vegetable diet, and the animals themselves are comparatively inactive owing to their heavy build, more plantigrade feet and long digging claws. They are mostly found in the Northern Hemisphere, outside the tropics.

Common Badger (*Meles meles*). This exhibits the characters mentioned

[*Charles Reid.*

BADGER (*Meles meles*).
The Badger is essentially nocturnal in habits, lying up by day in deep, often branching burrows, known as " sets."

above in a marked degree. The hair of the upper side is long and coarse and grizzled with black and grey, the legs and underside are black, but the face is white, with a broad black stripe on each side. The tail is only about six inches long, the head and body being some two feet four inches, the height about one foot and the weight up to forty pounds.

It is essentially nocturnal in habits, lying up by day in deep, often branching burrows, known as " sets," which may be occupied by successive generations for long periods and extend far underground. These burrows are kept scrupulously clean and are sometimes shared by foxes. The diet is very varied, consisting of eggs, mice, young rabbits, worms, snails, insects, as well as acorns, roots, bulbs and other vegetable substances. The cubs, usually three or four in number, are born in the spring or summer in a

By courtesy of]   [*The High Commissioner for Canada.*
AMERICAN BADGER (*Taxidea taxus*).
The so-called Badger of North America, though resembling our species in habits, size and somewhat in appearance, is only remotely related to it.

special nursery in the burrow, which the female lines with grass or moss.

Owing to its burrowing and nocturnal habits, the Badger is seldom seen, and is much commoner in Ireland and Great Britain than is usually supposed. It ranges from Western Europe into Asia and is represented by related forms as far east as Japan. But it is not found in America, the so-called Badger (*Taxidea taxus*) of North America, though resembling our species in habits, size and somewhat in appearance, being only remotely related to it.

Skunks (*Conepatus, Mephitis and Spilogale*). These also form a very distinct group, restricted to America, where they range from Canada to Patagonia. But they are tolerably similar to the Badger in habits, being mainly nocturnal and feeding upon smaller mammals, birds even as large as poultry, frogs, insects, etc. They are also like small Badgers in shape, but have long, bushy tails and are always characteristically coloured black or dark brown, relieved by white stripes. They are decorated, indeed, with a very distinctive livery by which they may be at once recognized and are the stock instance in mammals of the phenomenon of "warning coloration," which is associated with some special method of defence in an animal that would otherwise be preyed upon. In the Skunks, as is well known, their method is the discharge from glands beneath the tail of a pungent, volatile, suffocating liquid, insupportably offensive in odour and so enduring that clothes once tainted with it require repeated washings before they can be worn again. It is not

By courtesy of]   [*Carl Hagenbeck's Tierpark, Stellingen.*
CANADIAN SKUNKS (*Mephitis mephitis*).
This is as big as a half-grown cat, and has a wide range in North America.

[W. S. Berridge.
LITTLE SKUNK (*Spilogale putorius*).
This inhabits Central America and Texas, and is about the size of a Polecat.

supposed that the carnivorous mammals, like wolves, foxes, lynxes, cougars, and raptorial birds like eagles, have instinctive knowledge of the Skunk's nature, but it has been experimentally proved that dogs, accustomed to killing game, regard the Skunk at first sight as vermin to be as easily and promptly destroyed as a house cat or rabbit. So horrible, however, are the effects of the attack that the hound thereafter gives all Skunks a wide berth, readily identifying the little beasts by their conspicuous pattern. The Skunks themselves are instinctively well aware of their safety, and fearlessly go about their business in the open, rather courting observation than otherwise, by waving their tails in the air, and turn aside for no living thing they may meet.

There are many different kinds of Skunks, represented by the Canadian Skunk (*Mephitis mephitis*), which is as big as a small cat and has a wide range in North America ; the Hog-nosed Skunk (*Conepatus*), which spreads from the southern states of the Union of Patagonia, where it is represented by Humboldt's Skunk (*C. humboldtii*) ; and the Little Skunk (*Spilogale putorius*) of Central America and Texas, which is about the size of a Polecat.

Ratel or Honey-badger (*Mellivora ratel*). This is like a badger in size and appearance and is commonly so-called in India, but it has hardly a trace of the external ear and the teeth are of the flesh-eating type seen in the weasel group. The colour is usually grey or white above and black below and on the legs. Its range is from India into Africa, south of the Sahara. As may be guessed from its

[F. W. Bond.
RATEL (*Mellivora ratel*).
This has the reputation of being one of the most difficult to kill of all the smaller mammals.

800

SNOW LEOPARD OR OUNCE (*Felis uncia*)

By courtesy of]   [British Museum (Natural History)

CLOUDED LEOPARD (*Felis nebulosa*)

colour, the Ratel is protected, like the skunk, by the foetid discharge from its glands and, like many animals so protected, it is extraordinarily tenacious of life and has the reputation of being one of the most difficult to kill of all the smaller mammals. It is also a desperate and fearless

ZORILLA (*Ictonyx*).

[*Neville Kingston.*

This is a skunk-like, African animal which combines to a great extent the characters of the Meline and Musteline groups.

fighter and unusually strong, using both teeth and claws with deadly effect on any enemy that ventures to attack it. In virtue of its thick skin, it is indifferent to the quills of the porcupine and boldly enters the burrow of that animal and kills it. It also eats quantities of honey, being equally indifferent to the stings of wild bees ; and since it is known to destroy cobras, its hide is probably impervious to their poison. Nothing, indeed, comes amiss to it in the way of animal food, and its diet is partly vegetarian as well. It lives in burrows, caves, rock-clefts and other sheltered places and, being strictly nocturnal, is seldom seen.

Zorilla (*Ictonyx*). This is another well-known African type, which combines to a great extent the characters of the Meline and Musteline groups. The most familiar species is the Muishond or Cape Polecat (*I. capensis*) of South Africa. It is a beautiful little animal, conspicuously banded black and white, and is of interest on account of its adaptive resemblance to the skunks in habits and in its warning livery, which is associated with stink glands almost equally nauseating in odour.

[*W. S. Berridge.*

LITTLE CLAWLESS OTTER (*Amblonyx*).

This little animal, from India and tropical Asia, has, at most, tiny claws on the fore paws.

Otters (*Lutrinae*). The Otters may be at once distinguished by their structural characters in adaptation to aquatic life, the hind feet being much larger than the fore feet, and provided with very

[*W. S. Berridge.*
COMMON OTTER (*Lutra lutra*).
The range of this species extends from Ireland into eastern Asia and from the
Arctic coast to North Africa.

long, fully-webbed digits; the fore feet, also, are usually webbed, and the tail is thick, especially close to the body. The head is flattened, with small eyes and ears and valvular nostrils, and the fur is dense and impervious to water.

Otters are found almost all over the world, except in Australia; but, apart from the Sea Otter, the species (about fifteen in number) are very similar in habits, appearance and structure, though differing somewhat in size and a few other points.

Common Otter (*Lutra lutra*). This extends from Ireland into eastern Asia and from the Arctic coast to North Africa, and may be selected as an example. The colour is dark brown, the head and body measure about two and a half feet in length, the tail one and three-quarter feet, and the weight is usually from twenty to twenty-five pounds, but sometimes more, the female being smaller. Although perfectly at home in the water, swimming by means of sinuous twists of its long body and tail, or by strokes of its feet, it is tolerably active on land, often covering long distances between stream and stream. The diet is varied, consisting of fish, crayfish, mussels, water-rats, water-fowl, occasionally poultry and rabbits, if procurable, varied with insects and a taste of vegetable food. For fishing purposes, the animal frequently enters the sea. The " holt," as the den is called, is either a burrow, a rock crevice or a hollow beneath a tree root, usually near the water, and in this, on a bed of rushes, the young, usually two or three in number, are born blind and helpless in winter. The " dog " Otter stays with the " bitch " until the young are nearly independent and then family parties may be seen fishing and sporting in the water together.

Of the several species inhabiting India and tropical Asia, one of the most interesting is the Little Clawless Otter (*Amblonyx*). This has, at most, tiny claws on the fore paws, which are exceedingly sensitive and used for feeling for fish or crabs lurking under stones at the bottom of streams. A similar variation is met with in one or two African species. In America there are a few species, the Canadian Otter (*L. canadensis*) being closely allied to ours, whereas the large Brazilian Otter (*Pteronura brasiliensis*), the largest of the group, has the tail keeled for swift swimming.

802

Sea Otter (*Latax lutris*). This, with its heavily-built body, short neck and tail and huge hind feet, in which the toes increase in length from the first to the fifth, is a very different-looking animal from the freshwater species, although its colour is much the same. The tail is barely one foot long and about one-fourth the length of the head and body. The weight is seventy pounds or more. Although formerly abundant on the North Pacific coasts, it has been almost exterminated for the sake of its fur, which is of rare quality and highly prized. It is a slow swimmer and fetches its food, which consists mostly of shell-fish and crabs, from the bottom. For crushing the hard shells of its prey, its teeth are broad, with low, rounded cusps. When feeding, it holds its food in its fore paws, frequently lying on its back at the surface, and it has been seen to nurse its cub, of which there is seldom more than one, in this attitude.

Raccoons and Kinkajous (Family *Procyonidae*)

This family is mainly distinguished from the Mustelidae by possessing two or more cheek-teeth on each side and by the presence of a groove between the main cusps of the upper " carnassial tooth," the absence of which is characteristic of the Mustelidae. The number of genera and species is comparatively small, but the genera are as diversified structurally as those of the Mustelidae. They are found only in America.

Common North American Raccoon (*Procyon lotor*). This is about the size of a large cat, has a short, thick-set body, a short, broad head with a pointed muzzle, and a tail only about half as long as the head and body. The fur is long, thick and grey. The face has a broad black stripe below the eyes, with a white stripe above them and white on the muzzle, and the tail is ringed. The feet have the toes free from webbing, the fore feet being exceedingly delicate organs of touch and used for the finding and holding of food. It is the Raccoon's habit of dipping its food in water before eating it that suggested the scientific name "*lotor*," the washer, for the animal. Its diet is omnivorous, consisting of small mammals, birds, reptiles, frogs, fish, crabs, crayfish, insects, fruits, berries, and the like. It hunts

[*Alston Photo. Finishing Co.*

COMMON RACCOON (*Procyon lotor*).

The Raccoon's habit of dipping its food in water before eating it suggested the
scientific name " *lotor* " the washer.

803

WHITE-NOSED COATIMUNDI (*Nasua narica*).
[*F. W. Bond.*]
Coatis are found in Central and the warmer parts of South America.

on the ground by night, but spends the day mostly in trees. It also breeds in trees, making a rough nest for its young, which, four or five in number, are born in the spring. In colder districts of America, raccoons hibernate. An allied species, the Crab-eating Raccoon (*P. cancrivora*), is found in South America.

Coatis (*Nasua*). These are something like raccoons, but have exceedingly long, pig-like probing snouts, very long tails and the toes of the feet webbed and armed with long digging claws. Their diet is as varied as that of the raccoons and, being good climbers, they search for food both on the ground and in trees, a dozen or more sometimes hunting together. They are found in Central and the warmer parts of South America, and there are several different kinds; the best known being the Ring-tailed Coati (*N. nasua*), which has the tail banded and the snout dark, and is not uncommonly red in colour; and the White-nosed Coati (*N. narica*), which has the tail unbanded and the snout white.

Kinkajou (*Potos flavus*). This is a very different-looking animal from the preceding. The head is short and rounded, the tail very long and prehensile and the feet are armed with short, sharp claws for climbing. The colour is yellowish-brown, the fur is shortish, but soft and almost woolly, and the tongue is very long and extensile. The Kinkajou inhabits Central and South America and is almost exclusively arboreal, lying up in holes in trees and feeding by night on any small animals it can catch and on fruits of all kinds as well as honey. The Kinkajou shares with the binturong (page 764) the distinction of being the only carnivorous mammals with a prehensile tail.

KINKAJOU (*Potos flavus*).
[*W. S. Berridge.*]
This animal feeds by night on small animals, fruits of all kinds and honey.

False Kinkajou (*Bassaricyon alleni* and others). This superficially so closely

804

resembles the true Kinkajou as to be often mistaken for it. The habits, too, are similar; but the tail is not prehensile and there are many other anatomical differences. It is found in Central and South America.

Cacomistles (*Bassariscus*). These differ from the other members of this family in having the teeth more sharply cusped and adapted to the more predatory habits of the animals, which superficially closely resemble the genets, except that the fur is unspotted. Like the raccoons, they are

By courtesy of] [*Richard T. Doonor, Philadelphia, and the Academy of Natural Sciences of Philadelphia, U.S.A.* (*founded* 1812).

GIANT PANDA (*Ailuropoda melanoleuca*).

This is related to the true Panda, but resembles the bears, particularly in size and appearance.

partly terrestrial and partly arboreal, the young, from four to six in number, being born in holes in trees.

Pandas (Family *Ailuridae*)

The Panda or Cat Bear (*Ailurus fulgens*), although sometimes classified with the raccoons, differs in so many important anatomical characters that it is now referred to a separate family. It is about the size of a raccoon, but has the body longer, and the head shorter and rounder; the legs are more robust, with the paws hairy beneath and armed with sharp, partly retractile claws: the tail is much longer. The colour is very dark red above, black below and on the legs, with the whitish face striped on each side with red and the tail ringed. The head and body measure about two feet in length and the tail one and a half feet. Unlike the true raccoons, which are American, the Panda is found in south China and the north-eastern Himalayas. Its broad, flat-crowned teeth are adapted to a vegetable diet of bamboo-shoots, roots and fruits of various kinds. Although slow and awkward on the ground, the Panda is a good climber and spends most of its time in trees, the female making use of a hollow trunk as a home for her two cubs.

Giant Panda (*Ailuropoda melanoleuca*). This is related to the true Panda, but resembles the bears, with which it was formerly classified,

[F. W. Bond.
PANDA OR CAT BEAR (*Ailurus fulgens*).
The Panda, a native of south China and the north-eastern Himalayas, spends most of its time in trees.

in some respects, particularly in size and appearance. It is sometimes called the Parti-coloured Bear on account of its singular colouring, the head and body being white, with a black patch over each eye, black ears and legs and a stripe of the same colour on the shoulder. It is exactly like a bear in shape, with a very short tail and broad, flat feet. It inhabits the dense bamboo forests of China; but although nothing seems to have been recorded of its habits, there is no doubt from the massiveness of its jaws and its large, flat-crowned grinding teeth, that it feeds upon tough vegetable substances, probably on sugar-canes.

BEARS (Family *Ursidae*)

The Bears (*Ursidae*) may be distinguished from all other Carnivora, except the Giant Panda, by their large size and heavy build, associated with a very short tail, loose, protrusible lips, and broad, short, nearly plantigrade feet, provided with five short toes, all close together and with long, strong claws. Their dentition is remarkable for the uselessness of the front cheek-teeth and the large size of the remaining four, which have flat crushing crowns without trace of the cutting blades marking the " carnassial " teeth characteristic of the Order.

Bears, although represented by a comparatively small number of species,

BEARS (FAMILY URSIDAE)

SYRIAN BROWN BEAR (*Ursus arctos syriacus*).
In districts where the cold of winter is excessive, both sexes of Brown Bears hibernate after fattening themselves upon beechmast, acorns and nuts in the autumn.

were found all over Europe and Asia, as far to the south-east as Borneo, only in Morocco in Africa, all over North America, and in the northern parts of South America. They are mainly vegetarian in diet and breed only once a year, but although some of them are the largest of land carnivora, their cubs, seldom more than three to the litter, are remarkably small.

Brown Bear (*Ursus arctos*). This is the species most commonly exhibited in this country. The colour as indicated by the name is typically some shade of brown, but varies considerably, the hair, which is thick and long and forms a mat on the shoulder, is usually dark brown near the skin but paler, sometimes buff, red or even grey at the tips ; the legs are darker than the body and head. The size, too, is very variable individually and locally, females being smaller than males. In Europe, where the animal is now very rare, although still lingering in forested districts, a good-sized male stands about three and a half feet at the shoulder. But the species extends from Europe into Asia and North America, where it is represented by many local races, some smaller, some larger than the European bear, the largest of all being found in Alaska.

The Syrian race (*U. a. syriacus*) is paler fawn in colour than the European : the Himalayan race (*U. a. isabellinus*), not uncommon in Kashmir, where it is known as the " Snow

Photos]   [*W. S. Berridge.*
RED BEAR (*Ursus arctos isabellinus*).
This is the Himalayan race of the Brown Bear. It is a little smaller and sometimes reddish-brown.

Bear " or " Red Bear," is a little smaller than the European and sometimes reddish, brown or silvery. Another kind, the Hoary or Frosted Bear, inhabiting Tibet and central Asia, has the coat black, with silver or red tips and a broad, white collar over the neck. But the most imposing of all are the Alaskan Brown Bears, which stand four and a half feet at the shoulder and measure eight or nine feet long, rivalling the Polar Bear in dimensions.

In habits these Bears are very similar. In districts where the cold of winter is excessive, both sexes hibernate after fattening themselves upon beechmast, acorns and nuts in the autumn. During spring and summer, they eat grasses, roots and other vegetable food, varied with fish, insects and any ground animals like mice, which they can catch ; and in settled districts they raid farmyards after pigs, cattle and other livestock.

These depredations and the value of their hides are the main causes of their scarcity in places where they were formerly plentiful. They seldom attack man, except in self-defence ; but are formidable foes when cornered, biting savagely and dealing deadly blows with their forepaws. " Bruin's hug," however, is a myth. As is well known, they are skilful but slow climbers, ascending trunks of trees by gripping the bark with their strong, curved claws. The young are born in the winter-quarters of the mother, often under the snow, and have been found in north Europe as early as January, when the outside temperature was over 80° below zero.

Grizzly Bear (*U. a. horribilis*). This Bear of the Rockies and Barren grounds of North America, is so nearly related to the Brown Bear, which it resembles very closely in size, appearance and habits, that it is needless to describe it in detail. Greatly exaggerated stories of its ferocity have

By courtesy of]   *[Canadian Pacific Railway.*
AMERICAN BLACK BEAR (*Ursus americanus*).
This bear was formerly found almost everywhere in North America, from Canada to the Gulf of Mexico.

BEARS (FAMILY URSIDAE)

By courtesy of]   [Carl Hagenbeck's Tierpark, Stellingen.
POLAR BEAR (*Thalarctos maritimus*).
In this Bear the soles of the feet are much more overgrown with hair than in other species ; a safeguard against slipping on
the ice.

been told ; but there seems to be no reason to doubt the accounts of its
ability to knock down a bison with a blow of its paw or to drag away the
carcase of a wapiti weighing a thousand pounds.

American Black Bear (*Ursus americanus*). This is a smaller kind than
the foregoing, standing only about two and a half feet, or a little more,
at the shoulder. The colour is typically black, with the muzzle brown, but
it varies to cinnamon, slate-grey, or even dirty white, bears of the last-
mentioned tint being like little Polar Bears. It was formerly found almost
everywhere in North America, from Canada to the Gulf of Mexico. Its
habits do not seem to differ in any important particulars from those of
the Brown Bear.

Polar or White Bear (*Thalarctos maritimus*). This bear differs from
the Brown, Grizzly and Black Bear group (*Ursus*) in having smaller
grinding teeth, larger canines and incisors, the soles of the feet much more
overgrown with hair, and in its white colour. All these characters are
adaptations to life in the Arctic Regions. Its white colour prevents the
loss of internal heat and aids the successful stalking of seals in the snow ;
the hairs on the feet keep them warm and are a safeguard against slipping
on the ice and the teeth are better fitted for killing living prey such as
seals and walruses, and for tearing the flesh of stranded whales. These
mammals are the diet it is partial to, but it also eats fish and seaweed and
in summer, grass and lichens. It is the nature of its habitat near the shores
of the Arctic Ocean in Europe, Asia and America, where vegetable food is
only obtainable in small quantities in summer, that has driven this bear
to be mainly carnivorous. Although a capital swimmer, the Polar Bear
is unable to overtake seals in the water ; but he catches them either by a
swift pounce when they rise to the surface of their blow holes to breathe or

809

POLAR BEARS AT PLAY.
The Polar Bear is a capital swimmer.

[W. S. Berridge.

by stealthily stalking them when lying on the edges of the ice-floes. The testimony of Arctic travellers regarding the hibernation of this bear is contradictory. In certain districts males and half-grown young have been observed abroad in mid-winter. In others no bears are to be seen at that period; but whether their disappearance is due to migration urging them to follow the southward advance of the ice, to be as near as possible to open water where seals are obtainable, has not been ascertained. It is generally agreed, however, that the females retire in autumn to winter-quarters, under the snow, to give birth to their young, but whether they lapse into the state of profound torpidity characteristic of hibernation is not known. The cubs, generally two in number, are small but covered with hair, and are very like the pups of a large dog.

Himalayan Black Bear (*Selenarctos tibetanus*). This Bear differs in many particulars from those described above, notably in the nakedness of the underside of the wrist; the coat, too, is much smoother and shorter and the ears are larger. The colour is black, with the nose tan, and a white, angular stripe on the breast. The height is about two and a half feet in the Himalayas, but less elsewhere. It has a wide range, extending from Persia through the Himalayas to China and Japan, the Japanese (*S. japonicus*) being a small bear, usually about two feet high. Its habits are very similar to those of the Brown Bear; but owing to the structure of the feet, it is a better climber, and has the reputation of

[Charles Reid.
HIMALAYAN BLACK BEAR (*Selenarctos tibetanus*).
This Bear is black, with the nose tan, and a white, angular stripe on the breast.

810

being a fiercer animal and has been seen to drive a leopard off its kill. In the Himalayas it is found in the forests from the foothills up to about ten thousand feet, or more, in summer ; but even at tolerably high altitudes, it is only a partial hibernator, issuing from its winter-quarters on milder days to feed.

Malayan Bear (*Helarctos malayanus*). This is sometimes called the Honey Bear, and is a little, smooth-coated, short-eared, bandy-legged species, like the Himalayan Bear in its feet, but differing in its more mobile lips, longer extensile tongue and other characters. It ranges from Assam, through the Malay countries to Borneo, and is essentially a forest animal and a very active climber, feeding on fruits and honey, as well as small animals.

Sloth Bear (*Melursus ursinus*). This Bear differs from other species in having closable nostrils, very protrusible lips and tongue, associated with the loss of the two upper median incisor teeth, and the toes united to the tips. It has a long, shaggy coat and is typically black, with a mealy muzzle, although brown specimens now and then occur. Its height is about two and a half feet. It is found throughout

[*W. S. Berridge.*

SLOTH BEAR (*Melursus ursinus*).
Although mainly frugivorous, this Bear is particularly fond of white ants. It tears the ant hills open with its claws and licks up the insects with its long tongue.

Hindustan, except in the deserts, and in Ceylon, living in forest and jungle and frequently lying up in caves. Although mainly frugivorous, it eats honey and animal food, especially insects, and is particularly fond of white ants, which it obtains by tearing open the ant hills with its claws and puffing the galleries clear of earth before licking the insects with its long tongue or sucking them out by means of deep inhalations.

Spectacled Bear (*Tremarctos ornatus*). This Bear is so-called from the fawn-coloured ring usually encircling the eyes, and is a small species mainly of interest from being an inhabitant of South America, where it is found in the Andes from Ecuador to Chile. Its colour is black, relieved by some white on the muzzle and throat, and its height a little over two feet. Nothing remarkable is known of its habits.

MAMMALIA (ORDER CARNIVORA)

SEALS AND WALRUSES (Pinnipedia or Fin-footed Carnivora)

The Seals and Walruses are distinguished from other Carnivora by the conversion of all the limbs into swimming paddles, the foot being long in comparison with the rest of the limb, which is mostly imbedded in the body. But in all essential points they agree with the bear-like carnivores, of which they are a specialized offshoot. The tail is always short and never used for swimming.

Although typically marine and feeding in the sea, rivers or lakes, the Pinnipedes spend much of their time ashore and always pair and breed on land. The female produces almost invariably only a single pup, which differs from those of the typical, or fissipede, carnivores in being of relatively large size and well-developed at birth, with its eyes open ; also in shedding its milk teeth either just before or soon after it is born. The warmer parts of the Indian Ocean are the only seas from which Pinnipedes are absent.

There are three families, the Eared Seals or Sea-lions (*Otariidae*), the Walruses (*Odobenidae*) and the typical Seals (*Phocidae*).

Sea-lions or Eared Seals (Family *Otariidae*)

The Sea-lions (*Otariidae*) have huge flippers and can turn the hind flippers forwards and apply their soles to the ground for locomotion. They are provided with small ears, and swim by means of powerful strokes with their fore flippers. There is a large number of species found in the Pacific and in the southern oceans. They feed mainly on fish and their habits are everywhere very similar.

The different kinds are distinguished by size, the shape of their skulls and the nature of their fur, some of them yielding the valuable " seal-furs " of the trade.

Northern Fur Seal or Sea-bear (*Otaria ursina*). This is the most prized of the fur producers. It was formerly widely distributed in the North Pacific, but now breeds mainly, under strict protection, in the Pribylov Islands. It is of medium size, the males measuring about eight feet long. From November till May or June, these seals keep to the sea, following the fish southwards ; but in the early summer they return north, the males being the first to arrive, formerly literally in thousands, and come ashore fighting furiously for space to accommodate the females, which land a few weeks later, each male securing as many as possible for himself. The females give birth to their pups soon after arriving ; and the pairing season, in preparation for next year's families, follows. The pups when about two months old, begin to practise swimming with their mothers in November. But after once securing their stations, the males keep to the land, enduring a long fast all through the summer and subsisting the while on the fat accumulated by their fishing activities in the preceding winter.

Southern Fur Seal (*O. pusilla*). Frequenting the coasts of South America, South Africa and Australasia, this Seal is less valuable than the

Northern Fur Seal and also smaller, the males being about six feet long. Its habits, however, are tolerably similar.

Hair Seals. This is the name given to the species without fur. There are several inhabiting the Pacific and Australian Seas. Of these the best known, from its frequent importation into this country for exhibition is the Californian Sealion (*O. californiana*), a medium-sized species

By courtesy of] [*Carl Hagenbeck's Tierpark, Stellingen.*
CALIFORNIAN SEA-LION (*Otaria californiana*).
This is the best known of the Hair Seals. It is a medium-sized species some
seven feet in length.

about seven feet long. Larger still is the Patagonian Sea-lion (*O. byronii*), but the largest of the whole family is the Northern or Steller's Sea-lion (*O. stelleri*), which reaches a length of twelve feet and inhabits the same districts as the Northern Fur Seal.

Walrus (Family *Odobenidae*)

Although the Walrus resembles the sea-lions in the structure and use of the hind feet, it differs in the loss of all trace of external ear, apart from the orifice, its heavy build, and nearly naked wrinkled skin, but especially

[*Gibson & Sons.*
GREY SEAL (*Halichoerus grypus*).
This is the commonest species on the western sea-board of the British Isles.

in the peculiarities of its teeth. The upper canines form a pair of long, stout, downwardly-directed tusks projecting sometimes as much as one and a half feet below the mouth, with six inches or so imbedded in large sockets, greatly expanding the muzzle. They are present in both sexes. The rest of the teeth, however,

813

are reduced in size and number. Another striking feature is the great length and thickness of the " whiskers."

The Walrus is a huge, ungainly beast, inactive on the land and a slow swimmer as compared with the sea-lions. It is not dependent upon the capture of fishes, being mainly a bottom-feeder, eating clams and other molluscs, which it tears off the rocks or digs from the mud with its tusks. The tusks are also used for hauling the animal up slopes and in rival combats by the males and as weapons in case of attack, for although usually inoffensive, the Walrus fights fiercely if interfered with and has the herd instinct so strongly developed that in the past sailors who hunted them in open boats did so at the risk of being swamped by the combined assault of a dozen or more of these huge beasts. A big male measures ten feet long and weighs between two and three thousand pounds.

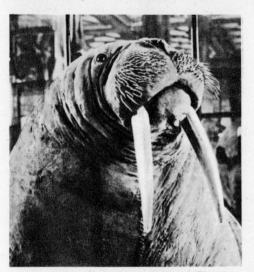

[*Photopress.*
ATLANTIC WALRUS (*Odobenus rosmarus*).
The tusks sometimes project as much as one and a half feet below the mouth.

The Walrus is restricted to the coast and ice-floes of the Arctic Ocean and seldom ventures out into the open sea. Specimens, however, have been seen off the coast of northern Scotland and formerly the animal was plentiful in America as far south as New-foundland. But it has been so persistently slaughtered that its last refuge is now in the extreme north, where, apart from man, its only enemy is the polar bear.

There are two alleged species of Walrus, *Odobenus rosmarus*, inhabiting the North Atlantic, and *O. obesus*, the North Pacific Ocean.

True Seals (Family *Phocidae*)

The typical Seals are distinguished by the hind limbs being extended backwards and incapable of being turned forwards for locomotion on land, which is effected by spasmodic jerks of the body, aided by the strong claws of the fore feet. Swimming is performed by means of sinuous curves of the hinder part of the body, the broadened flippers playing the part of tail-fin. The external ear is usually represented merely by its valvular orifice.

The two commonest species on the British coasts are the Grey Seal and the Common Seal.

Grey Seal (*Halichoerus grypus*). This has simple, peg-like cheek-teeth

COMMON SEAL (PHOCA VITULINA)

and is comparatively large, the males measuring eight or nine feet long and weighing up to about six hundred pounds.

The colour is very variable, ranging from light grey to black, or a blotched mixture of the two. The species is restricted to the North Atlantic and is the commonest species on our western seaboard,

ELEPHANT SEAL OR SEA-ELEPHANT (*Mirounga*).
The males, or " bulls," may attain a length of over twenty feet, and have a remarkably developed and inflatable nasal organ like an elephant's trunk.

being partial to rocky coasts. It is mainly a fish-eater and a great enemy to salmon. The pups, born in caves or on the rocks, usually in autumn but sometimes as late as early spring, are covered at first with whitish hair, which is shed some six weeks after birth.

Common Seal (*Phoca vitulina*). This is often confused with the last-named Seal. It has cusped, two-rooted cheek-teeth, and is smaller, the males measuring from four and a half feet to six feet long, and weighing about one hundred and fifty pounds. The colour is typically grey, mottled with black or brown. It is very widely distributed, occurring in the North Pacific as well as the North Atlantic; but it usually shuns rough rock-bound coasts, preferring sand-bank and mud-flat, and is nowhere plentiful in British Seas, except in the north. Its habits are tolerably similar to those of the Grey Seal, but the pups, born in May and June, are not white at birth.

Photos by courtesy of]   [Carl Hagenbeck's Tierpark, Stellingen.
YOUNG WALRUS.
The Walrus is restricted to the coast and ice-floes of the Arctic Ocean and seldom ventures out into the open sea.

A Seal that sometimes wanders to the shores of Britain is the Greenland or " Harp " Seal, sometimes known as the " Saddleback " (*P. groenlandica*). It takes its name from the two semicircular bands reaching from the shoulders nearly to the tail. Its habitat is the coasts of Greenland and the frozen regions of the Arctic.

MAMMALIA (ORDER CARNIVORA)

A small Seal of the North Atlantic is the Ringed Seal (*Phoca hispida*) ; measuring between three and four feet in length. The Lake Baikal Seal (*P. sibirica*) is of interest as it would appear to point to this great lake being at one time connected with the oceans.

Another Seal of the Northern Hemisphere is the Monk Seal (*Monachus monachus*), interesting from having the first and fifth toes of the hind foot considerably longer than the rest. It frequents the Mediterranean and neighbouring parts of the Atlantic.

The Bladder-nose or Hooded Seal (*Cystophora cristata*), sometimes known as the Crested Seal, is remarkable because the male has a curious hood of skin over the head and muzzle. This can be blown out when the animal is excited. It is a large, spotted Seal, fiercer than other species, and frequents the coasts of Greenland and the polar regions.

[W. S. Berridge.

YOUNG CRESTED, HOODED OR BLADDER-NOSE SEAL
(*Cystophora cristata*).
The male has a curious hood of skin over the head and muzzle, and this can be blown out when the animal is excited.

Leopard Seal (*Ogmorhinus leptonyx*). Several species of Seals are restricted to the southern oceans and may be seen in numbers on the Antarctic pack-ice. The largest of these, measuring nearly twelve feet, is the Leopard Seal, so called from its spotted pattern. It feeds mainly on fish and penguins.

Other interesting Seals of the southern oceans are the Crab-eating Seal (*Lobodon carcinophagus*) and Ross's Seal (*Ommatophoca rossi*).

Elephant Seal or Sea-elephant (*Mirounga*). This species takes its name from its gigantic size and the presence in the male of a proboscis about one foot long, which, when expanded with air, gives an indescribably grotesque appearance to the animal. The male measures twenty feet or so in length, but the female, which has no proboscis, is only about nine or ten feet in length. The colour is greyish-brown. The cheek-teeth are small and peg-like in adaptation to a diet of cuttlefish. It was formerly common on the islands of the southern oceans and up the western coast of America as far as California. There are two kinds, the Northern (*M. leonina*), which is the smaller, and the Southern (*M. patagonica*) of the Antarctic and Southern Pacific. Both are now very scarce and rapidly being exterminated for their blubber.

Order CETACEA (Whales, Porpoises and Dolphins)

The Whales have diverged more from the primitive structure-plan than any other order of Mammals; but from the evidence of extinct species, they are believed to be descended from the same primitive ancestral stock as the carnivores. They are completely adapted to aquatic life and, apart from variation in size, are unmistakably alike in general appearance. Their shape is fish-like without any marked division between head, body and

[Herbert G. Ponting.

KILLER WHALES OR GRAMPUS (*Orcinus orca*) RISING TO " BLOW."
This is the only Cetacean that habitually feeds on warm-blooded animals, sea-birds, seals, porpoises, as well as fish.

tail; the tail is provided with a horizontal fin, the " flukes "; all trace of the hind limbs has disappeared, the fore foot is converted into a flipper without visible external sign of digits; and in the head, the ear is represented by its orifice only, the eyes are minute, and the valvular nostrils are situated on the summit of the head, usually far behind the tip of the muzzle; the skin is smooth, hairs only being found in some cases upon the head and muzzle, and underneath the skin there is a layer of oily blubber to give buoyancy to the body and to withstand the extreme cold of polar seas and oceanic depths. Whales swim by means of up and down strokes of the powerful tail, the flippers, aided usually by a fin on the back, acting as balancers to preserve the position of the body in the water. They feed upon aquatic animals of all kinds, from seals, birds and fishes to minute marine shrimps, and their classification is based mainly upon the mechanisms for dealing with the particular food they affect.

Food is never masticated, but is swallowed entire, and the popular belief that Whales have a small gullet is only true of those, like the Whalebone Whales, which feed on shrimps, the Cachalot, which takes huge cuttlefish, and the Killer, which swallows seals and porpoises, having capacious throats.

Usually Whales, when undisturbed, rise to the surface to breathe every five or ten minutes; but the large Whales can remain submerged for nearly an hour. On reaching the surface after long submergence, the first act of the Whale is to expel the warm air with a whistling sound, called "blowing." When the water-vapour, with which the expired air is saturated, comes into contact with the cold atmosphere, it is condensed into a column of mist, a dozen or more feet high. This act is called "spouting," because the column of mist was mistaken for sea-water driven from the Whale's mouth through the nostrils.

The period of gestation is believed to be rather less than a year. The young, usually one but occasionally two, are active and capable at birth and about one-fourth or more the length of the mother, who frequently lies on her side in the water to suckle them.

The Whales are divided into two well-defined suborders, the *Mystacoceti*, the Whalebone or Baleen Whales, and the *Odontoceti*, the Toothed Whales.

CLASSIFICATION OF THE ORDER CETACEA
Suborder **Mystacoceti** (*Whalebone or Baleen Whales*)
> Right Whales, Fin-back Whales or Rorquals and Hump-backs.

Suborder **Odontoceti** (*Toothed Whales*)
> Sperm Whales, Bottle-nose Whale, Narwhal, White Whale, Black-fish, Killer Whale (Grampus), Porpoise, Dolphin, Freshwater Dolphin.

Whalebone or Baleen Whales (*Mystacoceti*)
These Whales have no teeth, their place in the upper jaw being taken by two series of closely-packed, horny plates of " baleen " or whalebone, which are broad above, narrowed below, and hang from the roof of the mouth on each side of the huge tongue. Their outer edges are entire, but their inner edges are frayed into horny fibres. They constitute a combined trap and sieve and are entirely subservient to dealing with a diet of small marine organisms swimming in shoals near the surface of the sea. The mechanism operates as follows : taking a mouthful of seawater teeming with these organisms, the Whale shuts its mouth, then by raising its tongue and closing its throat, forces the water between the plates of baleen,

letting it escape through the lips, sideways, while the tiny animals are caught by the frayed fibres and swallowed when the water is gone. To increase the size of the mouth, the bones of the lower jaw are arched out-wards and loosely connected in front. These Whales also have two nostrils or " blow-holes."

The largest known Whales, commonly called Right Whales, Hump-backs and Fin-back Whales or Rorquals, belong to this suborder.

Greenland Whale (*Balaena mysticetus*). This may be taken as typical of the Right Whales. It has an enormous head, the edge of the lower lip elevated and arched, and a cavernous mouth to accommodate the whale-bone of which there may be nearly four hundred plates on each side, those in the middle of the mouth being sometimes ten feet long. The prevailing colour is black, often relieved by white on the throat or elsewhere. and the

[*W. S. Berridge.*

PILOT WHALES OR BLACK-FISH (*Globiocephalus melas*) STRANDED.
These Whales go about in "schools," often of many hundreds, one individual leading the way as a guide or pilot.

total length is fifty or sixty feet. It feeds on oceanic shrimps and molluscs, and is a slow swimmer, seldom exceeding eight miles per hour going at speed. Large specimens will yield two hundred and fifty barrels of oil and three thousand pounds weight of whalebone. This Whale is restricted to the edges of the Arctic ice-floes in the Atlantic and Pacific; but being easily captured and of great value for its oil and whalebone, it has been hunted almost to the verge of extinction.

Atlantic Right Whale (*Eubalaena glacialis*). This was formerly plentiful in the Bay of Biscay and even entered the Mediterranean. It is nearly as large as the last but has a smaller head. a less arched lower lip, smaller baleen and a thicker tail. It has a very wide range and in the south is known as the Southern Right Whale. Like the Greenland Whale, and for similar reasons, it is now rare.

Pigmy Right Whale (*Neobalaena marginata*). This is found in the southern oceans, and is only about twenty feet in length.

Fin-backs or Rorquals (*Balaenoptera*). These are distinguished by having in the throat a great distensible food-pouch, marked externally, when empty, by a number of parallel grooves and ridges on the throat, by the smaller head, the straight edge of the lower lip, smaller whalebone plates and by a longer body, with a dorsal fin.

There are several species, varying considerably in size, the Lesser Rorqual (*B. acutirostris*) being about thirty feet long, the Common Rorqual (*B. physalus*) about sixty feet, and Sibbald's Rorqual (*B. musculus*), sometimes known as the "Blue Whale," from eighty to a hundred feet. These Whales are found in all seas and feed upon fish, especially herrings and pilchards, as well as marine shrimps. They are swift swimmers, and more dangerous to hunt and much less valuable than Right Whales on account of their smaller yield of oil and whalebone. The whalers, consequently, in former years left them alone. But since the Right Whales became scarce, the whaling industry has turned its attention to the Rorquals, with the result that they are annually decreasing in numbers.

Hump-back Whale (*Megaptera boöps*). This differs from the Rorquals in its shorter, deeper body, hump-like dorsal fin, larger flukes (tail-fin) and much longer flippers, attaining a quarter of the length of the whole animal, which is about forty or fifty feet long. It is found in all seas and, like the Rorquals, now forms an important item in the whaling industry.

Californian Grey Whale (*Rhachianectes glaucus*). This is distinguished from the preceding by having from two to four grooves only on the throat and the head rough with bristles. It reaches a length of about forty feet, and inhabits the North Pacific, but is now very rare.

Toothed Whales (*Odontoceti*)

In these Whales the mouth usually has teeth but never baleen plates, there is a single nostril, and the bones of the lower jaw are straight and firmly united in front.

The members of this group are known according to their size as Whales, Porpoises and Dolphins. There is a great number of species, exhibiting a wider range in structural characters and being on the average much smaller than the Whalebone Whales.

Sperm Whale or Cachalot (*Physeter catodon*). This is the largest and most important species. The male may reach a length of sixty feet, whereas the female is only half the length, a sexual discrepancy in size not met with elsewhere amongst mammals. The head in this Whale is of enormous size, about one-fourth of the total length, and this is due to the immense development of the snout, which is bluntly rounded at the end,

820

SPERM WHALE—BOTTLE-NOSE WHALE

considerably overlaps the lower jaw, and carries the single nostril at the tip of its summit. The upper jaw is toothless, but there are about twenty-four nearly conical teeth on each side of the lower jaw.

This Whale is addicted to the warmer oceans and usually occurs in " schools "; but relentless persecution by whalers, to whom the Cachalot was always a coveted prize on account of its spermaceti-permeated blubber, has made it a rarity. The bulk of this substance is obtained from a basin-shaped reservoir in the head. This Whale also yields an excretory product found floating in the sea, the valuable substance known as ambergris, used in the preparation of perfumes. The Cachalot is the most dangerous of all the Whales. In the old days it sometimes charged and sank small whaling vessels and frequently smashed harpooners' boats to matchwood with a stroke of its flukes. It feeds mainly on large squids and other

[*W. S. Berridge.*

PORPOISE (*Phocaena phocaena*).
The Porpoise, usually seen in small schools, is black above, white below and measures between five and six feet in length.

cuttlefish, which it is known to hunt at great depths. But it also takes large fish, like cod, in abundance.

Lesser Sperm Whale (*Kogia breviceps*). This is a small, mainly Antarctic species, measuring about ten feet long and provided with only ten or so teeth on each side of the lower jaw. In many respects it serves to connect the Cachalot with the more typical Toothed Whales.

Bottle-nose Whale (*Hyperoödon rostratus*). This species resembles the Sperm Whales in yielding spermaceti, and in some other respects. It differs, however, in the beak-like projection of its short jaws from the front of the swollen head, in the absence of functional teeth, and in the presence of a pair of grooves on the throat. It measures from twenty

821

to thirty feet in length and inhabits the North Atlantic, feeding on cuttlefish.

Narwhal or Sea Unicorn (*Monodon monoceros*). The Narwhal is distinguished from all Cetaceans by the presence in the male of an immense tusk, sometimes nine feet long, projecting like a great spear from the left side of the bluntly-rounded muzzle. This tusk, with its spirally arranged grooves, is the original of the horn of the unicorn of heraldry. Sometimes the right tusk is developed as well; but since in the female neither tusk cuts the gum, it may be inferred that the weapon is of use to the male in rival combats. This small Whale, mottled in colour and about eighteen feet long, lives in Arctic Seas, south of the ice-fields, and having a practically toothless mouth, feeds mainly on cuttlefish, though taking bony fishes as well.

White Whale (*Delphinapterus leucas*). This resembles the Narwhal in size, shape and habitat, but the tusk is absent and there are nine or ten teeth above and below on each side of the mouth.

Black-fish or Pilot Whale (*Globiocephalus melas*). This is also known as the Ca'ing Whale, and resembles the last in the number of its teeth and rounded head, but differs in colour, and in having a dorsal fin. It is about twenty-five feet in length and inhabits temperate and tropical seas, feeding mostly on cuttlefish and going about in "schools," often of many hundreds, one individual leading the way as a guide or pilot.

Killer Whale or Grampus (*Orcinus orca*). This is a well-known species, world-wide in distribution and sometimes seen off the British coasts, where it may be known by its high dorsal fin, black and white colouring and large size. It is a voracious, predatory Whale, with a dozen or so large teeth on each side of the upper and lower jaws, the male measuring between twenty and thirty feet in length, and the female about half that length. It is the only Cetacean that habitually feeds on warm-blooded animals, sea-birds, seals, porpoises, as well as fish. It is a swift swimmer, often hunting in packs. Several have been seen attacking a Greenland Whale, tearing at the lips to get at the tongue of the sluggish, defenceless monster. Its voracity may be gauged by the record of the finding of fourteen seals and thirteen porpoises in the stomach of a single individual measuring twenty-one feet in length.

Common Porpoise (*Phocaena phocaena*). This is the only Cetacean of frequent occurrence in British waters, where it may often be seen, usually in small schools. It is black above, white below and measures between five and six feet. Its head is bluntly rounded and its teeth, of which there are about two dozen above and below on each side, have spade-shaped crowns. It feeds on fish and often ascends tidal rivers in pursuit of them.

Common Dolphin (*Delphinus delphis*). Schools of dolphins, playing around the ship, are a familiar sight to travellers in the Atlantic and Mediterranean.

[*Topical Press.*

DOLPHINS, PHOTOGRAPHED FROM A SUBMARINE.

It is larger than the Porpoise, measuring between seven and eight feet, and has long, beak-like jaws and twice as many teeth, with simple, pointed crowns.

Several species, called, according to fancy, Porpoises or Dolphins, inhabit the upper waters of large tropical rivers. Many of these are closely related to the marine forms that pass under those names. One of them, the Camerun Dolphin (*Sotalia teuxi*), is of exceptional interest from being, in part, at least, apparently a vegetable feeder, judging from the leaves and grasses that have been found in its stomach. But some of these fresh-water Cetaceans found in India, China and South America are important from exhibiting several skeletal characters showing them to be more primitive types than the other Toothed Whales. The best known is the Susu (*Platanista gangetica*), found in the Brahmapootra, Ganges and Indus. It is eight feet long, and muddy in colour to match the turbid waters it frequents. It is blind and feeds mainly, apparently, on fishes it discovers in the mud at the bottom by probing with its long, slender, beak-like jaws, which are provided with a very large number of teeth. Another kind, the Ting Ling Dolphin (*Lipotes vexillifer*), which has slightly up-curved jaws, lives in the Ting Ling Lake, six hundred miles up the Yang-tse-Kiang River in China.

Order INSECTIVORA

Although obscure and unattractive, the animals of this Order are in several respects interesting. In their lowly organization they are not far from the primitive stock of placental mammals; but they admirably illustrate a phenomenon common in all classes of animals, namely the combination of primitive features with others that have averted extinction. In the struggle for existence they have saved themselves, either by acquiring protective weapons like spines and stink glands, by the adoption of particular habits like living in trees, water, or underground, or by finding their way to parts of the world where predatory foes are few. The adaptation to varied habitats has brought about variations in external characters producing creatures as dissimilar in appearance as otters are from mice.

The teeth, especially the incisors and canines, are extremely varied in number, size and arrangement. A common external feature is a long muzzle ending in a sensitive, probing snout.

The Order Insectivora is divided into two suborders. In the first, the *Lipotyphla*, the brain is less advanced in structure, and the dilatation of the intestine known as the caecum is absent. The Lipotyphla include two groups: to the first, distinguished by V-shaped molars, belong the Golden Moles and the Tenrecs; to the second, in which the principal cheek-teeth have broad crowns with W-shaped grinding surfaces, belong the Moles, Shrews, and Hedgehogs. The second suborder, *Menotyphla*, includes the Elephant-shrews and Tree-shrews, distinguished by the presence of a caecum, a higher type of brain, etc.

Suborder LIPOTYPHLA

The first group of the Lipotyphla is characterized by narrow molars with a V-shaped crown. It includes the Golden Moles, the Otter-shrew, and the Tenrecs.

Golden Moles, Otter-shrew and the Tenrecs

Golden Moles (Family *Chrysochloridae*). As their popular name indicates, this family is thoroughly adapted to subterranean life. There is no external trace of eyes, ears or tail, the head is conical, with the tip of the snout ending in a patch of naked skin probably used for boring in the soil. The legs are very short, with little more than the feet projecting from the body. The hind feet are not greatly modified, except that the claws, which no doubt aid in digging, are long and stout; but the fore feet are profoundly affected for work underground. The claws of the first, second and third digits progressively increase in size, those of the third being very long, stout and falciform and evidently the chief tool in digging. This foot is entirely different from the corresponding foot of the Common Mole, the superficial resemblance between the animals being a case of adaptation to similar fossorial habits.

824

The general colour of the Golden Moles is brownish, but the soft fur exhibits under reflected light a beautiful iridescent sheen, which is intensified by immersion in alcohol.

They are found in Central and South Africa and live in extensive burrows just beneath the surface of the soil, feeding upon worms, grubs, beetles and other insects. At the breeding time the female makes a nest of grass for the reception of her young.

There are several species of Golden Moles, the most familiar being the Cape Golden Mole (*Chrysochloris asiatica*), which is common in the western districts of Cape Colony, and measures about four and a half inches in length. A much larger species, the Giant Golden Mole (*Chrysospalax trevelyani*), measuring nine inches long, is found near King William's Town.

Otter-shrew. The family Potamogalidae includes only the Otter-shrew (*Potamogale velox*), an animal modified, as its name suggests, for aquatic life, and very closely resembling superficially a small otter, having a flattish head, short limbs and a powerful tail, as thick at the root as the body and flattened from side to side farther down. As the feet are not webbed, the tail is evidently the sole means of propulsion through the water. The animal is covered with thick brown fur and measures one and a half feet or more in total length, of which the tail is about nine or ten inches. It lives in the tropical forests of Central and West Africa, lurking under rocks in the banks of streams on the look-out for fish, which, on account of the astonishing speed with which it swims, it catches with ease.

The Golden Moles and Otter-shrew are examples of insectivores with V-shaped molars, which have probably survived on account of the adoption of subterranean and aquatic habitats respectively. There remain two families, with similar teeth, which have found refuge in isolated areas of the world.

Tenrecs (Family *Centetidae*). These are almost restricted to Madagascar, one of the homes of primitive types, and are represented by a considerable number of species varying in structure and habits, but although some are burrowers and some aquatic, the resulting modifications are unimportant in comparison with those of the Golden Moles and Otter-shrews.

On account of its large size and occasional exhibition in European menageries, the best-known member of this group is the Tailless Tenrec (*Centetes ecaudatus*), representing a division of the family in which the back is spiny, very much as in the hedgehogs. In this particular species, however, the spines, although present and arranged in bands in the comparatively defenceless young, almost entirely disappear, except on the neck, in the adult, which, being strongly built, nearly one and a half feet long and provided with long, piercing canine teeth, is more capable of taking care of itself. Its colour is yellowish-brown; and, like most insectivores, it has a long, probing snout used for uprooting worms and insects, the principal items in its diet, to which, no doubt, are added any small vertebrated

825

animals it can kill. Its home is mainly in the mountains of Madagascar and it has the habit of lying dormant in burrows from June to December. Even when brought to Europe, it keeps this custom, although supplied with plenty of food. Another peculiarity is its extraordinary fertility, the habitual number of young to the litter being over a dozen, sometimes as many as a score. This animal also occurs in some of the small islands near Madagascar, even in Mauritius and Reunion, where, no doubt, it has been artificially introduced.

Of the other species, distinguished by preserving their spines throughout life, reference need only be made to the Spiny Tenrec (*Ericulus spinosus*), which is as well armed in this respect as hedgehogs and closely resembles them superficially, although the spines are not so stout.

The members of this family, distinguished by their soft fur and the absence of spines, exhibit some interesting variations in habit and structure.

The Rice Tenrecs (*Nesoryctes tetradactyla* and *Oryzoryctes hova*) resemble large shrews, but have the claws of the fore feet enlarged for digging ; the colour is olive-brown and the tail short. They are great burrowers, doing considerable damage to rice crops by tunnelling in the roots in search of worms and grubs.

The Marsh Tenrec (*Limnogale mergulus*), on the contrary, is adapted to aquatic life. In size, colour and appearance, except for its long snout, it superficially resembles the water-rat, and its habits, no doubt, are like those of the Water-shrew ; but the fully-webbed hind feet suggest superior swimming powers.

Finally, the Mouse Tenrec (*Microgale longicaudata*) has the distinction of possessing relatively the longest tail in the class of mammals. This little creature is reddish-brown in colour and looks like a long-snouted mouse with a prodigious tail. The head and body measure a little over two inches, but the tail may be over five inches. Such tails are only found in jumpers, and since the Mouse Tenrec has long hind feet, it may be inferred that activity has been an important factor in its survival.

The *Solenodontidae* are distant relations of the Otter-shrew and the Tenrecs that have found refuge in the West Indian islands of Cuba and Hayti. The Cuban species (*Solenodon cubanus*) is known to the natives as the Almiqui, and the Haytian (*S. paradoxus*) as the Agouta. The latter was the first to be discovered and received its scientific name from the grooves on the canine-like incisors of the lower jaw and the puzzle its classification presented. They are the sole representatives of the family Solenodontidae. In size they equal the Tailless Tenrec of Madagascar, the head and body measuring about one foot in length, but differ from it superficially in the absence of spines, in possessing a long, scaly tail measuring some eight inches, very large claws on the feet, a more pronounced snout and in the position of the teats far back on the groins. The general colour is brownish, varied with darker and lighter tints, the

[W. S. Berridge.

CUBAN SOLENODON (*Solenodon cubanus*).
Solenodons are distant relatives of the Otter-shrew and Tenrecs that have found refuge in the West Indian islands of Cuba and Hayti.

Cuban Almiqui having the head tawny-yellow, whereas in the Haytian it is much browner. About the habits of these animals, which are rare, very little is known ; but the avidity with which captive specimens devour raw meat and the excitement they evince at the sight of live birds, even as large as fowls, suggest that they subsist on any living creatures they can find and overcome.

The remaining families of the Lipotyphla are distinguished by broader cheek-teeth, often with a W-shaped grinding surface.

Hedgehogs and Their Allies (Family *Erinaceidae*)

These are unknown in America, and have the large cheek-teeth flatter than in the moles and shrews, and without the high, sharp cusps and cutting edges seen in those animals. The Hedgehogs themselves, the most highly-organized members of the family, differ from Moles in many other characters ; but in south-eastern Asia there are several insectivores which serve in a measure to link the typical Hedgehogs with the Mole family. For want of an appropriate popular title they may be called the Gymnuras, a name derived from the scientific title of the best-known species, Raffles' Gymnura (*Gymnura gymnura*)

This animal differs superficially from the Hedgehogs in having no trace of spines and a long, nearly naked, scaly tail. It is one of the largest of the insectivores, the head and body measuring about one foot in length and the tail about eight inches. It ranges from Malaya to Borneo and is nocturnal, sheltering during the day under the roots of trees and coming out at dusk to

[D. Seth-Smith.

TENREC (*Centetes ecaudatus*).
These are hedgehog-like animals almost restricted to Madagascar. There are numerous species.

827

hunt for its food, which consists of insects of various kinds. It is very conspicuously coloured, usually a mixture of black and white, the white predominating on the head and forequarters, but some individuals are wholly white, and this conspicuous " warning " colouring, as in the case of the Indian " Musk Rat," described on page 833, is accompanied by a most unpleasant odour, said to resemble stale Irish stew, due to the secretion emitted by two glands, situated, not on the flanks as in the shrews, but beneath the tail.

There are several related but smaller genera and species, found in Burma, China and the Philippines, distinguished by variations in the number and structure of their teeth and other characters.

Typical Hedgehogs. These may be known at once by the shield of sharp, erectile, usually black and white spines which protects the back and the top of the head ; the face, limbs and underside being hairy. Although widely distributed and differentiated by their teeth, feet and other characters into a large number of genera and species, they are superficially very much alike, all tolerably closely resembling the typical European Hedgehog (*Erinaceus europaeus*).

The general appearance of this animal, with its heavily-built body, short tail and legs and pointed snout, is well known. Equally familiar is its power of rolling into a spiny ball when alarmed, with its limbs, head, tail and other vulnerable parts tucked out of harm's way. In habits it is nocturnal and very varied in its tastes, eating almost any animal substance, alive or dead, it can find, from carrion, insects, slugs, worms and the like to eggs and even fowls. It also kills rats and adders and the long-discredited stories of its sucking cows sleeping in the meadows at night have recently turned out to be true. The Hedgehog spends the day curled up asleep under dead leaves or low herbage ; but for its winter sleep, which lasts from late autumn till spring, with occasional periods of activity during exceptionally mild spells, it seeks a more secluded place, underground if possible, lining the retreat with grass, moss, etc. In a similar nest the young are born in the summer. The litter usually consists of four ; but although blind and helpless, the young are born with spines, which, soft at first, soon harden. The average length of the male is about ten inches.

This species, which is common in Ireland and Great Britain, is one of the largest of the Hedgehogs, being equalled, perhaps surpassed slightly, only by the Afghan Hedgehog (*E. megalotis*). No important difference in habits has been recorded between the species, although they range from Ireland to Central Asia and the south of India, and from Sweden to the Cape of Good Hope. It is only, however, in latitudes where winters are severe that hibernation takes place.

Moles (Family *Talpidae*)

The Moles and their allies have sharp-cusped cheek-teeth, but never have the front teeth modified as in the shrews, although otherwise these teeth are variable. The typical Moles are adapted for underground life, but some members of the family are aquatic.

Old-world Moles. The Common Mole (*Talpa europaea*), like other European species, has the most primitive dentition of all the insectivora,

COMMON EUROPEAN HEDGEHOG (*Erinaceus europaeus*).
This hedgehog eats almost any animal substance, alive or dead, from carrion, insects, slugs, worms and the like to eggs, and even fowls.

the six incisors above and below being small and subequal and the upper canine, tusk-like. But the shoulder bones and fore limbs are highly specialized for digging; the head, with its long snout, tiny eyes and obsolete ears, being thrust back between the shoulders and the fore feet, with five long, powerful claws, widened by a big bone arising from the wrist. For the rest, the body is cylindrical and covered with close, erect fur; the hind limbs are unmodified and the tail is short. The ordinary colour is glossy blackish-grey, but fawn is a not uncommon variation. The head and body are usually five and a half inches in length and the tail about one inch long. Although not found in Ireland, this Mole is common throughout Great Britain, whence it extends into temperate Europe. Related species are found in Spain, Italy and eastward in Europe and Asia as far as Japan and Burma.

Photos]   [*W. S. Berridge.*
LONG-EARED HEDGEHOG (*Hemiechinus megalotis*).
This is a large-eared Indian species.

The Mole spends most of its time underground, where, on account of the rapidity with which it can dig, it is safe from enemies, but it occasionally comes to the surface, where the slowness of its movements renders it an easy prey to foxes, weasels, owls and other predatory animals.

Formerly it was supposed that the Moles' burrows were excavated in accordance with a definite, symmetrical plan,

829

the construction being called the "fortress." But it is now known that they are driven in almost any direction through the soil, by the animal searching for earthworms and grubs, on which it principally feeds. The so-called "mole-hills," so familiar in the countryside and such a nuisance in private grounds to croquet and lawn-tennis players, are heaps of earth cast out, usually over the site of the nesting chamber. In this the young, naked, blind and usually three or four in number, are born on a bedding of leaves and grass in the spring.

North American Moles. These differ from those of the Old World in having the front upper incisors tusk-like; but their habits are similar. There are several different kinds, two being especially interesting. The Web-footed Mole (*Scalops aquaticus*) is distinguished by its webbed hind feet, which inspired the mistaken idea that the animal is aquatic. No doubt, the webs are useful for kicking back loosened earth in the burrows. The Star-nosed Mole (*Condylura cristata*) has the tail nearly as long as the body, but its chief peculiarity lies in the tip of the snout being provided with a number of radiating tactile filaments.

In their dentition the American Moles approach another section of the

[Stanley Crook.

COMMON MOLE (*Talpa europaea*).
Although not found in Ireland, the Mole is common throughout Great Britain.

family, the Desmans and their allies, which are not specialized diggers and have the fore feet normal in size and structure and smaller than the hind feet.

Desmans. The most familiar of these are two European species, the Spanish Desman (*Galemys pyrenaica*) and the Russian Desman (*Desmana moschata*), found in the countries from which they are named. They are thoroughly adapted to aquatic life, swimming by means of their long thick tails and enlarged, paddle-like hind feet, which have a fringe of stiff hair along the outer edge and the digits fully webbed. The snout also is peculiar, being very long, flattened, expanded at the tip and highly flexible. They live in deep burrows in the

[W. F. Taylor.

MODEL OF A MOLE HILL AT THE NATURAL HISTORY MUSEUM, LONDON.
Formerly it was supposed that the Mole's burrows were excavated in accordance with a definite symmetrical plan. But it
is now known that they are driven in almost any direction through the soil, by the animal searching for earthworms.

banks of streams, but spend most of their time in the water, hunting for
the insects, worms, molluscs and fish on which they feed. The Russian
Desman, the larger of the two, the head and body measuring about ten
inches and the tail, which is flattened from side to side for the greater part
of its length, six inches, has been compared to an otter in swimming
powers; but the Spanish Desman, with a total length of ten inches, of
which the tail, flattened only towards the end, is half, has been authori-
tatively described as inferior in aquatic agility to the Water-rat or Water-
shrew, despite its profound structural adaptations to life in water; and
this inferiority was ascribed to the handicap of its descent from inactive
fossorial ancestors of the Mole stock.

831

MAMMALIA (ORDER INSECTIVORA)

Shrews (Family *Soricidae*)

The Shrews are especially distinguished by the large size of their central front teeth, those of the upper jaw being hook-like and armed with a supplementary fang, and those of the lower jaw exceedingly long and projecting straight forwards. A few of the species are modified for aquatic life, but the majority are exclusively terrestrial in habits, mostly nocturnal, insectivorous animals with long, sensitive snouts, small eyes and soft fur, usually with a well-developed tail and unmodified feet. Their average size is much less than that of the other families, the largest having only the dimensions of a small rat and the smallest being the tiniest of all mammals. Judging, nevertheless, from their wide distribution and number of species, they have been the most successful of all the insectivora in the struggle for life. They are found in temperate and tropical parts of Europe, Asia and Africa, in North America and as far south in the New World as the northern parts of South America, but not in Madagascar or Australia.

Four species of the family are found in the British Isles. These may be dealt with, first.

Typical Shrews (*Sorex*). Of these the Common British Shrew or Shrew-mouse (*Sorex araneus*) is a familiar example. It is distinguished by having the tips of the teeth brown, by the uniform coating of short hairs on the tail and by their structural adaptation to terrestrial life. This species, which resembles a small, long-nosed mouse, is darker or lighter brown above and greyish below, the length of the head and body being between two and a half and three inches and of the tail about one and a half inches. It is common everywhere in the countryside of Great Britain ; and its food is mainly insects, worms, snails and the like. Its appetite is prodigious, a specimen has been known to eat at a meal five snails, each almost as large as itself. It spends its time eating and sleeping, always falling asleep after a meal. If deprived of food for a few hours, it invariably dies, and the necessity for constant feeding keeps it active day and night. It does not, however, hibernate. Sometimes it digs burrows for itself, but more frequently adopts those of field-mice. The female, however, commonly makes a nest for her young amongst thick grass or herbage. The breeding season lasts throughout the summer, the average number of young to the litter being half-a-dozen ; but there are probably three or four broods in the year. The span of its life is little more than a year. Its chief enemies are owls, kestrels and other predacious birds ; but although cats will kill it, they will not eat it, on account of the odour the little animal emits from a scent gland on the flanks.

The Pigmy-shrew (*Sorex minutus*) is smaller than the Common Shrew, the head and body measuring only a little over two inches. It is the only Shrew found in Ireland. Although not plentiful, it is widely distributed in Great Britain, whence, like the Common Shrew, it spreads eastwards to Central Asia.

SHREWS (FAMILY SORICIDAE)

The Water-shrew (*Neomys fodiens*), another British species, is about half-an-inch longer than the Common Shrew, blackish-grey in tint above and, in adaptation to swimming, has the feet fringed with stiff hairs and a crest of similar hairs on the underside of the tail. Al-though perfectly adapted for

COMMON SHREW OR SHREW-MOUSE (*Sorex araneus*).
If deprived of food for a few hours, this Shrew invariably dies, and the necessity for constant feeding keeps it active day and night.

water life and feeding mainly upon aquatic insects, snails, worms, small fish and the like, this Shrew is almost equally active on land, and may frequently be found in hedges or other places remote from streams. But it habitually makes its home near water, digging deep burrows in the banks of streams, and in these the females construct nests of grass or moss for their young, which, half-a-dozen or so in number and blind and naked, are born in early summer, a second litter probably being produced later in the year.

Brown-toothed Shrews are widely distributed in Europe and Asia and even in America, the commonest Shrew of America being known as *Blarina*. It extends as far south as Venezuela.

The last British species, Blair's Shrew (*Crocidura cassiteridum*), which is about the size of the Pigmy-shrew and restricted to the Scilly Isles, belongs to a group called from the colour of the teeth, the " White-toothed " Shrews. Of these there are many different kinds, widely distributed in Central Europe, Asia and Africa. They contain both the largest and smallest members of the family. The Etruscan Shrew (*Suncus etruscus*), for in-stance, is a tiny species, the head and body measuring only one and a half inches, the smallest mammal known. One of the biggest, on the other hand, is the familiar Indian " Musk Rat " (*S. caeruleus*), which is typically bluish-grey in colour, with the head and body six inches and the tail three to four inches long. This species is a good illustration of the phenomenon of protective

Photos]   [*W. S. Berridge.*
WATER-SHREW (*Neomys fodiens*).
In adaptation to swimming, this Shrew has the feet fringed with stiff hairs and a crest of similar hairs on the underside of the tail.

TONKIN TREE-SHREW (Family *Tupaiidae*). [*D. Seth-Smith.*
These animals, with their size and appearance and long, hairy
tails, could readily be mistaken for squirrels but for their long
snouts and slender, but not prehensile, thumbs.

advertisement, of which there are many instances in mammals.

It is a fearless little creature, invading houses after dark in search of food, and constantly squeaks as it noisily shuffles about, its pallid colouring making it look as if smeared with luminous paint, so that it is conspicuous in the dim light. Unmolested, it is inoffensive ; but when alarmed it gives off an intolerable smell of musk that adheres to everything the secretion from the gland on the flank touches. Many dogs, though eager to kill these Shrews, either resolutely refuse to touch them or, if they yield to the temptation, show unmistakable signs of disgust at the consequences.

Owing to their likeness to the rats which frequent the same houses in India, it is clear that the Shrews might easily be mistaken for those vermin and killed at sight by a dog or cat. Hence it is to their advantage to be as conspicuous and noisy and odorous as they can, so that a carnivore which has once experienced the unpleasantness of interference with one may recognize the next as something wisely left alone.

Some of the White-toothed Shrews are adapted to aquatic life. One of these, the Himalayan Water-shrew (*Chimarrogale himalayica*) closely resembles in habits and structural modifications the European species ; the other, the Tibetan Water-shrew (*Nectogale elegans*), is, on the contrary, much more modified and is like a diminutive Desman (page 830).

Another oriental species, the Short-tailed Shrew (*Anurosorex assamensis*) is evidently a specialized burrower, judging by its resemblance to the moles in its short legs and tail, tiny eyes, and obsolete ears. It occurs in Assam, and there is a related species in Tibet.

Suborder MENOTYPHLA
Tree-shrews or Tupaias (Family *Tupaiidae*)

These hold the highest place in the Order on account of superiority in the size of the brain, a better-developed cranium, and an annular orbit with large diurnal eyes. The hip-bones (pelvis) also form a long and complete union below, which is never the case in the lower types of the Order. The Menotyphla are sometimes regarded as a distinct Order of mammals.

The Tree-shrews in size and appearance, with their long, hairy tails,

834

diurnal habits and general activity, recall squirrels and could readily be mistaken for them but for their long snouts and slender, but not prehensile, thumbs. They are not, however, so agile as squirrels and, although some live in the tree-tops, they may mostly be seen running about in the forest amongst the roots of trees, hunting for insects and other small prey, which, varied with fruits, constitute their diet. Like all insectivora, they are quarrelsome amongst themselves and live in pairs or singly. The female is said to produce only one young one at a time.

The family ranges from India throughout the Malayan Islands, and is represented by many different kinds closely resembling each other in habits and general appearance, the best known being Elliot's Tree-shrew (*Anathana ellioti*), a rather pale, speckled species from southern India and Belanger's Tree-shrew (*Tupaia belangeri*), a browner species, common in Burma and Malaya. A much rarer kind is the Pen-tailed Tree-shrew (*Ptilocercus lowi*), from Borneo, distinguished by the feather-like arrangement of the hairs at the end of the tail, the rest being short-haired.

Elephant-shrews or Jumping-shrews (Family *Macroscelididae*)

Although related to the Tree-shrews, the Elephant-shrews are specially adapted for swift movements over open or rocky country, which when going at speed they traverse by a series of hops, their hind legs being greatly lengthened for the purpose. They are lively little animals, with large eyes, soft fur, dumpy bodies, the tail, as in all hopping mammals, being long; but the cylindrical, narrow snout, like india-rubber in flexibility, gives them a very quaint appearance.

They inhabit Africa, from Algeria to Cape Colony; and in habits are diurnal and insectivorous, living in burrows in sandy or rocky districts, especially where scrub affords shelter. There are many different kinds, the Saharan (*Elephantulus deserti*), a sandy-grey species, common in Algeria, and the Common Elephant-shrew (*Macroscelides proboscideus*), a redder species from the Cape flats, representing smallish examples with the head and body four or five inches long and the tail rather less. Nearly twice as large as these is the Four-toed Elephant-shrew (*Petrodromus tetradactylus*), which is darker in tint and inhabits East Africa.

[*W. S. Berridge.*

ROCK ELEPHANT-SHREW (*Elephantulus rupestris*).
Their hind legs being greatly lengthened, these little animals can traverse open or rocky country at speed by a series of hops.

Order CHIROPTERA (Bats)

The Bats are distinguished from all other mammals by the conversion of the fore limbs into wings capable of sustained and rapid flight ; and there are good reasons for thinking they were evolved from some arboreal insectivora which, like the Colugo (p. 842), planed from tree to tree by means of a well-developed patagium or wing-membrane. But the superiority of the bat's wing depends upon the extension of the patagium between all the digits of the fore foot, except the pollex, which is omitted to serve, with its sharp claw, as a climbing organ ; the digits concerned, as well as the other bones of the limb, being enormously elongated to give expanse to the membrane. The hind feet, which are not involved in the flight membrane, are of normal size and have five subequal digits armed with hooked claws by means of which the animal suspends itself in its natural resting attitude.

Only one young one is born at a time and this is carried about clinging to the breast of the mother.

By reason of their power of flight, Bats are more widely distributed than any Order of mammals, being found all over the world to the limits of tree-growth and in Oceanic Islands beyond the range of other mammals.

Classification of Bats. Bats are primarily divided into two groups or suborders, the *Microchiroptera* (Insectivorous Bats) and the *Megachiroptera* (Fruit-bats or Flying-foxes).

Suborder MICROCHIROPTERA (Insectivorous Bats)

These Bats take their scientific and popular names from the small average size of the species and the diet of insects which is characteristic of most of them. Their one distinguishing structural feature lies in the pinna, or broad upper part of the external ear, which is always open, never tubular, at the base ; typically, their cheek-teeth have broad, sharply-cusped crowns fitted for crushing insects and even hard-shelled beetles.

Their distribution is the same as that cited for the Order. They are classified into some seventeen families, based on differences in the teeth, skulls and other skeletal characters, as well as variations in external features into which it would be profitless to enter ; and the number of species (some six hundred) is so vast that only a few of the typical and of the more unusual types can be referred to.

To illustrate the habits and the structural features of the typical kinds, a few of the Common British species, which are also widely distributed in Europe, may be selected.

They are nocturnal, spending the day suspended by their hind legs in caves, old buildings or some sheltered spot and taking wing after sunset to feed. Their whole organization, apart from their eyes, which are minute and probably functional only for distinguishing light from darkness,

836

is adapted for capturing and devouring prey in the air ; and they find it not by eye-sight, but by their acutely-developed senses of hearing and touch. It has been proved experimentally that one of these bats, deprived of its eyes, can fly about a room with strings running across it in all directions from wall to wall, without touching one of them. Apparently, they have the faculty of perceiving some subtle difference in the atmosphere close to an object without actually touching it. And this sense, which lies in the wings, ears and flaps of naked skin often developed on the nose, is of service in enabling bats to fly without risk of injury about the recesses of caves in pitch darkness and, aided by their sharp hearing, to detect the proximity of insects on the wing at night.

The old country name " Flitter-mouse " given to our bats was inspired by their familiar flickering twilight flight. While thus occupied they are hunting for food. Gnats, midges and small moths are snapped up and swallowed without delay ; but larger moths and biggish, hard-shelled beetles, not so easily disposed of, are dealt with by the method called " pouching," that is to say, the bat curls its tail forwards and converts the membrane it supports into a receptacle for holding the prey, which, with head bent down, it masticates at leisure, keeping all the while on the wing.

[W. S. Berridge.
LONG-EARED BAT (*Plecotus auritus*).
In this species, the ears are enormous, nearly as long as the body.

But although flight is the principal means of locomotion, bats are by no means dependent upon it. Even the best fliers are tolerably skilful climbers on rough surfaces and can shuffle along the ground with some speed, the momentum gained from their straddled legs being supplemented by the action of the hook-like thumbs of their wings ; and British bats, it is believed, sometimes hunt insects in that way in crevices or on rock-surfaces and tree-trunks.

During the winter in temperate latitudes, animals dependent for food on insects which disappear at that season must either hibernate or migrate to warmer countries. British bats meet the difficulty by hibernation, retiring in late Autumn to the secluded haunts where they spend the daytime in summer, and there remaining more or less dormant until the warmth of Spring rouses them and insects alike from their lethargy. But during mild spells, even in mid-winter, they may awake, crawl about their retreats and probably feed, even if not venturing into the open. Hibernation, however, is not practised by all bats inhabiting colder temperate latitudes. Some American species living as far north as Canada in the summer habitually migrate in winter to southern districts where insects are obtainable.

MAMMALIA (ORDER CHIROPTERA)

Family Vespertilionidae (*Typical Bats*)

The majority of British bats, whose habits are epitomized above, belong to the cosmopolitan family *Vespertilionidae*, distinguished by the presence of a distinct flap, the tragus, at the base of the ear in front, by having a simple, hairy muzzle and the tail supporting throughout its length the membrane between the hind legs. The British members of this family are classified largely by variation in the numbers of their premolar teeth ; but there are certain external characters by which, with some practice, they can be identified. The Noctule (*Nyctalus noctula*), typically rather a high flyer, may be known by its comparatively large size and narrow wings. The Serotine (*Eptesicus serotinus*) is about as large, but has broader wings. The Pipistrelle (*Pipistrellus pipistrellus*), the commonest and one of the smallest of all our species, is allied to the Serotine, but is very much smaller. The

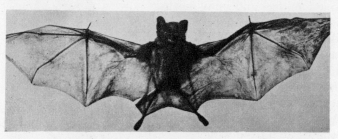

[*Clarke & Hyde.*
VAMPIRE (*Vampyrus spectrum*).
This species has been shown to be guiltless of the charge of blood-sucking, despite the belief to the contrary of the natives of Brazil.

Barbastelle (*Barbastella barbastellus* closely resembles the Pipistrelle in size, but has the ears united at the base on the summit of the head. Similar union of the ears occurs in the Long - eared Bat (*Plecotus auritus*), but in this striking species the ears are enormous, and nearly as long as the body.

Family Rhinolophidae (*Horse-shoe or Leaf-nosed Bats*)

Although most of the British bats belong to the Vespertilionidae, there are two referred to a second family known as the Horse-shoe or Leaf-nosed Bats (*Rhinolophidae*), so-called from the presence on the summit of the muzzle of an elaborately-folded, sensitive membrane somewhat resembling a horse-shoe in shape. The ear also has no tragus ; but otherwise these bats, called respectively the Greater Horse-shoe Bat (*Rhinolophus ferrumequinum*) and the Lesser (*Rh. hipposiderus*), which differ mainly in size, resemble the other British bats externally and in habits.

Family Nycteridae (*False Vampire Bats*)

Further variation in structure in adaptation to differences in diet and habits are illustrated by some exotic bats. In India there is a Leaf-nosed Bat, commonly known as the Indian Vampire Bat (*Megaderma lyra*),

GREATER HORSE-SHOE BAT
(*Rhinolophus ferrumequinum*).
This Bat gets its name from an elaborately-folded sensitive membrane somewhat resembling a horse-shoe in shape, and situated on the summit of the muzzle.

belonging to a family (*Nycteridae*) differing externally from the Horse-shoe Bats in having a tragus in the ear. This Bat is not by any means exclusively insectivorous. In addition to large insects, its prey consists of smaller bats, little birds, frogs and even fish. Feeding largely upon animals which it catches and devours when at rest, it has no need for the aerial activity of the species hitherto considered nor for "pouching" its prey. It has, therefore, lost its tail as a comparatively useless organ. These bats have large canine teeth, but those of the upper jaw are separated by a wide, toothless space indicated by a deep notch in the skull. This character serves to distinguish them from the true tropical American Vampire Bats, in which the space between the upper canines is provided with teeth.

American Vampires (*Phyllostomidae*)

In America the name "Vampire" is given to several different kinds of bats which are supposedly, or actually, blood-suckers. Most of them have a well-developed nose leaf shaped like a spear-head and from this feature they are sometimes called the American Leaf-nosed Bats and are referred to the family of Old World Leaf-nosed Bats, mentioned above. The name Vampire belongs by rights to one of these American species which has been shown to be guiltless of the charge of blood-sucking, despite the belief of the natives of Brazil to the contrary, and it was given the scientific name *Vampyrus spectrum* in accordance with the reputation it formerly bore, for which its somewhat uncanny appearance was responsible. It is the largest of the insectivorous bats, having a wing expanse of about twenty-eight inches and a body between five and six inches long. It also has large ears and long, powerful jaws, armed with strong, sharp teeth, but the tail is absent. This Bat is also interesting

Photos]   [*W. S. Berridge.*
GREAT LEAF-NOSED BAT.
This species is so named because of the leaf-like membrane on the nose.

from feeding mainly on forest fruits, as well as insects, this mixed diet being unusual in Bats of this suborder.

Another large American Bat for which the popular name Javelin Vampire (*Phyllostomus hastatus*) has been proposed also has the reputation, supported by the testimony of some English naturalists, of being addicted to blood-sucking. But this requires confirmation. This species is nearly as large as the true Vampire and has a similar nose-leaf, but may be at once distinguished by possessing a tail.

Long-tongued Vampires. An interesting group of these bats, known as the Long-tongued Vampires (*Glossophaga soricina* and others), differs

[W. S. Berridge.
FLYING-FOX, OR FRUIT-BAT
(*Pteropus giganteus*).
This species inhabits India and Ceylon. Each Bat will eat in a few hours fruit amounting to twice its own weight if it can secure it.

from the foregoing in having a very long and highly-extensile tongue, beset with tooth-like warts, which in some cases is known to be used for clearing out the soft pulp of fruits after the Bat has bitten through the rind with its teeth. But in some of the species which, like the one quoted, feed apparently mainly, if not exclusively, on insects, the tongue is probably employed for licking them from the depths of flowers. The Bat in question is a smallish species, measuring about two inches long, and there is no truth in the view at one time held that it feeds on blood.

Blood-sucking Vampires (*Desmodontidae*). The true Blood-sucking Vampires are readily distinguished by the adaptation of their teeth to the habit from which they take their name. Two of the upper incisor teeth are very large, shear-like and meet in the middle of the jaw ; and the canines behind them are similar in size and form. They have a small nose-leaf, but no tail. The best-known species (*Desmodus rufus*) is not a large Bat, its body measuring only about three inches long. It lies up by day in caves or hollow trees in Brazil and comes out after dark to search for the animals on whose blood it feeds, usually attacking them while asleep, and is a great pest to the live-stock of those camping in the forest at night. With its sharp teeth it insidiously scrapes away the outer skin even of horses and dogs and sucks up the blood that flows from the wounds.

Molossidae. In the account of the general habits of the Microchiroptera given above it was stated that the British species can climb and crawl with some agility, despite the impediment of their wing-membranes. In some exotic species this method of progression has been elaborated by increase in the use and strength of the hind legs and in the width of the foot. These Bats form a special family, the *Molossidae*, and the species which exhibits these adaptations for movement on the ground, tree-trunks or walls of caves, in the highest degree is the Naked Bat (*Chiromeles torquatus*) of the Malaysian Islands. It is a clumsy, ugly animal with a somewhat pig-like head; the skin is nearly naked and wrinkled, the tail is long, and the toes of the broad feet are capable of being spread to give an extended grip and area of support. But its chief peculiarity lies in the wings, which rise close to the middle of the back, instead of from the flank, while beneath them a flap of the membrane forms a pouch, containing the nipples of the female, who carries her young in it. This bat is of large size, the head and body measuring about five inches in length.

[*Otho Webb.*

GREY-HEADED FRUIT-BATS OR FLYING-FOXES (*Pteropus poliocephalus*).
These are native to the east coast of Australia. They are nocturnal, spending the day hanging to the branches of trees or to the walls of caves.

Sucker-footed Bats. Another modification subservient to climbing and locomotion on the ground, is the development of an adhesive disc on the thumb and sole of the foot. These suckers have been developed in two families of bats, the *Myzopodidae* and the *Thyropteridae*, which are otherwise akin to the Vespertilionidae. The former is represented by the Madagascar Sucker-footed Bat (*Myzopoda aurita*) and the latter by the tropical American Sucker-footed Bat (*Thyroptera tricolor*).

Suborder MEGACHIROPTERA (Fruit-bats or Flying-foxes)

In these bats the ear is tubular at the base, and since they feed upon easily-masticated fruit, the cheek-teeth have comparatively simple, narrow, weakly-cusped crowns. Although strong fliers, they have none of the general aerial activity of the smaller Bats, their flight being used to take

841

them to and from the roosting places and feeding grounds, and when on the wing they carry the hind legs stretched out behind to act as a rudder. Many of them are of large size, with an expanse of wing sometimes reaching four or five feet. They are confined to the Old World, where they range from Africa, through southern Asia to Australia. There are many different kinds, but all are referred to the family *Pteropodidae* and, so far as is known, are very similar in habits.

Living in countries where food is plentiful all the year round, they do not hibernate. But they are nocturnal, spending the day hanging to the branches of trees or the walls of caves, often in vast numbers. Towards sunset they take wing, making a bee-line for their feeding grounds and often travelling miles to reach them. When feeding, they hang head down, frequently by one foot only, using the other to hold the fruit steady while the mouth bites off pieces as large as it can take. They require a prodigious quantity of food, each Bat eating in a few hours fruit amounting to twice its own weight if it can secure it. Towards dawn they return to their cavern or tree. Perhaps the best known of these Bats are, the typical Flying-fox (*Pteropus giganteus*), from India and Ceylon, and the Grey-headed Fruit-bat (*P. poliocephalus*), from the east coast of Australia. A less familiar, but interesting, species is the Pigmy Fruit-bat (*Kiodotus minimus*), which is hardly larger than an average British Bat and is distinguished by having a very long, extensile tongue and greatly-reduced cheek-teeth. This modification of the tongue is similar to that of the Long-tongued Vampires (*Glossophaga*) in the Microchiroptera and serves the same purpose. This little Fruit-bat ranges from northern India throughout Malaya.

Order DERMOPTERA (Colugos or Flying Lemurs)

The classification of the Cobegos or Colugos (*Galeopithecus* and *Galeopterus*), also called Flying Lemurs, has been a great puzzle to zoologists. With the lemurs they have no near affinity ; and although they have been placed in the Insectivora, the many peculiarities they present entitle them to rank as an Order by themselves. Their chief interest, perhaps, lies in their representing a stage through which the bats must have passed in their evolution. As in the typical bats, the skin is developed into great flaps involving the neck, limbs and tail, the neck being greatly lengthened to increase its extent. For the same purpose, the fore legs also are lengthened, so as to exceed the hind legs. But the great difference between the Colugos and the bats lies in the structure of the fore foot, which in the Colugo is a typical hand-like, padded paw with five normal digits armed with sharp claws, quite different from the " wing " of the bats.

In all the features mentioned above in connection with the flight membrane or *patagium*, the Colugos differ from the Insectivora, and in the conversion of each of the four front lower incisors into a comb composed of about nine teeth, they are unique in the mammalia.

842

COLUGOS OR FLYING LEMURS

There are two species of Colugos, the typical form originally regarded as a Flying Lemur (*Galeopithecus volans*), inhabiting the forests of the Philippine Islands, and Temminck's Colugo (*Galeopterus temminckii*), ranging from Siam and the Malay States to Borneo. But the differences between them are trivial and their habits are the same.

HAMMERHEAD BAT (*Hypsignathus monstrosus*).
In this African species the head and muzzle are large and exceptionally hammer shaped.

They are fairly large animals, comparable in size to a small cat, are nocturnal, arboreal and, so far as is certainly known, vegetable feeders, devouring fruits and leaves, although insects and small birds are said to be taken by them at times. So completely is their organization adapted to life in the trees and to their patagiate flight, that they are almost helpless on the ground. Of true flight, as exhibited by bats, they are incapable. The most they can achieve is planing from the higher branches of one tree to the lower branches of another, dropping about one foot in five on their course, although the distance thus covered may be as much as seventy yards. Colugos have not inaptly been described as Nature's experimental failure in the art of flying.

During the day they sleep hanging back downwards on the underside of branches, with the head and tail tucked between the fore and hind limbs respectively. Many travellers have testified to the difficulty of detecting them in this position or when clinging to a tree trunk, owing to the obliterative effect of their coloration. The colour varies individually but is usually some shade of olive-brown or black, profusely mottled on the upper-side with silvery-white spots simulating the lichen which speckles

Photos]   [*W. S. Berridge.*
TUBE-NOSED BAT.
As will be seen from the illustration, this species derives its name from its tube-like nostrils.

the big boughs and trunks of the trees ; and it is noticeable that the mottling does not affect the parts that are tucked out of sight when the Colugo assumes its sleeping attitude. The teats, like those of bats and primates, are on the breast ; and the single young one, which is born blind and naked, is carried about by its mother as in those Orders and not reared in a retreat or nursery.

843

Order PRIMATES

In his classification of the Mammalia, Man very naturally gives pride of place to the Order containing himself and his next of kin. So far as the higher members of the Order are concerned, this position is justified by brain-development and the intelligence that goes with it. But this does not apply to the lower, and the general organization of the Order is less specialized than in many others.

Owing to the survival of tolerably primitive types, the number of distinctive characters by which the Primates may be defined are not many. Apart from Man, however, one external feature serves to distinguish them from the rest of the placental mammals, namely the mobility of the hallux, the "great toe" in Man, which is usually very large, prehensile and opposable to the other digits of the foot. Even when quite small, as in the Marmosets, it can be folded inwards across the sole. The feet always have five digits and the hand also, except in one animal, the Potto, where the second digit is vestigial. For the rest, there are never more than two incisor and six cheek-teeth above and below on each side, making at the most a total of thirty-six. Usually, only a single young one, occasionally two, is born at a time in a tolerably advanced state of development, so that it is soon capable of being carried by its mother, clinging to her back or to her breast when suckling.

The Order Primates may be grouped in three Suborders as follows :

Suborder 1. **Lemuroidea** (Lemurs).
> Families *Lemuridae* (Endrinas, Sifakas, Typical Lemurs and Mouse Lemurs), *Daubentoniidae* (Aye-aye), and *Galagidae* (Galagos, Lorises and Pottos).

Suborder 2. **Tarsioidea** (Tarsiers).
> Family *Tarsiidae.*

Suborder 3. **Pithecoidea** or **Anthropoidea** (Monkeys and Apes).
> A. *Platyrrhini* (American Monkeys and Marmosets).
>> Families *Cebidae* (Douroucoulis, Sakis and Uakaris, Titis, Capuchins, Squirrel Monkeys, Woolly Monkeys, Spider Monkeys and Howlers), *Hapalidae* (Marmosets and Tamarins).
> B. *Catarrhini* (Old World Monkeys and Apes).
>> Families *Cercopithecidae* (Macaques, Mangabeys, Baboons, etc.), *Colobidae* (Langurs and Guerezas), *Simiidae* ("Man-like" Apes, i.e. Gibbons, Orang-utans, Chimpanzees and Gorillas).

Suborder LEMUROIDEA (Lemurs)

Although in their general shape, usually long tails, structure of their hands and feet, and short-haired faces set off by the longer hair of the head, the Lemurs resemble the typical monkeys, they may be at once distinguished by their narrow and pointed or long, fox-like muzzles, resembling those of ordinary mammals in the nostrils opening on an area of moist skin that divides the upper lip, which is adherent to the gum in front and is not protrusible ; also the fourth digit of the hand and foot is the longest and the second digit of the foot always carries a claw, used for scratching the skin, the rest usually having flat nails.

There are also peculiarities in the teeth. These are usually the same in number as in the typical South American monkeys, but there is almost always a gap between the median upper incisors and the canines of the lower jaw, when present, lie alongside the small projecting incisors, forming with them a comb, which is kept clean by a finely-toothed plate on the lower side of the tongue, and is used for scraping the fur. In the skull the orbit, although encircled by bone, is not closed, but communicates freely with the space behind it.

The Lemurs are restricted to the warmer parts of the Old World and are the only members of the Primates found in Madagascar.

Madagascar Lemurs (Family *Lemuridae*)

Typical Lemurs (Lemurinae)

All the typical Lemurs commonly seen in captivity belong to the sub-family *Lemurinae*. They have the full number of teeth found in the Primates. The hands and feet are of moderate length, and are provided with well-developed, striated pads ; the toes are free from webbing. These Lemurs are mainly arboreal animals and extremely active climbers, resembling the Old World monkeys in the way they leap about trees and in their quadrupedal walk on the ground. They are gregarious and active mostly after sundown and are very noisy, making the forest resound with their unearthly cries.

Ruffed Lemur (*Lemur variegatus*). This is the largest and handsomest species of the genus, its colour being black and white

[*Neville Kingston.*
BLACK AND WHITE RUFFED LEMUR
(*Lemur variegatus*).
This is the largest and handsomest species, and inhabits north-eastern Madagascar.

845

or black and red in various proportions, and there is a conspicuous ruff on the sides of the neck. The head and body measure about two feet and the tail the same. It inhabits north-eastern Madagascar.

Black Lemur (*L. macaco*). This is a smaller species, about the size of a cat, and takes its name from the colour of the male, which is black from birth, whereas the female is reddish-brown, with some white on the cheeks. In both sexes the ears carry fringes of long hairs. It is found in north-west Madagascar.

Brown Lemur (*L. fulvus*). This Lemur is about the same size as the last, but has shorter fringes on the ears and the sexes are usually alike in hue, but otherwise the colour is very variable, sometimes local, sometimes individual, and many different varieties have been named, such as the *Black-fronted*, the *Yellow-whiskered*, the *Red-footed*, the *White-fronted* and so forth. It is widely distributed in Madagascar and is found also in the Comoro Islands.

Ring-tailed Lemur (*L. catta*). This is the prettiest and commonest of all in captivity, its general colour being greyish-buff, with the tail conspicuously banded black and white. It is the only species of this group which has the heel of the foot naked beneath. This peculiarity is, perhaps, connected with its different habitat, for it lives in dry, poorly-timbered rocky districts of southern Madagascar and is only seldom found in the forest.

Mouse Lemurs
(*Chirogalinae*)

Another group of the Madagascar Lemurs, called Mouse Lemurs, contains a number of species of small size, distinguished by the great length of the foot, the presence of very large, coarsely-striated pads on the palms and soles, and by the larger ears. They are nocturnal, arboreal and exceedingly active, passing from branch to branch by means of great leaps ; but the most interesting feature they exhibit is the habit

[*F. W. Bond.*
SMITH'S MOUSE LEMUR (*Microcebus murinus*).
Mouse Lemurs are nocturnal, arboreal and exceedingly active, passing from branch to branch by means of great leaps.

846

many, at least, of them practise of lying up in a nest of leaves in a hollow tree and remaining torpid during the dry season when all food is scarce, living on a quantity of fat accumulated on the tail during the previous season. One of the most commonly imported is Coquerel's Mouse Lemur (*Microcebus coquereli*), which is brown in colour and about the size of a squirrel; the typical Mouse Lemur (*M. murinus*), the size of a half-grown rat, is usually greyish in colour and has very large ears.

[*W. S. Berridge.*
RING-TAILED LEMUR (*Lemur catta*) AND YOUNG.
The general colour is greyish-buff, with the tail conspicuously banded black and white.

Endrinas and Sifakas
(*Indrisinae*)

The Lemurs popularly known as Endrinas and Sifakas are usually regarded as the highest types of this section. They are distinguished from the typical Lemurs by the reduction in the number of their teeth, their lengthened hands and feet, the smooth, padded palms and soles, and the webbing of the three inner toes. They are not exclusively nocturnal; they are gregarious and mainly arboreal, but on the ground their gait is not quadrupedal but semi-erect, the fore limbs not being employed for support. Their diet is purely vegetarian.

Endrina (*Indris brevicaudata*). This has a short, stumpy tail and big, hairy ears. It is the largest of existing Lemurs, standing when erect about three and a half feet high. Its colour is usually black, with the rump white, and it is restricted to the forests of eastern Madagascar.

Sifakas (*Propithecus*). These are a little smaller and have much longer tails, usually nearly as long as the head and body. They are found all over Madagascar and are represented by several species and local races, each restricted to its own area. The colour varies from white to black, white with brown or grey patches being common; all these varieties of

847

colour occur in the Dia-
demed Sifaka (*Propithe-
cus diadema*) of eastern
Madagascar.

Aye-aye (Family *Daubentoniidae*)

The Aye-aye (*Dau-
bentonia,* or *Chiromys,
madagascariensis*) forms
a family by itself,
mainly distinguished

AYE-AYE (*Daubentonia,* or *Chiromys, madagascariensis*).
The animal takes its popular name from the peculiar cry it utters.

from all other Lemurs by the resemblance of its teeth to those of the
Rodents, there being only two very large gnawing incisors, above and
below, separated by a long space from the small, flat-crowned cheek-teeth,
which are reduced in number. This dentition is accompanied by various
changes in the structure of the skull. Superficially, also, the Aye-aye
differs in having coarse, shaggy hair, huge, leathery ears, and sharp claws
on the thin fingers and toes, except on the hallux, and the fingers are long,
the third being exceptionally slender. The animal is about the size of
a cat and blackish-grey in colour. It is purely arboreal and nocturnal,
feeding very largely on wood-boring beetle larvae, which it detects by its
acute hearing and extracts by means of its thin, flexible finger when it
has gnawed away the wood to expose their tunnels. Pairs only are found
together and the female makes a nest of leaves for her single young one.
Its home is on the eastern side of Madagascar, and it takes its popular
name from the peculiar cry it utters.

Photos]   [*W. S. Berridge.*
MONGOOSE LEMUR (*Lemur mongoz*).

African and Asiatic Lemurs (Family *Galagidae*)

The African and
Asiatic Lemurs are dis-
tinguished from the
typical Madagascar
Lemurs by a few ana-
tomical characters and
constitute a group by
themselves. They are
popularly known as
Galagos, Pottos and
Lorises.

Galaginae. The

848

GALAGOS, POTTOS AND LORISES

Galagos or "Bush-babies" (*Galago*) superficially resemble the Mouse Lemurs of Madagascar, having long feet, long, hairy tails and large, membraneous ears and, like Mouse Lemurs, they are extraordinarily active climbers, taking prodigious leaps from branch to branch. On the ground they bound like kangaroos. But they are mainly arboreal and, being also nocturnal, spend the day curled up asleep in a hollow tree stem or in a nest made of leaves in the fork of a tree, coming out at night to hunt for food, which consists of fruit, insects, eggs or occasionally small birds. They are found only in the forests of tropical and southern Africa,

and are represented by several species, of which two are the best known. The Thick-tailed or Garnett's Galago (*G. crassicaudatus*) is a tolerably large animal, the head and body being about a foot long, or a little more, and the tail about the same. The colour varies locally, but is usually brownish-grey. It is widely distributed. The other, the Moholi Galago (*G. moholi*) is only about half the size of the other, but exhibits similar local variation in colour and is equally widely distributed. In South Africa this pretty little animal, which is often kept as a pet, is known as the "Bush-baby."

Lorisinae. The Pottos and Lorises differ from the Galagos in having the tail short, the ears small, the foot only as long as the hand, and the

[*F. W. Bond.*

DEMIDOFF'S GALAGO (*Galago demidoffi*).
Galagos are extraordinarily active climbers, taking prodigious leaps from branch to branch. On the ground they bound like kangaroos.

thumb as large as the great-toe, both being capable of great backward extension so that the span is very large. These differences are adaptations to differences of habit. Although nocturnal and arboreal, the Pottos and Lorises are unable to leap, and when prowling about the trees at night, they move with a slow, deliberate walk, gripping the branches with astonishing tenacity. In diet they resemble the Galagos and, despite their slowness, are adepts at catching resting insects with their hands.

Pottos. The Pottos (*Perodicticus*) are distinguished by having only three complete fingers, besides the thumb, on the hand, the forefinger being vestigial. The Common Potto (*P. potto*) has a tail usually about two inches long; its general colour is reddish or greyish-brown and its

N.H.　　　　　HHH　　　　　849

total length about one foot. It inhabits the forests of Central Africa. Another rare species, the Calabar Potto (*Arctocebus calabariensis*), has no visible tail and larger ears. It has been found only at Calabar in West Africa.

Lorises. The Lorises have the forefinger of the hand well developed and no visible tail. There are two very distinct kinds restricted to tropical Asia. The best known is the Slow Loris (*Nycticebus coucang*), which in its short,

SLENDER LORIS (*Loris tardigradus*).
This Loris has remarkably long and thin arms and legs, and is found only in southern India and Ceylon.

strong limbs and robust build resembles the Pottos and has many local varieties, differing in colour. It ranges from Assam to Cochin China and Borneo.

The Slender Loris (*Loris tardigradus*) is less stoutly built, has remarkably long and thin arms and legs, and is found only in southern India and Ceylon.

Suborder TARSIOIDEA (Tarsiers)

Photos]   [*W. S. Berridge.*
THICK-TAILED OR GARNETT'S GALAGO
(*Galago crassicaudatus*).
Galagos are found only in the forests of tropical and southern Africa.

The sole survivor of an extinct group is the little Primate known as the Tarsier (*Tarsius*). It stands nearly midway between monkeys and lemurs and is sometimes classified with the former, sometimes with the latter, or as a compromise, is given independent rank. In the genus there are seven species known to science. In its skull and teeth, and the structure of its lips and nose, it is more monkey-like; but in general appearance, in its large eyes and very long, hopping feet it re-

COMMON POTTO (*Perodicticus potto*).
The general colour of this animal is reddish or greyish-brown and its total length
about one foot.

sembles a little lemur of the galago group (page 849), except that the eyes are enormously larger. The fingers and toes have flat nails, except for the second and third toes which have claws. All the fingers and toes have at their extremities sucker-like discs, which enable the animal to cling firmly to the branches of trees. The size about equals that of a small rat, the tail is nearly twice as long as the head and body, and the soft fur is generally brownish, but varies in tint in different kinds. It ranges from Sumatra to the Philippines and Celebes. In habits it is nocturnal, insectivorous, arboreal and extraordinarily active; but it passes from branch to branch by hopping and traverses the ground in the same way. During the day it lies up in holes in tree stems or under projecting roots. It has the very unusual power of turning the head round so that the face can look backwards without the body moving. Under a bright light the pupil of the eye contracts to a narrow slit as in cats. The typical species (*T. tarsius*) is found in the Malayan Islands.

Suborder PITHE-COIDEA or ANTHRO-POIDEA (Monkeys and Apes)

This suborder, comprising the Apes and Monkeys, is distinguishable at a glance from the Lemuroidea by the structure of the muzzle, which is man-like in having no area of naked,

Photos]   [*W. S. Berridge.*
SLOW LORIS (*Nycticebus coucang*).
This Loris ranges from Assam to Cochin China and Borneo.

851

moist skin surrounding the nostrils and dividing the upper lip, the upper lip itself being free from the gum and, like the lower lip, protrusible so that water can be sucked into the mouth, instead of lapped. In the hands and feet the third or middle digit is usually longer, never shorter, than the fourth. With regard to the teeth, the median upper incisors are never separated by a gap, the lower canines and incisors never project forwards to form a fur-comb. The tongue has no finely-toothed plate on its lower side and in the skull the eye-sockets (orbits) are closed at the back by bone.

There are two divisions of the Anthropoidea, the *Platyrrhini*, or Monkeys and Marmosets of America, and the *Catarrhini*, or Apes and Monkeys of Africa and Asia.

AMERICAN MONKEYS AND MARMOSETS (Platyrrhini)

These are distinguished from the monkeys of the Old World by having three premolar teeth above and below in each jaw and in the absence of a bony floor to the ear opening in the skull. Generally, but not always, the nostrils are widely separated. The tail is frequently prehensile, which is never the case among the Old World Monkeys.

There are two families, the *Cebidae* (Spider Monkeys, Howlers, Capuchins, etc.) and the *Hapalidae* (Marmosets).

Family Cebidae (*Douroucoulis, Sakis and Uakaris, Titis, Capuchins, Squirrel Monkeys, Woolly Monkeys, Spider Monkeys and Howlers*)

In this family the fingers and toes have compressed nails, and the hallux is large and opposable to the other digits of the foot.

[*Neville Kingston.*
HUMBOLDT'S SAKI OR HAIRY SAKI (*Pithecia monachus*).
Among the Sakis are some of the quaintest-looking and ugliest monkeys in the world; the growth of the hair on the head is very varied but always eccentric.

These monkeys do not differ in habits from the arboreal Monkeys of Africa and Asia, except that they are less active climbers.

Douroucoulis or **"Night Apes"** (*Aotes*). These are distinguished from the rest of the South American monkeys by having, relatively, very large eyes adapted for nocturnal vision and the pads on the hands and feet exceptionally well developed, c o a r s e l y

852

striated and no doubt, highly sensitive for feeling in the dark. In both of these particulars, these monkeys adaptively resemble the nocturnal lemurs. In the skull the most noticeable peculiarity is the enormous size of the orbits to accommodate the eyes. They are small monkeys, with

[W. S. Berridge.
NIGHT APE (*Aotes*).
The eyes are, relatively, very large and adapted for nocturnal vision.

long, non-prehensile, bushy tails, small, round faces, weak jaws, and small ears. The general colour is usually greyish or brownish, but the face is white, broken by black stripes and black round the eyes. They are widely distributed in the forests of South America and are arboreal, spending the day asleep in some hollow tree-trunk and coming out at night to hunt for insects, eggs, small birds and fruit on which they feed. Their voice is loud, resembling a " caterwaul." A very large number of names have been given to various kinds, differing slightly in colour, the best-known being the Three-banded Douroucouli (*A. trivirgatus*) from the northern districts of South America.

Sakis and Uakaris (*Pithecia*, etc.). The Sakis represent a group distinguished by having very long, projecting incisor teeth. To this group belong some of the quaintest-looking and ugliest monkeys in the world, the growth of the hair on the head is very varied, but always eccentric, and the hair on the body is long and shaggy. These monkeys inhabit the forests on the banks of the large rivers of South America, seldom coming to the ground, but they are not active climbers and apparently feed solely on fruits. There are many different kinds, but only one or two of the most striking can be mentioned.

The Red-backed Saki (*Chiropotes chiropotes*) has the head, arms, legs and tail black and the back reddish. The head is very human in appearance owing to the hairs on the crown rising on each side from a parting and falling over the ears, while the cheeks and throat are provided with whiskers and beard growing like a " Newgate Frill." It inhabits the banks of the Amazon and Orinoco in northern Brazil and Venezuela, and is of medium size, the head and body measuring about one and a half feet and the tail one and a quarter feet. The scientific name of this monkey alludes to its alleged habit of drinking by picking up water in its hands.

The Red Uakari (*Cacajao rubicundus*) is a very different-looking monkey from the Red-backed Saki. It is red all over, even the skin of the face ;

and the tail is short, shorter than the hind legs. More marked still is the difference in the hair of the head. The " Newgate Frill " is developed, but instead of the luxuriant crop on the crown, the hair here is so short that it looks as if cropped close with a pair of scissors, so that at a little distance the head seems bald. This monkey is found in the forests to the north of the Amazon.

The White-headed Saki (*Pithecia pithecia*) has a long tail like the Red-backed Saki, but the coat is longer and shaggier and curly on the tail. The face is encircled with white hairs, forming bushy whiskers on the cheek, the rest of the head and body being covered with black hairs in the male and black, grey-tipped hairs in the female. This species also inhabits northern Brazil and Guiana.

[W. S. Berridge.
RED UAKARI (*Cacajao rubicundus*).
This monkey is red all over, even the skin of the face.

Titis (*Callicebus*). These form a group by themselves, distinguished by skull characters. In their small size, varied colouring and non-prehensile tails, they resemble the Squirrel Monkeys (page 856), but they have longer and shaggier fur. They are infrequently imported to this country. The Collared Titi (*C. torquatus*) is brown above, red below, with the neck and hands white, and the tail and feet black ; it inhabits northern Brazil. The Grey Titi (*C. gigot*), from southern Brazil, is grey with a red tail and black hands. These two are, perhaps, the commonest species.

The Capuchins and Squirrel Monkeys constitute a group that approaches the Spider Monkeys and their allies, but differs in skull-characters and in the absence of the features subservient to the special arboreal activities typical of that group. In general form they more closely resemble the Old World Monkeys, especially in the proportions of their limbs, their more efficient thumbs, shorter hands, and relatively longer feet. In trees they leap from branch to branch and run along their upper sides when climbing at speed. Their diet consists mainly of insects, eggs and berries.

854

Capuchins (*Cebus*). These have the tail prehensile, but not nearly so efficiently as in the Spider Monkeys, its underside being typically hairy to the tip. It is used for climbing, and, in captivity, at least, for carrying objects like paper-bags. Like other South American monkeys, they are arboreal, going about in troops, but in their habits there is nothing specially noteworthy. In captivity they are lively, intelligent and, on the whole, docile. Their habitat is the forested districts of Central and South America. A large number of different kinds have been described, but they are not well understood. A well-marked species, however, is the White-throated Capuchin (*C. capucinus*), in which the forehead is bald and the body black, with a white throat and cheeks. The head and body are about one and a half feet in length and the tail a little more. It is found in Central America and Colombia. In the rest of the Capuchins the tip of the tail is hairy. As an example may be cited the Brown

CAPUCHIN (*Cebus*).
The tail is used for climbing, and, in captivity, at least, for carrying objects like paper-bags.

Photos]   [*W. S. Berridge.*
COMMON SQUIRREL MONKEY (*Saimiri sciurea*).
This is a native of Guiana and Venezuela.

855

Capuchin (*C. fatuellus*), which is typically brown in tint and has the hair on the top of the head, especially in the males, raised into two crests. It is about the size of the last-named species, and is common in Guiana.

Squirrel Monkeys (*Saimiri*) are smaller and more delicately built than the Capuchins and have weaker jaws, longer heads and a non-prehensile tail. They are also more brightly coloured, the face being commonly flesh-coloured, with bluish lips, the body greyish, washed with yellow or red, the head sometimes black with white cheeks and the throat and the hands and feet ochre. In size the head and body measure about one foot and the tail is one and a quarter feet long. Several kinds, differing in colour, from various parts of the forested districts of South and Central America have been described: the Common Squirrel Monkey (*S. sciurea*), inhabiting Guiana, Venezuela, etc.; and the Red-backed Squirrel Monkey (*S. orstedii*), from Panama and Nicaragua being the commonest. In their habits and diet these pretty little monkeys resemble the Capuchins.

[*W. S. Berridge.*
RED-FACED SPIDER MONKEY
(*Ateles paniscus*).
This is typically black all over, with the face flesh-coloured.

The Woolly Monkeys, Spider Monkeys and Howlers form a group distinguished from the preceding by some well-marked characters in the skull and by the perfection of the tail as a prehensile organ, several inches of its lower side at the end being quite naked, very sensitive and finger-like. They are the most highly-specialized climbers amongst the South American Monkeys, not leaping from branch to branch, but traversing trees rather after the manner of the Orang-utan, with the added help of the tail.

Woolly Monkey. The least modified of the group is the Woolly Monkey (*Lagothrix*), distinguished by having a well-developed thumb set close to the next finger of the hand and the vocal organs unmodified. There are one or two species which derive their popular name, for which " Negro Monkey " is sometimes substituted, from their soft, thick, woolly fur. The better-known of the two species usually imported to this country is Humboldt's Woolly Monkey (*L. humboldtii*), which is grey in colour, with a black-faced head. It is a tolerably large monkey, the head and body measuring about two feet, and the tail a little over. It inhabits the forests of the Upper Amazon, and feeds on fruits of various kinds.

Spider Monkeys. The Spider Monkeys differ from the Woolly Monkey in having the thumb absent or vestigial and, when vestigial, not close to the next finger of the hand. They are also more slenderly built.

One rare species, the Woolly Spider Monkey (*Brachyteles arachnoides*), is of interest from its resemblance in the woolliness of its

WOOLLY MONKEY (*Lagothrix*).
Because of the soft, thick, woolly fur, this is often called the "Negro Monkey."

coat to the true Woolly Monkey. It is at least as large as the latter and its general colour, although very variable, is greyish-brown, the face being pale. Nothing has been recorded of its habits, except that it lives in the forests of south-eastern Brazil.

The true Spider Monkeys (*Ateles*) have long, shaggy coats; their arms are longer than their legs, with the hands nearly equalling the feet. They live in the tree-tops of the forests of the warmer parts of Central and South America, and feed mainly on berries and other fruits. Constant hunting by the Indians, who are partial to their flesh, has made them shy of human beings in the wild state and they greet the appearance of passers-by on the ground beneath by uttering barking cries, probably to warn their companions of danger, and by breaking off twigs and fruits and letting them fall upon them. But in captivity they are fearless, docile and lively when in health. The tail is used not only for securing a firm hold upon branches, but for grasping and plucking

Photos]   [*W. S. Berridge.*
VARIEGATED SPIDER MONKEY (*Ateles variegatus*).
Spider Monkeys use the tail not only for securing a firm hold on the branches, but for grasping and plucking fruit beyond the reach of the hands.

857

fruit beyond the reach of the hands. It resembles an elephant's trunk in sensitiveness, flexibility and grasping power.

Many different kinds, differing from each other mainly in colour, have been described, but most of them are probably local or individual varieties of the Red-faced Spider Monkey (*Ateles paniscus*), which is typically black all over, with the face flesh-coloured, and which inhabits the valley of the Amazon. A second, the Black Spider Monkey (*A. ater*), inhabiting the same district, differs only in having the face black. But the most curious variety of all is the Hooded Spider Monkey (*A. cucullatus*), in

[F. W. Bond.
BLACK HOWLER (*Alouatta caraya*).
These monkeys derive their name from the resonant and discordant howls they emit from the tree-tops.

which the hairs of the forehead project over the face, like an eye-shade. Its general colour is yellowish-brown, due to a mixture of black and yellow hairs ; its distribution is unknown. The average length of Spider Monkeys is rather less than two feet for the head and body, the tail being a little more.

Howlers (*Alouatta*). These resemble the Woolly Monkey in the structure of the hands, feet and tail, but are distinguished from them and from all the other members of the family by the modifications of the skull connected with the organs of voice which produce the resonant howls from which they take their name. The principal modification is the expansion of the bone, the hyoid, at the upper end of the wind-pipe into a great hollow sound-box, the lower jaw being much enlarged and spread to accommodate and protect this structure. These monkeys, found in the forests of Central and South America, are almost exclusively arboreal, but are slow, inactive climbers, feeding mainly on foliage. All travellers acquainted with them testify to the unearthly, discordant noise they emit from the tree-tops, but accounts differ as to the time the chorus is performed, some affirming that it starts at dark and is carried on till dawn, others that it is performed to salute the rising sun or that it may be stimulated by dull, cloudy weather at any hour of the day. The full-grown males have the most resonant voices ; but the purpose of the howling is quite unknown. Several species of Howlers have been named, mostly on trivial characters like colour. As instances may be quoted : the Red Howler (*Alouatta seniculus*), the Black Howler (*A. caraya*), the Yellow-handed Howler (*A. belzebul*). They do not appear to differ in habits, and in captivity they seem dull, lazy, unintelligent animals, never living for long.

858

MARMOSETS (FAMILY HAPALIDAE)

Family Hapalidae (*Marmosets and Tamarins*)

These little Monkeys, squirrel-like in size and arboreal activity, differ from the Cebidae in having the nails converted into claws for gripping the bark of trees, and the hallux, no longer required for grasping branches, reduced so as to be of very little use for prehension. Typically, also, they have only five, instead of six, cheek-teeth, the last molar being lost. Hence, numerically these teeth are the same as in the Old World Monkeys, but there are three premolars and two molars, instead of two premolars and three molars. In all the species the tail is long and hairy, never prehensile. Their habitat is the forests of South and Central America, Brazil being their headquarters.

They are mainly insectivorous in diet, eating moths, flies, which they skilfully catch with their hands, spiders, grubs and so forth. Although very popular as pets, they never thrive long in captivity without abundance of insect food. Of the many different kinds, a few only are commonly imported to this country.

Göldi's Marmoset (*Callimico goeldii*) must be mentioned as a connecting link between the Marmosets and the other South American Monkeys, having the hands and feet of the former and the teeth of the latter, there being six cheek-teeth above and below on each side, instead of five as in other Marmosets.

The best-known Marmoset is the Ouistiti (*Hapale jacchus*), distinguished by the long, fringe-like tuft of white or black hair on the ears, the mottled black, greyish-buff body-colour, and the banded tail.

[*W. S. Berridge.*
COMMON MARMOSET OR OUISTITI
(*Hapale jacchus*).
This is distinguished by the long, fringe-like tuft of white or black hair on the ears, and the banded tail.

The Marmosets called Tamarins (*Mystax*) are blacker in colour than the typical species and have no tufts on the ears, but are principally distinguished by the lower incisor teeth being short, shorter than the canines, instead of lengthened to equal the canines. The Negro Tamarin (*M. ursulus*) may be known by its tolerably uniformly black colour; the Red-handed Tamarin (*M. midas*) by its reddish hands and feet; and the

859

Moustache Tamarin (*M. mystax*) by a conspicuous tuft of white hair, like a moustache, on the upper lip.

The Pinché Marmoset (*Oedipomidas oedipus*) resembles the Tamarins in tooth-structure, but has the ears much reduced in size and the cheeks naked, or nearly so. It is a particoloured species, with a white crest on the crown, the body is brownish above, white below, the limbs are reddish, and the tail mostly black. It inhabits Colombia.

The Lion Marmoset (*Leontocebus rosalia*), so-called from the long, mane-like hair on the neck and shoulders, while resembling the Tamarin and Pinché in its teeth, is distinguished from them and from the typical Marmosets by having the hands lengthened to equal the feet. The colour is golden-brown all over.

[*W. S. Berridge.*
MOUSTACHE TAMARIN (*Mystax mystax*).
This Tamarin has a conspicuous tuft of white hair, like a moustache, on the upper lip.

It is sometimes known as the Silky Tamarin, and is a native of south-eastern Brazil.

CATARRHINI (Apes and Monkeys of Africa and Asia)

Two characters in the skull serve to distinguish this group from the Platyrrhini, namely the presence of two premolar teeth only above and below on each side, and the lengthening of the orifice of the ear by a floor of bone. The scientific name Catarrhini alludes to the narrowness of the space between the lower ends of the nostrils, which in these Monkeys and Apes are typically convergent slits, whereas in the American Monkeys the nostrils are

[*F. W. Bond.*
LION MARMOSET (*Leontocebus rosalia*).
This is so-called from the long, mane-like hair on the neck and shoulders.

usually widely separated. But the character is too variable to be cited as distinctive.

In the Catarrhini the tail is never prehensile, as it sometimes is in the Platyrrhini, but the former often possess large cheek-like pouches and frequently have bare patches on the hindquarters, which are never features of the New World Monkeys.

The Catarrhini

[W. S. Berridge.
GRIVET MONKEY (*Cercopithecus aethiops*).

themselves are referred to two tribes, the *Cynomorpha* or Dog-like Monkeys, and the *Anthropomorpha*, containing the family Simiidae, or the Man-like Apes.

CYNOMORPHA (Dog-like Monkeys)

The Monkeys of Asia and Africa have the arms and legs nearly equal in length, the hands much shorter than the feet, with the weak thumb tied closely to the palm and emerging from the middle of its inner edge, and the pads of the soles and palms comparatively well-developed. In walking on the ground in the quadrupedal attitude, the fore and hindquarters are nearly on a level, part or whole of the palm of the hand is applied to the ground, but the heel of the hind foot is raised off it ; rapid progression through trees is effected by a series of leaps, the propelling power lying in the strong, springy hindquarters and legs. It is on

[James's Press.
WHITE-COLLARED MANGABEY (*Cercocebus collaris*).
This handsome species is blackish and chestnut in colour, with a white collar, and is found in Nigeria.

861

account of their resemblance to typical quadrupedal mammals in their attitude and way of moving on the ground that these monkeys are called *Cynomorpha*, or dog-like ; and in their method of climbing they do not differ essentially from arboreal mammals like squirrels. The period of gestation is seven months.

There are two families in this group : the *Cercopithecidae*, including the Mangabeys, Macaques, Baboons and their allies, and the *Colobidae*, including the Langurs and Guerezas.

Family Cercopithecidae
(*Mangabeys*, *Baboons*, *Macaques*, *etc.*)

The monkeys of this family are distinguished by having cheek-pouches and a simple saccular stomach. Their diet and habits are very varied. They are omnivorous, eating fruits, nuts and vegetables of all kinds, as well as quantities of insects, even crabs sometimes, and small mammals, birds and their eggs. Their habitat may be forest, bush or rocky hillsides ; but the arboreal species are never so active in the trees as the Langurs and Guerezas (pages 870-872). Except that the young are typically duskier in hue, they do not differ appreciably

[*D. Seth-Smith.*
ANOTHER VIEW OF THE GRIVET MONKEY
(*Cercopithecus aethiops*).
This monkey is mainly arboreal and a native of Abyssinia.

GUENONS (FAMILY CERCOPITHECIDAE)

from their parents in colour.

These monkeys are found all over Africa, except in the deserts, and in south-eastern Asia, from India, China and Japan to Celebes.

A group of these monkeys, sometimes called Guenons (*Cercopithecus*) and distinguished by some peculiarities in dentition, is found all over Africa, south of the Sahara. They are mainly arboreal and all have long, straight tails. The

[F. W. Bond.
SCHMIDTS' WHITE-NOSED MONKEY
(*Cercopithecus petaurista schmidti*).
A heart-shaped patch of white hair on the nose is one of the distinguishing marks of this monkey.

species, of which there are a great many different kinds, fall into two ill-defined groups, one of which is represented by the so-called Grass Monkeys, which are greenish-grey in colour, with sooty-black faces. As examples may be cited the Green Monkey (*C. sabaeus*) of Sierra Leone, the Grivet (*C. aethiops*) of Abyssinia, and the Vervet (*C. pygerythrus*) of South Africa. They are about the size of house cats and usually frequent the bush and jungles on the river banks. The second group contains a large number of species, often handsomely coloured and quaintly decorated on the head in a variety of

[D. Seth-Smith.
ROLOWAY DIANA MONKEY (*Cercopithecus diana roloway*).
The black face, white brow-band and white, pointed beard are characteristic of the Diana monkey.

ANUBIS BABOON (*Papio anubis*). ·
[*James's Press.*
This is a large olive-green species ranging from East Africa to Nigeria.

ways. The Diana (*C. diana*) has a black face, with a white brow-band and a white, pointed beard ; the White-nosed Monkey and the Putty-nosed Monkey (*C. petaurista* and *C. nictitans*) have a heart-shaped patch of white hair on the nose ; the Moustached Monkey (*C. cephus*) has a blue band on the upper lip and a patch of yellow on the cheek. Many more instances could be cited. These monkeys are found mainly in the forested parts of Africa, and no doubt their patterns are protective, since patchy faces, like those described, would never be seen peering through the foliage.

The Patas Monkey (*Erythrocebus patas*), called in the trade the Hussar, on account of its sandy-red colour, is a large, long-legged relation of the Grass Monkeys, inhabiting open bush and rocky country in the Soudan. It is mainly terrestrial and so swift a runner that it requires a tolerably good pony to overtake it.

Mangabeys. The Mangabeys (*Cercocebus*) are long-tailed, very active arboreal monkeys inhabiting the forests of Central Africa, and differing from the last genus in the structure of their teeth, their larger size and other particulars. There are several species, including the Sooty Mangabey (*C. fuliginosus*), a uniformly slate-grey Monkey inhabiting Sierra Leone and the White-collared Mangabey (*C. collaris*), a

[*F. W. Bond.*
CHACMA BABOON (*Papio porcarius*).
This is a South African species.

864

[British Museum (Natural History)]

GELADA BABOON (*Theropithecus gelada*)

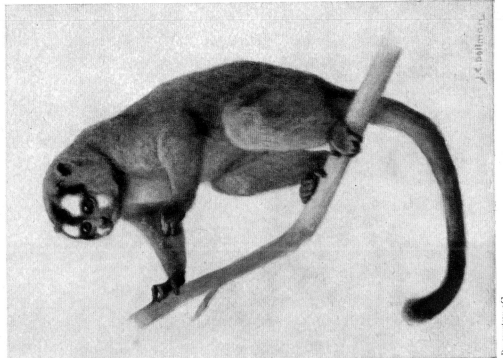

By courtesy of]

DOUROUCOULI (*Aotus trivirgatus*)

handsome species, blackish and chestnut in colour, with a white collar, found in Nigeria. An interesting point connected with these Monkeys is their kinship with the Baboons, of which they represent the ancestral stock.

Baboons. The Baboons, or Dog-faced Monkeys (*Papio*) resemble, as stated, the Mangabeys in many respects, but are distinguished by their large, dog-like muzzle due to the lengthening of the jaws and the development of a definite nose with the nostrils on it opening forwards. The tail, too, is only moderately long and is always carried in an arch. Baboons are large, powerfully-built monkeys, mainly terrestrial in habit and living on rocky hill-sides, for the climbing of which their fingers and toes are thick and short. They are, perhaps, the most intelligent of the Monkeys,

By courtesy of]   [*Carl Hagenbeck's Tierpark, Stellingen.*
HAMADRYAS OR ABYSSINIAN BABOON (*Papio hamadryas*).
This Baboon is greyish in colour and the male carries a great cloak of long hair on his shoulders and a tuft on his tail.

with the troop-instinct highly developed even to the extent of combination in the capture of prey. Several, for example, have been known to hide in the bushes fringing a forest path and spring upon passing antelope as large as sheep. In South Africa lambs and kids are sometimes killed by them. They feed, indeed, to a greater extent upon animal food than any of the Monkeys, devouring scorpions, centipedes and a variety of beetles and other insects, in search of which they overturn big stones; but they also eat roots, fruits and other vegetables. By reason of their great strength, they are formidable beasts to interfere with. A full-grown male is a match for a large dog and a troop has been known to turn upon a leopard which pounced upon a young one.

Baboons are found all over Africa, south of the Sahara, outside the Congo forest area. Five well-defined species are known, namely the Chacma Baboon (*P. porcarius*) of South Africa, the Yellow Baboon (*P. cynocephalus*) of East Africa; the Anubis Baboon (*P. anubis*), a large olive-green species ranging from East Africa to Nigeria; the Guinea Baboon (*P. papio*), the smallest of all and ginger in hue; and lastly, the Hamadryas Baboon (*P. hamadryas*), from the mountains of Abyssinia and southern Arabia, which is greyish in colour, the male carrying a great cloak of long hair on his shoulders and a tuft on his tail. This species, also known as the Sacred Baboon, is depicted on ancient Egyptian monuments.

The Mandrill (*Mandrillus sphinx*) and the Drill (*M. leucophaeus*) differ from the typical Baboons in having the tail reduced to a mere stump; the foot also has a very much longer prehensile great-toe, which is adapted for grasping the thick boughs of the trees in which they live. For, unlike the Baboons, these species are mainly arboreal, escaping to trees when hunted and sleeping in them at night. They are found in the forests of West Africa and are as large and powerfully built as Baboons. The adult male Mandrill is one of the most eccentric-looking of all Monkeys. The general hue is dark olive, but the rump is rainbow-tinted; on the top of the muzzle there are two bluish, sausage-shaped swellings, the end of the nose round the nostrils is carmine and the chin has a short, yellow beard. The Drill is browner in colour, with the face black.

Besides the Hamadryas Baboon another big monkey, the Gelada (*Theropithecus gelada*), lives in the mountains of Abyssinia and has the shoulders maned and the tail tufted, and is remarkable for its small, paw-like hands and feet adapted to rock climbing. It is as big as a medium-sized dog and mostly blackish-brown in colour, and has a deep but short muzzle and a small, fleshy nose. Its habits seem to be the same as those of Baboons and it is generally, but quite erroneously, supposed to be one of those animals.

[F. W. Bond.

BONNET MACAQUE (*Macaca radiata*).
The name is derived from the quaint-looking cap of radiating hair on the crown of the head.

866

Macaques. The Monkeys of Asia belonging to this family are popularly known as Macaques (*Macaca*). They are most nearly related to the Mangabeys, but differ from them in certain cranial and other characters and in being less arboreal in their habits. They range all over south-eastern Asia as far as Celebes, and there are about a dozen well-defined species, differing from each other in size, colour and particularly in the length of the tail. Their habitat is also varied from jungles on river banks to rocky hill-sides.

The species commonly exhibited in this country is the

[W. S. Berridge.

MANDRILL (*Mandrillus sphinx*).
On the top of the muzzle of the adult male there are two bluish, sausage-shaped swellings, the end of the nose round the nostrils is carmine and the chin has a short, yellow beard.

Rhesus or Bandar Macaque (*M. mulatta*), which may always be known by its tail of medium length and by the bright, orange-red hue of its hindquarters. It is common in the plains of northern India, up to five thousand feet in the Himalayas, and ranges thence eastward to Siam and northward as far as Pekin. In some places it frequents precipitous hill faces, in others, jungles on the river banks.

Equally commonly imported is the Bonnet Macaque (*M. radiata*) of southern India, which has a near ally in Ceylon known as the Toque (*M. sinica*). In these the tail is long, and their names are derived from the quaint-looking cap of radiating hair on the crown of the head.

A third Indian species, much rarer than the last, is the Wanderoo (*M. silenus*), which is black, with a thick ruff of long, grey hair round the face and a shortish, tufted tail. It is restricted to the forests of Travancore.

The so-called Common Macaque (*M. irus*), also known as the Crab-eating

867

Macaque, is like the Bonnet Macaque in having a long tail, but is without the cap on the crown. It ranges from Burma and Siam all over the Malayan Islands to the Philippines, and is represented by numerous local races differing in colour from olive or reddish to black. In Burma it frequents creeks and river banks, feeding, amongst other things, on crabs, whence its popular name is derived.

PIG-TAILED MACAQUE (*Macaca nemestrina*).
This is a formidable and powerful animal that derives its popular name from its short, thin tail carried in an arch over the buttocks.

The finest of all these Monkeys is the Pig-tailed Macaque (*M. nemestrina*), the male of which is as big as a Baboon or small mastiff and is a formidable, powerful animal, known, from its record of occasionally killing children, to be dangerous to human life in the Malay Peninsula, whence the typical race, brown and black in colour, ranges to Borneo. A smaller, greyer kind inhabits Burma and Siam. Its popular name is derived from its short, thin tail carried in an arch over the buttocks as in the Baboons.

Of the remaining species inhabiting eastern Asia, it is only necessary to mention the Stump-tailed Macaque (*M. speciosa*), inhabiting Assam, Burma and Siam ; the Japanese Macaque (*M. fuscata*), a thick-coated, dusky-hued monkey, with the tail rather shorter than in the Rhesus ; and the Moor Macaque (*M. maura*), a very short-tailed species found in Celebes and the neighbouring

Photos]   *[W. S. Berridge.*
WANDEROO OR LION-TAILED MACAQUE (*Macaca silenus*).
This is a black species, with a thick ruff of long, grey hair round the face. The tail is shortish and tufted.

868

GIBRALTAR OR BARBARY APE (*Macaca sylvana*).
This species has no visible trace of a tail.

islands. But one of the most interesting of all the group is the Gibraltar or Barbary Ape (*M. sylvana*), which somewhat resembles the Japanese Macaque, but has no visible trace of the tail. The natural home of this Monkey is the mountainous parts of Morocco and Algeria, its wide geographical isolation from the rest of the group being remarkable. A troop generally believed to be the descendants of specimens brought from Barbary and liberated, inhabits the precipitous cliffs of Gibraltar, where it lives under the protection of the Governor and has been maintained by fresh importations from northern Africa.

The last of the Macaque group is the Black Ape (*Cynopithecus niger*), often, but wrongly, supposed to belong to the Baboons on account of the ridges on the upper side of the muzzle. This feature and a crest on the top of the head serve to distinguish it from the Moor Macaque of the same country, with which it is often confused. But quite recently it has been found to intergrade with the Moor Macaque.

Most of the Monkeys of this family referred to above are commonly imported for exhibition or for sale to private owners. They are usually captured when quite young, perhaps about a year old, and

Photos]   *[W. S. Berridge.*
BLACK APE (*Cynopithecus niger*).
Because of the ridges on the upper side of the muzzle, this Macaque is often, but wrongly, supposed to belong to the Baboons.

869

are then attractive, amusing, if exacting pets. They reach maturity at about five years old; and thereafter they become more and more unmanageable and subject to fits of violent temper, which, coupled with their fearlessness of men and their terrible canine teeth, make them dangerous to keep any longer. This applies particularly to the males, which are more courageous and powerful than the females. The age to which they attain under natural conditions is unknown, but a Common and a Rhesus Macaque have been kept in captivity for twenty-nine and thirty years respectively; and a Mandrill that was exhibited some years ago in the Zoological Gardens, London, died when he was several years older than that.

Family Colobidae (*Langurs and Guerezas*)

[F. W. Bond.

DUSKY LANGUR.

Langurs are found in tropical Asia and Africa; but, as a rule, do not thrive well in captivity.

The *Colobidae* are distinguished by the absence of cheek-pouches and the presence of accessory, sack-like swellings in the stomach. The newly-born young differ remarkably in colour from their parents. These Monkeys feed mainly on the foliage of the trees in which they spend most of their time and in which they are perfectly at home, passing from branch to branch with prodigious leaps, often swinging from one to another with their hands. As in all active arboreal Monkeys, the tail is long, to serve as a balance. They are found in tropical Asia and Africa; but, as a rule, do not thrive well in captivity.

Langurs. The most familiar to Europeans is the typical Indian species, the Langur, Hanuman or Entellus Monkey (*Semnopithecus entellus*), a big black-faced, mostly greyish species represented by many local races in India and Ceylon. Its familiarity is due to its being regarded as sacred in many districts, and being unmolested, it is so fearless of Man that it may frequently be seen about the temples or on the roofs of village houses. But its natural home is in the hill forests, where it is almost as active in getting about over rocky ground as in the trees. The finest specimens are found in the Himalayas, where it is known as the Grey Ape. It may ascend to twelve thousand feet or so, and has been seen in the pine trees laden with snow. It is a large, powerful Monkey, the head and body measuring between two and a half and three feet, the tail being a little more in length. In addition to leaves and shoots, this Langur eats fruits and in the villages it does great damage by raiding gardens and grain fields.

In the countries between and including Burma and Borneo, there is a large number of other species and local races, differing in colour, size and a variety of ways and known to the Malays as Lotongs.

Closely resembling the Himalayan Langur in size, habits and its power to withstand cold is the Snub-nosed Monkey (*Rhinopithecus roxellanae*), which inhabits the forests of Szechwan in China, and takes its name from the face being disfigured by a little, triangular nose, up-tipped in such a way that the nostrils open forwards. The colour of this Monkey is brownish above and yellowish below and on the cheeks ; but other species from China are differently coloured.

Still more eccentric in appearance than the last is the Proboscis Monkey (*Nasalis larvatus*) of the tropical forests of Borneo. In the female there is a shortish, thick nose projecting forwards above

D. Seth-Smith.

CAPPED LANGUR AND YOUNG.
Langurs feed mainly on the foliage of the trees in which they spend most of their time.

871

the upper lip; but in the full-grown male this snout is much longer and thicker and hangs down over the mouth to the level of the chin. The use of these noses is quite unknown. The Proboscis Monkey is about the size of the Himalayan Langur, and its general colour is reddish-yellow.

Guerezas. The Guerezas (*Colobus*) differ from the Langur group in having, at most, a vestige of the thumb. They are restricted to the forests of Central Africa. There are many species

[*W. S. Berridge.*
SNUB-NOSED MONKEY
(*Rhinopithecus roxellanae*).
The small, triangular nose is up-tipped so that the nostrils open forwards.

belonging to two categories known as the "Red" and the "Black and White" Guerezas respectively. The former are typically red and black in varying proportions; the Bay Guereza (*C. badius*), of West Africa, being an example. The Black and White Guerezas have long coats varying in colour from wholly black, as in the West African Black Guereza (*C. satanas*), to mostly white, as in the white-tailed Kilimanjaro race of the Common Guereza (*C. abyssinicus*). In

[*Gambier Bolton.*
PROBOSCIS MONKEY (*Nasalis larvatus*).
In the full-grown male, the snout hangs down over the mouth to the level of the chin.

this race the crown of the head, the shoulders, the limbs and the root of the tail are black ; but the flanks and loins are covered with a cloak of

long, white, silky hair and the end of the tail is similarly adorned. A fancied resemblance between the coats of these Black and White Guerezas and the clerical garments known as the cassock and surplice has earned for these animals the name of " Bishop Monkeys." Their handsome liveries are said to render these Monkeys indistinguishable from the festoons of white lichen which grow on the boughs of the trees they frequent.

ANTHROPOMORPHA
(Man-like Apes)
Family Simiidae (*Gibbons, Orang-utans, Chimpanzees and Gorillas*)

Setting Man on one side and neglecting certain anatomical differences, the Man-like Apes are distinguished from the typical Monkeys of the Old World by having the arms much longer than the legs, the hands never much shorter than the feet, with the thumb more freely jointed from the wrist and the pads of the soles and palm practically undeveloped ; also there is never a trace of an external tail. In walking in the quadruped attitude, the palms of the

[*W. S. Berridge.*
WHITE-HANDED GIBBON (*Hylobates lar*).
The long arms easily reach the ground when the animal is standing in an upright attitude.

873

hands are never applied to the ground, the bent knuckles of the fingers being used instead and the entire sole of the foot, or its outer edge, supports the weight of the hindquarters, which, as compared with the shoulders, are weak and light. In tree-climbing the powerful arms are principally employed for swinging from branch to branch, when speed is desired, the legs being too feeble for long leaps.

The period of gestation, where known (*Chimpanzee*), is nine months.

Gibbons (*Hylobates*). These are the smallest of the Apes and differ from the rest in having horny sitting pads on the rump, as in the Old World Monkeys, a more lightly-built body, longer limbs, the arms easily reaching the ground in the upright attitude despite the longer legs, and the thumb and great toe better developed. There is no difference between the sexes in size. They live in the East Indies, ranging from Assam to Cochin China and Borneo, and are represented by some five or six species, all tolerably closely allied and exhibiting great individual variation in colour. The Hoolock (*H. hoolock*), from Assam and Burma, is black or brown, with a white band over the brows; the Lar or Wau-wau (*H. lar*), from Malaya, is black or fawn and has white hands and feet; Harlan's Gibbon (*H. concolor*), from Cochin China, has the hair on the crown erect, and is black or grey when full grown, fawn when young. There is no marked difference in their size. Standing erect, they are usually about two and a half feet, the head and body measuring one foot eight inches or so.

The habits of all the different kinds are very similar. They are diurnal, gregarious and essentially forest dwellers, spending most of their time in the tree-tops, but not infrequently coming to the ground, and by reason of their lightness of build, longer arms and better-developed legs, greatly excel the other Apes, both in arboreal activity and in the speed with which they traverse the ground. When walking slowly on the ground, they assume the erect posture, spreading the great toe inwards as a prop, but do not use the knuckles of the hand to rest on, merely the tips of the fingers now and again touching the ground lightly. In this posture they can run at very considerable speed, especially when young, and the arms are then raised aloft as balancers. Their balancing power in the upright attitude is surprising. They can walk with ease along a horizontal branch or rope, gripping it with the great toe and holding the arms out sideways. No less remarkable is the speed and precision with which they can traverse the forests, swinging arm over arm from bough to bough with the legs tucked up out of harm's way. No other Ape or Monkey can travel through the trees as they do, and Man is the only Primate which excels them in bipedal running on the ground.

Their diet consists of fruit, leaves, insects and spiders, eggs and small birds when they can catch them. They drink either by dipping their mouths into water, or by picking it up on their fingers.

MAN-LIKE APES (ANTHROPOMORPHA)

They are very noisy animals, shouting and calling in concert from the tree-tops, especially in the early morning and evening; the names "Hoolock," given to the Burmese species, and "Wau-wau," to the Malayan Gibbons, being derived from their voices, which are a better

From the Paramount Film]   ["Rango."
ORANG-UTAN (*Simia satyrus*).
In trees these Apes are perfectly at home, their whole organization being adapted to climbing.

guide to their identification than colour or other characters. One of them, indeed, the Siamang (*H. syndactylus*), a larger black species found in Sumatra, has a great vocal sac which expands like a bladder under the jaws and gives a booming, resonant, far-carrying cry.

Although Gibbons are commonly exhibited in our larger menageries, they seldom live long in captivity; and, apart from their spectacular acrobatic feats and their not unmelodious concerts, they are not so entertaining as the higher Apes or the commoner Monkeys.

Orang-utan (*Simia satyrus*). This Ape is less human in organization than either the Gorilla or the Chimpanzee. The crown of the head is higher, the ears very small, and the less prominent brows and flatter nose give a very different expression to the face. The arms are longer even than in the Chimpanzee, reaching to the ankles when the Ape is erect, but the legs are weaker, the hands and feet narrower, with the thumb and great toe smaller, but the other digits are longer; the foot, moreover, is jointed to the ankle in such a way that its outer edge rests on the ground during progression. The body is covered with long, shaggy, reddish-brown hair, shorter on the head, where it often forms a fringe on the forehead and passes down in front of the ear to the chin like the whiskers and beard of Man. The skin of the face is slate-grey. The adult male stands about four and a half feet, about the same height as the Chimpanzee, but the body is bulkier and the head larger. The female is much smaller, not more than four feet high.

This Ape is restricted to the forests of Sumatra and Borneo. There seems to be only one species, although it was at one time thought that males which develop great fibrous expansions on the sides of the face represented a species different from those in which these swellings do not appear. This is now regarded as an individual variation only. As might be inferred from the structure of its limbs, the Orang is almost exclusively arboreal, seldom descending to the ground, where its movements are slow and laboured. On account of the weakness of its legs, the twist of its foot and the weight of its body, the adults never stand erect and are probably unable to do so for more than a moment. The young, however, can both stand and walk on their legs, without the aid of their arms, although not easily. In trees these Apes are perfectly at home, their whole organization being adapted to climbing. They sometimes travel along the upper side of branches, but just as frequently beneath them, like a sloth, their long, hook-like digits giving them a secure hold. They never leap, but often swing from branch to branch, using their arms alone, but are careful not to let go the hold of one hand till the other has got a firm grip. They are not truly gregarious, being met with only in small family parties. In their native haunts they are said to be purely vegetable feeders, living on fruits and leaves, but probably they eat eggs. A specimen in the Zoological Gardens, London, at all events, was very fond of them, taking a whole hen's egg into his mouth, crushing it, and spitting out the shell, without losing a drop of the semifluid contents. For resting at night they make a platform by cleverly twisting branches together, the work being effected with great rapidity.

The span of life of Orang-utans in captivity in Europe is generally short, but they may live several years. A male, for instance, exhibited several years ago in the Zoological Gardens, London, was kept in Singapore for eight years before being imported to England in 1905. He died in 1929; assuming, therefore, that he was two or three years old when captured, he was about thirty-five years old at the time of death. In Singapore he was taught to smoke, and nothing pleased him more than a pull at a pipe or cigar, his way of expelling the fumes through his nostrils being most human.

Chimpanzee (*Anthropopithecus*). The Chimpanzee shares with the Gorilla the distinction of being the most man-like of the Apes. It is much smaller than the Gorilla both in stature and bulk and may be at once distinguished from it at all ages by its much larger ears and the unswollen rims of the nostrils. The

By courtesy of]　　　　　[Carl Hagenbeck's Tierpark, Stellingon.
CHIMPANZEE (*Anthropopithecus troglodytes*).
Chimpanzees inhabit the forests of West and Central Africa. There are several different kinds, distinguished principally by colour.

arms also are a little shorter, reaching about to the knees when the Ape is erect ; and the hands and the feet are narrower, more adapted for climbing, the toes being unwebbed. The height of the male standing upright is about four and a half feet, of the female, about six inches less.

They inhabit the forests of West and Central Africa and are more plentiful than Gorillas. Several different kinds, distinguished principally by colour, have been named, but to all intents and purposes they are local races of the typical Chimpanzee (*A. troglodytes*). The head and body are usually covered with coarse black hair, but the head may be bald as in the kind known as the Nshicgo-Mbouvé. Sometimes the hair is brown and the skin of the face may be black or pallid, the muzzle in Sierra Leone specimens being white.

In their habits Chimpanzees do not differ greatly from Gorillas, except that they are more arboreal, better climbers and altogether more active both in trees and on the ground. On the ground their gait is quadrupedal when traversing an open space ; but where the undergrowth is thick and especially when they are alarmed, they go through it in a slanting position, often at some speed, using their arms to push aside the creepers or to help themselves along by the tree-stems. When climbing they never leap from branch to branch, but either move along their upper sides, using both hands and feet, or swing from one to another, arm over arm, beneath, never letting go the grasp of one hand until the other has got a hold. But when they wish to descend rapidly to the ground, they drop from bough to bough, checking their fall with their hands as they come down. When shot at aloft, they usually descend in this way and make off on the ground or they hide in the foliage, never bounding away through the tree-tops like Monkeys. They also differ from the Gorilla, usually a silent animal, in periodically making the forest resound with concerted vociferous howls and cries.

Chimpanzees withstand conditions of captivity much better than Gorillas and are temperamentally more lively. They frequently live many years even under the unfavourable conditions of Zoological Gardens, and in Cuba they have been bred and reared to maturity. From observations on Chimpanzees kept in that island, it has been ascertained that the young are weaned in about twelve months, and reach maturity when ten to twelve years old, a little earlier in the female than in the male. It has been estimated that under favourable conditions the span of life is not far short of Man's. Within the last few years these Apes have also been bred in England and on the Continent.

Gorilla (*Gorilla*). This Ape may be distinguished from the other Man-like Apes by its much greater size, the thickly-expanded rims of the nostrils, beetling brows, broad hands with short, stumpy fingers, and broad foot with the four small toes tied together by webs in the basal half. The arms, when the animal is standing up, reach halfway between the knees and ankles, being intermediate in that respect between these limbs in the Chimpanzee and Orang-utan ; and the ears, although much smaller than in the Chimpanzee, are larger than in the Orang. In none of these three Apes are there horny sitting pads on the rump, which are present in Gibbons.

The standing height of a large male Gorilla is up to about five and a half feet, sometimes more ; but it may attain the prodigious weight of six hundred pounds. The female is much smaller, seldom exceeding four and a half feet. The head and body are massive and heavy, as compared with the short legs ; and the head, on account of the shortness of the neck, appears to arise between the shoulders.

878

GORILLA (GORILLA)

Its habitat is the forest of equatorial Africa, from the Cameroons and Gaboon eastward to the Great Lakes. Several different kinds have been named, mostly on variations in the colour, which is typically black, generally grizzled, especially in old animals ; a grey saddle on the back is a common feature in the males and there is often a good deal of reddish-brown on the head, neck or even shoulders.

[D. Seth-Smith.

YOUNG GORILLA (*Gorilla*).
A large male may stand up to a height of five and a half feet or more, and may attain the prodigious weight of six hundred pounds.

The Gorillas that were first made known to Europeans came from the Gaboon and other parts of West Africa, and exaggerated accounts of their ferocity and prowess, based mainly on native reports, were published in earlier natural histories. They were said to carry off negro women, to lower themselves from the forest trees and grasp with their feet the throats of natives passing beneath, to belabour with clubs the trunks of elephants plucking the foliage and to attack men at sight unprovoked. None of

879

these stories is true ; and later familiarity with them has shown that they are comparatively inoffensive, making off through the forest on the approach of Man, although terrible antagonists if wounded and forced to fight. Alike erroneous is the prevalent idea that they habitually stand and walk upright, an idea fostered to this day by the manner of mounting them in museums. They raise themselves on their legs to get a wider range of vision or to look inquisitively at an intruder and may beat their breasts with their hands, as the old stories said ; but when undisturbed, their gait is quadrupedal, the immense weight of the body and comparative weakness of the legs making bipedal progression for any distance a practical impossibility in the adult. The young, however, stand and walk with some facility and not infrequently in the erect attitude. Although good, if on the whole slow, climbers, they generally keep to the ground, the males even sleeping at the foot of trees, but the females and young go aloft and repose in platform nests made of interwoven branches. Their terrestrial habits may be explained by the absence of enemies. A leopard might pounce on a stray young one or possibly a female, but these are usually in the company of the male of the family party, a beast too formidable to be faced. They are purely vegetarian in diet, eating fruits and succulent green plants, very occasionally, it is said, raiding the plantations of the natives.

The typical Gaboon Gorilla (*Gorilla gorilla*) lives in hot, tropical forests ; but the so-called Mountain Gorilla, which is found just to the west of the Great Lakes of Africa, occurs at tolerably high altitudes, where the jungle is often drenched in mist and even Europeans require fires for warmth at night.

Young Gorillas have from time to time been exhibited in the Zoological Gardens ; but in the past these Apes, as a rule, have never lived long in menageries in Europe. It is hoped, however, that the difficulties of keeping these Apes alive in captivity in England have now been overcome. A few years ago a young male, known as " John," was kept by a lady as a private pet in London and enjoyed perfect health for two years. At the end of that period the owner was unfortunately compelled to part with him, and he did not long survive the loss of the companionship to which he was accustomed. He differed from all the other young Gorillas previously imported to this country in being docile and affectionate with human beings from the first ; this was probably due to his having been suckled and nursed, it was alleged, by a negress in Africa before being shipped to England.

INDEX

INDEX

INDEX

INDEX

885

INDEX

INDEX

INDEX